Introduction to
MATHEMATICAL LOGIC

THE UNIVERSITY SERIES IN UNDERGRADUATE MATHEMATICS

PATRICK SUPPES—Introduction to Logic
PAUL R. HALMOS—Finite-Dimensional Vector Spaces, 2nd Ed.
EDWARD J. MCSHANE and TRUMAN A. BOTTS—Real Analysis
JOHN G. KEMENY and J. LAURIE SNELL—Finite Markov Chains
PATRICK SUPPES—Axiomatic Set Theory
PAUL R. HALMOS—Naive Set Theory
JOHN L. KELLEY—Introduction to Modern Algebra
IVAN NIVEN—Calculus: An Introductory Approach
A. SEIDENBERG—Lectures in Projective Geometry
MAYNARD J. MANSFIELD—Introduction to Topology
FRANK M. STEWART—Introduction to Linear Algebra
LEON W. COHEN and GERTRUDE EHRLICH—The Structure of the Real Number System
ELLIOTT MENDELSON—Introduction to Mathematical Logic
HERMAN MEYER—Precalculus Mathematics—A Modern Introduction
ALBERT G. FADELL—Calculus with Analytic Geometry

A series of distinguished texts for undergraduate mathematics. Additional titles will be listed and announced as published.

Introduction to
MATHEMATICAL LOGIC

by

ELLIOTT MENDELSON
Associate Professor of Mathematics
Queens College
Flushing, New York

D. VAN NOSTRAND COMPANY, INC.
PRINCETON, NEW JERSEY
TORONTO · NEW YORK · LONDON

D. VAN NOSTRAND COMPANY, INC.
120 Alexander St., Princeton, New Jersey (*Principal office*)
24 West 40 Street, New York 18, New York

D. VAN NOSTRAND COMPANY, LTD.
358, Kensington High Street, London, W.14, England

D. VAN NOSTRAND COMPANY (Canada), LTD.
25 Hollinger Road, Toronto 16, Canada

Published simultaneously in Canada by
D. VAN NOSTRAND COMPANY (Canada), LTD.

First Published January 1964

Reprinted February 1965

PRINTED IN THE UNITED STATES OF AMERICA

To Arlene

PREFACE

In this book we have attempted to present a compact introduction to some of the principal topics of mathematical logic. In order to give a full and precise treatment of the more important basic subjects, certain subsidiary topics, such as modal, combinatory, and intuitionistic logics, and some interesting advanced topics, such as degrees of recursive unsolvability, have had to be omitted.

In the belief that beginners should be exposed to the most natural and easiest proofs, free-swinging set-theoretic methods have been used. The significance of a demand for constructive proofs can be evaluated only after a certain amount of experience with mathematical logic has been obtained. After all, if we are to be expelled from "Cantor's paradise" (as non-constructive set theory was called by Hilbert), at least we should know what we are missing.

The five chapters of the book can be covered in two semesters, but, for a one-semester course, Chapters 1 through 3 will be quite adequate (omitting, if hurried, Sections 5 and 6 of Chapter 1 and Sections 10, 11, and 12 of Chapter 2). The convention has been adopted of prefixing a superscript "*D*" to any section or exercise which will probably be difficult for a beginner, and a superscript "*A*" to any section or exercise which presupposes familiarity with a topic that has not been carefully explained in the text.

The present book is an expansion of lecture notes for a one-semester course in mathematical logic given by the author at Columbia University from 1958 to 1960 and at Queens College in 1961 and 1962. The author hopes that it can be read with ease by anyone with a certain amount of experience in abstract mathematical thought, but there is no specific prerequisite. The author would like to thank J. Barkley Rosser for encouragement and guidance during his graduate studies in logic, and he would like to acknowledge also the obvious debt owed to the books of Hilbert-Bernays, 1934, 1939; Kleene, 1952; Rosser, 1953; and Church, 1956.

ELLIOTT MENDELSON

Queens, New York
January 1963

TABLE OF CONTENTS

INTRODUCTION

One of the most popular definitions of logic is that it is the analysis of methods of reasoning. In studying these methods, logic is interested in the form rather than the content of the argument. For example, consider the two deductions:

(1) All men are mortal. Socrates is a man. Hence Socrates is mortal.
(2) All rabbits like carrots. Sebastian is a rabbit. Hence, Sebastian likes carrots.

Both have the same form: All A are B. S is an A. Hence S is a B. The truth or falsity of the particular premisses and conclusions is of no concern to the logician. He wants to know only whether the truth of the premisses implies the truth of the conclusion. The systematic formalization and cataloguing of valid methods of reasoning is one of the main tasks of the logician. If his work uses mathematical techniques and if it is primarily devoted to the study of mathematical reasoning, then it may be called mathematical logic. We can narrow the domain of mathematical logic if we define its principal aim to be a precise and adequate definition of the notion of "mathematical proof".

Impeccable definitions have little value at the beginning of the study of a subject. The best way to find out what mathematical logic is about is to start doing it, and the student is advised to begin reading the book even though (or especially if) he has qualms about the meaning or purposes of the subject.

Although logic is basic to all other studies, its fundamental and apparently self-evident character discouraged any deep logical investigations until the late nineteenth century. Then, under the impetus of the discovery of non-Euclidean geometries and of the desire to provide a rigorous foundation for analysis, interest in logic revived. This new interest, however, was still rather unenthusiastic until, around the turn of the century, the mathematical world was shocked by the discovery of the paradoxes, i.e., arguments leading to contradictions. The most important of these paradoxes are the following.

Logical Paradoxes

(1) (Russell, 1902) By a set, we mean any collection of objects, e.g., the set of all even integers, the set of all saxophone players in Brooklyn, etc. The objects which make up a set are called its members. Sets may themselves be members of sets, e.g., the set of all sets of integers has sets as its members. Most sets are not members of themselves; the set of cats, for example, is not a member of itself, because the set of cats is not a cat. However, there may be sets which do belong to themselves, e.g., the set of all sets. Now, consider the set A of all those sets X such that X is not a member of X. Clearly, by definition, A is a member of A if and only if A is not a member of A. So, if A is a member of A, then A is also not a member of A; and if A is not a member of A, then A is a member of A. In any case, A is a member of A and A is not a member of A.

(2) (Cantor, 1899) This paradox involves a certain amount of the theory of cardinal numbers and may be skipped by those having no previous acquaintance with that theory. The cardinal number $\overline{\overline{Y}}$ of a set Y is defined to be the set of all sets X which are equinumerous with Y (i.e., for which there is a one-one correspondence between Y and X, cf. page 8). We define $\overline{\overline{Y}} \leqslant \overline{\overline{Z}}$ to mean that Y is equinumerous with a subset of Z; by $\overline{\overline{Y}} < \overline{\overline{Z}}$ we mean $\overline{\overline{Y}} \leqslant \overline{\overline{Z}}$ and $\overline{\overline{Y}} \neq \overline{\overline{Z}}$. Cantor proved that, if $\mathscr{P}(Y)$ is the set of all subsets of Y, then $\overline{\overline{Y}} < \overline{\overline{\mathscr{P}(Y)}}$ (cf. page 183). Let C be the universal set, i.e., the set of all sets. Now, $\mathscr{P}(C)$ is a subset of C, so it follows easily that $\overline{\overline{\mathscr{P}(C)}} \leqslant \overline{\overline{C}}$. On the other hand, by Cantor's Theorem, $\overline{\overline{C}} < \overline{\overline{\mathscr{P}(C)}}$. The Schröder-Bernstein Theorem (cf. page 182) asserts that if $\overline{\overline{Y}} \leqslant \overline{\overline{Z}}$ and $\overline{\overline{Z}} \leqslant \overline{\overline{Y}}$, then $\overline{\overline{Y}} = \overline{\overline{Z}}$. Hence, $\overline{\overline{C}} = \overline{\overline{\mathscr{P}(C)}}$, contradicting $\overline{\overline{C}} < \overline{\overline{\mathscr{P}(C)}}$.

(3) (Burali-Forti, 1897) This paradox is the analogue in the theory of ordinal numbers of Cantor's Paradox and will make sense only to those already familiar with ordinal number theory. Given any ordinal number, there is a still larger ordinal number. But the ordinal number determined by the set of all ordinal numbers is the largest ordinal number.

Semantic Paradoxes

(4) The Liar Paradox. A man says, "I am lying." If he is lying, then what he says is true, and so he is not lying. If he is not lying,

then what he says is true, and so he is lying. In any case, he is lying and he is not lying.†

(5) (Richard, 1905) Some phrases of the English language denote real numbers, e.g., "the ratio between the circumference and diameter of a circle" denotes the number π. All phrases of the English language can be enumerated in a standard way: order all phrases having k letters lexicographically (as in a dictionary), and then place all phrases with k letters before all phrases with a larger number of letters. Hence, all phrases of the English language denoting real numbers can be enumerated merely by omitting all other phrases in the given standard enumeration. Call the nth real number in this enumeration the nth Richard number. Consider the phrase: "the real number whose n^{th} decimal place is 1 if the nth decimal place of the nth Richard number is not 1, and whose n^{th} decimal place is 2 if the nth decimal place of the nth Richard number is 1". This phrase defines a Richard number, say the kth Richard number; but, by its definition, it differs from the kth Richard number in the kth decimal place.

(6) (Berry, 1906) There are only a finite number of syllables in the English language. Hence, there are only a finite number of English expressions containing fewer than forty syllables. There are, therefore, only a finite number of positive integers which are denoted by an English expression containing fewer than forty syllables. Let k be *the least positive integer which is not denoted by an expression in the English language containing fewer than forty syllables.* The italicized English phrase contains fewer than forty syllables and denotes the integer k.

(7) (Grelling, 1908) An adjective is called *autological* if the property denoted by the adjective holds for the adjective itself. An adjective is called *heterological* if the property denoted by the adjective does not apply to the adjective itself. For example, "polysyllabic" and "English" are autological, while "monosyllabic", "French", and "blue" are heterological. Consider the adjective "heterological". If "heterological" is heterological, then it is not heterological. If "heterological" is not heterological, then it is heterological. In any case, "heterological" is both heterological and not heterological.

All of these paradoxes are genuine in the sense that they contain no obvious logical flaws. The logical paradoxes involve only notions from

† The Cretan "paradox", known in antiquity (e.g., cf. Paul, *Epistle to Titus*, I:12), is similar to the Liar Paradox. The Cretan philosopher Epimenides said, "All Cretans are liars." If what he said is true, then, since Epimenides is a Cretan, it must be false. Hence, what he said is false. Thus, there must be some Cretan who is not a liar. This is not logically impossible, so we do not have a genuine paradox. However, the fact that the utterance by Epimenides of that false sentence could imply the existence of some Cretan who is not a liar is rather unsettling.

the theory of sets, whereas the semantic paradoxes also make use of concepts like "denote", "true", "adjective", which need not occur within our standard mathematical language. For this reason, the logical paradoxes are a much greater threat to a mathematician's peace of mind than the semantic paradoxes.

Analysis of the paradoxes has led to various proposals for avoiding them. All of these proposals are restrictive in one way or another of the "naive" concepts which enter into the derivation of the paradoxes. Russell noted the self-reference present in all the paradoxes and suggested that every object must have a definite non-negative integer as its "type". Then an expression, "x is a member of the set y", is *meaningful* if and only if the type of y is one greater than the type of x. This approach, known as the theory of types and systematized and developed by Russell-Whitehead [1910–1913], is successful in eliminating the known paradoxes,† but it is clumsy in practice and has certain other drawbacks as well. A different criticism of the logical paradoxes is aimed at their assumption that, for every property $P(x)$, there exists a corresponding set of all objects x which satisfy $P(x)$. If we reject this assumption, then the logical paradoxes are no longer derivable.‡ It is necessary, however, to provide new postulates that will enable us to prove the existence of those sets which are a daily necessity to the practicing mathematician. The first such axiomatic set theory was invented by Zermelo [1908]. In Chapter IV we shall present an axiomatic theory of sets which is a descendant of Zermelo's system (with some new twists given to it by von Neumann, R. Robinson, Bernays, and Gödel). There are also various hybrid theories combining some aspects of type theory and axiomatic set theory, e.g., Quine's system NF (cf. Rosser [1953]).

A more radical interpretation of the paradoxes has been advocated by Brouwer and his intuitionist school (cf. Heyting [1956]). They refuse to accept the universality of certain basic logical laws, such as the law of excluded middle: P or not-P. Such a law, they claim, is true for finite sets, but it is invalid to extend it on a wholesale basis to all sets. Likewise, they say it is invalid to conclude that "there exists an object x such that not-$P(x)$" follows from "not-(for all x, $P(x)$)";

† Russell's Paradox, for example, depends upon the existence of the set A of all sets which are not members of themselves. Because, according to the theory of types, it is meaningless to say that a set belongs to itself, there can be no such set A.

‡ Russell's Paradox then proves that there is no set A of all sets which do not belong to themselves; the paradoxes of Cantor and Burali-Forti show that there is no universal set and no set containing all ordinal numbers. The semantic paradoxes cannot even be formulated, since they involve notions not expressible within the system.

we are justified in asserting the existence of an object having a certain property only if we know an effective method for constructing (or finding) such an object. The paradoxes are, of course, not derivable (or even meaningful) if we obey the intuitionist strictures, but, alas, so are many beloved theorems of everyday mathematics, and, for this reason, intuitionism has found few converts among mathematicians.

Whatever approach one takes to the paradoxes, it is necessary first to examine the language of logic and mathematics to see what symbols may be used, to determine the ways in which these symbols are put together to form terms, formulas, sentences, and proofs, and to find out what can and cannot be proved if certain axioms and rules of inference are assumed. This is one of the tasks of mathematical logic, and, until it is done, there is no basis for comparing rival foundations of logic and mathematics. The deep and devastating results of Gödel, Tarski, Church, Rosser, Kleene, and many others have been ample reward for the labor invested and have earned for mathematical logic its status as an independent branch of mathematics.

For the absolute novice a summary will be given here of some of the basic ideas and results used in the text. The reader is urged to skip these explanations now, and, if necessary, to refer to them later on.

A *set* is a collection of objects.† The objects in the collection are called *elements* or *members* of the set, and we shall write "$x \in y$" for the statement that x is a member of y. (Synonymous expressions are "x belongs to y" and "y contains x".) The negation of "$x \in y$" will be written "$x \notin y$".

By "$x \subseteq y$" we mean that every member of x is also a member of y, or, in other words, that x is a *subset* of y (or, synonymously, that x is *included* in y). We shall write "$t = s$" to mean that "t" and "s" denote the same object. As usual, "$t \neq s$" is the negation of "$t = s$". For sets x and y, we assume that $x = y$ if and only if $x \subseteq y$ and $y \subseteq x$; that is, if and only if x and y have the same members. A set x is called a *proper* subset of a set y, written "$x \subset y$", if $x \subseteq y$ but $x \neq y$.

The union $x \cup y$ of sets x and y is defined to be the set of all elements which are members of x or y or both. Hence, $x \cup x = x$, $x \cup y = y \cup x$, and $(x \cup y) \cup z = x \cup (y \cup z)$. The *intersection* $x \cap y$ is the set of elements which x and y have in common. It is easy to verify that

† Which collections of objects form sets will not be specified here. Care will be exercised to avoid using any ideas or procedures which may lead to the paradoxes; all the results can be formalized in the axiomatic set theory of Chapter IV. The term "class" is sometimes used as a synonym for "set", but it will be avoided here because it has a different meaning in Chapter IV. If the property $P(x)$ does determine a set, this set is often denoted $\{x \mid P(x)\}$, or $\hat{x}(P(x))$.

$x \cap x = x$, $x \cap y = y \cap x$, $x \cap (y \cap z) = (x \cap y) \cap z$, $x \cap (y \cup z) = (x \cap y) \cup (x \cap z)$, and $x \cup (y \cap z) = (x \cup y) \cap (x \cup z)$. The *relative complement* $x - y$ is the set of members of x which are not members of y. We also postulate the existence of the *empty set* (or *null set*) 0, i.e., a set which has no members at all. Then, $x \cap 0 = 0$, $x \cup 0 = x$, $x - 0 = x$, $0 - x = 0$, and $x - x = 0$. Two sets x and y are called *disjoint* if $x \cap y = 0$.

Given any objects $b_1, \ldots, b_k$, the set which contains $b_1, \ldots, b_k$ as its only members is denoted $\{b_1, \ldots, b_k\}$. In particular, $\{x, y\}$ is a set having x and y as its only members and, if $x \neq y$, is called the *unordered pair* of x and y. The set $\{x, x\}$ is written $\{x\}$ and is called the *unit set* of x. Notice that $\{x, y\} = \{y, x\}$. On the other hand, by $\langle b_1, \ldots, b_k \rangle$ we mean the *ordered k-tuple* of $b_1, \ldots, b_k$. The basic property of ordered k-tuples is that $\langle b_1, \ldots, b_k \rangle = \langle c_1, \ldots, c_k \rangle$ if and only if $b_1 = c_1$, $b_2 = c_2, \ldots, b_k = c_k$. Thus, $\langle b_1, b_2 \rangle = \langle b_2, b_1 \rangle$ if and only if $b_1 = b_2$. Ordered 2-tuples are called ordered *pairs*. If X is a set and k is a positive integer, we denote by X^k the set of all ordered k-tuples $\langle b_1, \ldots, b_k \rangle$ of elements $b_1, \ldots, b_k$ of X. We also make the convention that X^1 stands for X. X^k is called the *Cartesian product* of X with itself k times. If Y and Z are sets, then by $Y \times Z$ we denote the set of all ordered pairs $\langle y, z \rangle$ such that $y \in Y$ and $z \in Z$. $Y \times Z$ is called the Cartesian product of Y and Z.

An *n-place relation* (or a *relation with n arguments*) on a set X is a subset of X^n, i.e., a set of ordered n-tuples of elements of X. For example, the 3-place relation of betweenness for points on a line is the set of all 3-tuples $\langle x, y, z \rangle$ such that the point x lies between the points y and z. A 2-place relation is called a *binary* relation, e.g., the binary relation of fatherhood on the set of human beings is the set of all ordered pairs $\langle x, y \rangle$ such that x and y are human beings and x is the father of y. A 1-place relation on X is a subset of X, and is called a *property* on X.

Given a binary relation R on a set X, the *domain* of R is defined to be the set of all y such that $\langle y, z \rangle \in R$ for some z; the *range* of R is the set of all z such that $\langle y, z \rangle \in R$ for some y; and the *field* of R is the union of the domain and range of R. The *inverse* relation R^{-1} of R is the set of all ordered pairs $\langle y, z \rangle$ such that $\langle z, y \rangle \in R$. For example, the domain of the relation $<$ on the set ω of non-negative integers is ω, its range is $\omega - \{0\}$, and the inverse of $<$ is $>$. Notation: Very often $x \, R \, y$ is written instead of $\langle x, y \rangle \in R$. Thus, in the example just given, we usually write $x < y$ instead of $\langle x, y \rangle \in \, <$.

A binary relation R is said to be *reflexive* if $x \, R \, x$ for all x in the field of R. R is *symmetric* if $x \, R \, y$ implies $y \, R \, x$, and R is *transitive* if $x \, R \, y$ and $y \, R \, z$ imply $x \, R \, z$. Examples: The relation $\leqslant$ on the set of integers is reflexive and transitive but not symmetric. The relation "having at least one parent in common" on the set of human beings is reflexive and symmetric but not transitive.

A binary relation which is reflexive, symmetric, and transitive is called an *equivalence relation.* Examples of equivalence relations: (1) the *identity relation* I_X on a set X consisting of all pairs $\langle y, y\rangle$, where $y \in X$; (2) the relation of parallelism between lines in a plane; (3) given a fixed positive integer n, the relation $x \equiv y \pmod{n}$ holds when x and y are integers and $x - y$ is divisible by n; (4) the relation between directed line segments in three-dimensional space which holds when and only when they have the same length and the same direction; (5) the congruence relation on the set of triangles in a plane; (6) the similarity relation on the set of triangles in a plane. Given an equivalence relation R on a set X, and given any $y \in X$, define $[y]$ as the set of all z in X such that $y\ R\ z$. Then $[y]$ is called the *R-equivalence class* of y. It is easy to check that $[y] = [z]$ if and only if $y\ R\ z$ and that, if $[y] \neq [z]$, then $[y] \cap [z] = 0$, i.e., different R-equivalence classes have no elements in common. Hence, the set X is completely partitioned into the R-equivalence classes. For some of the examples above: (1) the equivalence classes are just the unit sets $\{y\}$, where $y \in X$; (2) the equivalence classes can be considered to be the directions in the plane; (3) there are n equivalence classes, the kth equivalence class ($k = 0, 1, \ldots, n - 1$) being the set of all numbers which leave the remainder k upon division by n; (4) the equivalence classes are the three-dimensional vectors.

A *function* f is a binary relation such that $\langle x, y\rangle \in f$ and $\langle x, z\rangle \in f$ imply $y = z$. Thus, for any element x of the domain of a function f, there is a unique y such that $\langle x, y\rangle \in f$; this unique element y is denoted $f(x)$. If x is in the domain of f, then $f(x)$ is said to be defined. A function f with domain X and range Y is said to be a *function from X onto Y*. If f is a function from X onto Y, and $Y \subseteq Z$, then f is called a *function from X into Z*. For example, if $f(x) = 2x$ for every integer x, f is a function from the set of integers onto the set of even integers, and f is a function from the set of integers into the set of integers. A function the domain of which consists of n-tuples is said to be a *function of n arguments*. A *(total) function of n arguments on a set* X is a function f whose domain is X^n. We usually write $f(x_1, \ldots, x_n)$ instead of $f(\langle x_1, \ldots, x_n\rangle)$. A *partial* function of n arguments on a set X is a function whose domain is a subset of X^n; e.g. ordinary division is a partial, but not total, function of two arguments on the set of integers (since division by zero is not defined). If f is a function with domain X and range Y, then the *restriction* f_Z of f to a set Z is the function $f \cap (Z \times Y)$. Clearly, $f_Z(u) = v$ if and only if $u \in Z$ and $f(u) = v$.

The *image* of the set Z under the function f is the range of f_Z. The *inverse image* of a set W under the function f is the set of all elements u of the domain of f such that $f(u) \in W$. We say that f *maps* X onto (into) Y if X is a subset of the domain of f and the image of X under f is (a subset of) Y. By an *n-place operation* (or *operation with n arguments*) *on a set* X we mean a function from X^n into X. For example, ordinary addition is a binary (i.e., 2-place) operation on the set of natural numbers $\{0, 1, 2, \ldots\}$. But ordinary subtraction is not a binary operation on the set of natural numbers, though it is a binary operation on the set of integers.

Given two functions f and g, the *composition* $f \circ g$ (also sometimes denoted fg) is the function such that $(f \circ g)(x) = f(g(x))$; $(f \circ g)(x)$ is defined if and only if $g(x)$ is defined and $f(g(x))$ is defined. For example, if $g(x) = x^2$ and $f(x) = x + 1$ for every integer x, then $(f \circ g)(x) = x^2 + 1$ and $(g \circ f)(x) = (x + 1)^2$. Also, if $h(x) = -x$ for every real number x and $f(x) = \sqrt{x}$ for every non-negative real number x, then $(f \circ h)(x)$ is defined only for $x \leqslant 0$, and, for such x, $(f \circ h)(x) = \sqrt{-x}$. A function f such that $f(x) = f(y)$ implies $x = y$ is called a 1–1 (*one–one*) function. Examples: (1) The identity relation I_X on a set X is a 1–1 function, since $I_X(y) = y$ for any $y \in X$; (2) the function $g(x) = 2x$, for every integer x, is a 1–1 function; (3) the function $h(x) = x^2$, for every integer x, is not 1–1, since $h(-1) = h(1)$. Notice that a function f is 1–1 if and only if its inverse relation f^{-1} is a function. If the domain and range of a 1–1 function f are X and Y, respectively, then f is said to be a 1–1 (*one–one*) *correspondence between* X *and* Y; then f^{-1} is a 1–1 correspondence between Y and X, and $(f^{-1} \circ f) = I_X$ and $(f \circ f^{-1}) = I_Y$. If f is a 1–1 correspondence between X and Y, and g is a 1–1 correspondence between Y and Z, then $g \circ f$ is a 1–1 correspondence between X and Z. Sets X and Y are said to be *equinumerous* (written $X \simeq Y$) if and only if there is a 1–1 correspondence between X and Y. Clearly, $X \simeq X$; $X \simeq Y$ implies $Y \simeq X$; and $X \simeq Y$ and $Y \simeq Z$ imply $X \simeq Z$. One can prove (cf. Schröder-Bernstein Theorem, page 182) that if $X \simeq Y_1 \subseteq Y$ and $Y \simeq X_1 \subseteq X$, then $X \simeq Y$. If $X \simeq Y$, one sometimes says that X and Y *have the same cardinal number*, and if X is equinumerous with a subset of Y but Y is not equinumerous with a subset of X, one says that the *cardinal number of* X *is smaller than* the cardinal number of Y.†

A set X is *denumerable* if it is equinumerous with the set of positive

† One can attempt to define the cardinal number of a set X as the collection $[X]$ of all sets equinumerous with X. However, in certain systems of set theory, $[X]$ does not exist, whereas in others (cf. page 184), $[X]$ exists but is not a set. For cardinal numbers $[X]$ and $[Y]$, one can define $[X] \leqslant [Y]$ to mean that X is equinumerous with a subset of Y.

integers. A denumerable set is said to have cardinal number $\aleph_0$, and any set equinumerous with the set of all subsets of a denumerable set is said to have the cardinal number $2^{\aleph_0}$ (or to have the *power of the continuum*). A set X is *finite* if it is empty or if it is equinumerous with the set of all positive integers $\{1, 2, \ldots, n\}$ which are less than or equal to some positive integer n. A set which is not finite is said to be *infinite*. A set is *countable* if it is either finite or denumerable. Clearly, any subset of a denumerable set is countable. A *denumerable sequence* is a function s whose domain is the set of positive integers; one usually writes s_n instead of $s(n)$. A *finite sequence* is a function whose domain is $\{1, 2, \ldots, n\}$, for some positive integer n.

Let $P(x, y_1, \ldots, y_k)$ be some relation on the set of non-negative integers. In particular, P may involve only the variable x and thus be a property. If $P(0, y_1, \ldots, y_k)$ holds, and, if, for any n, $P(n, y_1, \ldots, y_k)$ implies $P(n + 1, y_1, \ldots, y_k)$, then $P(x, y_1, \ldots, y_k)$ is true for all non-negative integers x (*Principle of Mathematical Induction*). In applying this principle, one usually proves that, for any n, $P(n, y_1, \ldots, y_k)$ implies $P(n + 1, y_1, \ldots, y_k)$ by assuming $P(n, y_1, \ldots, y_k)$ and then deducing $P(n + 1, y_1, \ldots, y_k)$; in the course of this deduction, $P(n, y_1, \ldots, y_k)$ is called the *inductive hypothesis*. If the relation P actually involves variables $y_1, \ldots, y_k$ other than x, then the proof of "for all x, $P(x)$" is said to proceed by *induction on* x. A similar induction principle holds for the set of integers greater than some fixed integer j. Example: to prove by mathematical induction that the sum of the first n odd integers $1 + 3 + 5 + \ldots + (2n - 1)$ is n^2, first show that $1 = 1^2$ (i.e., $P(1)$), and then, that if $1 + 3 + 5 + \ldots + (2n - 1) = n^2$, then $1 + 3 + 5 + \ldots + (2n - 1) + (2n + 1) = (n + 1)^2$ (i.e., if $P(n)$ then $P(n + 1)$). From the Principle of Mathematical Induction one can prove the *Principle of Complete Induction*: if, for every non-negative integer x the assumption that $P(u, y_1, \ldots, y_k)$ is true for all $u < x$ implies that $P(x, y_1, \ldots, y_k)$ holds, then, for all non-negative integers x, $P(x, y_1, \ldots, y_k)$ is true. (Exercise: show, by complete induction, that every integer greater than 1 is divisible by a prime number.)

A *partial order* is a binary relation R such that R is transitive and, for every x in the field of R, $x\, R\, x$ is false. (If R is a partial order, then the relation R' which is the union of R and the set of all ordered pairs $\langle x, x\rangle$, where x is in the field of R, we shall call a *reflexive partial order*; in the literature, "partial order" is used for either partial order or reflexive partial order. Notice that ($x\, R\, y$ and $y\, R\, x$) is impossible if R is a partial order, while ($x\, R\, y$ and $y\, R\, x$) implies $x = y$ if R is a reflexive partial order.) A (reflexive) *total order* is a (reflexive) partial order R such that, for any x and y in the field of R, either $x = y$ or $x\, R\, y$ or $y\, R\, x$. Examples: (1) the relation $<$ on the set of integers is a total order, while $\leqslant$ is a reflexive total order; (2) the relation $\subset$ on the set of all subsets of the set of positive integers is a partial order, but not a total order, while the relation $\subseteq$ is a reflexive partial order but not a reflexive total order. If C is the field of a relation R, and if B is a subset of C, then an element y of B is called an *R-least element* of B if $y\ R\ z$ for every element z of B different from y. A *well-order* (or *well-ordering relation*) is a total order R such that every non-empty subset of the field of R has an R-least element. Examples: (1) the relation $<$ on the set of non-negative integers is a well-order; (2) the relation $<$ on the set of non-negative rational numbers is a total order but not a well-order; (3) the relation $<$ on the set of integers is a total order but not a well-order. Associated with every well-order R having field X there is a corresponding *Complete Induction Principle*: if P is a property such that, for any u in X, whenever all z in X such that $z\ R\ u$ have the property P, then u has the property P, then it follows that all members of X have the property P. If the set X is infinite, a proof using this principle is called a proof by *transfinite induction*. One says that a *set X can be well-ordered* if there exists a well-order whose field includes X. An assumption which is useful in modern mathematics but about the validity of which there has been considerable controversy is the *Well-Ordering Principle*: every set can be well-ordered. The Well-Ordering Principle is equivalent (given the usual axioms of set theory) to the *Axiom of Choice* (*Multiplicative Axiom*): given any set X of non-empty pairwise disjoint sets, there is a set Y (called a *choice set*) which contains exactly one element in common with each set in X.

Let B be a non-empty set, f a function from B into B, and g a function from B^2 into B. Let us write x' for $f(x)$, and $x \cap y$ for $g(x, y)$. Then $\langle B, f, g\rangle$ is called a *Boolean algebra* if and only if the following conditions are satisfied:

(i) $x \cap y = y \cap x$ for all x, y in B.
(ii) $(x \cap y) \cap z = x \cap (y \cap z)$ for all x, y, z in B.
(iii) $x \cap y' = z \cap z'$ if and only if $x \cap y = x$ for any x, y, z in B.

We let $x \cup y$ stand for $(x' \cap y')'$; and we write $x \leqslant y$ for $x \cap y = x$. It is easily proved that $z \cap z' = w \cap w'$ for any w, z in B; we denote the value of $z \cap z'$ by 0. (The symbols $\cap$, $\cup$, 0 should not be confused with the corresponding symbols used in set theory.) We let 1 stand for $0'$. Then: $z \cup z' = 1$ for all z in B; $\leqslant$ is a reflexive partial order on B; and $\langle B, f, \cup\rangle$ is a Boolean algebra. An *ideal* in $\langle B, f, g\rangle$ is a non-empty subset J of B such that: (1) if $x \in J$ and $y \in J$, then $x \cup y \in J$, and (2) if $x \in J$ and $y \in B$, then $x \cap y \in J$. Clearly, $\{0\}$ and B are ideals. An ideal different from B is called a *proper ideal*. A *maximal ideal* is a proper ideal which is included in no other proper ideal. It can be shown that a proper ideal J is maximal if and only if, for any u in B, $u \in J$ or $u' \in J$. From the Well-Ordering Principle (or the Axiom of Choice) it follows that every Boolean algebra contains a maximal ideal, or, equivalently, that every proper ideal is included in some maximal ideal. Example: let B be the set of all subsets of a set X; for $Y \in B$, let $Y' = X-Y$, and for Y, Z in B, let $Y \cap Z$ be the ordinary set-theoretic intersection of Y and Z. Then $\langle B, ', \cap \rangle$ is a Boolean algebra. The 0 of B is the empty set 0, and 1 is X. Given an element u in X, let J_u be the set of all subsets of X which do not contain u. Then J_u is a maximal ideal. For a detailed study of Boolean algebras, cf. Sikorski [1960].

CHAPTER 1

THE PROPOSITIONAL CALCULUS

§ 1. Propositional Connectives. Truth Tables.

Sentences may be combined in various ways to form more complicated sentences. Let us consider only *truth-functional* combinations, in which the truth or falsity of the new sentence is determined by the truth or falsity of its component sentences.

Negation is one of the simplest operations on sentences. Although a sentence in a natural language may be negated in many ways, we shall adopt a uniform procedure, that of placing a sign for negation, the symbol $\sim$, in front of the entire sentence. Thus, if A is a sentence, then $\sim A$ denotes the negation of A.

The truth-functional character of negation is made apparent in the following *truth table*.

A	$\sim A$
T	F
F	T

When A is true, $\sim A$ is false; when A is false, $\sim A$ is true. We use T and F to denote the *truth values* Truth and Falsity.

Another common truth-functional operation is *conjunction*: "and". The conjunction of sentences A and B will be designated by $A \wedge B$ and has the following truth table.

A	B	$A \wedge B$
T	T	T
F	T	F
T	F	F
F	F	F

$A \wedge B$ is true when and only when both A and B are true. A and B are called the *conjuncts* of $A \wedge B$. Note that there are four rows in the table, corresponding to the number of possible assignments of truth values to A and B.

In natural languages, there are two distinct uses of "or", the inclusive and the exclusive. According to the inclusive usage, "A or B" means "A or B or both", whereas according to the exclusive usage, the meaning is "A or B, but not both". We shall introduce a special sign, $\vee$, for the inclusive connective. Its truth table is as follows:

A	B	$A \vee B$
T	T	T
F	T	T
T	F	T
F	F	F

Thus, $A \vee B$ is false when and only when both A and B are false. "$A \vee B$" is called a *disjunction*, with the *disjuncts* A and B.

EXERCISE

Write the truth table for the exclusive usage of "or".

Another important truth-functional operation is the *conditional*: "If A, then B." Ordinary usage is unclear here. Surely, "If A, then B" is false when the *antecedent* A is true and the *consequent* B is false. However, in other cases, there is no well-defined truth value. For example, the following sentences would be considered neither true nor false:

(1) If $1 + 1 = 2$, then Paris is the capital of France.
(2) If $1 + 1 \neq 2$, then Paris is the capital of France.
(3) If $1 + 1 \neq 2$, then Rome is the capital of France.

Their meaning is unclear, since we are accustomed to the assertion of some sort of relationship (usually causal) between the antecedent and the consequent. We shall make the convention that "If A, then B" is false when and only when A is true and B false. Thus, sentences (1)–(3) are assumed to be true. Let us denote "If A, then B" by "$A \supset B$". An expression "$A \supset B$" is called a *conditional*. Then $\supset$ has the following truth table:

A	B	$A \supset B$
T	T	T
F	T	T
T	F	F
F	F	T

This sharpening of the meaning of "If A, then B" involves no conflict with ordinary usage, but rather only an extension of that usage.†

A justification of the truth table for $\supset$ is the fact that we wish "If A and B, then B" to be true in all cases. Thus, the case in which A and B are true justifies the first line of our truth table for $\supset$, since A and B and B are both true. If A is false and B true, then A and B is false while B is true. This corresponds to the second line of the truth table. Finally, if A is false and B is false, A and B is false and B is false. This gives the fourth line of the truth table. Still more support for our definition comes from the meaning of statements such as, "For every x, if x is an odd positive integer, then x^2 is an odd positive integer." This asserts that, for every x, the statement "if x is an odd, positive integer, then x^2 is an odd, positive integer" is true. Now, we certainly do not want to consider cases in which x is not an odd, positive integer as counterexamples to our general assertion. This provides us with the second and fourth lines of our truth table. In addition, any case in which x is an odd, positive integer and x^2 is an odd, positive integer confirms our general assertion. This corresponds to the first line of the truth table.

Let us denote "A if and only if B" by "$A \equiv B$". Such an expression is called a *biconditional*. Clearly, $A \equiv B$ is true when and only when A and B have the same truth value. Its truth table, therefore, is

A	B	$A \equiv B$
T	T	T
F	T	F
T	F	F
F	F	T

The symbols $\sim$, $\wedge$, $\vee$, $\supset$, $\equiv$ will be called *propositional connectives*.‡ Any sentence built up by application of these connectives has a truth value which depends on the truth values of the constituent sentences.

† There seems to be a common non-truth-functional interpretation of "If A, then B", connected with causal laws. The sentence, "If this piece of iron is placed in water at time t, then the iron will dissolve", is regarded as false even in the case that the piece of iron is not placed in water at time t, i.e., even when the antecedent is false. Another non-truth-functional usage of "If . . ., then __" occurs in so-called counterfactual conditionals, such as, "If Sir Walter Scott had not written any novels, then there would have been no War Between the States." This sentence might be asserted to be true even though the antecedent is admittedly false. Fortunately, causal laws and counterfactual conditionals are not needed in mathematics and logic. For a clear treatment of conditionals and other connectives, cf. Quine [1951].

‡ We shall avoid the use of quotation marks to form names, whenever this is not likely to cause confusion. Strictly speaking, the given sentence should have quotation marks around each of the connectives. Cf. Quine [1951], pages 23–27.

In order to make this dependence apparent, let us apply the name *statement form* to an expression built up from the *statement letters* A, B, C, etc., by appropriate applications of the propositional connectives. More precisely,

(1) All statement letters (capital Roman letters) and such letters with numerical subscripts† are statement forms.
(2) If $\mathscr{A}$ and $\mathscr{B}$ are statement forms, then so are $(\sim \mathscr{A})$, $(\mathscr{A} \wedge \mathscr{B})$, $(\mathscr{A} \vee \mathscr{B})$, $(\mathscr{A} \supset \mathscr{B})$, and $(\mathscr{A} \equiv \mathscr{B})$.
(3) Only those expressions are statement forms which are determined to be so by means of (1) and (2).‡

For every assignment of truth values T or F to the statement letters occurring in a statement form, there corresponds, by virtue of the truth tables for the propositional connectives, a truth value for the statement form. Thus, each statement form determines a *truth function*, which can be graphically represented by a truth table for the statement form. For example, the statement form $(((\sim A) \vee B) \supset C)$ has the following truth table:

A	B	C	$(\sim A)$	$((\sim A) \vee B)$	$(((\sim A) \vee B) \supset C)$
T	T	T	F	T	T
F	T	T	T	T	T
T	F	T	F	F	T
F	F	T	T	T	T
T	T	F	F	T	F
F	T	F	T	T	F
T	F	F	F	F	T
F	F	F	T	T	F

Each row represents an assignment of truth values to the letters A, B, C, and the corresponding truth values assumed by the statement forms which appear in the construction of $(((\sim A) \vee B) \supset C)$.

The truth table for $((A \equiv B) \supset ((\sim A) \wedge B))$ is as follows:

A	B	$(A \equiv B)$	$(\sim A)$	$((\sim A) \wedge B)$	$((A \equiv B) \supset ((\sim A) \wedge B))$
T	T	T	F	F	F
F	T	F	T	T	T
T	F	F	F	F	T
F	F	T	T	F	F

† For example, $A_1, A_2, A_{17}, B_{31}, C_2, \ldots$.

‡ This can be rephrased as follows: $\mathscr{C}$ is a statement form if and only if there is a finite sequence $\mathscr{A}_1, \ldots, \mathscr{A}_n$ $(n \geqslant 1)$ such that $\mathscr{A}_n = \mathscr{C}$, and if $1 \leqslant i \leqslant n$, $\mathscr{A}_i$ is either a statement letter or is a negation, conjunction, disjunction, conditional, or biconditional constructed from previous expressions in the sequence. Notice that we use script letters $\mathscr{A}, \mathscr{B}, \mathscr{C}, \ldots$ to stand for arbitrary expressions, whereas Roman letters are being used as statement letters.

If there are n distinct letters in a statement form, then there are 2^n possible assignments of truth values to the statement letters and, hence, 2^n rows in the truth table.

EXERCISE

Construct truth tables for the statement forms $((A \supset B) \vee (\sim A))$ and $((A \supset (B \supset C)) \supset ((A \supset B) \supset (A \supset C)))$.

A truth table can be abbreviated by writing only the full statement form, putting the truth values of the statement letters underneath all occurrences of these letters, and writing, step by step, the truth value of each component statement form under the principal connective† of the form. As an example, for $((A \equiv B) \supset ((\sim A) \wedge B))$, we obtain

((A	≡	B)	⊃	((∼	A)	∧	B))
T	T	T	F	F	T	F	T
F	F	T	T	T	F	T	T
T	F	F	T	F	T	F	F
F	T	F	F	T	F	F	F

EXERCISES

1. Write the abbreviated truth tables for $((A \supset B) \wedge A)$ and $((A \vee (\sim C)) \equiv B)$.

2. Write the following sentences as statement forms, using statement letters to stand for the *atomic sentences*, i.e., those sentences which are not built up out of other sentences.

(a) If Mr. Jones is happy, Mrs. Jones is unhappy, and if Mr. Jones is unhappy, Mrs. Jones is unhappy.

(b) Either Sam will come to the party and Max will not, or Sam will not come to the party and Max will enjoy himself.

(c) A necessary and sufficient condition for the sheik to be happy is that he has wine, women, and song.

(d) Fiorello goes to the movies only if a comedy is playing.

(e) A sufficient condition for x to be odd is that x is prime.

(f) A necessary condition for a sequence s to converge is that s be bounded.

(g) The bribe will be paid if and only if the goods are delivered.

(h) The Giants will win the pennant unless the Dodgers win today.

(i) If x is positive, x^2 is positive.

† The *principal connective* of a statement form is the one which is applied last in constructing the form.

§2. Tautologies.

A *truth function* of n arguments is defined to be a function of n arguments, the arguments and values of which are the truth values T or F. As we have seen, any statement form determines a corresponding truth function.†

A statement form which is always true, no matter what the truth values of its statement letters may be, is called a *tautology*. A statement form is a tautology if and only if its corresponding truth function takes only the value T, or, equivalently, if, in its truth table, the column under the statement form contains only T's. If $(\mathscr{A} \supset \mathscr{B})$ is a tautology, $\mathscr{A}$ is said to *logically imply* $\mathscr{B}$ (according to the propositional calculus), or, alternatively, $\mathscr{B}$ is said to be a *logical consequence* of $\mathscr{A}$ (according to the propositional calculus). If $(\mathscr{A} \equiv \mathscr{B})$ is a tautology, $\mathscr{A}$ and $\mathscr{B}$ are said to be *logically equivalent* (according to the propositional calculus).‡ Examples of tautologies are $(A \vee (\sim A))$ (Law of the Excluded Middle); $(\sim(A \wedge (\sim A)))$; and $(A \equiv (\sim(\sim A)))$. Note also that $(A \wedge B)$ logically implies A, $(A \wedge (A \supset B))$ logically implies B, and $(A \supset B)$ and $((\sim A) \vee B)$ are logically equivalent. By means of truth tables, we have an effective procedure for determining whether a statement form is a tautology.

EXERCISES

1. Determine whether the following are tautologies.

(a) $(((A \supset B) \supset B) \supset B)$.
(b) $((A \equiv B) \equiv (A \equiv (B \equiv A)))$.

† If we wish to be precise, we should enumerate all statement letters as follows $A, B, \ldots, Z, A_1, B_1, \ldots, Z_1, A_2, \ldots$. If a statement form contains the $i_1{}^{\text{th}}, \ldots, i_n{}^{\text{th}}$ statement letters in this enumeration, where $i_1 < \ldots < i_n$, then the corresponding truth function is to have $x_{i_1}, \ldots, x_{i_n}$, in that order, as its arguments, where x_{i_j} corresponds to the $i_j{}^{\text{th}}$ statement letter. For example, $A \supset B$ generates the truth function

x_1	x_2	$f(x_1, x_2)$
T	T	T
F	T	T
T	F	F
F	F	T

while $B \supset A$ generates the truth function

x_1	x_2	$f(x_1, x_2)$
T	T	T
F	T	F
T	F	T
F	F	T

‡ From now on in this chapter, we shall always omit the qualifying phrase, "according to the propositional calculus".

2. Verify or disprove:

(a) $(A \equiv B)$ logically implies $(A \supset B)$.
(b) $((\sim A) \vee B)$ is logically equivalent to $((\sim B) \vee A)$.

3. Show that $\mathscr{A}$ and $\mathscr{B}$ are logically equivalent if and only if, in their truth tables, the columns under $\mathscr{A}$ and $\mathscr{B}$ are the same.

A statement form which is false for all possible truth values of its statement letters is called a *contradiction*. Its truth table has only F's in the column under the statement form.

Example. $(A \equiv (\sim A))$

A	$\sim A$	$(A \equiv (\sim A))$
T	F	F
F	T	F

Another example of a contradiction is $(A \wedge (\sim A))$.

Notice that a statement form $\mathscr{A}$ is a tautology if and only if $(\sim \mathscr{A})$ is a contradiction, and vice versa.

A sentence (in some natural language like English, or in a formal theory†) which arises from a tautology by substitution of sentences for all the statement letters, occurrences of the same letter being replaced by the same sentence, is said to be *logically true* (according to the propositional calculus). Such a sentence may be said to be true by virtue of its truth-functional structure alone. An example is the English sentence, "If it is raining or snowing, and it is not snowing, then it is raining", which arises by substitution from the tautology $(((A \vee B) \wedge (\sim B)) \supset A)$. A sentence which comes from a contradiction by means of substitution is said to be *logically false* (according to the propositional calculus).

Now let us prove a few general facts about tautologies.

PROPOSITION 1.1. *If $\mathscr{A}$ and $(\mathscr{A} \supset \mathscr{B})$ are tautologies, then so is $\mathscr{B}$.*

PROOF. Assume that $\mathscr{A}$ and $(\mathscr{A} \supset \mathscr{B})$ are tautologies. If $\mathscr{B}$ took the value F for some assignment of truth values to the statement letters of $\mathscr{A}$ and $\mathscr{B}$, then, since $\mathscr{A}$ is a tautology, $\mathscr{A}$ would take the value T, and, therefore, $(\mathscr{A} \supset \mathscr{B})$ would have the value F for that assignment. This contradicts the assumption that $(\mathscr{A} \supset \mathscr{B})$ is a tautology. Hence $\mathscr{B}$ never takes the value F.

PROPOSITION 1.2. *If $\mathscr{A}$ is a tautology containing as statement letters*

† By a formal theory, we mean an artificial language in which the notions of "meaningful expression", axioms, and rules of inference are precisely described; cf. pp. 29–30.

$A_1, A_2, \ldots, A_n$, and $\mathscr{B}$ arises from $\mathscr{A}$ by substituting statement forms $\mathscr{A}_1, \mathscr{A}_2, \ldots, \mathscr{A}_n$ for $A_1, A_2, \ldots, A_n$, respectively, then $\mathscr{B}$ is a tautology, i.e., substitution in a tautology yields a tautology.

PROOF. Assume that $\mathscr{A}$ is a tautology. For any assignment of truth values to the statement letters in $\mathscr{B}$, the forms $\mathscr{A}_1, \ldots, \mathscr{A}_n$ have truth values $x_1, \ldots, x_n$ (where each x_i is T or F). If we assign the values $x_1, \ldots, x_n$ to $A_1, \ldots, A_n$, respectively, then the resulting truth value of $\mathscr{A}$ is the truth value of $\mathscr{B}$ for the given assignment of truth values. Since $\mathscr{A}$ is a tautology, this truth value must be T. Thus, $\mathscr{B}$ always takes the value T.

PROPOSITION 1.3. *If $\mathscr{B}_1$ arises from $\mathscr{A}_1$ by substitution of $\mathscr{B}$ for one or more occurrences of $\mathscr{A}$, then $((\mathscr{A} \equiv \mathscr{B}) \supset (\mathscr{A}_1 \equiv \mathscr{B}_1))$ is a tautology. Hence, if $\mathscr{A}$ and $\mathscr{B}$ are logically equivalent, then so are $\mathscr{A}_1$ and $\mathscr{B}_1$.*

PROOF. Consider any assignment of truth values to the statement letters. If $\mathscr{A}$ and $\mathscr{B}$ have opposite truth values under this assignment, then $(\mathscr{A} \equiv \mathscr{B})$ takes the value F, and so $((\mathscr{A} \equiv \mathscr{B}) \supset (\mathscr{A}_1 \equiv \mathscr{B}_1))$ is T. If $\mathscr{A}$ and $\mathscr{B}$ take the same truth values, then so do $\mathscr{A}_1$ and $\mathscr{B}_1$, since $\mathscr{B}_1$ differs from $\mathscr{A}_1$ only in containing $\mathscr{B}$ in some places where $\mathscr{A}_1$ contains $\mathscr{A}$. Hence, in this case, $(\mathscr{A} \equiv \mathscr{B})$ is T, $(\mathscr{A}_1 \equiv \mathscr{B}_1)$ is T, and, therefore, $((\mathscr{A} \equiv \mathscr{B}) \supset (\mathscr{A}_1 \equiv \mathscr{B}_1))$ is T.

It would be profitable, at this point, to agree on some conventions to avoid the use of so many parentheses in writing formulas. This will make the reading of complicated expressions easier. First, we may omit the outer pair of parentheses of a statement form. (In the case of a statement letter, there is no outer pair of parentheses.) Second, when a form contains only one binary connective (namely, $\supset$, $\equiv$, $\wedge$, or $\vee$), parentheses are omitted by association to the left.

Examples. $A \supset B \supset A \supset C$ stands for $((A \supset B) \supset A) \supset C$, and $B \vee B \vee A \vee C \vee A$ stands for $((((B \vee B) \vee A) \vee C) \vee A)$.

Third, the connectives are ordered as follows: $\equiv$, $\supset$, $\vee$, $\wedge$, $\sim$, and parentheses are eliminated according to the rule that, first, $\sim$ applies to the smallest statement form following it, then $\wedge$ is to connect the smallest statement forms surrounding it, then $\vee$ connects the smallest forms surrounding it, and similarly for $\supset$ and $\equiv$. In applying this rule to occurrences of the same connective, we proceed from left to right.

Examples. Parentheses are restored to $A \vee \sim B \supset C \equiv A$ in the following steps.

$$A \vee (\sim B) \supset C \equiv A$$
$$(A \vee (\sim B)) \supset C \equiv A$$
$$((A \vee (\sim B)) \supset C) \equiv A$$
$$(((A \vee (\sim B)) \supset C) \equiv A)$$

As an exercise, show that $D \equiv C \equiv A \wedge D \wedge B \vee \sim D \supset B$ stands for

$$((D \equiv C) \equiv ((((A \wedge D) \wedge B) \vee (\sim D)) \supset B))$$

Not every form can be represented without use of parentheses. For example, parentheses cannot be further eliminated from $A \supset (B \supset C)$, nor from $\sim(A \vee B)$, nor from $A \wedge (B \supset C)$.

EXERCISES

1. Eliminate as many parentheses as possible from the forms

$$((B \equiv ((\sim C) \vee (D \wedge A))) \equiv (B \supset B))$$

and

$$(((A \wedge (\sim B)) \wedge C) \vee D)$$

2. Restore the parentheses to the forms $C \supset \sim(A \vee C) \wedge A \equiv B$ and $C \supset A \supset A \equiv \sim A \vee B$.

3. If we write $\sim\mathscr{A}$ instead of $(\sim\mathscr{A})$; $\supset\mathscr{A}\mathscr{B}$ instead of $(\mathscr{A} \supset \mathscr{B})$; $\wedge\mathscr{A}\mathscr{B}$ instead of $(\mathscr{A} \wedge \mathscr{B})$; $\vee\mathscr{A}\mathscr{B}$ instead of $(\mathscr{A} \vee \mathscr{B})$; and $\equiv\mathscr{A}\mathscr{B}$ instead of $(\mathscr{A} \equiv \mathscr{B})$, then there is no need of parentheses. For example $((\sim A) \supset (B \vee (\sim D)))$ becomes $\supset \sim A \vee B \sim D$. Write $(A \vee ((B \wedge (\sim D)) \supset A))$ in this notation. If we count $\supset$, $\wedge$, $\vee$, $\equiv$ each as $+1$, each statement letter as -1, and $\sim$ as 0, then, in this parenthesis free notation, an arbitrary expression $\mathscr{A}$ is a statement form if and only if the sum of the symbols is -1, and the sum of the symbols in any proper initial segment of $\mathscr{A}$ is non-negative.

4. Determine whether each of the following is a tautology, a contradiction, or neither.

(a) $A \equiv (A \vee A)$
(b) $(A \supset B) \supset ((B \supset C) \supset (A \supset C))$
(c) $((A \supset B) \wedge B) \supset A$
(d) $(\sim A) \supset (A \wedge B)$
(e) $A \wedge (\sim(A \vee B))$
(f) $(A \supset B) \equiv ((\sim A) \vee B)$
(g) $(A \supset B) \equiv \sim(A \wedge (\sim B))$

5. Prove that if $\mathscr{A} \wedge \mathscr{B}$ is a tautology, so are $\mathscr{A}$ and $\mathscr{B}$, and that if $\mathscr{A}$ is a tautology, then so are $\mathscr{A} \vee \mathscr{B}$ and $\mathscr{B} \vee \mathscr{A}$.

6. Apply Proposition 1.2 when $\mathscr{A}$ is $(A_1 \wedge A_2) \supset A_1$, $\mathscr{A}_1$ is $B \wedge D$, and $\mathscr{A}_2$ is $\sim B$.

7. Show that the following pairs are logically equivalent.

(a) $\sim(A \vee B)$ and $(\sim A) \wedge (\sim B)$
(b) $\sim(A \wedge B)$ and $(\sim A) \vee (\sim B)$

(c) $A \wedge (B \vee C)$ and $(A \wedge B) \vee (A \wedge C)$
(d) $A \vee (B \wedge C)$ and $(A \vee B) \wedge (A \vee C)$
(e) $A \vee (A \wedge B)$ and A
(f) $A \supset B$ and $\sim B \supset \sim A$ ($\sim B \supset \sim A$ is called the *contrapositive* of $A \supset B$)
(g) $(A \wedge B) \vee (\sim B)$ and $A \vee (\sim B)$
(h) $A \wedge (A \vee B)$ and A
(i) $A \wedge B$ and $B \wedge A$
(j) $A \vee B$ and $B \vee A$
(k) $(A \wedge B) \wedge C$ and $A \wedge (B \wedge C)$
(l) $(A \vee B) \vee C$ and $A \vee (B \vee C)$
(m) $A \equiv B$ and $B \equiv A$
(n) $(A \equiv B) \equiv C$ and $A \equiv (B \equiv C)$

8. (Principle of Duality)

(a) If $\mathscr{A}$ is a statement form involving only $\sim$, $\wedge$, and $\vee$, and $\mathscr{A}'$ arises from $\mathscr{A}$ by replacing each $\wedge$ by $\vee$, and each $\vee$ by $\wedge$, show that $\mathscr{A}$ is a tautology if and only if $\sim \mathscr{A}'$ is a tautology. Hence, if $\mathscr{A} \supset \mathscr{B}$ is a tautology, so is $\mathscr{B}' \supset \mathscr{A}'$, and if $\mathscr{A} \equiv \mathscr{B}$ is a tautology, so is $\mathscr{A}' \equiv \mathscr{B}'$. (Hint: Use 7(a) and 7(b).)

(b) Derive Exercise 7(b) from 7(a), and 7(d) from 7(c).

(c) If $\mathscr{A}$ is a statement form involving only $\sim$, $\wedge$, and $\vee$, and $\mathscr{A}^\star$ results from $\mathscr{A}$ by interchanging $\wedge$ and $\vee$, and replacing every statement letter by its negation, show that $\mathscr{A}^\star$ is logically equivalent to $\sim \mathscr{A}$. Find a statement form logically equivalent to the negation of $(A \vee \sim B) \wedge A \wedge (\sim C \vee (A \wedge C))$.

9. A statement form containing only the connective $\equiv$ is a tautology if and only if each statement letter occurs an even number of times.

10. (Shannon [1935], Hohn [1960]). An electric circuit containing only on-off switches (when a switch is on, it passes current; otherwise, not) can be represented by a diagram in which, next to each switch, we put a letter representing a necessary and sufficient condition for the switch to be on; see Fig. 1.1. The condition that a current flows through this network can be given by a statement form $(A \wedge B) \vee (C \wedge \sim A)$.

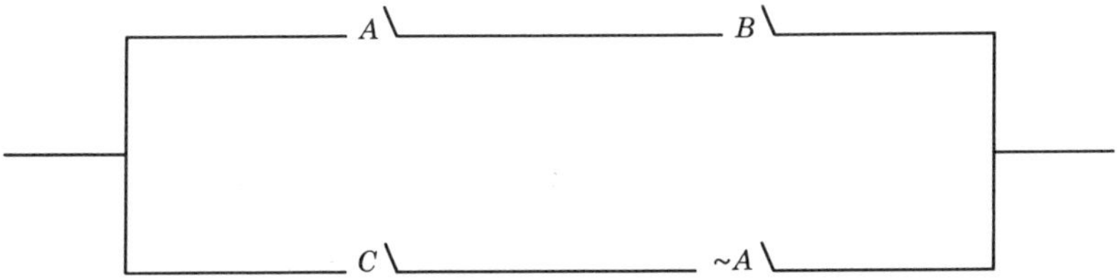

FIG. 1.1

A statement form representing the circuit shown in Fig. 1.2 is $(A \wedge B) \vee ((C \vee A) \wedge \sim B)$.

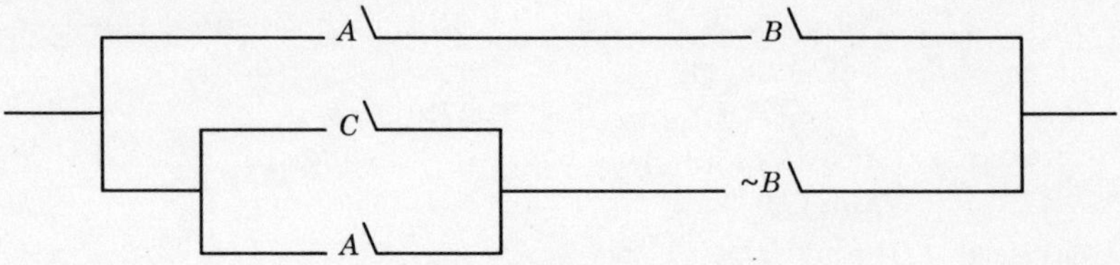

FIG. 1.2

Using Exercise 7(d,e,g,j,l), we find that this is logically equivalent to $((A \wedge B) \vee (C \vee A)) \wedge ((A \wedge B) \vee \sim B)$, which, in turn, is logically equivalent to $(((A \wedge B) \vee A) \vee C) \wedge (A \vee \sim B)$, then to $(A \vee C) \wedge (A \vee \sim B)$, and finally to $A \vee (C \wedge \sim B)$. Hence, the given circuit is equivalent to the simpler circuit shown in Fig. 1.3. (Two circuits are

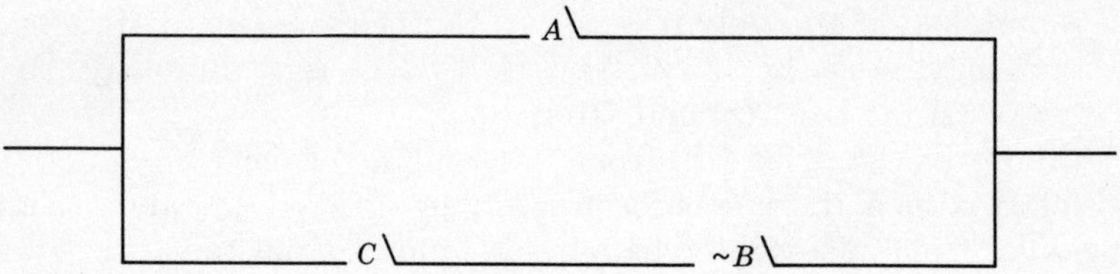

FIG. 1.3

said to be equivalent if current flows through one if and only if it flows through the other; and one circuit is simpler if it contains fewer switches.)

(a) Find simpler equivalent circuits for those shown in Figs. 1.4, 1.5, and 1.6.

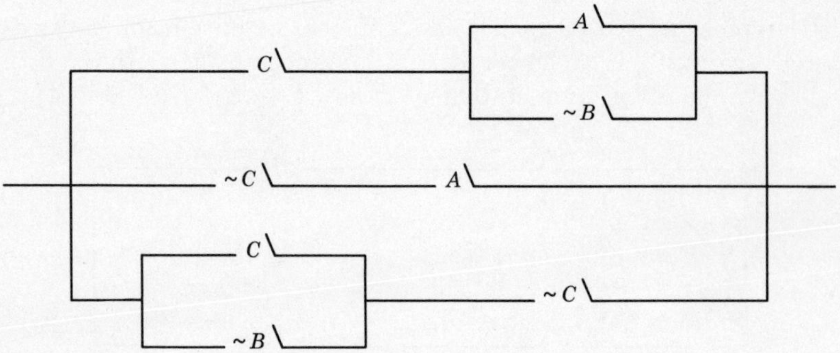

FIG. 1.4

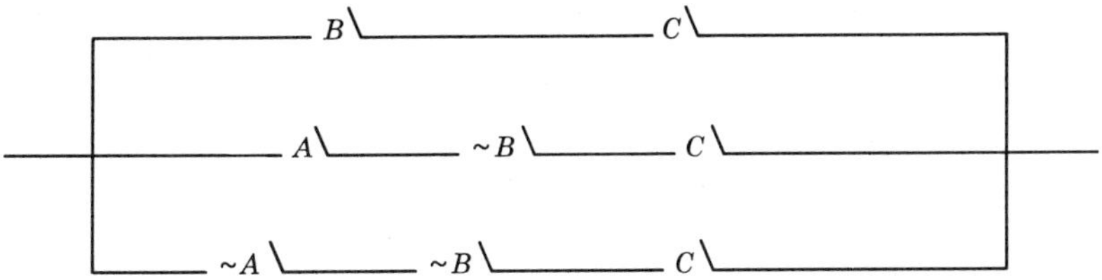

FIG. 1.5

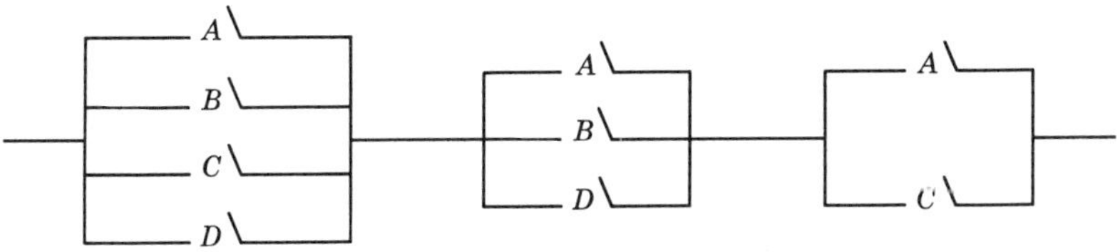

FIG. 1.6

(b) Assume that each of the three members of a committee votes Yes on a proposal by pressing a button. Devise as simple a circuit as you can which will allow current to pass when and only when at least two of the members vote in the affirmative.

(c) We wish a light to be controlled by three different switches in a room in such a way that flicking any one of these switches will turn the light on if it is off and will turn it off if it is on. Construct a simple circuit which will do the required job.

11. Determine whether the following arguments are logically correct by representing each sentence as a statement form and checking whether the conclusion is logically implied by the conjunction of the assumptions.

(a) If Jones is a Communist, Jones is an atheist. Jones is an atheist. Hence Jones is a Communist.

(b) If fallout shelters are built, other countries will feel endangered and our people will get a false sense of security. If other countries will feel endangered, they may start a preventive war. If our people will get a false sense of security, they will put less effort into preserving peace. If fallout shelters are not built, we run the risk of tremendous losses in the event of war. Hence, either other countries may start a preventive war and our people will put less effort into preserving peace, or we run the risk of tremendous losses in the event of war.

(c) If Jones did not meet Smith last night, then either Smith was the murderer or Jones is lying. If Smith was not the murderer, then Jones did not meet Smith last night and the murder took place after midnight. If the murder took place after midnight, then either Smith was the murderer or Jones is lying. Hence, Smith was the murderer.

(d) If capital investment remains constant, then government spending will increase or unemployment will result. If government spending will not increase, taxes can be reduced. If taxes can be reduced and capital investment remains constant, then unemployment will not result. Hence, government spending will increase.

12. Check each of the following sets of statements for consistency by representing the sentences as statement forms and then testing their conjunction to see whether it is a contradiction.

(a) Either the witness was not intimidated, or, if Doherty committed suicide, a note was found. If the witness was intimidated, then Doherty did not commit suicide. If a note was found, then Doherty committed suicide.

(b) If the party is dull, Alicia starts crying or Anatol tells jokes. If Sylvester comes to the party, either the party is dull or Alicia starts crying. If Anatol tells jokes, then Alicia does not start crying. Sylvester comes to the party if and only if Anatol does not tell jokes. If Alicia starts crying, Anatol tells jokes.

(c) If the bond market goes up or if interest rates decrease, either the stock market goes down or taxes are not raised. The stock market goes down when and only when the bond market goes up and taxes are raised. If interest rates decrease, then the stock market does not go down or the bond market does not go up. Either taxes are raised or the stock market goes down and interest rates decrease.

§3. Adequate Sets of Connectives

Every statement form containing n statement letters generates a corresponding truth function of n arguments. The arguments and values of the function are T or F. Logically equivalent forms generate the same truth function. The question naturally presents itself as to whether all truth functions are so generated.

PROPOSITION 1.4. *Every truth function is generated by a statement form involving the connectives* $\sim$, $\wedge$, *and* $\vee$.

PROOF. Let $f(x_1, \ldots, x_n)$ be a truth function. Clearly f can be represented by a truth table of 2^n rows, where each row represents some assignment of truth values to the variables $x_1, \ldots, x_n$, followed by the corresponding value of $f(x_1, \ldots, x_n)$. If $1 \leqslant i \leqslant 2^n$, let C_i be the conjunction $U_1^i \wedge U_2^i \wedge \ldots \wedge U_n^i$, where U_j^i is A_j if, in the ith row of the truth table, x_j takes the value T, and U_j^i is $\sim A_j$ if x_j takes the value F.

Let D be the disjunction of all those C_i's such that f has the value T for the ith row of the truth table. (If there are no such rows, then f always takes the value F, and we let D be $A_1 \wedge \sim A_1$, which satisfies the theorem.) As its corresponding truth function, D has f. For, let there be given an assignment of truth values to the statement letters $A_1, \ldots, A_n$, and assume that the corresponding assignment to the variables $\text{x}_1, \ldots, \text{x}_\text{n}$ is row k of the truth table for f. Then C_k has the value T for this assignment, whereas every other C_i has the value F. If f has the value T for row k, then C_k is a disjunct of D. Hence, D would also have the value T for this assignment. If f has the value F for row k, then C_k is not a disjunct of D and all the disjuncts of D take the value F for this assignment. Therefore, D would also have the value F. Thus, D generates the truth function f.

Examples

(a)

x_1	x_2	$\text{f}(\text{x}_1, \text{x}_2)$
T	T	F
F	T	T
T	F	T
F	F	T

$$D \text{ is } (\sim A_1 \wedge A_2) \vee (A_1 \wedge \sim A_2) \vee (\sim A_1 \wedge \sim A_2)$$

(b)

x_1	x_2	x_3	$\text{g}(\text{x}_1, \text{x}_2, \text{x}_3)$
T	T	T	T
F	T	T	F
T	F	T	T
F	F	T	T
T	T	F	F
F	T	F	F
T	F	F	F
F	F	F	T

D is

$$(A_1 \wedge A_2 \wedge A_3) \vee (A_1 \wedge \sim A_2 \wedge A_3) \vee (\sim A_1 \wedge \sim A_2 \wedge A_3) \vee (\sim A_1 \wedge \sim A_2 \wedge \sim A_3)$$

EXERCISE

Find a statement form in the connectives $\sim$, $\wedge$, and $\vee$ which has the following truth function $\text{f}(\text{x}_1, \text{x}_2, \text{x}_3)$.

x_1	x_2	x_3	$f(x_1, x_2, x_3)$
T	T	T	T
F	T	T	T
T	F	T	F
F	F	T	F
T	T	F	F
F	T	F	F
T	F	F	F
F	F	F	T

COROLLARY 1.5. *Every truth function corresponds to a statement form containing as connectives only* $\wedge$ *and* $\sim$, *or only* $\vee$ *and* $\sim$, *or only* $\supset$ *and* $\sim$.

PROOF. Notice that $A \vee B$ is logically equivalent to $\sim(\sim A \wedge \sim B)$. Hence, by Proposition 1.3 (second part), any statement form in $\wedge$, $\vee$, and $\sim$ is logically equivalent to a statement form in only $\wedge$ and $\sim$ (obtained by replacing all expressions $\mathscr{A} \vee \mathscr{B}$ by $\sim(\sim\mathscr{A} \wedge \sim\mathscr{B})$). The other parts of the corollary are similar consequences of the following tautologies:

$$A \wedge B \equiv \sim(\sim A \vee \sim B)$$
$$A \vee B \equiv (\sim A) \supset B$$
$$A \wedge B \equiv \sim(A \supset \sim B)$$

We have just seen that there are certain pairs of connectives, e.g., $\sim$ and $\wedge$, in terms of which all other truth functions are definable (in the sense of Corollary 1.5). It turns out that there is a single connective, $\downarrow$ (joint denial), which will do the same job. Its truth table is

A	B	$A \downarrow B$
T	T	F
F	T	F
T	F	F
F	F	T

$A \downarrow B$ is true when and only when neither A nor B is true. Clearly, $\sim A \equiv (A \downarrow A)$ and $(A \wedge B) \equiv ((A \downarrow A) \downarrow (B \downarrow B))$ are tautologies. Hence, the adequacy of $\downarrow$ for the construction of all truth functions follows from Corollary 1.5.

Another connective, $|$ (alternative denial), is also adequate for this purpose. Its truth table is

A	B	$A \mid B$
T	T	F
F	T	T
T	F	T
F	F	T

$A \mid B$ is true when and only when not both A and B are true. The adequacy of $\mid$ follows from the tautologies $\sim A \equiv (A \mid A)$ and $(A \vee B) \equiv ((A \mid A) \mid (B \mid B))$.

PROPOSITION 1.6. *The only binary connectives which alone are adequate for the construction of all truth functions are* $\downarrow$ *and* $\mid$.

PROOF. Assume that $h(A, B)$ is an adequate connective. Now, if $h(T, T)$ were T, then any statement form built up using only h would take the value T when all its statement letters take the value T. Hence, $\sim A$ would not be definable in terms of h. So, $h(T, T) = F$. Likewise, $h(F, F) = T$. Thus, we have the truth table

A	B	$h(A, B)$
T	T	F
F	T	
T	F	
F	F	T

If the second and third entries in the last column are F, F or T, T, then his $\downarrow$ or $\mid$. If they are F, T, then $h(A, B) \equiv \sim B$ would be a tautology; and if they are T, F, then $h(A, B) \equiv \sim A$ is a tautology. In both cases, h would be definable in terms of $\sim$. But $\sim$ is not adequate by itself, because the only truth functions of one variable definable from it are the identity function and negation itself, whereas the truth function that is always T would not be definable.

EXERCISES

1. Prove that each of the pairs, $\supset$, $\vee$ and $\sim$, $\equiv$ is not alone adequate to express all truth functions.

2. A statement form is in *disjunctive normal form* if it is a disjunction consisting of one or more disjuncts, each of which is a conjunction of one or more statement letters and negations of statement letters, e.g., $(A \wedge B) \vee (\sim A \wedge C)$, $(A \wedge B \wedge \sim A) \vee (C \wedge \sim B) \vee (A \wedge \sim C)$, A, $A \wedge B$, $A \vee (B \wedge C)$. A form is in *conjunctive normal form* if it is a conjunction of one or more conjuncts, each of which is a disjunction of one or more statement letters and negations of statement letters. Note that we consider statement letters and their negations as (degenerate) conjunctions or disjunctions. The proof of Proposition

1.4 shows that every statement form $\mathscr{A}$ is logically equivalent to one in disjunctive normal form. By applying this result to $\sim\mathscr{A}$, prove that $\mathscr{A}$ is also logically equivalent to a form in conjunctive normal form.

3. Find logically equivalent disjunctive and conjunctive normal forms for $(A \supset B) \vee (\sim A \wedge C)$ and $A \equiv (B \wedge \sim A)$.

Suggestion: instead of relying on Proposition 1.4, it is usually easier to use Exercise 7, pp. 20–21. For example, let $((A \supset \sim B) \wedge C) \vee (\sim A \equiv C)$ be given. To obtain the conjunctive form, first we eliminate $\supset$ and $\equiv$, obtaining $((\sim A \vee \sim B) \wedge C) \vee ((A \vee C) \wedge (\sim C \vee \sim A))$. Then, by Exercise 7(d), we have $(\sim A \vee \sim B \vee A \vee C) \wedge (\sim A \vee \sim B \vee \sim C \vee \sim A) \wedge (C \vee A \vee C) \wedge (C \vee \sim C \vee \sim A)$, which is logically equivalent to $(\sim A \vee \sim B \vee \sim C) \wedge (C \vee A)$, which is in conjunctive normal form. To obtain the disjunctive form, we first eliminate $\supset$ and $\equiv$, obtaining $((\sim A \vee \sim B) \wedge C) \vee ((\sim A \wedge C) \vee (A \wedge \sim C))$, and then, by Exercise 7(c), $(\sim A \wedge C) \vee (\sim B \wedge C) \vee (\sim A \wedge C) \vee (A \wedge \sim C)$, which is logically equivalent to $(\sim A \wedge C) \vee (\sim B \wedge C) \vee (A \wedge \sim C)$.

4. Let us call a statement letter A and its negation $\sim A$ *literals* with the letter A. A disjunctive (conjunctive) normal form is called *full* if no disjunct (conjunct) contains two occurrences of literals with the same letter and if a letter occurring in one disjunct (conjunct) also occurs in all the others. For example, $(A \wedge \sim A \wedge B) \vee (A \wedge B)$, $(A \wedge A \wedge B) \vee (A \wedge B)$, $(A \wedge B) \vee A$ are not full, whereas $(A \wedge \sim B) \vee (B \wedge A)$, and $(A \wedge B \wedge \sim C) \vee (A \wedge B \wedge C) \vee (A \wedge \sim B \wedge \sim C)$ are full disjunctive normal forms. Find full disjunctive and conjunctive normal forms for $(A \supset B) \vee (\sim A \wedge C)$ and $A \equiv (B \wedge \sim A)$. Prove that every non-contradictory (non-tautologous) statement form $\mathscr{A}$ is logically equivalent to a full disjunctive (conjunctive) normal form $\mathscr{F}$, and if $\mathscr{F}$ contains exactly n letters, then $\mathscr{A}$ is a tautology (contradiction) if and only if $\mathscr{F}$ has 2^n disjuncts (conjuncts).

5. A certain country is inhabited only by people who either always tell the truth or always tell lies, and who will respond to questions only with a yes or a no. A tourist comes to a fork in the road, where one branch leads to the capital and the other does not. There is no sign indicating which branch to take, but there is an inhabitant, Mr. R., standing at the fork. What yes-or-no question should the tourist ask him to determine which branch to take?

Hint: let A stand for "Mr. R always tells the truth", and let B stand for "The left-hand branch leads to the capital". Construct, by means of a suitable truth table, a statement form involving A and B such that the native's answer to the question as to whether this statement form is true will be "Yes" when and only when B is true.

§4. An Axiom System for the Propositional Calculus

Truth tables enable us to answer most of the significant questions concerning the truth-functional connectives, such as whether a given statement form is a tautology, contradiction, or neither, and whether it logically implies or is logically equivalent to some other given statement form. The more complex parts of logic which we shall treat later, however, cannot be handled by truth tables, or by any other similar effective procedure. Consequently, another approach, by means of formal theories, will have to be tried. Although, as we have seen, the propositional calculus surrenders completely to the truth table method, it will be instructive to illustrate the axiomatic method in this simple branch of logic.

A formal theory $\mathscr{S}$ is defined when the following conditions are satisfied.

(1) A countable set of symbols† is given as the symbols of $\mathscr{S}$. A finite sequence of symbols of $\mathscr{S}$ is called an *expression* of $\mathscr{S}$.

(2) There is a subset of the expressions of $\mathscr{S}$ called the set of *well-formed formulas* (abbreviated "wfs") of $\mathscr{S}$. (There is usually an effective procedure to determine whether a given expression is a wf.)

(3) A set of wfs is set aside and called the set of *axioms* of $\mathscr{S}$. (Most often, one can effectively decide whether a given wf is an axiom, and, in such a case, $\mathscr{S}$ is called an *axiomatic* theory.)

(4) There is a finite set $R_1, \ldots, R_n$ of relations among wfs, called *rules of inference*. For each R_i, there is a unique positive integer j such that, for every set of j wfs and each wf $\mathscr{A}$, one can effectively decide whether the given j wfs are in the relation R_i to $\mathscr{A}$, and, if so, $\mathscr{A}$ is called a *direct consequence* of the given wfs by virtue of R_i.

A *proof* in $\mathscr{S}$ is a sequence $\mathscr{A}_1, \ldots, \mathscr{A}_n$ of wfs such that, for each i, either $\mathscr{A}_i$ is an axiom of $\mathscr{S}$ or $\mathscr{A}_i$ is a direct consequence of some of the preceding wfs by virtue of one of the rules of inference.

A *theorem* of $\mathscr{S}$ is a wf $\mathscr{A}$ of $\mathscr{S}$ such that there is a proof the last wf of which is $\mathscr{A}$. Such a proof is called a *proof of* $\mathscr{A}$.

Even if $\mathscr{S}$ is axiomatic, i.e., if there is an effective procedure for checking any given wf to see whether it is an axiom, the notion of "theorem" is not necessarily effective, since, in general, there is no mechanical method (effective procedure) for determining, given any wf $\mathscr{A}$, whether there is a proof of $\mathscr{A}$. A theory for which there is such a mechanical method is said to be *decidable*; otherwise, it is called *undecidable*. A decidable theory is, roughly speaking, one for which a machine can be devised to test wfs for theoremhood, whereas, in an

† If desired, these "symbols" can be taken to be arbitrary objects rather than just linguistic objects.

undecidable theory, ingenuity is required to determine whether wfs are theorems.

A wf $\mathscr{A}$ is said to be a *consequence* in $\mathscr{S}$ of a set Γ of wfs if and only if there is a sequence $\mathscr{A}_1, \ldots, \mathscr{A}_n$ of wfs such that $\mathscr{A} = \mathscr{A}_n$ and, for each i, either $\mathscr{A}_i$ is an axiom or $\mathscr{A}_i$ is in Γ, or $\mathscr{A}_i$ is a direct consequence by some rule of inference of some of the preceding wfs in the sequence. Such a sequence is called a *proof* (or *deduction*) *of* $\mathscr{A}$ *from* Γ. The members of Γ are called the *hypotheses* or *premisses* of the proof. We use $\Gamma \vdash \mathscr{A}$ as an abbreviation for "$\mathscr{A}$ is a consequence of Γ". In order to avoid confusion when dealing with more than one theory, we write $\Gamma \vdash_{\mathscr{S}} \mathscr{A}$, adding the subscript $\mathscr{S}$ to indicate the theory in question. If Γ is a finite set $\{\mathscr{B}_1, \ldots, \mathscr{B}_n\}$, we write $\mathscr{B}_1, \ldots, \mathscr{B}_n \vdash \mathscr{A}$ instead of $\{\mathscr{B}_1, \ldots, \mathscr{B}_n\} \vdash \mathscr{A}$. If Γ is the empty set 0, then $0 \vdash \mathscr{A}$ if and only if $\mathscr{A}$ is a theorem. It is customary to omit the sign "0" and simply write $\vdash \mathscr{A}$. Thus, $\vdash \mathscr{A}$ is another way of asserting that $\mathscr{A}$ is a theorem.

The following are simple properties of the notion of consequence.

(1) If $\Gamma \subseteq \Delta$ and $\Gamma \vdash \mathscr{A}$, then $\Delta \vdash \mathscr{A}$.

(2) $\Gamma \vdash \mathscr{A}$ if and only if there is a finite subset Δ of Γ such that $\Delta \vdash \mathscr{A}$.

(3) If $\Delta \vdash \mathscr{A}$, and, for each $\mathscr{B}$ in Δ, $\Gamma \vdash \mathscr{B}$, then $\Gamma \vdash \mathscr{A}$.

Assertion (1) represents the fact that if $\mathscr{A}$ is provable from a set Γ of premisses, then, if we add still more premisses, $\mathscr{A}$ is still provable. Half of (2) follows from (1). The other half is obvious when we notice that any proof of $\mathscr{A}$ from Γ uses only a finite number of premisses from Γ. Proposition (3) is also quite simple: if $\mathscr{A}$ is provable from premisses in Δ, and each premiss in Δ is provable from the premisses in Γ, then $\mathscr{A}$ is provable from premisses in Γ.

We now introduce a formal axiomatic theory L for the propositional calculus.

(1) The symbols of L are $\sim$, $\supset$, (,), and the letters A_i with positive integers i as subscripts: $A_1, A_2, A_3, \ldots$. The symbols $\sim$ and $\supset$ are called *primitive connectives*, and the letters A_i are called *statement letters*.

(2)(a) All statement letters are wfs. (b) If $\mathscr{A}$ and $\mathscr{B}$ are wfs, so are $(\sim \mathscr{A})$ and $(\mathscr{A} \supset \mathscr{B})$.† Thus, a wf of L is just a statement form built up from the statement letters A_i by means of the connectives $\sim$ and $\supset$.

† To be precise, we should add the so-called extremal clause: (c) An expression is a wf only if it can be shown to be a wf on the basis of clauses (a) and (b). This definition can be made rigorous using as a model the definition in the footnote on page 15.

(3) If $\mathscr{A}$, $\mathscr{B}$, and $\mathscr{C}$ are any wfs of L, then the following are axioms of L.

(A1). $(\mathscr{A} \supset (\mathscr{B} \supset \mathscr{A}))$
(A2). $((\mathscr{A} \supset (\mathscr{B} \supset \mathscr{C})) \supset ((\mathscr{A} \supset \mathscr{B}) \supset (\mathscr{A} \supset \mathscr{C})))$
(A3). $((\sim\mathscr{B} \supset \sim\mathscr{A}) \supset ((\sim\mathscr{B} \supset \mathscr{A}) \supset \mathscr{B}))$.

(4) The only rule of inference of L is *modus ponens*: $\mathscr{B}$ is a direct consequence of $\mathscr{A}$ and $\mathscr{A} \supset \mathscr{B}$. We shall abbreviate application of this rule by MP.

We shall use our conventions for eliminating parentheses.

Notice that the infinite set of axioms of L is given by means of three axiom schemas (A1)–(A3), each schema standing for an infinite number of axioms. One can easily check for any given wf whether or not it is an axiom; therefore, L is axiomatic. It is our intention, in setting up the system L, to obtain as theorems precisely the class of all tautologies.

We introduce other connectives by definition.

(D1). $(\mathscr{A} \wedge \mathscr{B})$ for $\sim(\mathscr{A} \supset \sim\mathscr{B})$
(D2). $(\mathscr{A} \vee \mathscr{B})$ for $(\sim\mathscr{A}) \supset \mathscr{B}$
(D3). $(\mathscr{A} \equiv \mathscr{B})$ for $(\mathscr{A} \supset \mathscr{B}) \wedge (\mathscr{B} \supset \mathscr{A})$.

The meaning of D1, for example, is that, for any wfs $\mathscr{A}$ and $\mathscr{B}$, "$(\mathscr{A} \wedge \mathscr{B})$" is an abbreviation for "$\sim(\mathscr{A} \supset \sim\mathscr{B})$".†

LEMMA 1.7. *For any* wf $\mathscr{A}$, $\vdash_{L} \mathscr{A} \supset \mathscr{A}$.

PROOF.‡ We shall construct a proof in L of $\mathscr{A} \supset \mathscr{A}$.

† When we say that "$(\mathscr{A} \wedge \mathscr{B})$" is an abbreviation for "$\sim(\mathscr{A} \supset \sim\mathscr{B})$" we mean that "$(\mathscr{A} \wedge \mathscr{B})$" is to be taken as another name in the English language (or in whatever language $\mathscr{L}$ we happen to be using to talk about the theory L) for the expression "$\sim(\mathscr{A} \supset \sim\mathscr{B})$". Notice that as a name of an expression built up by juxtaposing various other expressions we use the expression in English (or in $\mathscr{L}$) made by juxtaposing the names of these other expressions; in addition, we use parentheses and the connectives as their own names except, of course, when this may cause confusion. For example, if "$\mathscr{A}$" is the name of the expression $(A_1 \supset A_2)$ and "$\mathscr{B}$" is the name of the expression $(\sim A_1)$, then we use "$(\mathscr{A} \supset \mathscr{B})$" as the name of the expression $((A_1 \supset A_2) \supset (\sim A_1))$. These conventions are quite natural and would not be noticed by most people if we had not explicitly pointed them out. For further elucidation, consult Quine's discussion of quasi-quotation (Quine [1951]); Carnap's treatment of autonymous symbols (Carnap [1934], § 4, and § 42); Rosser [1953], Chapter III; Suppes [1957], Chapter 6; Church [1956], Introduction and pages 74–77.

‡ The word "proof" is used in two distinct senses. First, it has a precise meaning defined above as a certain kind of finite sequence of wfs of L. However, in another sense, it also designates certain sequences of sentences of the English language (supplemented by various technical terms) which are supposed to serve as an argument justifying some assertion about the language L (or other formal theories). In general, the language we are studying (in this case L) is called the *object language*, while the language in which we formulate and prove results about the object language is called the *metalanguage*. The metalanguage might also be

(1) $(\mathscr{A} \supset ((\mathscr{A} \supset \mathscr{A}) \supset \mathscr{A})) \supset ((\mathscr{A} \supset (\mathscr{A} \supset \mathscr{A})) \supset (\mathscr{A} \supset \mathscr{A}))$
(Instance of Axiom Schema A2)
(2) $\mathscr{A} \supset ((\mathscr{A} \supset \mathscr{A}) \supset \mathscr{A})$ Axiom Schema A1
(3) $(\mathscr{A} \supset (\mathscr{A} \supset \mathscr{A})) \supset (\mathscr{A} \supset \mathscr{A})$ From 1, 2 by MP
(4) $\mathscr{A} \supset (\mathscr{A} \supset \mathscr{A})$ Axiom Schema A1
(5) $\mathscr{A} \supset \mathscr{A}$ From 3, 4 by MP

EXERCISES

Prove:

1. $\vdash_L (\sim\mathscr{A} \supset \mathscr{A}) \supset \mathscr{A}$.
2. $\mathscr{A} \supset \mathscr{B}, \mathscr{B} \supset \mathscr{C} \vdash_L \mathscr{A} \supset \mathscr{C}$.
3. $\mathscr{A} \supset (\mathscr{B} \supset \mathscr{C}) \vdash_L \mathscr{B} \supset (\mathscr{A} \supset \mathscr{C})$.
4. $\vdash_L (\sim\mathscr{B} \supset \sim\mathscr{A}) \supset (\mathscr{A} \supset \mathscr{B})$.

In mathematical arguments, one often proves a statement $\mathscr{B}$ on the assumption of some other statement $\mathscr{A}$ and then concludes that "If $\mathscr{A}$ then $\mathscr{B}$" is true. This procedure is justified for the system L by the following theorem.

PROPOSITION 1.8 (DEDUCTION THEOREM).† *If Γ is a set of* wfs, *and $\mathscr{A}$ and $\mathscr{B}$ are* wfs, *and $\Gamma, \mathscr{A} \vdash \mathscr{B}$, then $\Gamma \vdash \mathscr{A} \supset \mathscr{B}$. In particular, if $\mathscr{A} \vdash \mathscr{B}$, then $\vdash \mathscr{A} \supset \mathscr{B}$.* (Herbrand [1930].)

PROOF. Let $\mathscr{B}_1, \ldots, \mathscr{B}_n$ be a proof of $\mathscr{B}$ from $\Gamma \cup \{\mathscr{A}\}$, where $\mathscr{B}_n = \mathscr{B}$. Let us prove, by induction on i, that $\Gamma \vdash \mathscr{A} \supset \mathscr{B}_i$ for $1 \leqslant i \leqslant n$. First of all, $\mathscr{B}_1$ must be in Γ or an axiom of L or $\mathscr{A}$. By Axiom (A1), $\mathscr{B}_1 \supset (\mathscr{A} \supset \mathscr{B}_1)$ is an axiom. Hence, in the first two cases, by MP, $\Gamma \vdash \mathscr{A} \supset \mathscr{B}_1$. For the third case, when $\mathscr{B}_1$ is $\mathscr{A}$, we have $\vdash \mathscr{A} \supset \mathscr{B}_1$, by Lemma 1.7, and, therefore, $\Gamma \vdash \mathscr{A} \supset \mathscr{B}_1$. This takes care of the case $i = 1$. Assume now that $\Gamma \vdash \mathscr{A} \supset \mathscr{B}_k$ for all $k < i$. Either $\mathscr{B}_i$ is an axiom or $\mathscr{B}_i$ is in Γ, or $\mathscr{B}_i$ is $\mathscr{A}$, or $\mathscr{B}_i$ follows by modus ponens from some $\mathscr{B}_j$ and $\mathscr{B}_m$, where $j < i$, $m < i$, and $\mathscr{B}_m$

formalized and made the subject of study, which we would carry out in a meta-metalanguage, etc. However, we shall use the English language as our (unformalized) metalanguage, although, for a substantial part of this book, we employ only a mathematically weak portion of the English language. The contrast between object language and metalanguage is also present in the study of a foreign language; for example, in a German class, German is the object language, while the metalanguage, the language we use, is English. The distinction between "proof" and "metaproof" (i.e., a proof in the metalanguage) leads to a distinction between theorems of the object language and *metatheorems* of the metalanguage. To avoid confusion, we generally use "proposition" instead of "metatheorem". The word "metamathematics" refers to the study of logical and mathematical object languages; sometimes the word is restricted to those investigations which use what appear to the metamathematician to be constructive (or so-called *finitary*) methods.

† We use $\Gamma, \mathscr{A} \vdash \mathscr{B}$ to stand for $\Gamma \cup \{\mathscr{A}\} \vdash \mathscr{B}$. In general, we let $\Gamma, \mathscr{A}_1, \ldots, \mathscr{A}_n \vdash \mathscr{B}$ stand for $\Gamma \cup \{\mathscr{A}_1, \ldots, \mathscr{A}_n\} \vdash \mathscr{B}$.

has the form $\mathscr{B}_j \supset \mathscr{B}_i$. In the first three cases, $\Gamma \vdash \mathscr{A} \supset \mathscr{B}_i$, as in the case i = 1 above. In the last case, we have, by inductive hypothesis, $\Gamma \vdash \mathscr{A} \supset \mathscr{B}_j$ and $\Gamma \vdash \mathscr{A} \supset (\mathscr{B}_j \supset \mathscr{B}_i)$. But, by Axiom (A2), $\vdash (\mathscr{A} \supset (\mathscr{B}_j \supset \mathscr{B}_i)) \supset ((\mathscr{A} \supset \mathscr{B}_j) \supset (\mathscr{A} \supset \mathscr{B}_i))$. Hence, by MP, $\Gamma \vdash (\mathscr{A} \supset \mathscr{B}_j) \supset (\mathscr{A} \supset \mathscr{B}_i)$, and, again by MP, $\Gamma \vdash \mathscr{A} \supset \mathscr{B}_i$. Thus, the inductive proof is complete. The case i = n is the desired result. (Notice that, given a deduction of $\mathscr{B}$ from Γ and $\mathscr{A}$, the proof just given enables us to construct a deduction of $\mathscr{A} \supset \mathscr{B}$ from Γ. Also note that only Axiom Schemas (A1)–(A2) are used in proving the Deduction Theorem.)

COROLLARY 1.9.

(i) $\mathscr{A} \supset \mathscr{B}, \mathscr{B} \supset \mathscr{C} \vdash \mathscr{A} \supset \mathscr{C}$.

(ii) $\mathscr{A} \supset (\mathscr{B} \supset \mathscr{C}), \mathscr{B} \vdash \mathscr{A} \supset \mathscr{C}$.

PROOF. (1)

(a)	$\mathscr{A} \supset \mathscr{B}$	Hyp (abbreviation for "Hypothesis")
(b)	$\mathscr{B} \supset \mathscr{C}$	Hyp
(c)	$\mathscr{A}$	Hyp
(d)	$\mathscr{B}$	(a), (c) MP
(e)	$\mathscr{C}$	(b), (d) MP

Thus, $\mathscr{A} \supset \mathscr{B}, \mathscr{B} \supset \mathscr{C}, \mathscr{A} \vdash \mathscr{C}$. So, by the Deduction Theorem, $\mathscr{A} \supset \mathscr{B}, \mathscr{B} \supset \mathscr{C} \vdash \mathscr{A} \supset \mathscr{C}$.

(2) Exercise (Use the Deduction Theorem).

LEMMA 1.10. *For any* wfs $\mathscr{A}$, $\mathscr{B}$, *the following are theorems of L.*

(a) $\sim\sim\mathscr{B} \supset \mathscr{B}$

(b) $\mathscr{B} \supset \sim\sim\mathscr{B}$

(c) $\sim\mathscr{A} \supset (\mathscr{A} \supset \mathscr{B})$

(d) $(\sim\mathscr{B} \supset \sim\mathscr{A}) \supset (\mathscr{A} \supset \mathscr{B})$

(e) $(\mathscr{A} \supset \mathscr{B}) \supset (\sim\mathscr{B} \supset \sim\mathscr{A})$

(f) $\mathscr{A} \supset (\sim\mathscr{B} \supset \sim(\mathscr{A} \supset \mathscr{B}))$

(g) $(\mathscr{A} \supset \mathscr{B}) \supset ((\sim\mathscr{A} \supset \mathscr{B}) \supset \mathscr{B})$

PROOF.

(a) $\vdash \sim\sim\mathscr{B} \supset \mathscr{B}$

1.	$(\sim\mathscr{B} \supset \sim\sim\mathscr{B}) \supset ((\sim\mathscr{B} \supset \sim\mathscr{B}) \supset \mathscr{B})$	Axiom (A3)
2.	$\sim\mathscr{B} \supset \sim\mathscr{B}$	Lemma 1.7†
3.	$(\sim\mathscr{B} \supset \sim\sim\mathscr{B}) \supset \mathscr{B}$	1,2, Corollary 1.9(ii)
4.	$\sim\sim\mathscr{B} \supset (\sim\mathscr{B} \supset \sim\sim\mathscr{B})$	Axiom (A1)
5.	$\sim\sim\mathscr{B} \supset \mathscr{B}$	3,4, Corollary 1.9(i)

† Instead of writing down here the complete proof of $\sim\mathscr{B} \supset \sim\mathscr{B}$, we simply cite Lemma 1.7. In this way, we indicate how the proof of $\sim\sim\mathscr{B} \supset \mathscr{B}$ could be written down, if we wished to take the time and space to do so. This, of course, is nothing more than the ordinary application of previously obtained theorems.

(b) $\vdash \mathscr{B} \supset \sim\sim\mathscr{B}$

1. $(\sim\sim\sim\mathscr{B} \supset \sim\mathscr{B}) \supset ((\sim\sim\sim\mathscr{B} \supset \mathscr{B}) \supset \sim\sim\mathscr{B})$ — Axiom (A3)
2. $\sim\sim\sim\mathscr{B} \supset \sim\mathscr{B}$ — Part (a) above
3. $(\sim\sim\sim\mathscr{B} \supset \mathscr{B}) \supset \sim\sim\mathscr{B}$ — 1,2, MP
4. $\mathscr{B} \supset (\sim\sim\sim\mathscr{B} \supset \mathscr{B})$ — Axiom (A1)
5. $\mathscr{B} \supset \sim\sim\mathscr{B}$ — 3,4, Corollary 1.9(i)

(c) $\vdash \sim\mathscr{A} \supset (\mathscr{A} \supset \mathscr{B})$

1. $\sim\mathscr{A}$ — Hyp
2. $\mathscr{A}$ — Hyp
3. $\mathscr{A} \supset (\sim\mathscr{B} \supset \mathscr{A})$ — Axiom (A1)
4. $\sim\mathscr{A} \supset (\sim\mathscr{B} \supset \sim\mathscr{A})$ — Axiom (A1)
5. $\sim\mathscr{B} \supset \mathscr{A}$ — 2,3, MP
6. $\sim\mathscr{B} \supset \sim\mathscr{A}$ — 1,4, MP
7. $(\sim\mathscr{B} \supset \sim\mathscr{A}) \supset ((\sim\mathscr{B} \supset \mathscr{A}) \supset \mathscr{B})$ — Axiom (A3)
8. $(\sim\mathscr{B} \supset \mathscr{A}) \supset \mathscr{B}$ — 6,7, MP
9. $\mathscr{B}$ — 5,8, MP

Thus, by 1–9, $\sim\mathscr{A}, \mathscr{A} \vdash \mathscr{B}$. Therefore, by the Deduction Theorem, $\sim\mathscr{A} \vdash \mathscr{A} \supset \mathscr{B}$, and, again by the Deduction Theorem, $\vdash \sim\mathscr{A} \supset (\mathscr{A} \supset \mathscr{B})$.

(d) $\vdash (\sim\mathscr{B} \supset \sim\mathscr{A}) \supset (\mathscr{A} \supset \mathscr{B})$

1. $\sim\mathscr{B} \supset \sim\mathscr{A}$ — Hyp
2. $\mathscr{A}$ — Hyp
3. $(\sim\mathscr{B} \supset \sim\mathscr{A}) \supset ((\sim\mathscr{B} \supset \mathscr{A}) \supset \mathscr{B})$ — Axiom (A3)
4. $\mathscr{A} \supset (\sim\mathscr{B} \supset \mathscr{A})$ — Axiom (A1)
5. $(\sim\mathscr{B} \supset \mathscr{A}) \supset \mathscr{B}$ — 1,3, MP
6. $\mathscr{A} \supset \mathscr{B}$ — 4,5, Corollary 1.9(i)
7. $\mathscr{B}$ — 2,6, MP

Thus, by 1–7, $\sim\mathscr{B} \supset \sim\mathscr{A}, \mathscr{A} \vdash \mathscr{B}$, and two applications of the Deduction Theorem yield the desired result.

(e) $\vdash (\mathscr{A} \supset \mathscr{B}) \supset (\sim\mathscr{B} \supset \sim\mathscr{A})$

1. $\mathscr{A} \supset \mathscr{B}$ — Hyp
2. $\sim\sim\mathscr{A} \supset \mathscr{A}$ — Part (a)
3. $\sim\sim\mathscr{A} \supset \mathscr{B}$ — 1,2, Corollary 1.9(i)
4. $\mathscr{B} \supset \sim\sim\mathscr{B}$ — Part (b)
5. $\sim\sim\mathscr{A} \supset \sim\sim\mathscr{B}$ — 3,4, Corollary 1.9(i)
6. $(\sim\sim\mathscr{A} \supset \sim\sim\mathscr{B}) \supset (\sim\mathscr{B} \supset \sim\mathscr{A})$ — Part (d)
7. $(\sim\mathscr{B} \supset \sim\mathscr{A})$ — 5,6, MP

Thus, by 1–7, $\mathscr{A} \supset \mathscr{B} \vdash \sim\mathscr{B} \supset \sim\mathscr{A}$, and, by the Deduction Theorem, (e) follows.

(f) $\vdash \mathscr{A} \supset (\sim\mathscr{B} \supset \sim(\mathscr{A} \supset \mathscr{B}))$

Clearly, $\mathscr{A}, \mathscr{A} \supset \mathscr{B} \vdash \mathscr{B}$ by MP. Hence, $\vdash \mathscr{A} \supset ((\mathscr{A} \supset \mathscr{B}) \supset \mathscr{B})$ by two uses of the Deduction Theorem By Part (e), $\vdash ((\mathscr{A} \supset \mathscr{B}) \supset \mathscr{B}) \supset (\sim\mathscr{B} \supset \sim(\mathscr{A} \supset \mathscr{B}))$. Hence, using Corollary 1.9(i),

$$\vdash \mathscr{A} \supset (\sim\mathscr{B} \supset \sim(\mathscr{A} \supset \mathscr{B}))$$

(g) $\vdash (\mathscr{A} \supset \mathscr{B}) \supset ((\sim\mathscr{A} \supset \mathscr{B}) \supset \mathscr{B})$

1.	$\mathscr{A} \supset \mathscr{B}$	Hyp
2.	$\sim\mathscr{A} \supset \mathscr{B}$	Hyp
3.	$(\mathscr{A} \supset \mathscr{B}) \supset (\sim\mathscr{B} \supset \sim\mathscr{A})$	Part (e)
4.	$\sim\mathscr{B} \supset \sim\mathscr{A}$	1,3, MP
5.	$(\sim\mathscr{A} \supset \mathscr{B}) \supset (\sim\mathscr{B} \supset \sim\sim\mathscr{A})$	Part (e)
6.	$\sim\mathscr{B} \supset \sim\sim\mathscr{A}$	2,5, MP
7.	$(\sim\mathscr{B} \supset \sim\sim\mathscr{A}) \supset ((\sim\mathscr{B} \supset \sim\mathscr{A}) \supset \mathscr{B})$	Axiom (A3)
8.	$(\sim\mathscr{B} \supset \sim\mathscr{A}) \supset \mathscr{B}$	6,7, MP
9.	$\mathscr{B}$	4,8, MP

Thus, $\mathscr{A} \supset \mathscr{B}, \sim\mathscr{A} \supset \mathscr{B} \vdash \mathscr{B}$. Two applications of the Deduction Theorem yield (g).

EXERCISES

1. Show that the following are theorems of L:

(a) $((\mathscr{A} \supset \mathscr{B}) \supset \mathscr{A}) \supset \mathscr{A}$; (b) $\mathscr{A} \supset (\mathscr{B} \supset (\mathscr{A} \wedge \mathscr{B}))$.

2. Exhibit a complete proof in L of Lemma 1.10(c). (Hint: apply the procedure used in the proof of the Deduction Theorem to the demonstration given above of Lemma 1.10(c).) Greater fondness for the Deduction Theorem will result if the reader tries to prove Lemma 1.10 without using the Deduction Theorem.

It is our purpose to show that a wf of L is a theorem of L if and only if it is a tautology. Half of this is very easy.

PROPOSITION 1.11. *Every theorem of* L *is a tautology.*

PROOF. As an exercise, verify that all the axioms of L are tautologies. By Proposition 1.1, modus ponens leads from tautologies to other tautologies. Hence, every theorem of L is a tautology.

The following lemma is to be used in the proof that every tautology is a theorem of L.

LEMMA 1.12. *Let* $\mathscr{A}$ *be a* wf, *and let* $B_1, \ldots, B_k$ *be the statement letters occurring in* $\mathscr{A}$. *For a given assignment of truth values to* $B_1, \ldots, B_k$, *let* B_i' *be* B_i *if* B_i *takes the value* T; *and let* B_i' *be* $\sim B_i$ *if* B_i *takes the value* F. *Let* $\mathscr{A}'$ *be* $\mathscr{A}$, *if* $\mathscr{A}$ *takes the value* T *under the assignment; and let* $\mathscr{A}'$ *be* $\sim\mathscr{A}$ *if* $\mathscr{A}$ *takes the value* F. *Then* $B_1', \ldots, B_k' \vdash \mathscr{A}'$.

For example, let $\mathscr{A}$ be $\sim(\sim A_2 \supset A_5)$. Then, for each row of the truth table

A_2	A_5	$\sim(\sim A_2 \supset A_5)$
T	T	F
F	T	F
T	F	F
F	F	T

Lemma 1.12 asserts a corresponding deducibility relation. For instance, corresponding to the third row there is $A_2, \sim A_5 \vdash \sim\sim(\sim A_2 \supset A_5)$, and, to the fourth row, $\sim A_2, \sim A_5 \vdash \sim(\sim A_2 \supset A_5)$.

PROOF. By induction on the number n of occurrences of primitive connectives in $\mathscr{A}$. (We assume $\mathscr{A}$ written without abbreviations.) If $n = 0$, then $\mathscr{A}$ is just a statement letter B_1, and then the Lemma reduces to $B_1 \vdash B_1$ and $\sim B_1 \vdash \sim B_1$. Assume now that the Lemma holds for all $j < n$.

Case 1. $\mathscr{A}$ is $\sim\mathscr{B}$. Then $\mathscr{B}$ has fewer than n occurrences of primitive connectives.

Subcase 1a. Let $\mathscr{B}$ take the value T under the given truth value assignment. Then $\mathscr{A}$ takes the value F. So, $\mathscr{B}'$ is $\mathscr{B}$, and $\mathscr{A}'$ is $\sim\mathscr{A}$. By the inductive hypothesis applied to $\mathscr{B}$, $B_1', \ldots, B_k' \vdash \mathscr{B}$. Then, by Lemma 1.10(b) and MP, $B_1', \ldots, B_k' \vdash \sim\sim\mathscr{B}$. But $\sim\sim\mathscr{B}$ is $\mathscr{A}'$.

Subcase 1b. Let $\mathscr{B}$ take the value F. Then $\mathscr{B}'$ is $\sim\mathscr{B}$, and $\mathscr{A}'$ is $\mathscr{A}$. By inductive hypothesis, $B_1', \ldots, B_k' \vdash \sim\mathscr{B}$. But $\sim\mathscr{B}$ is $\mathscr{A}'$.

Case 2. $\mathscr{A}$ is $(\mathscr{B} \supset \mathscr{C})$. Then $\mathscr{B}$ and $\mathscr{C}$ have fewer occurrences of primitive connectives than $\mathscr{A}$. So, by inductive hypothesis, $B_1', \ldots, B_k' \vdash \mathscr{B}'$ and $B_1', \ldots, B_k' \vdash \mathscr{C}'$.

Case 2a. $\mathscr{B}$ takes the value F. Hence, $\mathscr{A}$ takes the value T. Then $\mathscr{B}'$ is $\sim\mathscr{B}$, and $\mathscr{A}'$ is $\mathscr{A}$. So, $B_1', \ldots, B_k' \vdash \sim\mathscr{B}$. By Lemma 1.10(c), $B_1', \ldots, B_k' \vdash \mathscr{B} \supset \mathscr{C}$. But $\mathscr{B} \supset \mathscr{C}$ is $\mathscr{A}'$.

Case 2b. $\mathscr{C}$ takes the value T. Hence $\mathscr{A}$ takes the value T. Then $\mathscr{C}'$ is $\mathscr{C}$ and $\mathscr{A}'$ is $\mathscr{A}$. Now, $B_1', \ldots, B_k' \vdash \mathscr{C}$. Then, by Axiom (A1), $B_1', \ldots, B_k' \vdash \mathscr{B} \supset \mathscr{C}$. But $\mathscr{B} \supset \mathscr{C}$ is $\mathscr{A}'$.

Case 2c. $\mathscr{B}$ takes the value T and $\mathscr{C}$ the value F. Then $\mathscr{A}$ has the value F, $\mathscr{B}'$ is $\mathscr{B}$, $\mathscr{C}'$ is $\sim\mathscr{C}$, and $\mathscr{A}'$ is $\sim\mathscr{A}$. Now, $B_1', \ldots, B_k' \vdash \mathscr{B}$ and $B_1', \ldots, B_k' \vdash \sim\mathscr{C}$. So, by Lemma 1.10(f), $B_1', \ldots, B_k' \vdash \sim(\mathscr{B} \supset \mathscr{C})$. But $\sim(\mathscr{B} \supset \mathscr{C})$ is $\mathscr{A}'$.

PROPOSITION 1.13 (COMPLETENESS THEOREM). *If a* wf $\mathscr{A}$ *of* L *is a tautology, then it is a theorem of* L.

PROOF. (Kalmár) Assume $\mathscr{A}$ a tautology, and let $B_1, \ldots, B_k$ be the statement letters in $\mathscr{A}$. For any truth value assignment to $B_1, \ldots, B_k$, we have, by Lemma 1.12, $B_1', \ldots, B_k' \vdash \mathscr{A}$. ($\mathscr{A}'$ is $\mathscr{A}$, because $\mathscr{A}$ always takes the value T.) Hence, if B_k takes the value T, $B_1', \ldots, B_{k-1}', B_k \vdash \mathscr{A}$, and, if B_k takes the value F, $B_1', \ldots, B_{k-1}', \sim B_k \vdash \mathscr{A}$. So, by the Deduction Theorem, $B_1', \ldots, B_{k-1}' \vdash B_k \supset \mathscr{A}$ and $B_1', \ldots, B_{k-1}' \vdash \sim B_k \supset \mathscr{A}$. Then, by Lemma 1.10(g), $B_1', \ldots, B_{k-1}' \vdash \mathscr{A}$. Similarly, B_{k-1} may be T or F, and again applying the Deduction Theorem and Lemma 1.10(g), we can eliminate B_{k-1}' just as we eliminated B_k'. After k such steps, we finally obtain $\vdash \mathscr{A}$.

COROLLARY 1.14. *If $\mathscr{B}$ is an expression involving the signs $\sim$, $\supset$, $\wedge$, $\vee$, $\equiv$ which is an abbreviation for a* wf *$\mathscr{A}$ of L, then $\mathscr{B}$ is a tautology if and only if $\mathscr{A}$ is a theorem of L.*

PROOF. In Definitions D1–D3, the abbreviating formulas replace wfs to which they are logically equivalent. Hence, by Proposition 1.3, $\mathscr{A}$ and $\mathscr{B}$ are logically equivalent, and $\mathscr{B}$ is a tautology if and only if $\mathscr{A}$ is. The corollary now follows from Proposition 1.13.

COROLLARY 1.15. *The system L is consistent, i.e., there is no* wf *$\mathscr{A}$ such that both $\mathscr{A}$ and $\sim \mathscr{A}$ are theorems of L.*

PROOF. By Proposition 1.11, every theorem of L is a tautology. The negation of a tautology cannot be a tautology, and, therefore, it is impossible for both $\mathscr{A}$ and $\sim \mathscr{A}$ to be theorems of L.

Notice that L is consistent if and only if not all wfs of L are theorems. For, clearly, if L is consistent, then there are wfs which are not theorems (e.g., the negations of theorems). On the other hand, by Lemma 1.10(c), $\vdash_L \sim \mathscr{A} \supset (\mathscr{A} \supset \mathscr{B})$, and so, if L were inconsistent, i.e., if some wf $\mathscr{A}$ and its negation $\sim \mathscr{A}$ were provable, then, by MP, any wf $\mathscr{B}$ would be provable. (This equivalence holds for any theory having modus ponens as a rule of inference and in which Lemma 1.10(c) is provable.) A theory in which not all wfs are theorems is often said to be *absolutely consistent*, and this definition is applicable even to theories not containing a negation sign.

EXERCISES

1. Verify that, for any wfs $\mathscr{A}$, $\mathscr{B}$, $\mathscr{C}$, the following are tautologies, and hence theorems of L.

   (a) $((\mathscr{A} \vee \mathscr{B}) \wedge (\mathscr{A} \supset \mathscr{C}) \wedge (\mathscr{B} \supset \mathscr{C})) \supset \mathscr{C}$.
   (b) $\mathscr{A} \supset (\mathscr{B} \supset \mathscr{C}) \equiv (\mathscr{A} \wedge \mathscr{B}) \supset \mathscr{C}$.

2. Let $\mathscr{A}$ be a statement form which is not a tautology. Let L^+ be the formal theory obtained from L by adding as new axioms all formulas obtainable from $\mathscr{A}$ by substituting arbitrary statement forms for the statement letters in $\mathscr{A}$, the same forms being substituted for all occurrences of a statement letter. Show that L^+ is inconsistent.

§ 5. Independence. Many-Valued Logics.

Given an axiomatic theory, a subset X of the axioms is said to be *independent* if some wf in X cannot be proved from the rest of the axioms by means of the rules of inference.

PROPOSITION 1.16. *Each of Axiom Schemas* (A1)–(A3) *is independent.*

PROOF

(a) Independence of (A1). Consider the following tables.

A	$\sim A$
0	1
1	1
2	0

A	B	$A \supset B$
0	0	0
1	0	2
2	0	0
0	1	2
1	1	2
2	1	0
0	2	2
1	2	0
2	2	0

Given any assignment of the values 0, 1, 2 to the statement letters of a wf $\mathscr{A}$, these tables determine a corresponding value of $\mathscr{A}$. If it always takes the value 0, $\mathscr{A}$ is called *select.* Now, modus ponens preserves selectness. Check that, if $\mathscr{A} \supset \mathscr{B}$ and $\mathscr{A}$ are select, so is $\mathscr{B}$. Verify also that all instances of Axioms (A2)–(A3) are select. Hence, any wf derivable from (A2)–(A3) by modus ponens is select. However, $A_1 \supset (A_2 \supset A_1)$, which is an instance of (A1), is not select, since it takes the value 2 when A_1 is 1 and A_2 is 2.

(b) Independence of (A2). Consider the following tables.

A	$\sim A$
0	1
1	0
2	1

A	B	$A \supset B$
0	0	0
1	0	0
2	0	0
0	1	2
1	1	2
2	1	0
0	2	1
1	2	0
2	2	0

Let us call a wf which always takes the value 0 according to these tables *grotesque.* Modus ponens preserves grotesqueness, and all instances of Axioms (A1) and (A3) are grotesque. (Exercise.) However, the instance $A_1 \supset (A_2 \supset A_3) \supset ((A_1 \supset A_2) \supset (A_1 \supset A_3))$ of (A2) takes the value 2 when A_1 is 0, A_2 is 0, and A_3 is 1, and, therefore, is not grotesque.

(c) Independence of (A3). If $\mathscr{A}$ is any wf, let h($\mathscr{A}$) be the wf obtained by erasing all negation signs in $\mathscr{A}$. For each instance $\mathscr{A}$ of Axioms (A1)–(A2), h($\mathscr{A}$) is a tautology. Also, modus ponens preserves the property of a wf $\mathscr{A}$ that h($\mathscr{A}$) is a tautology; for, if h($\mathscr{A} \supset \mathscr{B}$) and h($\mathscr{A}$) are tautologies, then h($\mathscr{B}$) is a tautology. (Just note that h($\mathscr{A} \supset \mathscr{B}$) is h($\mathscr{A}$) $\supset$ h($\mathscr{B}$).) Hence, every wf $\mathscr{A}$ derivable from (A1)–(A2) by modus ponens has the property that h($\mathscr{A}$) is a tautology. But h($(\sim A_1 \supset \sim A_1) \supset ((\sim A_1 \supset A_1) \supset A_1)$) is $(A_1 \supset A_1) \supset ((A_1 \supset A_1) \supset A_1)$, which is not a tautology. Hence, $(\sim A_1 \supset \sim A_1) \supset ((\sim A_1 \supset A_1) \supset A_1)$, an instance of (A3), is not derivable from (A1)–(A2) by modus ponens.

EXERCISE. Prove the independence of Axiom Schema (A3) by constructing tables for the connectives $\sim$ and $\supset$.

The idea used in the proof of independence of Axiom Schemas (A1)–(A2) may be generalized to the notion of a many-valued logic. Call the numbers 0, 1, 2, . . . , n "truth values", and let $0 \leqslant m < n$. The numbers 0, 1, . . . , m are called *designated values*. Take a finite number of "truth tables" representing functions from the set {0, 1, . . . , n} into itself. For each truth table, introduce a sign, which is called the corresponding *connective*. Using these connectives and statement letters, we may construct "statement forms", and every such statement form defines a "truth function" from {0, 1, 2, . . . , n} into itself. A statement form whose corresponding truth function takes only designated values is said to be *exceptional*. The numbers n, m, and the basic truth tables are said to define a (finite) *many-valued logic* M. An axiomatic theory involving statement letters and the connectives of M is said to be *suitable* for M if and only if the theorems of the theory coincide with the exceptional statement forms of M. (All these notions can obviously be generalized to the case of an infinite number of truth values.)

If n = 1 and m = 0, and the truth tables are those given for $\sim$ and $\supset$ in § 1, the corresponding 2-valued logic is that studied in this chapter. The exceptional wfs in this case were called tautologies. The system L is suitable for this logic, as proved in Propositions 1.11 and 1.13. In the proofs of the independence of Axiom Schemas (A1)–(A2), two three-valued logics were used.

EXERCISES

1. (McKinsey-Tarski) Consider the axiom system P in which there is exactly one binary connective $*$, the only rule of inference is modus

ponens (i.e., $\mathscr{B}$ follows from $\mathscr{A}$ and $\mathscr{A} * \mathscr{B}$), and the axioms are all wfs of the form $\mathscr{A} * \mathscr{A}$. Show that P is not suitable for any (finite) many-valued logic.

2. For any (finite) many-valued logic M, there is an axiomatic theory suitable for M.

Further information about many-valued logics can be gained from the monograph [1952] of Rosser and Turquette, and from the references mentioned therein.

§ 6. Other Axiomatizations

Although the axiom system L is quite simple, there are many other systems which would do as well. We can use, instead of $\sim$ and $\supset$, any collection of primitive connectives, so long as these are adequate for the definition of all other truth-functional connectives.

Examples.

L_1: $\vee$ and $\sim$ are the primitive connectives. We use $\mathscr{A} \supset \mathscr{B}$ as an abbreviation for $\sim\mathscr{A} \vee \mathscr{B}$. We have four axiom schemas: (1) $\mathscr{A} \vee \mathscr{A} \supset \mathscr{A}$; (2) $\mathscr{A} \supset \mathscr{A} \vee \mathscr{B}$; (3) $\mathscr{A} \vee \mathscr{B} \supset \mathscr{B} \vee \mathscr{A}$; (4) $(\mathscr{B} \supset \mathscr{C}) \supset (\mathscr{A} \vee \mathscr{B} \supset \mathscr{A} \vee \mathscr{C})$. The only rule of inference is modus ponens. This system is developed in Hilbert-Ackermann [1950].

L_2: $\wedge$ and $\sim$ are the primitive connectives. $\mathscr{A} \supset \mathscr{B}$ is an abbreviation for $\sim(\mathscr{A} \wedge \sim\mathscr{B})$. There are three axiom schemas: (1) $\mathscr{A} \supset (\mathscr{A} \wedge \mathscr{A})$; (2) $\mathscr{A} \wedge \mathscr{B} \supset \mathscr{A}$; (3) $(\mathscr{A} \supset \mathscr{B}) \supset (\sim(\mathscr{B} \wedge \mathscr{C}) \supset \sim(\mathscr{C} \wedge \mathscr{A}))$. Modus ponens is the only rule. Consult Rosser [1953] for a detailed study.

L_3: This is just like our original system L except that, instead of the axiom schemas (A1)–(A3), we have three specific axioms: (1) $A_1 \supset (A_2 \supset A_1)$; (2) $(A_1 \supset (A_2 \supset A_3)) \supset ((A_1 \supset A_2) \supset (A_1 \supset A_3))$; (3) $(\sim A_2 \supset \sim A_1) \supset ((\sim A_2 \supset A_1) \supset A_2)$. In addition to modus ponens, we have a substitution rule: we may substitute any wf for all occurrences of a statement letter in a given wf.

L_4: The primitive connectives are $\supset$, $\wedge$, $\vee$, and $\sim$. Modus ponens is the only rule, and we have ten axiom schemas:

(1) $\mathscr{A} \supset (\mathscr{B} \supset \mathscr{A})$
(2) $(\mathscr{A} \supset (\mathscr{B} \supset \mathscr{C})) \supset ((\mathscr{A} \supset \mathscr{B}) \supset (\mathscr{A} \supset \mathscr{C}))$
(3) $\mathscr{A} \wedge \mathscr{B} \supset \mathscr{A}$
(4) $\mathscr{A} \wedge \mathscr{B} \supset \mathscr{B}$
(5) $\mathscr{A} \supset (\mathscr{B} \supset (\mathscr{A} \wedge \mathscr{B}))$
(6) $\mathscr{A} \supset (\mathscr{A} \vee \mathscr{B})$
(7) $\mathscr{B} \supset (\mathscr{A} \vee \mathscr{B})$
(8) $(\mathscr{A} \supset \mathscr{C}) \supset ((\mathscr{B} \supset \mathscr{C}) \supset (\mathscr{A} \vee \mathscr{B} \supset \mathscr{C}))$

(9) $(\mathscr{A} \supset \mathscr{B}) \supset ((\mathscr{A} \supset \sim\mathscr{B}) \supset \sim\mathscr{A})$

(10) $\sim\sim\mathscr{A} \supset \mathscr{A}$

We define, as usual, $\mathscr{A} \equiv \mathscr{B}$ to be $(\mathscr{A} \supset \mathscr{B}) \wedge (\mathscr{B} \supset \mathscr{A})$. This system may be found in Kleene [1952].

EXERCISES

1. (Hilbert-Ackermann [1950]). Prove the following results about the theory L_1.

(a) $\mathscr{A} \supset \mathscr{B} \vdash_{L_1} \mathscr{C} \vee \mathscr{A} \supset \mathscr{C} \vee \mathscr{B}$

(b) $\vdash_{L_1} (\mathscr{A} \supset \mathscr{B}) \supset ((\mathscr{C} \supset \mathscr{A}) \supset (\mathscr{C} \supset \mathscr{B}))$

(c) $\mathscr{C} \supset \mathscr{A}, \mathscr{A} \supset \mathscr{B} \vdash_{L_1} \mathscr{C} \supset \mathscr{B}$

(d) $\vdash_{L_1} \mathscr{A} \supset \mathscr{A}$ (i.e., $\vdash_{L_1} \sim\mathscr{A} \vee \mathscr{A}$)

(e) $\vdash_{L_1} \mathscr{A} \vee \sim\mathscr{A}$

(f) $\vdash_{L_1} \mathscr{A} \supset \sim\sim\mathscr{A}$

(g) $\vdash_{L_1} \sim\mathscr{B} \supset (\mathscr{B} \supset \mathscr{C})$

(h) $\vdash_{L_1} \mathscr{A} \vee (\mathscr{B} \vee \mathscr{C}) \supset ((\mathscr{B} \vee (\mathscr{A} \vee \mathscr{C})) \vee \mathscr{A})$

(i) $\vdash_{L_1} (\mathscr{B} \vee (\mathscr{A} \vee \mathscr{C})) \vee \mathscr{A} \supset \mathscr{B} \vee (\mathscr{A} \vee \mathscr{C})$

(j) $\vdash_{L_1} \mathscr{A} \vee (\mathscr{B} \vee \mathscr{C}) \supset \mathscr{B} \vee (\mathscr{A} \vee \mathscr{C})$

(k) $\vdash_{L_1} (\mathscr{A} \supset (\mathscr{B} \supset \mathscr{C})) \supset (\mathscr{B} \supset (\mathscr{A} \supset \mathscr{C}))$

(l) $\vdash_{L_1} (\mathscr{C} \supset \mathscr{A}) \supset ((\mathscr{A} \supset \mathscr{B}) \supset (\mathscr{C} \supset \mathscr{B}))$

(m) $\mathscr{A} \supset (\mathscr{B} \supset \mathscr{C}), \mathscr{A} \supset \mathscr{B} \vdash_{L_1} \mathscr{A} \supset (\mathscr{A} \supset \mathscr{C})$

(n) $\mathscr{A} \supset (\mathscr{B} \supset \mathscr{C}), \mathscr{A} \supset \mathscr{B} \vdash_{L_1} \mathscr{A} \supset \mathscr{C}$

(o) If $\Gamma, \mathscr{A} \vdash_{L_1} \mathscr{B}$, then $\Gamma \vdash_{L_1} \mathscr{A} \supset \mathscr{B}$ (Deduction Theorem)

(p) $\mathscr{B} \supset \mathscr{A}, \sim\mathscr{B} \supset \mathscr{A} \vdash_{L_1} \mathscr{A}$

(q) $\vdash_{L_1} \mathscr{A}$ if and only if $\mathscr{A}$ is a tautology. (Hint: prove the analogues of Lemma 1.12 and Proposition 1.13.)

2. (Rosser [1953]). Prove the following assertions about the theory L_2.

(a) $\mathscr{A} \supset \mathscr{B}, \mathscr{B} \supset \mathscr{C} \vdash_{L_2} \sim(\sim\mathscr{C} \wedge \mathscr{A})$

(b) $\vdash_{L_2} \sim(\sim\mathscr{A} \wedge \mathscr{A})$

(c) $\vdash_{L_2} \sim\sim\mathscr{A} \supset \mathscr{A}$

(d) $\vdash_{L_2} \sim(\mathscr{A} \wedge \mathscr{B}) \supset (\mathscr{B} \supset \sim\mathscr{A})$

(e) $\vdash_{L_2} \mathscr{A} \supset \sim\sim\mathscr{A}$

(f) $\vdash_{L_2} (\mathscr{A} \supset \mathscr{B}) \supset (\sim\mathscr{B} \supset \sim\mathscr{A})$

(g) $\sim\mathscr{A} \supset \sim\mathscr{B} \vdash_{L_2} \mathscr{B} \supset \mathscr{A}$

(h) $\mathscr{A} \supset \mathscr{B} \vdash_{L_2} \mathscr{C} \wedge \mathscr{A} \supset \mathscr{B} \wedge \mathscr{C}$

(i) $\mathscr{A} \supset \mathscr{B}, \mathscr{B} \supset \mathscr{C}, \mathscr{C} \supset \mathscr{D} \vdash_{L_2} \mathscr{A} \supset \mathscr{D}$

(j) $\vdash_{L_2} \mathscr{A} \supset \mathscr{A}$

(k) $\vdash_{L_2} \mathscr{A} \wedge \mathscr{B} \supset \mathscr{B} \wedge \mathscr{A}$

(l) $\mathscr{A} \supset \mathscr{B}, \mathscr{B} \supset \mathscr{C} \vdash_{L_2} \mathscr{A} \supset \mathscr{C}$

(m) $\mathscr{A} \supset \mathscr{B}, \mathscr{C} \supset \mathscr{D} \vdash_{L_2} \mathscr{A} \wedge \mathscr{C} \supset \mathscr{B} \wedge \mathscr{D}$

(n) $\mathscr{B} \supset \mathscr{C} \vdash_{L_2} \mathscr{A} \wedge \mathscr{B} \supset \mathscr{A} \wedge \mathscr{C}$

(o) $\vdash_{L_2} (\mathscr{A} \supset (\mathscr{B} \supset \mathscr{C})) \supset ((\mathscr{A} \wedge \mathscr{B}) \supset \mathscr{C})$
(p) $\vdash_{L_2} ((\mathscr{A} \wedge \mathscr{B}) \supset \mathscr{C}) \supset (\mathscr{A} \supset (\mathscr{B} \supset \mathscr{C}))$
(q) $\mathscr{A} \supset \mathscr{B}, \mathscr{A} \supset (\mathscr{B} \supset \mathscr{C}) \vdash_{L_2} \mathscr{A} \supset \mathscr{C}$
(r) $\vdash_{L_2} \mathscr{A} \supset (\mathscr{B} \supset \mathscr{A} \wedge \mathscr{B})$
(s) $\vdash_{L_2} \mathscr{A} \supset (\mathscr{B} \supset \mathscr{A})$
(t) If $\Gamma, \mathscr{A} \vdash_{L_2} \mathscr{B}$, then $\Gamma \vdash_{L_2} \mathscr{A} \supset \mathscr{B}$ (Deduction Theorem)
(u) $\vdash_{L_2} (\sim\mathscr{A} \supset \mathscr{A}) \supset \mathscr{A}$
(v) $\mathscr{A} \supset \mathscr{B}, \sim\mathscr{A} \supset \mathscr{B} \vdash_{L_2} \mathscr{B}$
(w) $\vdash_{L_2} \mathscr{A}$ if and only if $\mathscr{A}$ is a tautology. (Hint: prove analogues of Lemma 1.12 and Proposition 1.13.)

3. Show that the theory L_3 has the same theorems as the theory L.
4. (Kleene [1952]). Derive the following statements about the theory L_4.

(a) $\vdash_{L_4} \mathscr{A} \supset \mathscr{A}$
(b) If $\Gamma, \mathscr{A} \vdash_{L_4} \mathscr{B}$, then $\Gamma \vdash_{L_4} \mathscr{A} \supset \mathscr{B}$ (Deduction Theorem)
(c) $\mathscr{A} \supset \mathscr{B}, \mathscr{B} \supset \mathscr{C} \vdash_{L_4} \mathscr{A} \supset \mathscr{C}$
(d) $\vdash_{L_4} (\mathscr{A} \supset \mathscr{B}) \supset (\sim\mathscr{B} \supset \sim\mathscr{A})$
(e) $\mathscr{B}, \sim\mathscr{B} \vdash_{L_4} \mathscr{C}$
(f) $\vdash_{L_4} \mathscr{B} \supset \sim\sim\mathscr{B}$
(g) $\vdash_{L_4} \sim\mathscr{B} \supset (\mathscr{B} \supset \mathscr{C})$
(h) $\vdash_{L_4} \mathscr{B} \supset (\sim\mathscr{C} \supset \sim(\mathscr{B} \supset \mathscr{C}))$
(i) $\vdash_{L_4} \sim\mathscr{B} \supset (\sim\mathscr{C} \supset \sim(\mathscr{B} \vee \mathscr{C}))$
(j) $\vdash_{L_4} (\sim\mathscr{B} \supset \mathscr{A}) \supset ((\mathscr{B} \supset \mathscr{A}) \supset \mathscr{A})$
(k) $\vdash_{L_4} \mathscr{A}$ if and only if $\mathscr{A}$ is a tautology. (Prove analogues of Lemma 1.12 and Proposition 1.13.)

Axiomatizations can be found for the propositional calculus which contain only one axiom schema. For example, if $\sim$ and $\supset$ are the primitive connectives and modus ponens the only rule of inference, the axiom schema

$$[(((\mathscr{A} \supset \mathscr{B}) \supset (\sim\mathscr{C} \supset \sim\mathscr{D})) \supset \mathscr{C}) \supset \mathscr{E}] \supset [(\mathscr{E} \supset \mathscr{A}) \supset (\mathscr{D} \supset \mathscr{A})]$$

is sufficient (C. A. Meredith [1953]). Another single-axiom formulation, due to J. Nicod [1917], uses only alternative denial $|$. Its rule of inference is: $\mathscr{C}$ follows from $\mathscr{A} \mid (\mathscr{B} \mid \mathscr{C})$ and $\mathscr{A}$, and its axiom schema is

$$(\mathscr{A} \mid (\mathscr{B} \mid \mathscr{C})) \mid \{[\mathscr{D} \mid (\mathscr{D} \mid \mathscr{D})] \mid [(\mathscr{E} \mid \mathscr{B}) \mid (\mathscr{A} \mid \mathscr{E}) \mid (\mathscr{A} \mid \mathscr{E}))]\}.$$

Further information, including historical background, may be found in Church [1956] and in a paper by Lukasiewicz and Tarski [1956, IV].

EXERCISES

1. Show that Axiom Schema (A3) of the system L can be replaced by the schema $(\sim\mathscr{A} \supset \sim\mathscr{B}) \supset (\mathscr{B} \supset \mathscr{A})$ without altering the class of theorems.

2. If, in L_4, Axiom Schema (10) is replaced by the schema (10)′—$\sim\mathscr{A} \supset (\mathscr{A} \supset \mathscr{B})$—then the new system L_I is called the *intuitionistic* propositional calculus.

(a) Consider an n+1-valued logic with these connectives: $\sim\mathscr{A}$ is 0 when $\mathscr{A}$ is n, and otherwise it is n; $\mathscr{A} \wedge \mathscr{B}$ has the maximum of the values of $\mathscr{A}$ and $\mathscr{B}$, while $\mathscr{A} \vee \mathscr{B}$ has the minimum of these values; $\mathscr{A} \supset \mathscr{B}$ is 0 if $\mathscr{A}$ has a value not less than that of $\mathscr{B}$, and, otherwise, it has the same value as $\mathscr{B}$. If we take 0 as the only designated value, show that all theorems of L_I are exceptional.

(b) $A_1 \vee \sim A_1$ and $\sim\sim A_1 \supset A_1$ are not theorems of L_I.

(c) For any m, the wf

$$(A_1 \equiv A_2) \vee \ldots \vee (A_1 \equiv A_m) \vee (A_2 \equiv A_3) \vee \ldots \vee (A_2 \equiv A_m) \vee \ldots \vee (A_{m-1} \equiv A_m)$$

is not a theorem of L_I.

(d) (Gödel [1933]) L_I is not suitable for any finite many-valued logic.

(e) (i) If $\Gamma, \mathscr{A} \vdash_{L_I} \mathscr{B}$, then $\Gamma \vdash_{L_I} \mathscr{A} \supset \mathscr{B}$ (Deduction Theorem)
(ii) $\mathscr{A} \supset \mathscr{B}, \mathscr{B} \supset \mathscr{C} \vdash_{L_I} \mathscr{A} \supset \mathscr{C}$
(iii) $\vdash_{L_I} \mathscr{A} \supset \sim\sim\mathscr{A}$
(iv) $\vdash_{L_I} (\mathscr{A} \supset \mathscr{B}) \supset (\sim\mathscr{B} \supset \sim\mathscr{A})$
(v) $\vdash_{L_I} \mathscr{A} \supset (\sim\mathscr{A} \supset \mathscr{B})$
(vi) $\vdash_{L_I} \sim\sim(\sim\sim\mathscr{A} \supset \mathscr{A})$
(vii) $\sim\sim(\mathscr{A} \supset \mathscr{B}), \sim\sim\mathscr{A} \vdash_{L_I} \sim\sim\mathscr{B}$
(viii) $\vdash_{L_I} \sim\sim\sim\mathscr{A} \supset \sim\mathscr{A}$

D(f) $\vdash_{L_I} \sim\sim\mathscr{A}$ if and only if $\mathscr{A}$ is a tautology.

(g) $\vdash_{L_I} \sim\mathscr{A}$ if and only if $\sim\mathscr{A}$ is a tautology.

D(h) If $\mathscr{A}$ has $\wedge$ and $\sim$ as its only connectives, $\vdash_{L_I} \mathscr{A}$ if and only if $\mathscr{A}$ is a tautology.

For further information on intuitionist logic, cf. Heyting [1956], Kleene [1945], Jaskowski [1936]. The latter paper shows that L_I is suitable for a many-valued logic with denumerably many values.

A3. Let $\mathscr{A}$ and $\mathscr{B}$ be in the relation R if and only if $\vdash_L \mathscr{A} \equiv \mathscr{B}$. Show that R is an equivalence relation. Given equivalence classes $[\mathscr{A}]$ and $[\mathscr{B}]$, let $[\mathscr{A}] \cup [\mathscr{B}] = [\mathscr{A} \vee \mathscr{B}]$, $[\mathscr{A}] \cap [\mathscr{B}] = [\mathscr{A} \wedge \mathscr{B}]$ and $\overline{[\mathscr{A}]} = [\sim\mathscr{A}]$. Show that the equivalence classes under R form a Boolean algebra with respect to $\cup$, $\cap$, and $\overline{}$, called the Lindenbaum algebra $L^\star$ determined by L. The element 0 of $L^\star$ is the equivalence class consisting of all contradictions (i.e., negations of tautologies). The element 1 of $L^\star$ is the equivalence class consisting of all tautologies.

Notice that $\vdash_L \mathscr{A} \supset \mathscr{B}$ if and only if $[\mathscr{A}] \leqslant [\mathscr{B}]$ in $L^\star$, and that $\vdash_L \mathscr{A} \equiv \mathscr{B}$ if and only if $[\mathscr{A}] = [\mathscr{B}]$. Show that a Boolean function f (built up from variables, 0 and 1, using $\cup$, $\cap$, $\overline{}$) is equal to the constant function 1 in all Boolean algebras if and only if $\vdash_L \mathrm{f}\#$, where $\mathrm{f}\#$ is obtained from f by changing $\cup$, $\cap$, $\overline{}$, 0, 1 into $\vee$, $\wedge$, $\sim$, $A_1 \wedge \sim A_1$, $A_1 \vee \sim A_1$, respectively.

CHAPTER 2

QUANTIFICATION THEORY

§ 1. Quantifiers

There are various kinds of logical inference which obviously cannot be justified on the basis of the propositional calculus; for example:

(1) Any friend of Martin is a friend of John.
Peter is not John's friend.
Hence Peter is not Martin's friend.

(2) All men are immortal.
Socrates is a man.
Hence Socrates is immortal.

(3) All men are animals.
Hence the head of a man is the head of an animal.

The correctness of these inferences rests not only upon the truth-functional relations among the sentences involved, but also upon the internal structure of these sentences as well as upon the meaning of such expressions as "all", "any", etc.

In order to make the structure of complex sentences more transparent, it is convenient to introduce special notation to represent frequently occurring expressions. If $P(x)$ asserts that x has the property P, then $(x)P(x)$ is to mean that, for every x, property P holds, or, in other words, that everything has the property P. On the other hand, $(Ex)P(x)$ shall mean that there is an x having the property P, i.e., that there is at least one object having the property P. In $(x)P(x)$, the first "(x)" is called a *universal quantifier*; in $(Ex)P(x)$, "(Ex)" is called an *existential quantifier*. The study of quantifiers and related concepts is the principal subject of this chapter; hence the title "Quantification Theory".

Examples. Let m, j, p, s, $F(x, y)$, $M(x)$, $I(x)$, $A(x)$, $h(x)$ stand, respectively, for Martin, John, Peter, Socrates, x is a friend of y, x is a man, x is immortal, x is an animal, and the head of x.

Then (1)–(3) above become:

(1′)
$$\frac{\begin{array}{c}(x)(F(x, m) \supset F(x, j)) \\ \sim F(p, j)\end{array}}{\sim F(p, m)}$$

(2′)
$$\frac{\begin{array}{c}(x)(M(x) \supset I(x)) \\ M(s)\end{array}}{I(s)}$$

(3′)
$$\frac{(x)(M(x) \supset A(x))}{(x)((Ey)(x = h(y) \wedge M(y)) \supset (Ey)(x = h(y) \wedge A(y)))}$$

Notice that the validity of these inferences does not depend upon the particular meanings of m, j, p, s, F, M, I, A, and h.

Just as statement forms were used to indicate logical structure dependent upon the propositional connectives, so also the form of inferences involving quantifiers, such as (1)–(3), can be represented abstractly, as in (1′)–(3′). For this purpose, we shall use commas, parentheses, the symbols $\sim$ and $\supset$ of the propositional calculus, *individual variables* $x_1, x_2, \ldots, x_n, \ldots$; *individual constants* $a_1, a_2, \ldots, a_n, \ldots$; *predicate letters* $A_1^1, A_1^2, \ldots, A_k^j, \ldots$; and *function letters* $f_1^1, f_1^2, \ldots, f_k^j, \ldots$. The positive integer which is a superscript of a predicate or function letter indicates the number of arguments, whereas the subscript is just an indexing number to distinguish different predicate or function letters with the same number of arguments. In the examples above, m, j, p, s are individual constants, F and $=$ are binary predicate letters (i.e., letters with two arguments), M, I, A are monadic predicate letters (i.e., letters with one argument), and h is a function letter with one argument.

The function letters applied to the variables and individual constants generate the *terms*, that is,

(a) Variables and individual constants are terms.

(b) If f_i^n is a function letter, and $t_1, \ldots, t_n$ are terms, then $f_i^n(t_1, \ldots, t_n)$ is a term.

(c) An expression is a term only if it can be shown to be a term on the basis of clauses (a) and (b).

The predicate letters applied to terms yield the *atomic formulas*, i.e., if A_i^n is a predicate letter and $t_1, \ldots, t_n$ are terms, then $A_i^n(t_1, \ldots, t_n)$ is an atomic formula.

The well-formed formulas (wfs) of quantification theory are defined as follows:

(a) Every atomic formula is a wf.

(b) If $\mathscr{A}$ and $\mathscr{B}$ are wfs, and y is a variable, then $(\sim\mathscr{A})$, $(\mathscr{A} \supset \mathscr{B})$, and $((y)\mathscr{A})$ are wfs.

(c) An expression is a wf only if it can be shown to be a wf on the basis of clauses (a) and (b).

In $((y)\mathscr{A})$, "$\mathscr{A}$" is called the *scope* of the quantifier "(y)". Note that $\mathscr{A}$ need not contain the variable y. In that case, we ordinarily understand $((y)\mathscr{A})$ to mean the same thing as $\mathscr{A}$. The expressions $\mathscr{A} \wedge \mathscr{B}$, $\mathscr{A} \vee \mathscr{B}$, $\mathscr{A} \equiv \mathscr{B}$ are defined as in the system L of the propositional calculus (cf. page 31). It was unnecessary for us to use the symbol E as a primitive symbol, because we can define existential quantification as follows:

$$(Ex)\mathscr{A} \text{ stands for } \sim((x)(\sim\mathscr{A}))$$

This definition is obviously faithful to the meaning of the quantifiers.

The same conventions made in Chapter 1 as to omission of parentheses are made here, with the additional convention that quantifiers (y) and (Ey) rank in strength between $\equiv$, $\supset$, and $\vee$, $\wedge$, $\sim$.

Examples:

$$(x_1)A_1^1(x_1) \supset A_1^2(x_1, x_2) \text{ stands for } (((x_1)A_1^1(x_1)) \supset A_1^2(x_1, x_2))$$
$$(x_1)A_1^1(x_1) \vee A_1^2(x_1, x_2) \text{ stands for } ((x_1)(A_1^1(x_1) \vee A_1^2(x_1, x_2)))$$

EXERCISE. Restore parentheses to $(x_2) \sim A_1^1(x_1) \supset A_2^3(x_1, x_1, x_2) \vee (x_1)A_2^1(x_1)$, and to $\sim(x_1)A_1^1(x_1) \supset (Ex_2)A_2^1(x_2) \supset A_1^2(x_1, x_2) \vee A_1^1(x_2)$.

As an additional convention, we also omit parentheses around quantified formulas when they are preceded by other quantifiers.

Example.

$$(x_1)(Ex_2)(x_4)A_1^3(x_1, x_2, x_4) \text{ stands for } ((x_1)((Ex_2)(((x_4)A_1^3(x_1, x_2, x_4)))))$$

EXERCISE. Restore parentheses to $(x_1)(x_3)(x_4)A_1^1(x_1) \supset A_2^1(x_3) \wedge \sim A_1^1(x_1)$, and to $(Ex_1)(x_2)(Ex_3)A_1^1(x_1) \vee (Ex_2) \sim (x_3)A_1^2(x_3, x_2)$.

The notions of *free* and *bound* occurrences of variables in a wf are defined as follows: an occurrence of a variable x is *bound* in a wf if and only if either it is the variable of a quantifier "(x)" in the wf, or it is within the scope of a quantifier "(x)" in the wf. Otherwise, the occurrence is said to be *free* in the wf.

Examples.

(i) $A_1^2(x_1, x_2)$

(ii) $A_1^2(x_1, x_2) \supset (x_1)A_1^1(x_1)$

(iii) $(x_1)(A_1^2(x_1, x_2) \supset (x_1)A_1^1(x_1))$

In (i), the single occurrence of x_1 is free. In (ii), the first occurrence of x_1 is free, but the second and third occurrences are bound. In (iii), all occurrences of x_1 are bound. In all three wfs, every occurrence of x_2 is free. Notice that, as in (ii), a variable may have both free and bound occurrences in a given wf. Also notice that an occurrence of a variable may be bound in some wf $\mathscr{A}$, but free in a subformula of $\mathscr{A}$. For example, the first occurrence of x_1 is free in (ii), but is bound in the larger wf (iii).

EXERCISE

Pick out the free and bound occurrences of variables in the following:

1. $(x_3)(((x_1)A_1^2(x_1, x_2)) \supset A_1^2(x_3, a_1))$
2. $(x_2)A_1^2(x_3, x_2) \supset (x_3)A_1^2(x_3, x_2)$
3. $((x_2)(Ex_1)A_1^3(x_1, x_2, f_1^2(x_1, x_2))) \vee \sim(x_1)A_1^2(x_2, f_1^1(x_1))$

A variable is said to be free (bound) in a wf if and only if it has a free (bound) occurrence in the wf. Thus, a variable may be both bound and free in the same wf, e.g., x_1 is bound and free in example (ii).

We shall often indicate that a wf $\mathscr{A}$ has some of the free variables $x_{i_1}, \ldots, x_{i_k}$ by writing it as $\mathscr{A}(x_{i_1}, \ldots, x_{i_k})$. This does not mean that $\mathscr{A}$ contains these variables as free variables nor does it mean that $\mathscr{A}$ does not contain other free variables. This notation is convenient because we then can agree to write as $\mathscr{A}(t_1, \ldots, t_k)$ the result of substituting in $\mathscr{A}$ the terms $t_1, \ldots, t_k$ for all free occurrences (if any) of $x_{i_1}, \ldots, x_{i_k}$, respectively.

If $\mathscr{A}$ is a wf and t is a term, then t is said to be *free for x_i in $\mathscr{A}$* if and only if no free occurrences of x_i in $\mathscr{A}$ lie within the scope of any quantifier (x_j), where x_j is a variable in t.

Examples.

(a) The term x_j is free for x_i in $A_1^1(x_i)$, but x_j is not free for x_i in $(x_j)A_1^1(x_i)$. The term $f_1^2(x_1, x_3)$ is free for x_1 in $(x_2)A_1^2(x_1, x_2) \supset A_1^1(x_1)$, but is not free for x_1 in $(Ex_3)(x_2)A_1^2(x_1, x_2) \supset A_1^1(x_1)$.

(b) Any term containing no variables is free for any variable in any wf.

(c) A term t is free for any variable in $\mathscr{A}$ if none of the variables of t is bound in $\mathscr{A}$.

(d) x_i is free for x_i in any wf.

(e) Any term is free for x_i in $\mathscr{A}$ if $\mathscr{A}$ contains no free occurrences of x_i.

EXERCISES

1. Is the term $f_1^2(x_1, x_2)$ free for x_1 in:

(a) $A_1^2(x_1, x_2) \supset (x_2)A_1^1(x_2)$

(b) $((x_2)A_1^2(x_2, a_1)) \vee (Ex_2)A_1^2(x_1, x_2)$

2. Translate the following sentences into wfs.

(a) All fish except sharks are kind to children.

(b) Either every wine-drinker is very communicative or some pawnbroker is honest and doesn't drink wine.

(c) Not all birds can fly.

(d) Everyone loves somebody and no one loves everybody, or somebody loves everybody and someone loves nobody.

(e) You can fool some of the people all the time, and you can fool all the people some of the time, but you can't fool all the people all the time.

(f) Some people are witty only if they are drunk.

(g) No politician is honest.

(h) If anyone can do it, Jones can.

(i) Anyone who is persistent can learn logic.

(j) If all clever philosophers are cynics and only women are clever philosophers, then, if there are any clever philosophers, some women are cynics.

§ 2. Interpretations. Satisfiability and Truth. Models.

Wfs have meaning only when an interpretation is given for the symbols. An *interpretation* consists of a non-empty set D, called the *domain* of the interpretation, and an assignment to each predicate letter A_j^n of an n-place relation in D, to each function letter f_j^n of an n-place operation in D (i.e., a function from D^n into D), and to each individual constant a_i of some fixed element of D. Given such an interpretation, variables are thought of as ranging over the set D, and $\sim$, $\supset$, and quantifiers are given their usual meaning. (Remember that an n-place relation in D can be thought of as a subset of D^n, the set of all n-tuples of elements of D. For example, if D is the set of human beings, then the relation "father of" can be identified with the set of all ordered pairs (x, y) such that x is the father of y.)

For a given interpretation, a wf without free variables (called a *closed* wf) represents a proposition which is true or false, whereas a wf with free variables stands for a relation on the domain of the interpretation which may be satisfied (true) for some values in the domain of the free variables and not satisfied (false) for the others.

Examples.

(i) $A_1^2(x_1, x_2)$

(ii) $(x_2)A_1^2(x_1, x_2)$

(iii) $(Ex_2)(x_1)A_1^2(x_2, x_1)$

If we take as domain the set of positive integers and interpret $A_1^2(y, z)$ as $y \leqslant z$, then (i) represents the relation $y \leqslant z$ which is satisfied by all the ordered pairs (a, b) of positive integers such that a $\leqslant$ b; (ii) represents the property (i.e., relation with one argument) "For all positive integers y, z $\leqslant$ y", which is satisfied only by the integer 1; and (iii) is a true sentence asserting that there is a smallest positive integer. If we were to take as domain the set of all integers, then (iii) would be false.

EXERCISES

1. $A_1^2(f_1^2(x_1, x_2), a_1)$
2. $A_1^2(x_1, x_2) \supset A_1^2(x_2, x_1)$
3. $(x_1)(x_2)(x_3)(A_1^2(x_1, x_2) \supset (A_1^2(x_2, x_3) \supset A_1^2(x_1, x_3)))$

For the following interpretations and for each of 1–3, indicate for what values the wfs are satisfied (if they contain free variables) or whether they are true or false (if they contain no free variables).

(a) The domain is the set of positive integers, $A_1^2(y, z)$ is y $\geqslant$ z, $f_1^2(y, z)$ is y$\cdot$z, and a_1 is 1.

(b) The domain is the set of human beings, $A_1^2(y, z)$ is "y loves z", $f_1^2(y, z)$ is z, and a_1 is Hitler.

(c) The domain is the set of all sets of integers, $A_1^2(y, z)$ is y $\supseteq$ z, $f_1^2(y, z)$ is y $\cup$ z, and a_1 is the empty set 0.

The notions of satisfiability and truth are intuitively clear, but, for the skeptical, they can be made precise in the following way. (Tarski [1936]) Let there be given an interpretation with domain D. Let $\sum$ be the set of denumerable sequences of elements of D. We shall define what it means for a sequence s = (b$_1$, b$_2$, ...) in $\sum$ to satisfy a wf $\mathscr{A}$ under the given interpretation. As a preliminary step we define a function s* of one argument, with terms as arguments and values in D.

(1) If t is x_i, let s$^\star(t)$ be b$_i$.

(2) If t is an individual constant, then s$^\star(t)$ is the interpretation in D of this constant.

(3) If f_j^n is a function letter and g is the corresponding operation in D, and $t_1, \ldots, t_n$ are terms, then s$^\star(f_j^n(t_1, \ldots, t_n))$ = g(s$^\star(t_1)$, s$^\star(t_2)$, ..., s$^\star(t_n)$).

Thus, s* is a function, determined by the sequence s, from the set of terms into D. Intuitively, for a sequence s = (b$_1$, b$_2$, ...) and a term t, s$^\star(t)$ is the element of D obtained by substituting, for each i, b$_i$ for all occurrences of x_i in t, and then performing the operations of the interpretation corresponding to the function letters of t. For instance, if t is $f_2^2(x_3, f_1^2(x_1, a_1))$, and the interpretation has the set of integers as its domain, f_2^2 and f_1^2 are interpreted as ordinary multiplication and addition, and a_1 is interpreted as 2, then, for any sequence s = (b$_1$, b$_2$, ...) of integers, s$^\star(t)$ is the integer b$_3$ $\times$ (b$_1$ + 2).

Now we proceed to the definition proper, which is an inductive definition.

(i) If $\mathscr{A}$ is an atomic wf $A_j^n(t_1, \ldots, t_n)$ and B_j^n is the corresponding relation of the interpretation, then the sequence s satisfies $\mathscr{A}$ if and only if $B_j^n(s^\star(t_1), \ldots, s^\star(t_n))$, i.e., if the n-tuple $(s^\star(t_1), \ldots, s^\star(t_n))$ is in the relation B_j^n.†

(ii) s satisfies $\sim\mathscr{A}$ if and only if s does not satisfy $\mathscr{A}$.

(iii) s satisfies $\mathscr{A} \supset \mathscr{B}$ if and only if either s does not satisfy $\mathscr{A}$ or s satisfies $\mathscr{B}$.

(iv) s satisfies $(x_i)\mathscr{A}$ if and only if every sequence of $\sum$ which differs from s in at most the ith component satisfies $\mathscr{A}$.

Intuitively, a sequence s = $(b_1, b_2, \ldots)$ satisfies a wf $\mathscr{A}$ if and only if, when we substitute, for each i, a symbol representing b_i for all free occurrences of x_i in $\mathscr{A}$, the resulting proposition is true under the given interpretation.

A wf $\mathscr{A}$ is *true* (for the given interpretation) if and only if every sequence in $\sum$ satisfies $\mathscr{A}$.

$\mathscr{A}$ is *false* (for the given interpretation) if and only if no sequence in $\sum$ satisfies $\mathscr{A}$.

An interpretation is said to be a *model* for a set Γ of wfs if and only if every wf in Γ is true for the interpretation.

Verification of the following consequences of the definitions above is left to the reader. (Most of the results are also obvious if one wishes to use only the ordinary intuitive understanding of the notions of truth and satisfaction.)

(I) $\mathscr{A}$ is false for a given interpretation if and only if $\sim\mathscr{A}$ is true for that interpretation; and $\mathscr{A}$ is true if and only if $\sim\mathscr{A}$ is false.

(II) For a given interpretation, no wf can be both true and false.

(III) If $\mathscr{A}$ and $\mathscr{A} \supset \mathscr{B}$ are true for a given interpretation, so is $\mathscr{B}$.

(IV) For a given interpretation, $\mathscr{A} \supset \mathscr{B}$ is false if and only if $\mathscr{A}$ is true and $\mathscr{B}$ false.

(V) (i) A sequence s satisfies $\mathscr{A} \wedge \mathscr{B}$ if and only if s satisfies $\mathscr{A}$ and s satisfies $\mathscr{B}$. A sequence s satisfies $\mathscr{A} \vee \mathscr{B}$ if and only if s satisfies $\mathscr{A}$

† For example, if the domain of the interpretation is the set of real numbers, the interpretation of A_1^2 is the relation $\leqslant$ and the interpretation of $f_1^1(x)$ is e^x, then a sequence s = $(b_1, b_2, \ldots)$ of real numbers satisfies $A_1^2(f_1^1(x_2), x_5)$ if and only if $e^{b_2} \leqslant b_5$. If the domain is the set of points in a plane, the interpretation of $A_1^3(x, y, z)$ is "x and y are equidistant from z", and the interpretation of $f_1^2(x, y)$ is "the midpoint of the line segment connecting x and y", then a sequence s = $(b_1, b_2, \ldots)$ of points in the plane satisfies $A_1^3(f_1^2(x_1, x_2), f_1^2(x_3, x_1), x_4)$ if and only if the midpoint of the line segment between b_1 and b_2 is at the same distance from b_4 as the midpoint of the line segment between b_3 and b_1. If the domain is the set of integers, the interpretation of $A_1^4(x, y, u, v)$ is "$x \cdot v = u \cdot y$", and the interpretation of a_1 is 2, then a sequence s = $(b_1, b_2, \ldots)$ of integers satisfies $A_1^4(x_3, a_1, x_1, x_3)$ if and only if $b_3{}^2 = 2b_1$.

or s satisfies $\mathscr{B}$. A sequence s satisfies $\mathscr{A} \equiv \mathscr{B}$ if and only if s satisfies both $\mathscr{A}$ and $\mathscr{B}$ or s satisfies neither $\mathscr{A}$ nor $\mathscr{B}$†.

(ii) A sequence s satisfies $(Ex_i)\mathscr{A}$ if and only if there is a sequence s′ which differs from s in at most the ith place such that s′ satisfies $\mathscr{A}$.†

(VI) $\mathscr{A}$ is true (for a given interpretation) if and only if $(x_i)\mathscr{A}$ is true (for that interpretation). By the *closure* of $\mathscr{A}$ we mean the closed wf obtained from $\mathscr{A}$ by prefixing as universal quantifiers those variables (in order of decreasing subscripts) which are free in $\mathscr{A}$. If $\mathscr{A}$ has no free variables, the closure of $\mathscr{A}$ is defined to be $\mathscr{A}$ itself. (For example, if $\mathscr{A}$ is $A_1^2(x_2, x_5) \supset \sim(Ex_2)A_1^3(x_1, x_2, x_3)$, its closure is $(x_5)(x_3)(x_2)(x_1)\mathscr{A}$.) Hence $\mathscr{A}$ is true if and only if its closure is true.

(VII) Every instance of a tautology is true for any interpretation. (An *instance* of a statement form is a wf obtained from the statement form by substituting wfs for all statement letters, all occurrences of the same statement letter being replaced by the same wf.) (Hint: show that all instances of the axioms of L are true, and then use (III) and Proposition 1.13.)

(VIII) If the free variables (if any) of a wf $\mathscr{A}$ occur in the list $x_{i_1}, \ldots, x_{i_k}$, and if the sequences s and s′ have the same components in the $i_1{}^{th}, \ldots, i_k{}^{th}$ places, then s satisfies $\mathscr{A}$ if and only if s′ satisfies $\mathscr{A}$. (Hint: induction on the number of connectives and quantifiers in $\mathscr{A}$. First prove that if the variables in a term t occur in the list $x_{i_1}, \ldots, x_{i_k}$, and if s and s′ have the same components in the $i_1{}^{th}, \ldots, i_k{}^{th}$ places, then $s^\star(t) = (s')^\star(t)$. In particular, if t contains no variables at all, $s_1{}^\star(t) = s_2{}^\star(t)$ for any sequences s_1 and s_2.) (Although, by (VIII), a particular wf $\mathscr{A}$ with k free variables is essentially satisfied or not only by k-tuples, rather than by denumerable sequences, it is more convenient for a general treatment of satisfiability for all wfs to deal with infinite rather than finite sequences.)

The set of k-tuples $(b_{i_1}, \ldots, b_{i_k})$ of the domain D such that any sequence with $b_{i_1}, \ldots, b_{i_k}$ in its $i_1{}^{th}, \ldots, i_k{}^{th}$ places, respectively, satisfies $\mathscr{A}$ is called the relation (or property) of the interpretation associated with $\mathscr{A}$.‡ For example, if the domain D is the set of human beings, $A_1^2(x, y)$ is interpreted as "x is a brother of y", and $A_2^2(x, y)$ is interpreted as "x is a parent of y", then the binary relation on D corresponding to the wf $(Ex_3)(A_1^2(x_1, x_3) \wedge A_2^2(x_3, x_2))$ is the relation of unclehood. If the domain is the set of positive integers, A_1^2 is interpreted as $=$, f_1^2 is interpreted as multiplication, and a_1 is interpreted as 1, then the wf $\sim A_1^2(x_1, a_1) \wedge (x_2)((Ex_3)A_1^2(x_1, f_1^2(x_2, x_3)) \supset A_1^2(x_2, x_1) \vee A_1^2(x_2, a_1))$ determines the property of being a prime number.

† Remember that $\mathscr{A} \wedge \mathscr{B}$, $\mathscr{A} \vee \mathscr{B}$, $\mathscr{A} \equiv \mathscr{B}$, $(Ex_i)\mathscr{A}$ are abbreviations for $\sim(\mathscr{A} \supset \sim\mathscr{B})$, $\sim\mathscr{A} \supset \mathscr{B}$, $(\mathscr{A} \supset \mathscr{B}) \wedge (\mathscr{B} \supset \mathscr{A})$, $\sim(x_i)\sim\mathscr{A}$, respectively.

‡ We assume here that $x_{i_1}, \ldots, x_{i_k}$ are the free variables of $\mathscr{A}$.

(IX) If $\mathscr{A}$ is a closed wf, then, for any given interpretation, either $\mathscr{A}$ is true or $\sim\mathscr{A}$ is true (i.e., $\mathscr{A}$ is false). (Hint: corollary of (VIII).) Of course, $\mathscr{A}$ may be true for some interpretations and false for others (e.g., if $\mathscr{A}$ is $A_1^1(a_1)$).

If $\mathscr{A}$ is not closed, i.e., if $\mathscr{A}$ contains free variables, $\mathscr{A}$ may be neither true nor false for some interpretations. For example, if $\mathscr{A}$ is $A_1^2(x_1, x_2)$, and we consider an interpretation in which the domain is the set of integers and $A_1^2(y, z)$ is interpreted as $y < z$, then $\mathscr{A}$ is satisfied only by those sequences $s = (b_1, b_2, \ldots)$ of integers in which $b_1 < b_2$. Hence, $\mathscr{A}$ is neither true nor false for this interpretation.

(X) Lemma: if t and u are terms and s is a sequence in $\sum$, and t' results from t by substitution of u for all occurrences of x_i, and s′ results from s by substituting $s^\star(u)$ for the ith component of s, then $s^\star(t') = (s')^\star(t)$. (Hint: induction on the length† of t.)

Let $\mathscr{A}(x_i)$ be a wf, t a term free for x_i in $\mathscr{A}(x_i)$, and $\mathscr{A}(t)$ the wf obtained from $\mathscr{A}(x_i)$ by substituting t for all free occurrences of x_i in $\mathscr{A}(x_i)$. Then a sequence $s = (b_1, b_2, \ldots)$ satisfies $\mathscr{A}(t)$ if and only if the sequence s′ obtained from s by substituting $s^\star(t)$ for b_i in the ith place, satisfies $\mathscr{A}(x_i)$. (Hint: induction on the number of connectives and quantifiers in $\mathscr{A}(x_i)$, using the lemma.)

COROLLARY. *If $(x_i)\mathscr{A}(x_i)$ is satisfied by s, so is $\mathscr{A}(t)$. Hence, $(x_i)\mathscr{A}(x_i) \supset \mathscr{A}(t)$ is true for all interpretations.*

(XI) If $\mathscr{A}$ does not contain x_i free, then $(x_i)(\mathscr{A} \supset \mathscr{B}) \supset (\mathscr{A} \supset (x_i)\mathscr{B})$ is true for all interpretations.

EXERCISE

Verify (I)–(XI). As an example, let us prove (XI). Assume it is incorrect. Then $(x_i)(\mathscr{A} \supset \mathscr{B}) \supset (\mathscr{A} \supset (x_i)\mathscr{B})$ is not true for some interpretation. By clause (iii) of the definition above, there is a sequence s such that s satisfies $(x_i)(\mathscr{A} \supset \mathscr{B})$ and s does not satisfy $(\mathscr{A} \supset (x_i)\mathscr{B})$. From the latter and clause (iii), s satisfies $\mathscr{A}$ and s does not satisfy $(x_i)\mathscr{B}$. Hence this implies, by clause (iv), that there is a sequence s′ differing from s in at most the ith place such that s′ does not satisfy $\mathscr{B}$. Since x_i is free in neither $(x_i)(\mathscr{A} \supset \mathscr{B})$ nor $\mathscr{A}$, and since s satisfies both of these wfs, it follows by (VIII) that s′ also satisfies both $(x_i)(\mathscr{A} \supset \mathscr{B})$ and $\mathscr{A}$. Since s′ satisfies $(x_i)(\mathscr{A} \supset \mathscr{B})$, it follows, by clause (iv), that s′ satisfies $\mathscr{A} \supset \mathscr{B}$. Since s′ satisfies $\mathscr{A} \supset \mathscr{B}$ and $\mathscr{A}$, clause (iii) implies that s′ satisfies $\mathscr{B}$, which contradicts the fact that s′ does not satisfy $\mathscr{B}$. Hence (XI) is proved.

† The length of an expression is the number of occurrences of symbols in the expression.

A wf $\mathscr{A}$ is said to be *logically valid* (according to quantification theory) if and only if $\mathscr{A}$ is true for every interpretation.

$\mathscr{A}$ is said to be *satisfiable* (according to quantification theory) if and only if there is an interpretation for which $\mathscr{A}$ is satisfied by at least one sequence in $\sum$.

It is obvious that $\mathscr{A}$ is logically valid if and only if $\sim\mathscr{A}$ is not satisfiable; and $\mathscr{A}$ is satisfiable if and only if $\sim\mathscr{A}$ is not logically valid. If $\mathscr{A}$ is a closed wf, then we know that $\mathscr{A}$ is either true or false for any given interpretation, i.e., $\mathscr{A}$ is satisfied by all sequences or by none; therefore, if $\mathscr{A}$ is closed, then $\mathscr{A}$ is satisfiable if and only if $\mathscr{A}$ is true for some interpretation.

We say that $\mathscr{A}$ is *contradictory* (according to quantification theory) if and only if $\sim\mathscr{A}$ is logically valid, or, equivalently, if and only if $\mathscr{A}$ is false for every interpretation.

$\mathscr{A}$ is said to *logically imply* $\mathscr{B}$ (according to quantification theory) if and only if, in every interpretation, any sequence satisfying $\mathscr{A}$ also satisfies $\mathscr{B}$. (More generally, $\mathscr{B}$ is a *logical consequence* (according to quantification theory) of a set Γ of wfs if and only if, in every interpretation, every sequence which satisfies every wf in Γ also satisfies $\mathscr{B}$.) $\mathscr{A}$ and $\mathscr{B}$ are *logically equivalent* (according to quantification theory) if and only if they logically imply each other.

The following assertions are easy consequences of these definitions.

(a) $\mathscr{A}$ logically implies $\mathscr{B}$ if and only if $\mathscr{A} \supset \mathscr{B}$ is logically valid.

(b) $\mathscr{A}$ and $\mathscr{B}$ are logically equivalent if and only if $\mathscr{A} \equiv \mathscr{B}$ is logically valid.

(c) If $\mathscr{A}$ logically implies $\mathscr{B}$, and $\mathscr{A}$ is true in a given interpretation, so is $\mathscr{B}$.

(d) If $\mathscr{B}$ is a logical consequence of a set Γ of wfs, and all wfs in Γ are true in a given interpretation, so is $\mathscr{B}$.

Any sentence of a formal or natural language which is an instance of a logically valid wf is called *logically true* (according to quantification theory), and an instance of a contradictory wf is said to be *logically false* (according to quantification theory).†

Examples.

1. Every instance of a tautology is logically valid. (VII)
2. If $\mathscr{A}$ does not contain x free, then $(x)(\mathscr{A} \supset \mathscr{B}) \supset (\mathscr{A} \supset (x)\mathscr{B})$ is logically valid. (XI)
3. If t is free for x in $\mathscr{A}$, then $(x)\mathscr{A}(x) \supset \mathscr{A}(t)$ is logically valid. (X)
4. The wf $(x_2)(Ex_1)A_1^2(x_1, x_2) \supset (Ex_1)(x_2)A_1^2(x_1, x_2)$ is not logically valid. As a counterexample, let the domain D be the set of integers,

† From now on, we shall omit the phrase "according to quantification theory".

and let $A_1^2(y, z)$ be y < z. Then $(x_2)(Ex_1)A_1^2(x_1, x_2)$ is true, but $(Ex_1)(x_2)A_1^2(x_1, x_2)$ is false.

EXERCISES

1. Show that the following wfs are not logically valid.

(a) $[(x_1)(A_1^1(x_1)) \supset ((x_1)A_2^1(x_1))] \supset [(x_1)(A_1^1(x_1) \supset A_2^1(x_1))]$
(b) $[(x_1)(A_1^1(x_1) \vee A_2^1(x_1))] \supset [((x_1)A_1^1(x_1)) \vee ((x_1)A_2^1(x_1))]$

2. Show that the following wfs are logically valid.

(a) $\mathscr{A}(t) \supset (Ex_i)\mathscr{A}(x_i)$ if t is free for x_i in $\mathscr{A}(x_i)$
(b) $(x_i)\mathscr{A} \supset (Ex_i)\mathscr{A}$
(c) $(x_i)(x_j)\mathscr{A} \equiv (x_j)(x_i)\mathscr{A}$
(d) $(x_i)\mathscr{A} \equiv \sim(Ex_i)\sim\mathscr{A}$
(e) $(x_i)(\mathscr{A} \supset \mathscr{B}) \supset ((x_i)\mathscr{A} \supset (x_i)\mathscr{B})$
(f) $((x_i)\mathscr{A} \wedge (x_i)\mathscr{B}) \equiv (x_i)(\mathscr{A} \wedge \mathscr{B})$
(g) $((x_i)\mathscr{A} \vee (x_i)\mathscr{B}) \supset (x_i)(\mathscr{A} \vee \mathscr{B})$
(h) $(Ex_i)(Ex_j)\mathscr{A} \equiv (Ex_j)(Ex_i)\mathscr{A}$
(i) $(Ex_i)(x_j)\mathscr{A} \supset (x_j)(Ex_i)\mathscr{A}$

3. If $\mathscr{A}$ is a closed wf, show that $\mathscr{A}$ logically implies $\mathscr{B}$ if and only if $\mathscr{B}$ is true in every interpretation in which $\mathscr{A}$ is true. (This is not always the case when $\mathscr{A}$ has free variables. For example, let $\mathscr{A}$ be $A_1^1(x_1)$ and $\mathscr{B}$ be $(x_1)A_1^1(x_1)$; $\mathscr{B}$ is true whenever $\mathscr{A}$ is (by VI); produce an interpretation showing that $\mathscr{A}$ does not logically imply $\mathscr{B}$.)

4. Show that the wfs

(a) $(Ex)(y)(A_1^2(x, y) \wedge \sim A_1^2(y, x) \supset [A_1^2(x, x) \equiv A_1^2(y, y)])$
(b) $(x)(y)(z)(A_1^2(x, y) \wedge A_1^2(y, z) \supset A_1^2(x, z))$
$\wedge\ (x)\sim A_1^2(x, x) \supset (Ex)(y)\sim A_1^2(x, y)$
(c) $(x)(y)(z)(A_1^2(x, x) \wedge (A_1^2(x, z) \supset A_1^2(x, y) \vee A_1^2(y, z)))$
$\supset (Ey)(z)A_1^2(y, z)$

are not logically valid.

5. Prove: If the free variables of $\mathscr{A}$ are $y_1, \ldots, y_n$, then $\mathscr{A}$ is satisfiable if and only if $(Ey_1)\ldots(Ey_n)\mathscr{A}$ is satisfiable.

6. Introducing appropriate abbreviations, write the sentences of the following arguments as wfs, and determine whether the conclusion is logically implied by the conjunction of the premisses.

(a) Everyone who is sane can understand mathematics. None of Hegel's sons can understand mathematics. No madmen are fit to vote. Hence none of Hegel's sons is fit to vote.

(b) For every set x, there is a set y such that the cardinality of y is greater than the cardinality of x. If x is included in y, the cardinality of x is not greater than the cardinality of y. Every set is included in V. Hence, V is not a set.

(c) If every ancestor of an ancestor of an individual is also an ancestor of the same individual, and no individual is his own ancestor, then there must be a person who has no ancestor.

(d) Any barber in Jonesville shaves exactly those men who do not shave themselves. Hence there is no barber in Jonesville.

7. Exhibit a logically valid wf which is not an instance of a tautology. However, show that any logically valid open wf (i.e., a wf without quantifiers) must be an instance of a tautology.

§ 3. First-Order Theories

In the case of the propositional calculus, the method of truth tables provides an effective test as to whether any given statement form is a tautology. However, there does not seem to be any effective process to determine whether a given wf is logically valid, since, in general, one has to check the truth of a wf for interpretations with arbitrarily large finite or infinite domains. In fact, we shall see later that, according to a fairly plausible definition of "effective", it may actually be proved that there is no effective way to test for logical validity. The axiomatic method, which was a luxury in the study of the propositional calculus, thus appears to be a necessity in the study of wfs involving quantifiers,† and we therefore turn now to the consideration of *first-order theories*‡.

The symbols of a first-order theory K are essentially those introduced earlier in this chapter: the propositional connectives $\sim$, $\supset$; the punctuation marks (,), , (the comma is not strictly necessary but is convenient for ease in reading formulas); denumerably many individual variables x_1, x_2, . . . ; a finite or denumerable non-empty set of predicate

† There is still another reason for a formal axiomatic approach. Concepts and propositions which involve the notion of interpretation, and related ideas such as truth, model, etc., are often called *semantical* to distinguish them from *syntactical* concepts, which refer to simple relations among symbols and expressions of precise formal languages. Since semantical notions are set-theoretic in character, and since set theory, because of the paradoxes, is considered a rather shaky foundation for the study of mathematical logic, many logicians consider a syntactical approach, consisting in a study of formal axiomatic theories using only rather weak number-theoretic methods, to be much safer. For further discussions, see the pioneering study on semantics by Tarski [1936], Kleene [1952], Church [1956], and Hilbert-Bernays [1934].

‡ The adjective "first-order" is used to distinguish the theories we shall study from those in which there are predicates having other predicates or functions as arguments or in which predicate quantifiers or function quantifiers are permitted, or both. First-order theories suffice for the expression of known mathematical theories, and, in any case, most higher-order theories can be suitably "translated" into first-order theories. Examples of higher-order theories may be found in Church [1940], Gödel [1931], Tarski [1933], Scholz-Hasenjaeger [1961: §§ 200–219].

letters $A_j^n (n, j \geqslant 1)$; a finite or denumerable, possibly empty, set of function letters $f_j^n (n, j \geqslant 1)$; and a finite or denumerable, possibly empty, set of individual constants a_i $(i \geqslant 1)$. Thus, in a theory K, some or all of the function letters and individual constants may be absent, and some (but not all) of the predicate letters may be absent. Different theories may differ in which of these symbols they possess.

The definitions given in Section 2 for term, wf, and for the propositional connectives $\wedge$, $\vee$, $\equiv$, are adopted for any first-order theory. Of course, for a particular theory K, only those symbols occurring in K are used in the formation of terms and wfs.

The axioms of K are divided into two classes: the logical axioms and the proper (or non-logical) axioms.

Logical Axioms: If $\mathscr{A}$, $\mathscr{B}$, $\mathscr{C}$ are wfs of K, then the following are logical axioms of K.

(1) $\mathscr{A} \supset (\mathscr{B} \supset \mathscr{A})$
(2) $(\mathscr{A} \supset (\mathscr{B} \supset \mathscr{C})) \supset ((\mathscr{A} \supset \mathscr{B}) \supset (\mathscr{A} \supset \mathscr{C}))$
(3) $(\sim\mathscr{B} \supset \sim\mathscr{A}) \supset ((\sim\mathscr{B} \supset \mathscr{A}) \supset \mathscr{B})$
(4) $(x_i)\mathscr{A}(x_i) \supset \mathscr{A}(t)$, if $\mathscr{A}(x_i)$ is a wf of K and t is a term of K free for x_i in $\mathscr{A}(x_i)$. Note here that t may be identical with x_i, giving the axioms $(x_i)\mathscr{A}(x_i) \supset \mathscr{A}(x_i)$.
(5) $(x_i)(\mathscr{A} \supset \mathscr{B}) \supset (\mathscr{A} \supset (x_i)\mathscr{B})$ if $\mathscr{A}$ is a wf of K containing no free occurrences of x_i.

Proper Axioms: These cannot be specified, since they vary from theory to theory. A first-order theory in which there are no proper axioms is called a first-order *predicate calculus*.

The rules of inference of any first-order theory are

(i) Modus ponens: $\mathscr{B}$ follows from $\mathscr{A}$ and $\mathscr{A} \supset \mathscr{B}$.
(ii) Generalization: $(x_i)\mathscr{A}$ follows from $\mathscr{A}$.

(We shall use MP and Gen, respectively, to indicate applications of these rules.)

By a model of a first-order theory K we mean an interpretation in which all the axioms of K are true. By (III) and (VI), pp. 51–52, if the rules of modus ponens and generalization are applied to wfs true in a given interpretation, then the results of these applications are also true. Hence every theorem of K is true in any model of K.

As we shall see, the logical axioms are so designed that the logical consequences (in the semantic sense, cf. p. 54) of the closure of the axioms of K are precisely the theorems of K. In particular, if K is a first-order predicate calculus, it turns out that the theorems of K are precisely those wfs of K which are logically valid.

Some explanation is needed for the restrictions in Axiom Schema (4) and (5). In the case of (4), if t were not free for x_i in $\mathscr{A}$, the following unpleasant result would arise. Let $\mathscr{A}(x_1)$ be $\sim(x_2)A_1^2(x_1, x_2)$ and let t be x_2. Notice that t is not free for x_1 in $\mathscr{A}(x_1)$. Consider the instance of Axiom (4):

$$(\maltese) \quad (x_1)(\sim(x_2)A_1^2(x_1, x_2)) \supset \sim(x_2)A_1^2(x_2, x_2)$$

Now, take as interpretation any domain with at least two members and let A_1^2 stand for the identity relation. Then the antecedent of ($\maltese$) is true and the consequent false.

In the case of (5), relaxation of the restriction that x_i not be free in $\mathscr{A}$ would lead to the following misfortune. Let $\mathscr{A}$ and $\mathscr{B}$ both be $A_1^1(x_1)$. Thus, x_1 is free in $\mathscr{A}$. Consider the instance of (5):

$$(\maltese\maltese) \quad (x_1)(A_1^1(x_1) \supset A_1^1(x_1)) \supset (A_1^1(x_1) \supset (x_1)A_1^1(x_1))$$

The antecedent of ($\maltese\maltese$) is logically valid. However, if we take any interpretation in which A_1^1 holds for some but not all elements of the domain, then the consequent will not be true.

Examples of first-order theories.

(i) Partial order. Let K have a single predicate letter A_1^2 and no function letters and individual constants. We shall write $x_i < x_j$ instead of $A_1^2(x_i, x_j)$ and $x_i \nless x_j$ for $\sim(x_i < x_j)$. We have two proper axioms:

(a) $(x_1)(x_1 \nless x_1)$ (Irreflexivity)
(b) $(x_1)(x_2)(x_3)(x_1 < x_2 \wedge x_2 < x_3 \supset x_1 < x_3)$ (Transitivity)

A model of this theory is called a partially-ordered structure.

(ii) Group theory. Let K have one predicate letter A_1^2, one function letter f_1^2, and one individual constant a_1. (To conform with ordinary notation, we shall write $t = s$ instead of $A_1^2(t, s)$, $t + s$ instead of $f_1^2(t, s)$ and 0 instead of a_1.) As proper axioms we have:

(a) $(x_1)(x_2)(x_3)(x_1 + (x_2 + x_3) = (x_1 + x_2) + x_3)$ (Associativity)
(b) $(x_1)(0 + x_1 = x_1)$ (Identity)
(c) $(x_1)(Ex_2)(x_2 + x_1 = 0)$ (Inverse)
(d) $(x_1)(x_1 = x_1)$ (Reflexivity of =)
(e) $(x_1)(x_2)(x_1 = x_2 \supset x_2 = x_1)$ (Symmetry of =)
(f) $(x_1)(x_2)(x_3)(x_1 = x_2 \supset (x_2 = x_3 \supset x_1 = x_3))$ (Transitivity of =)
(g) $(x_1)(x_2)(x_3)(x_2 = x_3 \supset (x_1 + x_2 = x_1 + x_3 \wedge x_2 + x_1 = x_3 + x_1))$ (Substitutivity of =)

A model for this theory is called a group. If, in addition, the wf $(x_1)(x_2)(x_1 + x_2 = x_2 + x_1)$ is true in a group, the latter is called abelian (or commutative).

The theories of partial order and of groups are both axiomatic. In general, any theory with a finite number of proper axioms is axiomatic, since it is obvious that one can effectively decide whether any given wf is a logical axiom (cf. page 57).

§4. Properties of First-Order Theories

All the results in this section refer to an arbitrary first-order theory K, unless otherwise stated. Notice that any first-order theory is a formal theory (cf. pages 29–30).

PROPOSITION 2.1. *Every* wf $\mathscr{A}$ *of K which is an instance of a tautology is a theorem of K, and it may be proved using only Axioms* (1)–(3) *and* MP.

PROOF. $\mathscr{A}$ arises from a tautology W by substitution. By Proposition 1.13, there is a proof of W in L. In such a proof, make the same substitutions of wfs of K for statement letters as were used in obtaining $\mathscr{A}$ from W, and, for all statement letters in the proof which do not occur in W, substitute an arbitrary wf of K. Then the resulting sequence of wfs is a proof of $\mathscr{A}$, and this proof uses only Axiom Schemas (1)–(3) and MP.

PROPOSITION 2.2. *Any first-order predicate calculus K is consistent.*

PROOF. For each wf $\mathscr{A}$ of K, let $\mathrm{h}(\mathscr{A})$ be the expression obtained by erasing all the quantifiers and terms in $\mathscr{A}$ (together with the associated commas and parentheses). Examples: $\mathrm{h}((x_1)(A_1^2(x_1, x_2) \supset A_1^1(x_3))$ is $A_1^2 \supset A_1^1$; and $\mathrm{h}(\sim(x_7)A_2^3(x_4, a_1, x_7) \supset A_3^1(x_4)))$ is $\sim A_2^3 \supset A_3^1$. Then $\mathrm{h}(\mathscr{A})$ is essentially a statement form, with the symbols A_j^k playing the role of statement letters. Clearly, $\mathrm{h}(\sim\mathscr{A}) = \sim(\mathrm{h}(\mathscr{A}))$ and $\mathrm{h}(\mathscr{A} \supset \mathscr{B}) = \mathrm{h}(\mathscr{A}) \supset \mathrm{h}(\mathscr{B})$. Now, for every axiom $\mathscr{A}$ given by Schemas (1)–(5), $\mathrm{h}(\mathscr{A})$ is a tautology. This is clear for (1)–(3). An instance of (4), $(x_i)\mathscr{A}(x_i) \supset \mathscr{A}(t)$, is transformed by h into a tautology of the form $\mathscr{B} \supset \mathscr{B}$; and an instance of (5), $(x_i)(\mathscr{A} \supset \mathscr{B}) \supset (\mathscr{A} \supset (x_i)\mathscr{B})$ is transformed into a tautology of the form $(\mathscr{D} \supset \mathscr{E}) \supset (\mathscr{D} \supset \mathscr{E})$. In addition, if $\mathrm{h}(\mathscr{A})$ and $\mathrm{h}(\mathscr{A} \supset \mathscr{B})$ are tautologies, then, by Proposition 1.1, $\mathrm{h}(\mathscr{B})$ is also a tautology; and, if $\mathrm{h}(\mathscr{A})$ is a tautology, so is $\mathrm{h}((x_i)\mathscr{A})$, which is the same as $\mathrm{h}(\mathscr{A})$. Hence, $\mathrm{h}(\mathscr{A})$ is a tautology whenever $\mathscr{A}$ is a theorem of K. If there were a wf $\mathscr{B}$ of K such that $\vdash_{\mathrm{K}} \mathscr{B}$ and $\vdash_{\mathrm{K}} \sim\mathscr{B}$, then both $\mathrm{h}(\mathscr{B})$ and $\sim\mathrm{h}(\mathscr{B})$ would be tautologies, which is impossible. Thus, K is consistent. (The transformation h amounts to interpreting K in a domain with a single element. All the theorems of

K are true in such an interpretation, but no wf and its negation can be true in any interpretation.)

The Deduction Theorem (Proposition 1.8) for the propositional calculus cannot be carried over without modification to arbitrary first-order theories K. For example, for any wf $\mathscr{A}$, $\mathscr{A} \vdash_K (x_1)\mathscr{A}$, but it is not always the case that $\vdash_K \mathscr{A} \supset (x_1)\mathscr{A}$. Consider a domain containing at least two elements c and d. Let K be a predicate calculus, and let $\mathscr{A}$ be $A_1^1(x_1)$. Interpret A_1^1 as a property which holds only for c. Then $A_1^1(x_1)$ is satisfied by any sequence $s = (b_1, b_2, \ldots)$ where $b_1 = c$, but $(x_1)A_1^1(x_1)$ is satisfied by no sequence at all. Hence, $A_1^1(x_1) \supset (x_1)A_1^1(x_1)$ is not true in this interpretation, and so it is not logically valid. But it is easy to see (Proposition 2.7) that every theorem of a predicate calculus is logically valid.

However, a modified, but still useful, form of the Deduction Theorem may be derived.

Let $\mathscr{A}$ be a wf in a set Γ of wfs; assume given a deduction $\mathscr{B}_1, \ldots, \mathscr{B}_n$ from Γ, together with justification for each step of the deduction. We shall say that $\mathscr{B}_i$ *depends upon* $\mathscr{A}$ in this proof if and only if:

(i) $\mathscr{B}_i$ is $\mathscr{A}$ and the justification for $\mathscr{B}_i$ is that it belongs to Γ; or

(ii) $\mathscr{B}_i$ is justified as a direct consequence by MP or Gen of some preceding wfs of the sequence, where at least one of these preceding wfs depends upon $\mathscr{A}$.

Example.

$$\mathscr{A}, (x_1)\mathscr{A} \supset \mathscr{C} \vdash (x_1)\mathscr{C}$$

$(\mathscr{B}_1)$	$\mathscr{A}$	Hyp
$(\mathscr{B}_2)$	$(x_1)\mathscr{A}$	$(\mathscr{B}_1)$, Gen
$(\mathscr{B}_3)$	$(x_1)\mathscr{A} \supset \mathscr{C}$	Hyp
$(\mathscr{B}_4)$	$\mathscr{C}$	$(\mathscr{B}_2)$, $(\mathscr{B}_3)$, MP
$(\mathscr{B}_5)$	$(x_1)\mathscr{C}$	$(\mathscr{B}_4)$, Gen

Here, $(\mathscr{B}_1)$ depends upon $\mathscr{A}$; $(\mathscr{B}_2)$ depends upon $\mathscr{A}$; $(\mathscr{B}_3)$ depends upon $(x_1)\mathscr{A} \supset \mathscr{C}$; $(\mathscr{B}_4)$ depends upon $\mathscr{A}$ and $(x_1)\mathscr{A} \supset \mathscr{C}$, and $(\mathscr{B}_5)$ depends upon $\mathscr{A}$ and $(x_1)\mathscr{A} \supset \mathscr{C}$.

PROPOSITION 2.3. *If $\mathscr{B}$ does not depend upon $\mathscr{A}$ in a deduction $\Gamma, \mathscr{A} \vdash \mathscr{B}$, then $\Gamma \vdash \mathscr{B}$.*

PROOF. Let $\mathscr{B}_1, \ldots, \mathscr{B}_n = \mathscr{B}$ be a deduction of $\mathscr{B}$ from Γ and $\mathscr{A}$, in which $\mathscr{B}$ does not depend upon $\mathscr{A}$. As inductive hypothesis, let us assume that the proposition is true for all deductions of length less than n. If $\mathscr{B}$ belongs to Γ or is an axiom, then $\Gamma \vdash \mathscr{B}$. If $\mathscr{B}$ is a direct consequence of one or two preceding wfs, then, since $\mathscr{B}$ does not depend upon $\mathscr{A}$, neither do these preceding wfs. By the inductive hypothesis, these preceding wfs are deducible from Γ alone. Consequently, so is $\mathscr{B}$.

PROPOSITION 2.4 (DEDUCTION THEOREM). *Assume that* $\Gamma, \mathscr{A} \vdash \mathscr{B}$, *where, in the deduction, no application of* Gen *to a* wf *which depends upon* $\mathscr{A}$ *has as its quantified variable a free variable of* $\mathscr{A}$. *Then* $\Gamma \vdash \mathscr{A} \supset \mathscr{B}$.

PROOF. Let $\mathscr{B}_1, \ldots, \mathscr{B}_n = \mathscr{B}$ be a deduction of $\mathscr{B}$ from $\Gamma, \mathscr{A}$ satisfying the assumption of our proposition. Let us show by induction that $\Gamma \vdash \mathscr{A} \supset \mathscr{B}_i$ for each $i \leqslant n$. If $\mathscr{B}_i$ is an axiom or belongs to Γ, then $\Gamma \vdash \mathscr{A} \supset \mathscr{B}_i$, since $\mathscr{B}_i \supset (\mathscr{A} \supset \mathscr{B}_i)$ is an axiom. If $\mathscr{B}_i$ is $\mathscr{A}$, then $\Gamma \vdash \mathscr{A} \supset \mathscr{B}_i$, since, by Proposition 2.1, $\vdash \mathscr{A} \supset \mathscr{A}$. If there exist j, k less than i such that $\mathscr{B}_k$ is $\mathscr{B}_j \supset \mathscr{B}_i$, then, by inductive hypothesis, $\Gamma \vdash \mathscr{A} \supset \mathscr{B}_j$ and $\Gamma \vdash \mathscr{A} \supset (\mathscr{B}_j \supset \mathscr{B}_i)$. Hence, $\Gamma \vdash \mathscr{A} \supset \mathscr{B}_i$, by Axiom (2) and MP. Finally, suppose there is some $j < i$ such that $\mathscr{B}_i$ is $(x_k)\mathscr{B}_j$. By hypothesis, $\Gamma \vdash \mathscr{A} \supset \mathscr{B}_j$ and either $\mathscr{B}_j$ does not depend upon $\mathscr{A}$ or x_k is not a free variable of $\mathscr{A}$. If $\mathscr{B}_j$ does not depend upon $\mathscr{A}$, then, by Proposition 2.3, $\Gamma \vdash \mathscr{B}_j$, and, consequently, by Gen, $\Gamma \vdash (x_k)\mathscr{B}_j$. Thus, $\Gamma \vdash \mathscr{B}_i$. Now, by Axiom (1), $\vdash \mathscr{B}_i \supset (\mathscr{A} \supset \mathscr{B}_i)$. So, $\Gamma \vdash \mathscr{A} \supset \mathscr{B}_i$, by MP. If x_k is not a free variable of $\mathscr{A}$, then, by Axiom (5), $\vdash (x_k)(\mathscr{A} \supset \mathscr{B}_j) \supset (\mathscr{A} \supset (x_k)\mathscr{B}_j)$. Since $\Gamma \vdash \mathscr{A} \supset \mathscr{B}_j$, we have, by Gen, $\Gamma \vdash (x_k)(\mathscr{A} \supset \mathscr{B}_j)$, and so, by MP, $\Gamma \vdash \mathscr{A} \supset (x_k)\mathscr{B}_j$, i.e., $\Gamma \vdash \mathscr{A} \supset \mathscr{B}_i$. This completes the induction, and our proposition is just the special case $i = n$.

The hypothesis of Proposition 2.4 is rather cumbersome, and the following weaker corollaries often prove to be more useful.

COROLLARY 2.5. *If a deduction* $\Gamma, \mathscr{A} \vdash \mathscr{B}$ *involves no application of* Gen *of which the quantified variable is free in* $\mathscr{A}$, *then* $\Gamma \vdash \mathscr{A} \supset \mathscr{B}$.

COROLLARY 2.6. *If* $\mathscr{A}$ *is a closed* wf, *and* $\Gamma, \mathscr{A} \vdash \mathscr{B}$, *then* $\Gamma \vdash \mathscr{A} \supset \mathscr{B}$.

In Propositions 2.3–2.6, the following additional conclusion can be drawn from the proof. The new proof of $\Gamma \vdash \mathscr{A} \supset \mathscr{B}$ (in the case of 2.3, of $\Gamma \vdash \mathscr{B}$) involves an application of Gen to a wf depending upon a wf $\mathscr{C}$ of Γ only if there is an application of Gen in the given proof of $\Gamma, \mathscr{A} \vdash \mathscr{B}$ which involves the same quantified variable and is applied to a wf which depends upon $\mathscr{C}$. (In the proof of Proposition 2.4, one should observe that $\mathscr{B}_j$ depends upon a premiss $\mathscr{C}$ of Γ in the original proof if and only if $\mathscr{A} \supset \mathscr{B}_j$ depends upon $\mathscr{C}$ in the new proof.)

This supplementary conclusion is useful when we wish to apply the Deduction Theorem several times in a row to a given deduction, e.g., to obtain $\Gamma \vdash \mathscr{D} \supset (\mathscr{A} \supset \mathscr{B})$ from $\Gamma, \mathscr{D}, \mathscr{A} \vdash \mathscr{B}$; from now on, it is to be considered as part of the statements of Propositions 2.3–2.6.

Example. $\vdash (x_1)(x_2)\mathscr{A} \supset (x_2)(x_1)\mathscr{A}$

PROOF.

1. $(x_1)(x_2)\mathscr{A}$ Hyp
2. $(x_1)(x_2)\mathscr{A} \supset (x_2)\mathscr{A}$ Axiom (4)
3. $(x_2)\mathscr{A}$ 1, 2, MP
4. $(x_2)\mathscr{A} \supset \mathscr{A}$ Axiom (5)
5. $\mathscr{A}$ 3, 4, MP
6. $(x_1)\mathscr{A}$ 5, Gen
7. $(x_2)(x_1)\mathscr{A}$ 6, Gen

Thus, by 1–7, we have $(x_1)(x_2)\mathscr{A} \vdash (x_2)(x_1)\mathscr{A}$, where, in the deduction, no application of Gen has as a quantified variable a free variable of $(x_1)(x_2)\mathscr{A}$. Hence, by Corollary 2.5, $\vdash (x_1)(x_2)\mathscr{A} \supset (x_2)(x_1)\mathscr{A}$.

EXERCISES

1. Show that
   (a) $\vdash (x_1)(\mathscr{A} \supset \mathscr{B}) \supset ((x_1)\mathscr{A} \supset (x_1)\mathscr{B})$.
   (b) $\vdash (x)(\mathscr{A} \supset \mathscr{B}) \supset ((Ex)\mathscr{A} \supset (Ex)\mathscr{B})$.
   (c) $\vdash (x)(\mathscr{A} \wedge \mathscr{B}) \equiv (x)\mathscr{A} \wedge (x)\mathscr{B}$.
   (d) $\vdash (y_1)\ldots(y_n)\mathscr{A} \supset \mathscr{A}$.

2. Let K be a first-order theory, and let K# be an axiomatic theory having the following axioms: (1) $(y_1)\ldots(y_n)\mathscr{A}$ where $\mathscr{A}$ is any axiom of K and $y_1, \ldots, y_n$ $(n \geqslant 0)$ are any variables; (2) $(y_1)\ldots(y_n)(\mathscr{A} \supset \mathscr{B}) \supset [(y_1)\ldots(y_n)\mathscr{A} \supset (y_1)\ldots(y_n)\mathscr{B}]$ where $\mathscr{A}$ and $\mathscr{B}$ are any wfs and $y_1, \ldots, y_n$ are any variables. Moreover, K# has the rule of modus ponens as its only rule of inference. Show that K# has the same theorems as K.

§ 5. Completeness Theorems

PROPOSITION 2.7. *Every theorem of a first-order predicate calculus is logically valid.*

PROOF. By property (VII) of the notion of truth (cf. page 52), Axioms (1)–(3) are logically valid. By properties (X)(Corollary) and (XI), Axioms (4)–(5) are logically valid. By (III) and (VI), the rules of inference MP and Gen preserve logical validity. Hence, every theorem of a predicate calculus is logically valid.

EXERCISES

1. For any first-order theory K, if $\Gamma \vdash_K \mathscr{A}$ and each wf in Γ is true in a given model M of K, then $\mathscr{A}$ is also true in M.

2. If a wf $\mathscr{A}$ without quantifiers is provable in a predicate calculus,

then it is an instance of a tautology, and, hence, by Proposition 2.1, has a proof without quantifiers using only Axioms (1)–(3) and MP. (Hint: if $\mathscr{A}$ were not a tautology, one could construct an interpretation having the set of terms occurring in $\mathscr{A}$ as its domain, in which $\mathscr{A}$ is false, contradicting Proposition 2.7.) Note that this implies the consistency of the predicate calculus and also provides a decision procedure for provability of wfs without quantifiers.

Proposition 2.7 establishes only half of the completeness result that we are seeking. The other half will follow from a much more general proposition established below. First, we must prove a few preliminary lemmas.

If x_i and x_j are distinct, then $\mathscr{A}(x_i)$ and $\mathscr{A}(x_j)$ are said to be *similar* if and only if x_j is free for x_i in $\mathscr{A}(x_i)$ and $\mathscr{A}(x_i)$ has no free occurrences of x_j. It is assumed here that $\mathscr{A}(x_j)$ arises from $\mathscr{A}(x_i)$ by substituting x_j for all free occurrences of x_i. If $\mathscr{A}(x_i)$ and $\mathscr{A}(x_j)$ are similar, then x_i is free for x_j in $\mathscr{A}(x_j)$ and $\mathscr{A}(x_j)$ has no free occurrences of x_i. Thus, similarity is a symmetric relation. Intuitively, $\mathscr{A}(x_i)$ and $\mathscr{A}(x_j)$ are similar if and only if $\mathscr{A}(x_j)$ has free occurrences of x_j in exactly those places where $\mathscr{A}(x_i)$ has free occurrences of x_i.

LEMMA 2.8. *If $\mathscr{A}(x_i)$ and $\mathscr{A}(x_j)$ are similar, then* $\vdash (x_i)\mathscr{A}(x_i) \equiv (x_j)\mathscr{A}(x_j)$.

PROOF. $\vdash (x_i)\mathscr{A}(x_i) \supset \mathscr{A}(x_j)$ by Axiom (4). By Gen,

$$\vdash (x_j)((x_i)\mathscr{A}(x_i) \supset \mathscr{A}(x_j))$$

and, by Axiom (5), $\vdash (x_i)\mathscr{A}(x_i) \supset (x_j)\mathscr{A}(x_j)$. In the same way, $\vdash (x_j)\mathscr{A}(x_j) \supset (x_i)\mathscr{A}(x_i)$. Hence, by the tautology $A_1 \supset (A_2 \supset (A_1 \wedge A_2))$, and Proposition 2.1, $\vdash (x_i)\mathscr{A}(x_i) \equiv (x_j)\mathscr{A}(x_j)$.

EXERCISE. If $\mathscr{A}(x_i)$ and $\mathscr{A}(x_j)$ are similar, $\vdash (Ex_i)\mathscr{A}(x_i) \equiv (Ex_j)\mathscr{A}(x_j)$.

LEMMA 2.9. *If a closed* wf $\sim\mathscr{A}$ *of K is not provable in K, then the theory K′, obtained from K by adding $\mathscr{A}$ as an axiom, is consistent.*

PROOF. Assume K′ inconsistent. Then, for some wf $\mathscr{B}$, $\vdash_{K'} \mathscr{B}$ and $\vdash_{K'} \sim\mathscr{B}$. Now, $\vdash_{K'} \mathscr{B} \supset (\sim\mathscr{B} \supset \sim\mathscr{A})$, by Proposition 2.1. So, $\vdash_{K'} \sim\mathscr{A}$. Hence, $\mathscr{A} \vdash_K \sim\mathscr{A}$. Since $\mathscr{A}$ is closed, we have $\vdash_K \mathscr{A} \supset \sim\mathscr{A}$, by Corollary 2.6 of the Deduction Theorem. However, by Proposition 2.1, $\vdash_K (\mathscr{A} \supset \sim\mathscr{A}) \supset \sim\mathscr{A}$. Hence, $\vdash_K \sim\mathscr{A}$, contradicting our hypothesis. (Similarly, if $\mathscr{A}$ is not provable in K, then the new theory obtained by adding $\sim\mathscr{A}$ as an axiom to K is consistent.)

LEMMA 2.10. *The set of expressions of a first-order theory K is denumerable. (Hence the same is true of the set of terms,* wfs, *closed* wfs, *etc.)*

PROOF. First assign a distinct odd number $g(u)$ to each symbol u as follows: $g(()=3$, $g())=5$, $g(,)=7$, $g(\sim)=9$, $g(\supset)=11$; $g(x_k)=5+8k$; $g(a_k)=7+8k$; $g(f_k^n)=9+8(2^n3^k)$; $g(A_k^n)=11+8(2^n3^k)$. Then, to an expression $u_1u_2\ldots u_r$, associate the number $2^{g(u_1)}3^{g(u_2)}\ldots p_r^{g(u_r)}$, where p_i is the ith prime number. We can enumerate all expressions in the order of their associated numbers.

Moreover, if we can effectively tell whether any given symbol is a symbol of K, then this enumeration can be effectively carried out, and, in addition, we can effectively decide whether any given number is the number of an expression of K. The same holds true for terms, wfs, closed wfs, etc. If K is also axiomatic, i.e., if we can effectively decide whether any given wf is an axiom of K, then we can effectively enumerate the theorems of K as follows: Starting with a list consisting of the first axiom of K, in the given enumeration (according to the associated numbers) of the axioms, add all the direct consequences of this axiom by MP and by Gen used only with x_1 as quantified variable. Add the second axiom to this new list (if it is not already there), and write down all new direct consequences of the wfs in this augmented list, this time with Gen used only with x_1, x_2. If at the kth step, we add the kth axiom and restrict Gen to the variables $x_1, \ldots, x_k$, we eventually obtain, in this manner, all theorems of K. However, in contradistinction to the case of expressions, wfs, terms, etc., it turns out that there are theories K for which we cannot tell in advance whether any given wf of K will eventually appear in the list of theorems.

We say that a first-order theory K is *complete* if and only if, for any closed wf $\mathscr{A}$ of K, either $\vdash_K \mathscr{A}$ or $\vdash_K \sim\mathscr{A}$.

A first-order theory K′ having the same symbols as a first-order theory K is said to be an *extension* of K if every theorem of K is a theorem of K′. (Obviously, it suffices to prove that every proper axiom of K is a theorem of K′.)

LEMMA 2.11 (LINDENBAUM'S LEMMA). *If K is a consistent first-order theory, then there is a consistent, complete extension of K.*

PROOF. Let $\mathscr{B}_1, \mathscr{B}_2, \ldots,$ be an enumeration of all closed wfs of K, by Lemma 2.10. Define a sequence $J_0, J_1, J_2, \ldots$ of theories in the following way. J_0 is K. Assume J_n defined, with $n \geqslant 0$. If it is not the case that $\vdash_{J_n} \sim\mathscr{B}_{n+1}$ then let J_{n+1} be obtained from J_n by adding $\mathscr{B}_{n+1}$ as an additional axiom. On the other hand, if $\vdash_{J_n} \sim\mathscr{B}_{n+1}$, let $J_{n+1} = J_n$. Let J be the first-order theory obtained by taking as axioms all the axioms of all the J_i's. Clearly, J_{n+1} is an extension of J_n, and J is an extension of all the J_i's, including $J_0 = K$. To show that J is consistent, it suffices to prove that all the J_i's are consistent, because a proof of a contradiction in J, involving as it does only a finite number of axioms, is also a proof of a contradiction in some J_n. We prove the consistency of the J_i's by induction. By hypothesis, $J_0 = K$ is consistent. Assume that J_i is consistent. If $J_{i+1} = J_i$, then J_{i+1} is consistent. If $J_i \neq J_{i+1}$ and, therefore, by the definition of J_{i+1}, $\sim \mathscr{B}_{i+1}$ is not provable in J_i, then, by Lemma 2.9, J_{i+1} is also consistent. Hence, J_{i+1} is consistent if J_i is, and, therefore, J is consistent. To prove the completeness of J, let $\mathscr{A}$ be any closed wf of K. Then $\mathscr{A} = \mathscr{B}_{j+1}$ for some $j \geqslant 0$. Now, either $\vdash_{J_j} \sim \mathscr{B}_{j+1}$ or $\vdash_{J_{j+1}} \mathscr{B}_{j+1}$, since, if not $\vdash_{J_j} \sim \mathscr{B}_{j+1}$, then $\mathscr{B}_{j+1}$ is added as an axiom in J_{j+1}. Therefore, either $\vdash_J \sim \mathscr{B}_{j+1}$ or $\vdash_J \mathscr{B}_{j+1}$. Thus, J is a complete consistent extension of K.

Note that even if one can effectively determine whether any wf is an axiom of K, it may not be possible to do the same with (or even to effectively enumerate) the axioms of J, i.e., J may not be axiomatic even if K is. This is due to the possibility of not being able to determine, at each step, whether or not $\sim \mathscr{B}_{n+1}$ is provable in J_n.

^{D}EXERCISE. Prove that every consistent, decidable first-order theory has a consistent, decidable, complete extension.

PROPOSITION 2.12.† *Every consistent first-order theory K has a denumerable model (i.e., a model in which the domain is denumerable).*

PROOF. Add to the symbols of K a denumerable set $\{b_1, b_2, \ldots\}$ of new individual constants. Call this new first-order theory K_0. Its axioms are those of K plus those logical axioms which involve the new constants. K_0 is consistent. For, if not, $\vdash_{K_0} \mathscr{A} \wedge \sim \mathscr{A}$ for some wf $\mathscr{A}$. Replace each b_i appearing in this proof by a variable which does not appear in the proof. This transforms axioms into axioms and preserves the correctness of the applications of the rules of inference. The final wf in the proof is still a contradiction, but now the proof does not involve any of the b_i's and therefore is a proof in K. This contradicts the consistency of K. Therefore, K_0 is consistent.

By Lemma 2.10, let $F_1(x_{i_1}), F_2(x_{i_2}), \ldots, F_k(x_{i_k}), \ldots$ be an enumeration of all wfs of K_0 having at most one free variable. (Let x_{i_k} be the free variable of F_k if the latter has a free variable; otherwise, let x_{i_k} be x_1.) Choose a sequence $b_{j_1}, b_{j_2}, \ldots$ of some of the new individual constants such that b_{j_k} is not contained in $F_1(x_{i_1}), F_2(x_{i_2}), \ldots, F_k(x_{i_k})$, and such that b_{j_k} is different from each of $b_{j_1}, b_{j_2}, \ldots, b_{j_{k-1}}$. Consider the wf:

$$(S_k) \qquad \sim (x_{i_k}) F_k(x_{i_k}) \supset \sim F_k(b_{j_k})$$

† The proof given here is due to Henkin [1949], as simplified by Hasenjaeger [1953]. The result was originally proved by Gödel [1930]. Other proofs have been published by Rasiowa-Sikorski [1951–52] and Beth [1951], using (Boolean) algebraic and topological methods, respectively. Still other proofs may be found in Hintikka [1955a, b] and in Beth [1959].

Let K_n be the first-order theory obtained by adding $(S_1), \ldots, (S_n)$ to the axioms of K_0, and let K_∞ be the theory obtained by adding all the (S_i)'s as axioms to K_0. Any proof in K_∞ contains only a finite number of the (S_i)'s, and will also be a proof in some K_n. Hence, if all the K_i's are consistent, so is K_∞. To demonstrate that all the K_i's are consistent, proceed by induction. We know that K_0 is consistent. Assume that K_{n-1} is consistent but that K_n is inconsistent ($n \geqslant 1$). Then, as we know, any wf is provable in K_n (by the tautology $A_1 \supset (\sim A_1 \supset A_2)$ and Proposition 2.1). In particular, $\vdash_{K_n} \sim(S_n)$. Hence, $(S_n) \vdash_{K_{n-1}} \sim(S_n)$. Since (S_n) is closed, we have, by Corollary 2.6, $\vdash_{K_{n-1}} (S_n) \supset \sim(S_n)$. But, by the tautology $(A_1 \supset \sim A_1) \supset \sim A_1$ and Proposition 2.1, we then have $\vdash_{K_{n-1}} \sim(S_n)$, i.e.,

$$\vdash_{K_{n-1}} \sim(\sim(x_{i_n})F_n(x_{i_n}) \supset \sim F_n(b_{j_n}))$$

Now, by the tautologies $\sim(A_1 \supset A_2) \supset (A_1 \wedge \sim A_2)$; $(A_1 \wedge A_2) \supset A_1$; $(A_1 \wedge A_2) \supset A_2$; $\sim\sim A_1 \supset A_1$, we obtain $\vdash_{K_{n-1}} \sim(x_{i_n})F_n(x_{i_n})$ and $\vdash_{K_{n-1}} F_n(b_{j_n})$. From the latter and from the fact that b_{j_n} does not occur in $(S_1), \ldots, (S_{n-1})$, we conclude $\vdash_{K_{n-1}} F_n(x_p)$, where x_p is a variable not occurring in the proof of $F_n(b_{j_n})$ in K_{n-1}. (Simply replace in the proof all occurrences of b_{j_n} by x_p.) By Gen, $\vdash_{K_{n-1}} (x_p)F_n(x_p)$, and, then, by Lemma 2.8, $\vdash_{K_{n-1}} (x_{i_n})F_n(x_{i_n})$. (We use the fact that $F_n(x_{i_n})$ and $F_n(x_p)$ are similar.) But $\vdash_{K_{n-1}} \sim(x_{i_n})F_n(x_{i_n})$. This contradicts the assumed consistency of K_{n-1}. Hence, K_n must also be consistent. In this way, all the K_i's are consistent, and so also is K_∞. Note that K_∞ is a consistent extension of K_0. Now, by Lemma 2.11, let J be a consistent, complete extension of K_∞.

By a *closed term*, we mean a term which contains no variables. The denumerable interpretation M of K_0 shall have as its domain the set of closed terms of K_0. (By Lemma 2.10, this is a denumerable set.) If c is an individual constant of K_0, its interpretation shall be c itself. If f_j^n is a function letter of K, then the associated operation $f_j^{n\star}$ in M shall have, for arguments $t_1, \ldots, t_n$ (which are closed terms of K_0), the value $f_j^n(t_1, \ldots, t_n)$, which is a closed term of K_0. If A_j^n is a predicate letter of K, then the associated relation $(A_j^n)^\star$ in M shall hold, for arguments $t_1, \ldots, t_n$, if and only if $\vdash_J A_j^n(t_1, \ldots, t_n)$. To show that M is a model for K_0, it suffices to prove that a closed wf $\mathscr{A}$ of K_0 is true for M if and only if $\vdash_J \mathscr{A}$, because all theorems of K_0 are theorems of J. We prove this, by induction on the number of connectives and quantifiers in $\mathscr{A}$. First, let $\mathscr{A}$ be a closed atomic wf. Then, by definition, $\mathscr{A}$ is true for M if and only if $\vdash_J \mathscr{A}$. Now, assume that, for the induction step, if $\mathscr{B}$ is any closed wf with fewer connectives and quantifiers than $\mathscr{A}$, $\mathscr{B}$ is true for M if and only if $\vdash_J \mathscr{B}$.

Case 1. $\mathscr{A}$ is $\sim\mathscr{B}$. If $\mathscr{A}$ is true for M, then $\mathscr{B}$ is false for M, and so, by inductive hypothesis, not-$\vdash_J \mathscr{B}$. Since J is complete and $\mathscr{B}$ is closed, $\vdash_J \sim\mathscr{B}$, i.e., $\vdash_J \mathscr{A}$. On the other hand, if $\mathscr{A}$ is not true for M, then $\mathscr{B}$ is true for M. Hence, $\vdash_J \mathscr{B}$. Since J is consistent, not-$\vdash_J \sim\mathscr{B}$, i.e., not-$\vdash_J \mathscr{A}$.

Case 2. $\mathscr{A}$ is $(\mathscr{B} \supset \mathscr{C})$. Since $\mathscr{A}$ is closed, so are $\mathscr{B}$ and $\mathscr{C}$. If $\mathscr{A}$ is false for M, then $\mathscr{B}$ is true and $\mathscr{C}$ is false. Hence, by inductive hypothesis, $\vdash_J \mathscr{B}$ and not-$\vdash_J \mathscr{C}$. By the completeness of J, $\vdash_J \sim\mathscr{C}$. Therefore, by the tautology $A_1 \supset (\sim A_2 \supset \sim(A_1 \supset A_2))$, $\vdash_J \sim(\mathscr{B} \supset \mathscr{C})$, i.e., $\vdash_J \sim\mathscr{A}$, and so, by the consistency of J, not-$\vdash_J \mathscr{A}$. On the other hand, if not-$\vdash_J \mathscr{A}$, then, by the completeness of J, $\vdash_J \sim\mathscr{A}$. By the tautologies $\sim(A_1 \supset A_2) \supset A_1$ and $\sim(A_1 \supset A_2) \supset \sim A_2$, we obtain $\vdash_J \mathscr{B}$ and $\vdash_J \sim\mathscr{C}$. Hence, $\mathscr{B}$ is true for M. By the consistency of J, not-$\vdash_J \mathscr{C}$, and, therefore, $\mathscr{C}$ is false for M. Thus, $\mathscr{A}$ is false for M.

Case 3. $\mathscr{A}$ is $(x_n)\mathscr{B}$. Let $\mathscr{B}$ be $F_k(x_{i_k})$. We may assume that x_n is x_{i_k}. (Otherwise, $\mathscr{B}$ is closed and does not contain x_n free. But, in this case, $\mathscr{A}$ is true if and only if $\mathscr{B}$ is true (by (VI) of page 52), and $\vdash_J \mathscr{A}$ if and only if $\vdash_J \mathscr{B}$. Therefore, the result for $\mathscr{A}$ follows from that for $\mathscr{B}$.) Assume that $\mathscr{A}$ is true for M, but not-$\vdash_J \mathscr{A}$. By the completeness of J, $\vdash_J \sim\mathscr{A}$, i.e., $\vdash_J \sim(x_{i_k})F_k(x_{i_k})$. But, $\vdash_J (S_k)$. Hence, $\vdash_J \sim F_k(b_{j_k})$. Since $\mathscr{A} = (x_{i_k})F_k(x_{i_k})$ is true for M, it follows (by (X), Corollary, page 53) that $F_k(b_{j_k})$ is true in M. So, by inductive hypothesis, $\vdash_J F_k(b_{j_k})$, contradicting the consistency of J. On the other hand, assume $\mathscr{A}$ false for M, but $\vdash_J \mathscr{A}$. Since $(x_{i_k})F_k(x_{i_k})$ is false for M, it follows from the fact that the domain of M is the set of closed terms of K_0, and from (iv) and the second paragraph of (X) (cf. pages 51 and 53),† that, for some closed term t of K_0, $F_k(t)$ is false. But $\vdash_J (x_{i_k})F_k(x_{i_k})$. Hence, by Axiom (4), $\vdash_J F_k(t)$. By inductive hypothesis, $F_k(t)$ is, therefore, true for M, contradicting the falsity of $F_k(t)$ for M.

Thus, M is a denumerable model for J, and hence also for K_0. Since all theorems of K are theorems of K_0, M is also a denumerable model for K. (Notice that M is not necessarily effectively constructible. The interpretation of predicate letters depends upon the concept of provability in J, and this, as was noted at the end of Lemma 2.11, may not be effectively decidable.)

COROLLARY 2.13. *Any logically valid* wf $\mathscr{A}$ *of a first-order theory K is a theorem of K.*

PROOF. We need only consider closed wfs $\mathscr{A}$, since a wf $\mathscr{B}$ is logically valid if and only if its closure is logically valid, and $\mathscr{B}$ is provable in K if and only if its closure is provable in K. So, let $\mathscr{A}$ be a logically valid

† It is necessary here to observe that $s^*(t) = t$ for any sequence s of elements of the domain of M and any closed term t.

closed wf of K. Now, assume that $\mathscr{A}$ is not a theorem of K. Then, if we add $\sim\mathscr{A}$ as an axiom to K, the new theory K′ is consistent (by Lemma 2.9). Hence, by Proposition 2.12, K′ has a model M. Since $\sim\mathscr{A}$ is an axiom of K′, $\sim\mathscr{A}$ is true in M; and, since $\mathscr{A}$ is logically valid, $\mathscr{A}$ is true in M. Hence, $\mathscr{A}$ is both true and false in M, which is impossible ((II), page 51). Thus, $\mathscr{A}$ must be a theorem of K.

COROLLARY 2.14 (GÖDEL'S COMPLETENESS THEOREM [1930]). *In any first-order predicate calculus, the theorems are precisely the logically valid* wfs.

PROOF. By Proposition 2.7 and Corollary 2.13. (Gödel's original proof runs along quite different lines. For a constructive proof of a related result, cf. Herbrand [1930] and, for still other proofs, cf. Dreben [1952], Hintikka [1955a, b], Beth [1951], and Rasiowa-Sikorski [1950, 1951].)

COROLLARY 2.15.

(a) $\mathscr{A}$ *is true in every denumerable model of* K *if and only if* $\vdash_K \mathscr{A}$. *Hence,* $\mathscr{A}$ *is true in every model of* K *if and only if* $\vdash_K \mathscr{A}$.

(b) *If, in every model of* K, *every sequence, satisfying all* wfs *in a set* Γ *of* wfs, *also satisfies* $\mathscr{B}$, *then* $\Gamma \vdash_K \mathscr{B}$.

(c) *If a* wf $\mathscr{B}$ *of* K *is a logical consequence* (*cf. page* 54) *of a set* Γ *of* wfs *of* K, *then* $\Gamma \vdash_K \mathscr{B}$.

(d) *If the* wf $\mathscr{B}$ *of* K *is a logical consequence of a* wf $\mathscr{A}$ *of* K, *then* $\mathscr{A} \vdash_K \mathscr{B}$.

PROOF.

(a) We may assume $\mathscr{A}$ closed. If not-$\vdash_K \mathscr{A}$, then the theory $K' = K + \{\sim\mathscr{A}\}$ is consistent.† Hence, K′ has a denumerable model M. However, $\sim\mathscr{A}$, being an axiom of K′, is true in M; and since M is also a model for K, $\mathscr{A}$ is true in M. Therefore, $\mathscr{A}$ is true and false in M, which is a contradiction.

(b) Consider the theory $K + \Gamma$. The wf $\mathscr{B}$ is true in every model of this theory. Hence, by (a), $\vdash_{K+\Gamma} \mathscr{B}$. So, $\Gamma \vdash_K \mathscr{B}$.

(c) is a consequence of (b), and (d) is a special case of (c).

EXERCISE. Show that $\vdash_K \mathscr{A}$ if and only if there is a wf $\mathscr{C}$ which is the closure of the conjunction of some axioms of K such that $\mathscr{C} \supset \mathscr{A}$ is logically valid.

Corollaries 2.13–2.15 show that the syntactical approach to quantification theory by means of first-order theories is equivalent to the semantical approach through the notions of interpretations, models,

† If K is a theory and Δ is a set of wfs of K, then $K + \Delta$ denotes the theory obtained from K by adding the wfs of Δ as additional axioms.

logical validity, etc. For the propositional calculus, Corollary 1.14 demonstrated the analogous equivalence between the semantical notions (tautology, etc.) and the syntactical notions (theorem of L, etc.). Notice also that, in the propositional calculus, completeness of the system L (cf. Proposition 1.13) led to a solution of the decision problem. However, for first-order theories, we cannot obtain a decision procedure for logical validity, or, equivalently, for provability in a first-order predicate calculus. We shall prove this and related results later on (Chapter V).

There is another important classical result which falls out of Proposition 2.12.

COROLLARY 2.16 (SKOLEM-LÖWENHEIM THEOREM [1919, 1915]). *Any first-order theory K which has a model has a denumerable model.*

PROOF. If K has a model, then K is consistent (by (II), page 51). Hence, by Proposition 2.12, K has a denumerable model.

We have another even stronger consequence of Proposition 2.12.

ACOROLLARY 2.17. *For any cardinal number* $\alpha \geqslant \aleph_0$, *any consistent first-order theory K has a model of cardinality* α.

PROOF. We know, by Proposition 2.12, that K has a denumerable model. Therefore, for our result, it suffices to prove the following lemma.

LEMMA. *If* α *and* β *are two cardinal numbers such that* $\alpha \leqslant \beta$ *and if K has a model of cardinality* α, *then K has a model of cardinality* β.

PROOF. Let M be a model of K with domain D of cardinality α. Let D′ be a set of cardinality β containing D. Extend the model M to an interpretation M′ having D′ as domain in the following way. Let c be a fixed element of D. We stipulate that the elements of D′ − D behave like c. For example, if B_j^n is the interpretation in M of the predicate letter A_j^n, and $(B_j^n)'$ is the new interpretation in M′, then, for any $d_1, \ldots, d_n$ in D′, $(B_j^n)'$ holds for $(d_1, \ldots, d_n)$ if and only if B_j^n holds for $(u_1, \ldots, u_n)$ where $u_i = d_i$ if $d_i \in D$ and $u_i = c$ if $d_i \in D' - D$. The interpretation of the function letters is extended in an analogous way, and the same interpretations as in M are taken for the individual constants. It is an easy exercise to show, by induction on the number of connectives and quantifiers in a wf, that any wf $\mathscr{A}$ is true in M′ if and only if it is true in M. Hence, M′ is a model of K of cardinality β.

EXERCISES

A1. If, for some cardinal $\alpha \geqslant \aleph_0$, a wf $\mathscr{A}$ is true in every interpretation of cardinality α, then $\mathscr{A}$ is logically valid.

[A]2. If a wf $\mathscr{A}$ is true in all interpretations of cardinality α, then $\mathscr{A}$ is true in all interpretations of cardinality $\leqslant \alpha$.

3. (a) For any wf $\mathscr{A}$, there are only a finite number of interpretations of $\mathscr{A}$ on a given domain of finite cardinality k.

(b) For any wf $\mathscr{A}$, there is an effective way of determining whether $\mathscr{A}$ is true in all interpretations with domain of some fixed finite cardinality k. (Hint: introduce new individual constants $b_1, \ldots, b_k$, and replace each wf $(x)\mathscr{B}(x)$ by $\mathscr{B}(b_1) \wedge \mathscr{B}(b_2) \wedge \ldots \wedge \mathscr{B}(b_k)$.)

4. Show that the following wf is true for all finite domains, but is false in some infinite domain.

$$\{(x)(y)(z)[A_1^2(x, x) \wedge (A_1^2(x, y) \wedge A_1^2(y, z) \supset A_1^2(x, z)) \wedge (A_1^2(x, y) \vee A_1^2(y, x))]\} \supset (Ey)(x)A_1^2(y, x)$$

5. (a) A closed prenex wf $(x_1)\ldots(x_n)(Ey_1)\ldots(Ey_m)\mathscr{A}$ (with $m \geqslant 0$, $n \geqslant 1$) is logically valid if and only if it is true in every interpretation with domain of n objects. ($\mathscr{A}$ is assumed to contain no quantifiers, function letters, or individual constants.)

(b) A closed prenex wf $(Ey_1)\ldots(Ey_m)\mathscr{A}$ (where $\mathscr{A}$ contains no quantifiers, function letters, or individual constants) is logically valid if and only if it is true for all domains of one element.

(c) There is an effective procedure to determine the logical validity of all wfs of the forms given in (a) or (b).

§ 6. Some Additional Metatheorems

For the sake of smoothness in working with particular first-order theories later, it is convenient to prove a few additional facts about first-order theories. We assume in this section that we are dealing with some arbitrary first-order theory K.

In many cases, one has proved $(x)\mathscr{A}(x)$ and one wants $\mathscr{A}(t)$, where t is a term free for x in $\mathscr{A}(x)$. This is justified by the

PARTICULARIZATION RULE A4. *If t is free for x in $\mathscr{A}(x)$, then $(x)\mathscr{A}(x) \vdash \mathscr{A}(t)$.*

PROOF. From $(x)\mathscr{A}(x)$ and the instance $(x)\mathscr{A}(x) \supset \mathscr{A}(t)$ of Axiom (4), we obtain $\mathscr{A}(t)$ by modus ponens.

PROPOSITION 2.18. *If $\mathscr{A}$ and $\mathscr{B}$ are* wfs *and x is not free in $\mathscr{A}$, the following are theorems of K.*

(a) $\mathscr{A} \supset (x)\mathscr{A}$ (hence, by Axiom (4), $\vdash \mathscr{A} \equiv (x)\mathscr{A}$)
(b) $(Ex)\mathscr{A} \supset \mathscr{A}$ (hence, by rule E4 below, $\vdash (Ex)\mathscr{A} \equiv \mathscr{A}$)
(c) $(x)(\mathscr{A} \supset \mathscr{B}) \equiv (\mathscr{A} \supset (x)\mathscr{B})$
(d) $(x)(\mathscr{B} \supset \mathscr{A}) \equiv ((Ex)\mathscr{B} \supset \mathscr{A})$

PROOF. Exercise.

A useful derived rule which is just the contrapositive of Rule A4 is the following.

EXISTENTIAL RULE E4. *If t is free for x in $\mathscr{A}(x)$, then* $\vdash \mathscr{A}(t) \supset (Ex)\mathscr{A}(x)$. *Hence,* $\mathscr{A}(t) \vdash (Ex)\mathscr{A}(x)$.

PROOF. By Axiom (4), $\vdash (x)\sim\mathscr{A}(x) \supset \sim\mathscr{A}(t)$. Hence, by the tautology $(A \supset \sim B) \supset (B \supset \sim A)$ and MP, $\vdash \mathscr{A}(t) \supset \sim(x)\sim\mathscr{A}(x)$ which is, in abbreviated form, $\vdash \mathscr{A}(t) \supset (Ex)\mathscr{A}(x)$. Hence, $\mathscr{A}(t) \vdash (Ex)\mathscr{A}(x)$.

EXERCISES

1. Prove the following derived rules:

   Conjunction Rule: $\mathscr{A}, \mathscr{B} \vdash \mathscr{A} \wedge \mathscr{B}$
   Disjunction Rule: $\mathscr{A} \supset \mathscr{C}, \mathscr{B} \supset \mathscr{D}, \mathscr{A} \vee \mathscr{B} \vdash \mathscr{C} \vee \mathscr{D}$

2. If $\mathscr{B}$ is obtained from $\mathscr{A}$ by erasing all quantifiers of the form (x) or (Ex) whose scope does not contain x free, then $\vdash \mathscr{A} \equiv \mathscr{B}$.

PROPOSITION 2.19. *For any* wfs $\mathscr{A}, \mathscr{B}$: $\vdash (x)(\mathscr{A} \equiv \mathscr{B}) \supset ((x)\mathscr{A} \equiv (x)\mathscr{B})$.

PROOF

1.	$(x)(\mathscr{A} \equiv \mathscr{B})$	Hyp
2.	$(x)\mathscr{A}$	Hyp
3.	$\mathscr{A} \equiv \mathscr{B}$	1, Rule A4
4.	$\mathscr{A}$	2, Rule A4
5.	$\mathscr{B}$	3, Tautology $(A \equiv B) \supset (A \supset B)$, MP
6.	$(x)\mathscr{B}$	5, Gen
7.	$(x)(\mathscr{A} \equiv \mathscr{B}), (x)\mathscr{A} \vdash (x)\mathscr{B}$	1–6
8.	$(x)(\mathscr{A} \equiv \mathscr{B}) \vdash (x)\mathscr{A} \supset (x)\mathscr{B}$	1–7, Prop. 2.4
9.	$(x)(\mathscr{A} \equiv \mathscr{B}) \vdash (x)\mathscr{B} \supset (x)\mathscr{A}$	Proved in a way similar to that for 8
10.	$(x)(\mathscr{A} \equiv \mathscr{B}) \vdash (x)\mathscr{A} \equiv (x)\mathscr{B}$	8,9, Conjunction Rule
11.	$\vdash (x)(\mathscr{A} \equiv \mathscr{B}) \supset ((x)\mathscr{A} \equiv (x)\mathscr{B})$	1–10, Prop 2.4

PROPOSITION 2.20 (EQUIVALENCE THEOREM). *If $\mathscr{B}$ is a subformula of $\mathscr{A}$, and $\mathscr{A}'$ is the result of replacing zero or more occurrences of $\mathscr{B}$ in $\mathscr{A}$ by a* wf *$\mathscr{C}$, and every free variable of $\mathscr{B}$ or $\mathscr{C}$ which is also a bound variable of $\mathscr{A}$ occurs in the list $y_1, \ldots, y_k$, then*

$$\vdash [(y_1)\ldots(y_k)(\mathscr{C} \equiv \mathscr{B})] \supset (\mathscr{A} \equiv \mathscr{A}')$$

PROOF. Induction on the number n of connectives and quantifiers of $\mathscr{A}$. Note that if zero occurrences are replaced, then $\mathscr{A}'$ is $\mathscr{A}$, and the wf to be proved is an instance of the tautology $B \supset (A \equiv A)$. If $\mathscr{B}$ is identical with $\mathscr{A}$, and this occurrence of $\mathscr{B}$ is replaced by $\mathscr{C}$ the wf to be proved, $(y_1)\ldots(y_k)(\mathscr{B} \equiv \mathscr{C}) \supset (\mathscr{B} \equiv \mathscr{C})$, is derivable (cf. page 62, Exercise 1(d)) from Axiom (4). Thus, we may assume that $\mathscr{B}$ is a proper part of $\mathscr{A}$ and that at least one occurrence of $\mathscr{B}$ is replaced. Also let us assume the theorem for all wfs with fewer connectives and quantifiers than $\mathscr{A}$.

Case 1. $\mathscr{A}$ is an atomic wf. Then $\mathscr{B}$ cannot be a proper part of $\mathscr{A}$.

Case 2. $\mathscr{A}$ is $\sim \mathscr{D}$. Let $\mathscr{A}'$ be $\sim \mathscr{D}'$. By inductive hypothesis, $\vdash (y_1)\ldots(y_k)(\mathscr{B} \equiv \mathscr{C}) \supset (\mathscr{D} \equiv \mathscr{D}')$. Hence, by the tautology $(A \equiv B) \supset (\sim A \equiv \sim B)$, $\vdash (y_1)\ldots(y_k)(\mathscr{B} \equiv \mathscr{C}) \supset (\mathscr{A} \equiv \mathscr{A}')$.

Case 3. $\mathscr{A}$ is $\mathscr{D} \supset \mathscr{E}$. Let $\mathscr{A}'$ be $\mathscr{D}' \supset \mathscr{E}'$. By inductive hypothesis, $\vdash (y_1)\ldots(y_k)(\mathscr{B} \equiv \mathscr{C}) \supset (\mathscr{D} \equiv \mathscr{D}')$ and $\vdash (y_1)\ldots(y_k)(\mathscr{B} \equiv \mathscr{C}) \supset (\mathscr{E} \equiv \mathscr{E}')$. Using the tautology $((A \equiv B) \wedge (C \equiv D)) \supset ((A \supset C) \equiv (B \supset D))$, we obtain $\vdash (y_1)\ldots(y_k)(\mathscr{B} \equiv \mathscr{C}) \supset (\mathscr{A} \equiv \mathscr{A}')$.

Case 4. $\mathscr{A}$ is $(x)\mathscr{D}$. Let $\mathscr{A}'$ be $(x)\mathscr{D}'$. By inductive hypothesis, $\vdash (y_1)\ldots(y_k)(\mathscr{B} \equiv \mathscr{C}) \supset (\mathscr{D} \equiv \mathscr{D}')$. Now, x does not occur free in $(y_1)\ldots(y_k)(\mathscr{B} \equiv \mathscr{C})$, for, if it were, then it would be free in $\mathscr{B}$ or $\mathscr{C}$, and, since it is bound in $\mathscr{A}$, it would be one of $y_1, \ldots, y_k$, and x would not be free in $(y_1)\ldots(y_k)(\mathscr{B} \equiv \mathscr{C})$. Hence, using Axiom (5), we obtain $\vdash (y_1)\ldots(y_k)(\mathscr{B} \equiv \mathscr{C}) \supset (x)(\mathscr{D} \equiv \mathscr{D}')$. However, by Proposition 2.19, $\vdash (x)(\mathscr{D} \equiv \mathscr{D}') \supset ((x)\mathscr{D} \equiv (x)\mathscr{D}')$. Thus,

$$\vdash (y_1)\ldots(y_k)(\mathscr{B} \equiv \mathscr{C}) \supset (\mathscr{A} \equiv \mathscr{A}').$$

COROLLARY 2.21 (REPLACEMENT THEOREM). *Let $\mathscr{A}$, $\mathscr{B}$, $\mathscr{A}'$, $\mathscr{C}$ be as in Proposition 2.20. If $\vdash \mathscr{B} \equiv \mathscr{C}$, then $\vdash \mathscr{A} \equiv \mathscr{A}'$. Also, if $\vdash \mathscr{B} \equiv \mathscr{C}$ and $\vdash \mathscr{A}$, then $\vdash \mathscr{A}'$.*

COROLLARY 2.22 (CHANGE OF BOUND VARIABLES). *If $(x)\mathscr{B}(x)$ is a subformula of $\mathscr{A}$, and $\mathscr{B}(y)$ is similar to $\mathscr{B}(x)$, and $\mathscr{A}'$ is the result of replacing one or more occurrences of $(x)\mathscr{B}(x)$ in $\mathscr{A}$ by $(y)\mathscr{B}(y)$, then $\vdash \mathscr{A} \equiv \mathscr{A}'$.*

PROOF. Apply Lemma 2.8 and Corollary 2.21.

EXERCISES

1. Prove $\vdash (Ex) \sim \mathscr{A} \equiv \sim (x)\mathscr{A}$ and $\vdash (x)\mathscr{A} \equiv \sim (Ex) \sim \mathscr{A}$.

2. Let $\mathscr{A}$ be a wf involving only quantifiers and $\wedge$, $\vee$, $\sim$, but not $\supset$, $\equiv$. Exchange universal and existential quantifiers, and exchange $\wedge$ and $\vee$. The result $\mathscr{A}^{\star}$ is called the *dual* of $\mathscr{A}$. Prove that (a) $\vdash \mathscr{A}$ if and only if $\vdash \sim \mathscr{A}^{\star}$; (b) $\vdash \mathscr{A} \supset \mathscr{B}$ if and

only if $\vdash \mathscr{B}^{\star} \supset \mathscr{A}^{\star}$; (c) $\vdash \mathscr{A} \equiv \mathscr{B}$ if and only if $\vdash \mathscr{A}^{\star} \equiv \mathscr{B}^{\star}$; (d) using $\vdash (x)(\mathscr{A} \wedge \mathscr{B}) \equiv (x)\mathscr{A} \wedge (x)\mathscr{B}$ (cf. page 62, Exercise 1(c)), prove $\vdash (Ex)(\mathscr{A} \vee \mathscr{B}) \equiv (Ex)\mathscr{A} \vee (Ex)\mathscr{B}$.

§7. Rule C

It is very common in mathematics to reason in the following way. Assume that we have proved a wf of the form $(Ex)\mathscr{A}(x)$. Then, we say, let b be an object such that $\mathscr{A}(b)$. We continue the proof, finally arriving at a formula which does not involve the arbitrarily chosen element b.

For example, let us say that we wish to show that $(Ex)(\mathscr{B}(x) \supset \mathscr{C}(x))$, $(x)\mathscr{B}(x) \vdash (Ex)\mathscr{C}(x)$.

1.	$(Ex)(\mathscr{B}(x) \supset \mathscr{C}(x))$	Hyp
2.	$(x)\mathscr{B}(x)$	Hyp
3.	$\mathscr{B}(b) \supset \mathscr{C}(b)$ for some b	1
4.	$\mathscr{B}(b)$	2, Rule A4
5.	$\mathscr{C}(b)$	3,4, MP
6.	$(Ex)\mathscr{C}(x)$	5, Rule E4
7.	$(Ex)(\mathscr{B}(x) \supset \mathscr{C}(x)), (x)\mathscr{B}(x) \vdash (Ex)\mathscr{C}(x)$	1–6

Such a proof seems to be perfectly legitimate, on an intuitive basis. In fact, we can achieve the same result without making an arbitrary choice of an element b as in step 3. This can be done as follows:

1.	$(x)\mathscr{B}(x)$	Hyp
2.	$(x) \sim \mathscr{C}(x)$	Hyp
3.	$\mathscr{B}(x)$	1, Rule A4
4.	$\sim \mathscr{C}(x)$	2, Rule A4
5.	$\sim (\mathscr{B}(x) \supset \mathscr{C}(x))$	3,4, Tautology $(A \wedge \sim B) \supset \sim (A \supset B)$
6.	$(x) \sim (\mathscr{B}(x) \supset \mathscr{C}(x))$	5, Gen
7.	$(x)\mathscr{B}(x), (x) \sim \mathscr{C}(x) \vdash (x) \sim (\mathscr{B}(x) \supset \mathscr{C}(x))$	1–6
8.	$(x)\mathscr{B}(x) \vdash [(x) \sim \mathscr{C}(x)] \supset [(x) \sim (\mathscr{B}(x) \supset \mathscr{C}(x))]$	7, Prop. 2.4
9.	$(x)\mathscr{B}(x) \vdash [\sim (x) \sim (\mathscr{B}(x) \supset \mathscr{C}(x))] \supset [\sim (x) \sim \mathscr{C}(x)]$	8, Tautology $(A \supset B) \supset (\sim B \supset \sim A)$
10.	$(x)\mathscr{B}(x) \vdash (Ex)(\mathscr{B}(x) \supset \mathscr{C}(x)) \supset (Ex)\mathscr{C}(x)$	Abbreviation of 9
11.	$(Ex)(\mathscr{B}(x) \supset \mathscr{C}(x)), (x)\mathscr{B}(x) \vdash (Ex)\mathscr{C}(x)$	10, MP

In general, any wf which can be proved using arbitrary acts of choice, can also be proved without such acts of choice. We shall call the rule which permits us to go from $(Ex)\mathscr{A}(x)$ to $\mathscr{A}(b)$, *Rule C* ("C" for "choice"). More precisely, the definition of a Rule C deduction in a first-order theory K is as follows:

$\Gamma \vdash_C \mathscr{A}$ if and only if there is a sequence of wfs $\mathscr{B}_1, \ldots, \mathscr{B}_n = \mathscr{A}$

such that the following four statements hold.

(I) For each i, either

(i) $\mathscr{B}_i$ is an axiom of K, or
(ii) $\mathscr{B}_i$ is in Γ, or
(iii) $\mathscr{B}_i$ follows by MP or Gen from preceding wfs in the sequence, or
(iv) There is a preceding wf $(Ex)\mathscr{C}(x)$ and $\mathscr{B}_i$ is $\mathscr{C}(d)$, where d is a new individual constant. (Rule C)

(II) As axioms in (I)(i), we can also use all logical axioms involving the new individual constants already introduced by applications of (I)(iv), Rule C.

(III) No application of Gen is made using a variable which is free in some $(Ex)\mathscr{C}(x)$ to which Rule C has been previously applied.

(IV) $\mathscr{A}$ contains none of the new individual constants introduced in any application of Rule C.

A word should be said about the reason for including clause (III). Without this clause, we could proceed as follows:

1.	$(x)(Ey)A_1^2(x, y)$	Hyp
2.	$(Ey)A_1^2(x, y)$	1, Rule A4
3.	$A_1^2(x, b)$	2, Rule C with b
4.	$(x)A_1^2(x, b)$	3, Gen
5.	$(Ey)(x)A_1^2(x, y)$	4, Rule E4
6.	$(x)(Ey)A_1^2(x, y) \vdash_C (Ey)(x)A_1^2(x, y)$	1–5

However, (cf. page 54, (4)), there is an interpretation for which $(x)(Ey)A_1^2(x, y)$ is true but $(Ey)(x)A_1^2(x, y)$ is false.

PROPOSITION 2.23. *If $\Gamma \vdash_C \mathscr{A}$, then $\Gamma \vdash \mathscr{A}$.* Moreover, from the proof below it is easy to verify that if there is an application of Gen in the new proof of $\mathscr{A}$ from Γ using a certain variable and applied to a wf depending upon a certain wf of Γ, then there was such an application of Gen in the original proof.†

PROOF. Let $(Ey_1)\mathscr{C}_1(y_1), \ldots, (Ey_k)\mathscr{C}_k(y_k)$ be the wfs, in order of occurrence, to which Rule C is applied in the proof of $\Gamma \vdash_C \mathscr{A}$, and let $c_1, \ldots, c_k$ be the corresponding new individual constants. Then $\Gamma, \mathscr{C}_1(c_1), \ldots, \mathscr{C}_k(c_k) \vdash \mathscr{A}$; but then, by clause (III) of the definition

† The first formulation of a version of Rule C similar to that given here seems to be due to Rosser [1953].

above, and the Deduction Theorem 2.4, $\Gamma, \mathscr{C}_1(c_1), \ldots, \mathscr{C}_{k-1}(c_{k-1}) \vdash \mathscr{C}_k(c_k) \supset \mathscr{A}$. Replace c_k everywhere by a variable z not occurring in the proof. Then

$\Gamma, \mathscr{C}_1(c_1), \ldots, \mathscr{C}_{k-1}(c_{k-1}) \vdash \mathscr{C}_k(z) \supset \mathscr{A}$, and, by Gen,
$\Gamma, \mathscr{C}_1(c_1), \ldots, \mathscr{C}_{k-1}(c_{k-1}) \vdash (z)(\mathscr{C}_k(z) \supset \mathscr{A})$. Hence, by Proposition 2.18(d),
$\Gamma, \mathscr{C}_1(c_1), \ldots, \mathscr{C}_{k-1}(c_{k-1}) \vdash (Ey_k)\mathscr{C}_k(y_k) \supset \mathscr{A}$. But,
$\Gamma, \mathscr{C}_1(c_1), \ldots, \mathscr{C}_{k-1}(c_{k-1}) \vdash (Ey_k)\mathscr{C}_k(y_k)$. Hence
$\Gamma, \mathscr{C}_1(c_1), \ldots, \mathscr{C}_{k-1}(c_{k-1}) \vdash \mathscr{A}$.

Repeating this argument, we can eliminate $\mathscr{C}_{k-1}(c_{k-1}), \ldots, \mathscr{C}_1(c_1)$ one after the other, obtaining $\Gamma \vdash \mathscr{A}$.

Example. $\vdash (x)(\mathscr{A}(x) \supset \mathscr{B}(x)) \supset ((Ex)\mathscr{A}(x) \supset (Ex)\mathscr{B}(x))$

1.	$(x)(\mathscr{A}(x) \supset \mathscr{B}(x))$	Hyp
2.	$(Ex)\mathscr{A}(x)$	Hyp
3.	$\mathscr{A}(b)$	2, Rule C with b
4.	$\mathscr{A}(b) \supset \mathscr{B}(b)$	1, Rule A4
5.	$\mathscr{B}(b)$	3,4, MP
6.	$(Ex)\mathscr{B}(x)$	5, Rule E4
7.	$(x)(\mathscr{A}(x) \supset \mathscr{B}(x)), (Ex)\mathscr{A}(x) \vdash_C (Ex)\mathscr{B}(x)$	1–6
8.	$(x)(\mathscr{A}(x) \supset \mathscr{B}(x)), (Ex)\mathscr{A}(x) \vdash (Ex)\mathscr{B}(x)$	7, Prop. 2.23
9.	$(x)(\mathscr{A}(x) \supset \mathscr{B}(x)) \vdash (Ex)\mathscr{A}(x) \supset (Ex)\mathscr{B}(x)$	8, Prop. 2.4
10.	$\vdash (x)(\mathscr{A}(x) \supset \mathscr{B}(x)) \supset ((Ex)\mathscr{A}(x) \supset (Ex)\mathscr{B}(x))$	9, Prop. 2.4

EXERCISES

Use Rule C and Proposition 2.23 to prove the following:

(1) $\vdash (Ex)(\mathscr{A}(x) \supset \mathscr{B}(x)) \supset ((x)\mathscr{A} \supset (Ex)\mathscr{B})$
(2) $\vdash ((x)\mathscr{A}(x) \vee (x)\mathscr{B}(x)) \supset (x)(\mathscr{A}(x) \vee \mathscr{B}(x))$.

§ 8. First-Order Theories with Equality

Let K be a first-order theory which has as one of its predicate letters A_1^2. Let us write $t = s$ as an abbreviation for $A_1^2(t, s)$, and $t \neq s$ as an abbreviation for $\sim A_1^2(t, s)$. Then K is called a first-order theory with equality if the following are theorems of K.

(6)† $(x_1)(x_1 = x_1)$ (Reflexivity of Equality)
(7) $x = y \supset (\mathscr{A}(x, x) \supset \mathscr{A}(x, y))$ (Substitutivity of Equality)

where x and y are any variables, $\mathscr{A}(x, x)$ is any wf, and $\mathscr{A}(x, y)$ arises from $\mathscr{A}(x, x)$ by replacing some, but not necessarily all, free occurrences of x by y, with the proviso that y is free for the occurrences of x which

† The numbering here is a continuation of the numbering of the Logical Axioms on page 57.

it replaces. Thus, $\mathscr{A}(x, y)$ may or may not contain free occurrences of x.

PROPOSITION 2.24. *In any first-order theory with equality,*

(a) *for any term t,* $\vdash t = t$
(b) $\vdash x = y \supset y = x$
(c) $\vdash x = y \supset (y = z \supset x = z)$.

PROOF. (a) From (6), $\vdash (x_1)(x_1 = x_1)$; hence, by Rule A4, $\vdash t = t$. (b) Let $\mathscr{A}(x, x)$ be $x = x$ and $\mathscr{A}(x, y)$ be $y = x$. Then, by (7), $\vdash x = y \supset (x = x \supset y = x)$. But, by (a), $\vdash x = x$. So, by the tautology $B \supset ((A \supset (B \supset C)) \supset (A \supset C))$, we have $\vdash x = y \supset y = x$. (c) Let $\mathscr{A}(y, y)$ be $y = z$ and $\mathscr{A}(y, x)$ be $x = z$. Then, by (7), with x and y interchanged, $\vdash y = x \supset (y = z \supset x = z)$. But, by (b), $\vdash x = y \supset y = x$. Hence, using the tautology $(A \supset B) \supset ((B \supset C) \supset (A \supset C))$, we have: $\vdash x = y \supset (y = z \supset x = z)$.

EXERCISES

Prove

(1) $\vdash (x)(\mathscr{B}(x) \equiv (Ey)(x = y \wedge \mathscr{B}(y)))$
(2) $\vdash (x)(\mathscr{B}(x) \equiv (y)(x = y \supset \mathscr{B}(y)))$
(3) $\vdash (x)(Ey)(x = y)$.

We can reduce condition (7) for equality to a few simpler cases.

PROPOSITION 2.25. *Let K be a first-order theory for which* (6) *holds and* (7) *holds only for atomic* wfs $\mathscr{A}(x, x)$. *Then K is a first-order theory with equality*, i.e., (7) *holds for all* wfs $\mathscr{A}(x, x)$.

PROOF. We must prove (7) for all wfs $\mathscr{A}(x, x)$. It holds for atomic wfs by assumption. Note that we have Proposition 2.24, since its proof used (7) only with atomic wfs. Proceeding by induction on the number n of connectives and quantifiers in $\mathscr{A}$, we assume that (7) holds for all k < n.

Case 1. $\mathscr{A}(x, x)$ is $\sim\mathscr{B}(x, x)$. By inductive hypothesis, we have $\vdash y = x \supset (\mathscr{B}(x, y) \supset \mathscr{B}(x, x))$, since $\mathscr{B}(x, x)$ arises from $\mathscr{B}(x, y)$ by replacing some occurrences of y by x. Hence, by Proposition 2.24(b), and the tautologies $(A \supset B) \supset (\sim B \supset \sim A)$ and $(A \supset B) \supset ((B \supset C) \supset (A \supset C))$, we obtain $\vdash x = y \supset (\mathscr{A}(x, x) \supset \mathscr{A}(x, y))$.

Case 2. $\mathscr{A}(x, x)$ is $\mathscr{B}(x, x) \supset \mathscr{C}(x, x)$. By inductive hypothesis, and Proposition 2.24(b), $\vdash x = y \supset (\mathscr{B}(x, y) \supset \mathscr{B}(x, x))$ and $\vdash x = y \supset (\mathscr{C}(x, x) \supset \mathscr{C}(x, y))$. Hence, by the tautology $(A \supset (B_1 \supset B)) \supset [(A \supset (C \supset C_1)) \supset (A \supset ((B \supset C) \supset (B_1 \supset C_1)))$, we have $\vdash x = y \supset (\mathscr{A}(x, x) \supset \mathscr{A}(x, y))$.

Case 3. $\mathscr{A}(x, x)$ is $(z)\mathscr{B}(x, x, z)$. By inductive hypothesis, $\vdash x = y \supset (\mathscr{B}(x, x, z) \supset \mathscr{B}(x, y, z))$. Now, by Gen and Axiom (5), $\vdash x = y \supset (z)(\mathscr{B}(x, x, z) \supset \mathscr{B}(x, y, z))$. By Exercise 1(a) on page 62, $\vdash (z)(\mathscr{B}(x, x, z) \supset \mathscr{B}(x, y, z)) \supset [(z)(\mathscr{B}(x, x, z)) \supset (z)(\mathscr{B}(x, y, z))]$, and so, by the tautology $(A \supset B) \supset ((B \supset C) \supset (A \supset C))$, $\vdash x = y \supset (\mathscr{A}(x, x) \supset \mathscr{A}(x, y))$.

The instances of (7) can be still further reduced.

PROPOSITION 2.26. *Let K be a first-order theory in which* (6) *holds and* (7) *holds for all atomic* wfs $\mathscr{A}(x, x)$ *such that no function letters occur in* $\mathscr{A}(x, x)$ *and* $\mathscr{A}(x, y)$ *comes from* $\mathscr{A}(x, x)$ *by replacing exactly one occurrence of* x *by* y. *In addition, we assume the following:* (∗) *for any function letter* f_j^n, *if* $z_1, \ldots, z_n$ *are variables and* $f_j^n(w_1, \ldots, w_n)$ *arises from* $f_j^n(z_1, \ldots, z_n)$ *by replacing one occurrence of* x *by* y, *then* $\vdash x = y \supset (f_j^n(z_1, \ldots, z_n) = f_j^n(w_1, \ldots, w_n))$. *Then K is a first-order theory with equality.*

PROOF. Note that, by repeated application, our assumptions can be extended to replacements of more than one occurrence of x by y. Also, Proposition 2.24 is still derivable. By Proposition 2.25, it suffices to prove (7) only for atomic wfs. But, one can easily prove $\vdash (y_1 = z_1 \wedge \ldots \wedge y_n = z_n) \supset (\mathscr{A}(y_1, \ldots, y_n) \supset \mathscr{A}(z_1, \ldots, z_n))$ for all variables $y_1, \ldots, y_n, z_1, \ldots, z_n$ and any atomic wf $\mathscr{A}$ without function letters. Hence, using Rule A4, we reduce the problem to showing that if $t(x, x)$ is a term and $t(x, y)$ comes from $t(x, x)$ by replacing some occurrences of x by y, then $\vdash x = y \supset (t(x, x) = t(x, y))$. But, this can be proved, using (∗), by induction on the number of function letters in t, and we leave this as an exercise.

EXERCISES

1. Let K_1 be a first-order theory having only $=$ as a predicate letter, and no function letters or individual constants; and let its proper axioms be $(x_1)(x_1 = x_1)$, $(x_1)(x_2)(x_1 = x_2 \supset x_2 = x_1)$, and $(x_1)(x_2)(x_3)(x_1 = x_2 \supset (x_2 = x_3 \supset x_1 = x_3))$. Show that K is a first-order theory with equality. Hint: by Proposition 2.26, it suffices to prove the following wfs:

$$x = y \supset (x = x \supset y = x)$$
$$x = y \supset (x = x \supset x = y)$$
$$x = y \supset (x = y \supset y = y)$$
$$x = y \supset (y = x \supset y = y)$$
$$x = y \supset (x = z \supset y = z)$$
$$x = y \supset (z = x \supset z = y)$$

K_1 is called the first-order theory of equality.

2. Let K_2 be a first-order theory having only $=$ and $<$ as predicate letters, and no function letters or individual constants. Let K_2 have the proper axioms:

(a) $(x_1)(x_1 = x_1)$
(b) $(x_1)(x_2)((x_1 = x_2) \supset (x_2 = x_1))$
(c) $(x_1)(x_2)(x_3)(x_1 = x_2 \supset (x_2 = x_3 \supset x_1 = x_3))$
(d) $(x_1)(Ex_2)(Ex_3)(x_1 < x_2 \wedge x_3 < x_1)$
(e) $(x_1)(x_2)(x_3)(x_1 < x_2 \wedge x_2 < x_3 \supset x_1 < x_3)$
(f) $(x_1)(x_2)(x_1 = x_2 \supset \sim x_1 < x_2)$
(g) $(x_1)(x_2)(x_1 < x_2 \vee x_1 = x_2 \vee x_2 < x_1)$
(h) $(x_1)(x_2)(x_1 < x_2 \supset (Ex_3)(x_1 < x_3 \wedge x_3 < x_2))$

Using Proposition 2.26, show that K_2 is a first-order theory with equality. (K_2 is the first-order theory of densely-ordered sets with neither first nor last element.)

3. Let K be any first-order theory with equality. (a) Prove that $\vdash_K x_1 = y_1 \wedge \ldots \wedge x_n = y_n \supset t(x_1, \ldots, x_n) = t(y_1, \ldots, y_n)$, where $t(y_1, \ldots, y_n)$ arises from a term $t(x_1, \ldots, x_n)$ by substitution of $y_1, \ldots, y_n$ for $x_1, \ldots, x_n$, respectively. (b) Prove that $\vdash_K x_1 = y_1 \wedge \ldots \wedge x_n = y_n \supset (\mathscr{A}(x_1, \ldots, x_n) \equiv \mathscr{A}(y_1, \ldots, y_n))$ where $\mathscr{A}(y_1, \ldots, y_n)$ is obtained by substituting $y_1, \ldots, y_n$ for one or more free occurrences of $x_1, \ldots, x_n$, respectively, in the wf $\mathscr{A}(x_1, \ldots, x_n)$, and $y_1, \ldots, y_n$ are free for $x_1, \ldots, x_n$, respectively, in the wf $\mathscr{A}(x_1, \ldots, x_n)$.

Examples. (In the literature, "elementary" is sometimes used instead of "first-order".)

1. Elementary Theory G of Groups: predicate letter $=$, function letter f_1^2, and individual constant a_1. We abbreviate $f_1^2(t, s)$ by $t + s$, and a_1 by 0. The proper axioms are:

(a) $x_1 + (x_2 + x_3) = (x_1 + x_2) + x_3$
(b) $x_1 + 0 = x_1$
(c) $(x_1)(Ex_2)(x_1 + x_2 = 0)$
(d) $x_1 = x_1$
(e) $x_1 = x_2 \supset x_2 = x_1$
(f) $x_1 = x_2 \supset (x_2 = x_3 \supset x_1 = x_3)$
(g) $x_1 = x_2 \supset (x_1 + x_3 = x_2 + x_3 \wedge x_3 + x_1 = x_3 + x_2)$

From Proposition 2.26, one easily proves that G is a first-order theory with equality. If one adds to the axioms the following wf

(h) $x_1 + x_2 = x_2 + x_1$

the new theory G_C is called the elementary theory of abelian groups.

2. Elementary Theory F of Fields: predicate letter $=$, function

letters f_1^2 and f_2^2, and individual constants a_1 and a_2. Abbreviate $f_1^2(t, s)$ by $t + s$ and $f_2^2(t, s)$ by $t \cdot s$ and a_1 and a_2 by 0 and 1. As proper axioms, take (a)–(h) of (1) above, plus

(i) $x_1 = x_2 \supset (x_1 \cdot x_3 = x_2 \cdot x_3 \wedge x_3 \cdot x_1 = x_3 \cdot x_2)$
(j) $(x_1 \cdot x_2) \cdot x_3 = x_1 \cdot (x_2 \cdot x_3)$
(k) $x_1 \cdot (x_2 + x_3) = (x_1 \cdot x_2) + (x_1 \cdot x_3)$
(l) $x_1 \cdot x_2 = x_2 \cdot x_1$
(m) $x_1 \cdot 1 = x_1$
(n) $x_1 \neq 0 \supset (Ex_2)(x_1 \cdot x_2 = 1)$

F is a first-order theory with equality. Axioms (a)–(m) define the elementary theory R_C of commutative rings with unit. If we add to F the predicate letter A_2^2, denoting $A_2^2(t, s)$ by $t < s$, and add the axioms (e), (f), (g) of Exercise 2 above, as well as $x_1 < x_2 \supset x_1 + x_3 < x_2 + x_3$ and $x_1 < x_2 \wedge 0 < x_3 \supset x_1 \cdot x_3 < x_2 \cdot x_3$, then the new theory $F_<$ is called the elementary theory of ordered fields.

EXERCISE. Show that the axioms (d)–(f) of equality (reflexivity, symmetry, transitivity), mentioned in Examples 1 and 2 above, can be replaced by (d) and (f′): $x = y \supset (z = y \supset x = z)$.

One often encounters first-order theories K in which $=$ may be defined, i.e., there is a wf $\mathscr{E}(x, y)$ with two free variables x, y such that, if we abbreviate $\mathscr{E}(t, s)$ by $t = s$, then (6) and (7) are provable in K. We make the convention that, if t and s are terms that are not free for x and y, respectively, in $\mathscr{E}(x, y)$ then we take $t = s$ to be the abbreviation not of $\mathscr{E}(t, s)$ but rather of a wf $\mathscr{E}^\star(t, s)$ obtained from $\mathscr{E}(t, s)$ by suitable changes of bound variables (cf. Corollary 2.22) so that t and s are free for x and y, respectively, in $\mathscr{E}^\star(x, y)$. Analogues of Propositions 2.25 and 2.26 hold for such theories if, in the propositions, we assume (7) also for suitable wfs of the form $\mathscr{E}^\star(t, s)$. (Exercise)

In first-order theories with equality, it is possible to define phrases using the expression "There exists one and only one x such that ..." in the following way.

DEFINITION. $(E_1 x)\mathscr{A}(x)$ for $(Ex)\mathscr{A}(x) \wedge (x)(y)(\mathscr{A}(x) \wedge \mathscr{A}(y) \supset x = y)$.

EXERCISES

1. $\vdash (x)(E_1 y)(x = y)$
2. $\vdash (E_1 x)\mathscr{A}(x) \equiv (Ex)(y)(x = y \equiv \mathscr{A}(y))$
3. $\vdash (x)(\mathscr{A}(x) \equiv \mathscr{B}(x)) \supset [(E_1 x)\mathscr{A}(x) \equiv (E_1 x)\mathscr{B}(x)]$

In any model for a first-order theory K with equality, the relation E in the model corresponding to the predicate letter = is an equivalence relation (by Proposition 2.24). If this relation E is the identity relation in the domain of the model, then the model is called *normal*.

Any model M for K can be *contracted* to a normal model M′ for K by taking the domain D′ of M′ to be the set of equivalence classes determined by the relation E in the domain D of M. For a predicate letter A_j^n with interpretation $(A_j^n)^\star$ in M, we define the new interpretation $(A_j^n)'$ in M′ as follows: for any equivalence classes $[\mathrm{b}_1], \ldots, [\mathrm{b}_\mathrm{n}]$ in D′ determined by the elements $\mathrm{b}_1, \ldots, \mathrm{b}_\mathrm{n}$ in D, $(A_j^n)'$ holds for $([\mathrm{b}_1], \ldots, [\mathrm{b}_\mathrm{n}])$ if and only if $(A_j^n)^\star$ holds for $\mathrm{b}_1, \ldots, \mathrm{b}_\mathrm{n}$. Notice that it makes no difference which representatives $\mathrm{b}_1, \ldots, \mathrm{b}_\mathrm{n}$ we select in the given equivalence classes, for, by (7), $\vdash x_1 = y_1 \wedge \ldots \wedge x_\mathrm{n} = y_\mathrm{n} \supset (A_j^n(x_1, \ldots, x_\mathrm{n}) \equiv A_j^n(y_1, \ldots, y_\mathrm{n}))$. Likewise, if $(f_j^n)^\star$ is the interpretation in M of f_j^n, then we define the new interpretation $(f_j^n)'$ in M′ as follows: for any equivalence classes $[\mathrm{b}_1], \ldots, [\mathrm{b}_\mathrm{n}]$ in D′ determined by the elements $\mathrm{b}_1, \ldots, \mathrm{b}_\mathrm{n}$ in D, $(f_j^n)'([\mathrm{b}_1], \ldots, [\mathrm{b}_\mathrm{n}]) = [(f_j^n)^\star(\mathrm{b}_1, \ldots, \mathrm{b}_\mathrm{n})]$. Again note that this is independent of the choice $\mathrm{b}_1, \ldots, \mathrm{b}_\mathrm{n}$ of representatives, since, by (7), $\vdash x_1 = y_1 \wedge \ldots \wedge x_\mathrm{n} = y_\mathrm{n} \supset f_j^n(x_1, \ldots, x_\mathrm{n}) = f_j^n(y_1, \ldots, y_\mathrm{n})$. If c is the interpretation in M of an individual constant a_i, then we take the equivalence class [c] to be the interpretation in M′ of a_i. The relation E′ corresponding to = in the model M′ is the identity relation in D′: $\mathrm{E}'([\mathrm{b}_1], [\mathrm{b}_2])$ if and only if $\mathrm{E}(\mathrm{b}_1, \mathrm{b}_2)$, i.e., if and only if $[\mathrm{b}_1] = [\mathrm{b}_2]$. Now, one can easily prove by induction the following lemma: if $\mathrm{s} = (\mathrm{b}_1, \mathrm{b}_2, \ldots)$ is a denumerable sequence of elements of D, $[\mathrm{b}_\mathrm{i}]$ is the equivalence class of b_i, and $\mathrm{s}' = ([\mathrm{b}_1], [\mathrm{b}_2], \ldots)$, then $\mathscr{A}$ is satisfied by s in M if and only if $\mathscr{A}$ is satisfied by s′ in M′. It follows that, for any wf $\mathscr{A}$, $\mathscr{A}$ is true in M if and only if $\mathscr{A}$ is true in M′. Hence, because M is a model of K, M′ is a normal model for K.

PROPOSITION 2.27 (Extension of Proposition 2.12; Gödel [1930]). *Any consistent first-order theory K with equality has a finite or denumerable normal model.*

PROOF. By Proposition 2.12, K has a denumerable model M. Hence the contraction of M to a normal model yields a finite or denumerable normal model M′, for the set of equivalence classes in a set D has cardinality less than or equal to the cardinality of D.

COROLLARY 2.28 (Extension of the Skolem-Löwenheim Theorem). *Any first-order theory* K *with equality which has an infinite normal model* M *has a denumerable normal model.*

PROOF. Add to K the new individual constants $b_1, b_2, \ldots$ together with the axioms $b_i \neq b_j$ for i ≠ j. Then the new theory K′ is consistent. For, if K′ were inconsistent, there would be a proof in K′ of a contradiction $\mathscr{C} \wedge \sim\mathscr{C}$ where we may assume that $\mathscr{C}$ is a wf of K. But this proof uses only a finite number of the new axioms: $b_{i_1} \neq b_{j_1}, \ldots, b_{i_n} \neq b_{j_n}$. Now M can be extended to a model of K with the axioms $b_{i_1} \neq b_{j_1}, \ldots, b_{i_n} \neq b_{j_n}$, for, since M is an infinite normal model, we can choose interpretations of $b_{i_1}, b_{j_1}, \ldots, b_{i_n}, b_{j_n}$ so that the wfs $b_{i_1} \neq b_{j_1}, \ldots, b_{i_n} \neq b_{j_n}$ are true in M. But, since $\mathscr{C} \wedge \sim\mathscr{C}$ is derivable from these wfs and the axioms of K, it would follow that $\mathscr{C} \wedge \sim\mathscr{C}$ is true in M, which is impossible ((II), page 51). Hence, K′ must be consistent. Now, by Proposition 2.27, K′ has a finite or denumerable normal model N. But, since the wfs $b_i \neq b_j$, for i ≠ j, are axioms of K′, they are true in N. Hence the elements in N which are the interpretations of $b_1, b_2, \ldots$ must be distinct, which implies that the domain of N is infinite, and, therefore, denumerable.

EXERCISES

1. We define $(E_n x)\mathscr{A}(x)$ by induction on n ⩾ 1. The case n = 1 has already been taken care of. Let $(E_{n+1}x)\mathscr{A}(x)$ stand for $(Ey)(\mathscr{A}(y) \wedge (E_n x)(x \neq y \wedge \mathscr{A}(x)))$. Show that $(E_n x)\mathscr{A}(x)$ asserts that there are exactly n objects for which $\mathscr{A}$ holds, in the sense that in any normal model for $(E_n x)\mathscr{A}(x)$ there are exactly n objects for which the property corresponding to $\mathscr{A}(x)$ holds.

2. If a first-order theory K with equality has arbitrarily large finite normal models, then it has a denumerable normal model. (Hint: the proof is analogous to that for Corollary 2.28.)

3. Any predicate calculus with equality is consistent. (Hint: let $\mathscr{A}$ be a wf. Cross out all quantifiers. Replace any wf $t = s$ by $\mathscr{B} \vee \sim\mathscr{B}$ for some fixed wf $\mathscr{B}$. Erase all terms, and all associated parentheses. If $\mathscr{A}$ is a theorem, show that the result of the indicated action yields an instance of a tautology. But $x_1 \neq x_1$ transforms into $\sim(\mathscr{B} \vee \sim\mathscr{B})$.)

4. Prove the independence of Axioms (1)–(7) in any predicate calculus with equality. (Hints: for the independence of (1)–(3), replace all $t = s$ by the statement form $A \supset A$; then erase all quantifiers, terms, and associated commas and parentheses; Axioms (4)–(6) go over into statement forms of the form $P \supset P$, and (7) into $(P \supset P) \supset (Q \supset Q)$. Now, for (2)–(3), use the same proofs as for Axioms (A2)–(A3) for the propositional calculus (cf. pages 38–39). For (1), the three-valued

truth table used on page 38 does not give the value 0 for $P \supset P$; instead, use the following four-valued truth tables:

A	$\sim A$
0	1
1	0
2	3
3	2

A	B	$A \supset B$	A	B	$A \supset B$
0	0	0	0	2	1
1	0	0	1	2	0
2	0	0	2	2	0
3	0	0	3	2	0
0	1	1	0	3	1
1	1	0	1	3	0
2	1	1	2	3	1
3	1	1	3	3	0

For (4), replace all universal quantifiers (x) by existential quantifiers (Ex). For (5), change all terms t to x_1 and replace all universal quantifiers by (x_1). For (6), replace all wfs $t = s$ by the negation of some fixed theorem. For (7), replace all wfs $t = s$ by some fixed theorem.) A predicate calculus with equality is assumed to have (6) and (7) as axioms.

5. Prove the independence of the rules of inference MP and Gen, in the sense that if we omit a rule it cannot be proved as a derived rule of inference. (Hint: for MP, note that Gen increases the number of quantifiers and connectives. For Gen, replace every $(x)\mathscr{A}$ by $(x) \sim (\mathscr{A} \supset \mathscr{A})$.)

6. Let a wf $\mathscr{A}$ be called k-valid if it is true in all interpretations having k elements. Call $\mathscr{A}$ precisely k-valid if it is k-valid but not (k + 1)-valid. Note that (k + 1)-validity implies k-validity. Give an example of a wf which is precisely k-valid. (For further information, cf. Hilbert-Bernays I [1934, § 4–5]; Wajsberg [1933].)

§ 9. Definitions of New Function Letters and Individual Constants

In mathematics, once we have proved, for any $y_1, \ldots, y_n$, the existence of a unique object u having the property $\mathscr{A}(u, y_1, \ldots, y_n)$, we often introduce a new function $f(y_1, \ldots, y_n)$ such that $\mathscr{A}(f(y_1, \ldots, y_n), y_1, \ldots, y_n)$ holds for all $y_1, \ldots, y_n$. In cases where we have proved the existence of a unique object u satisfying $\mathscr{A}(u)$, and $\mathscr{A}(u)$ contains u as its only free variable, then we introduce a new individual constant b. It is generally acknowledged that such definitions, though convenient, add nothing really new to the theory. This can be made precise in the following way.

PROPOSITION 2.29. *Let* K *be a first-order theory with equality. Assume that* $\vdash_K (E_1 u)\mathscr{A}(u, y_1, \ldots, y_n)$. *Let* K′ *be the first-order theory with equality obtained by adding to* K *a new function letter* f *of* n *arguments, and the proper axiom* $\mathscr{A}(f(y_1, \ldots, y_n), y_1, \ldots, y_n)$, *as well as all instances of* (1)–(7) *involving* f. *Then there is an effective transformation mapping each* wf $\mathscr{B}$ *of* K′ *into a* wf $\mathscr{B}'$ *of* K *such that*

(1) *if* f *does not occur in* $\mathscr{B}$, *then* $\mathscr{B}'$ *is* $\mathscr{B}$
(2) $(\sim \mathscr{B})'$ *is* $\sim(\mathscr{B}')$
(3) $(\mathscr{B} \supset \mathscr{C})'$ *is* $\mathscr{B}' \supset \mathscr{C}'$
(4) $((x)\mathscr{B})'$ *is* $(x)(\mathscr{B}')$
(5) $\vdash_{K'} \mathscr{B} \equiv \mathscr{B}'$
(6) if $\vdash_{K'} \mathscr{B}$, *then* $\vdash_{K} \mathscr{B}'$

Hence, if $\mathscr{B}$ *does not contain* f *and* $\vdash_{K'} \mathscr{B}$, *then* $\vdash_{K} \mathscr{B}$.

PROOF. A simple f-term is an expression $f(t_1, \ldots, t_n)$ where $t_1, \ldots, t_n$ are terms not containing f. Given an atomic wf $\mathscr{B}$ of K′, let $\mathscr{B}^\star$ be the result of replacing the left-most occurrence of a simple f-term $f(t_1, \ldots, t_n)$ in $\mathscr{B}$ by the first variable u not in $\mathscr{B}$. Call the wf $(Eu)(\mathscr{A}(u, t_1, \ldots, t_n) \wedge \mathscr{B}^\star)$ the f-transform of $\mathscr{B}$. If $\mathscr{B}$ does not contain f, let $\mathscr{B}$ be its own f-transform. Clearly, $\vdash_{K'} (Eu)(\mathscr{A}(u, t_1, \ldots, t_n) \wedge \mathscr{B}^\star) \equiv \mathscr{B}$. (Here we use $\vdash_K (E_1u)\mathscr{A}(u, y_1, \ldots, y_n)$ and the axiom $\mathscr{A}(f(y_1, \ldots, y_n), y_1, \ldots, y_n)$ of K′.) Since the f-transform $\mathscr{B}^\star$ of $\mathscr{B}$ contains one less f than $\mathscr{B}$, and $\vdash_{K'} \mathscr{B}^\star \equiv \mathscr{B}$, if we take successive f-transforms, eventually we obtain a wf $\mathscr{B}'$ which does not contain f, and such that $\vdash_{K'} \mathscr{B}' \equiv \mathscr{B}$. Call $\mathscr{B}'$ the f-less transform of $\mathscr{B}$. Extend the definition to all wfs of K′ by letting $(\sim\mathscr{B})'$ be $\sim(\mathscr{B}')$, $(\mathscr{B} \supset \mathscr{C})'$ be $\mathscr{B}' \supset \mathscr{C}'$, and $((x)\mathscr{B})'$ be $(x)(\mathscr{B}')$. Properties (1)–(5) of the theorem are then obvious. To prove (6), it suffices, by (1) and (5), to show that, if $\mathscr{B}$ does not contain f and $\vdash_{K'} \mathscr{B}$, then $\vdash_K \mathscr{B}$. We may assume that $\mathscr{B}$ is a closed wf, since a wf and its closure are deducible from each other.

Assume that M is a model of K. Let M_1 be the corresponding normal model of K (cf. page 80). We know that a wf is true in M if and only if it is true in M_1. Since $\vdash_K (E_1u)\mathscr{A}(u, y_1, \ldots, y_n)$, then, for any $b_1, \ldots, b_n$ in the domain of M_1, there is a unique c in the domain of M_1 such that $\mathscr{A}(c, b_1, \ldots, b_n)$ is true in M_1. If we define $f'(b_1, \ldots, b_n)$ to be c, then, taking f′ to be the interpretation of the function letter f, we obtain from M_1 a model M′ of K′. For, the logical axioms of K′ (including the equality axioms of K′) are true in any interpretation, and the axiom $\mathscr{A}(f(y_1, \ldots, y_n), y_1, \ldots, y_n)$ also holds in M′ by virtue of the definition of f′. Since the proper axioms of K do not contain f, and since they are true in M_1, they are also true in M′. But $\vdash_{K'} \mathscr{B}$. Hence, $\mathscr{B}$ is true in M′, but since $\mathscr{B}$ does not contain f, $\mathscr{B}$ is true in M_1, and hence also in M. Thus, $\mathscr{B}$ is true in every model of K. Therefore, by Corollary 2.15(a) of the Completeness Theorem, $\vdash_K \mathscr{B}$. (In the case where $\vdash_K (E_1u)\mathscr{A}(u)$ and $\mathscr{A}(u)$ contains only u as a free variable, we form K′ by adding a new individual constant b and the axiom $\mathscr{A}(b)$. Then the analogue of Proposition 2.29 follows from practically the same proof as the one just given.)

EXERCISE. Find the f-less transforms of

$$(x)(Ey)(A_1^3(x, y, f(x, y, \ldots, y)) \supset f(y, x, x, \ldots, x) = x)$$

and of

$$A_1^1(f(y_1, \ldots, y_{n-1}, f(y_1, \ldots, y_n)) \vee (Ex)A_1^2(x, f(y_1, \ldots, y_n))$$

Note that Proposition 2.29 also applies when we have introduced several new symbols $f_1, \ldots, f_n$, for we can assume that we have added each f_i to the theory already obtained by the addition of $f_1, \ldots, f_{i-1}$; then n successive applications of Proposition 2.29 are necessary. In addition, the wf $\mathscr{B}'$ of K in Proposition 2.29 can be considered an f-free translation of $\mathscr{B}$ into the language of K.

Examples.

1. In the elementary theory of groups G (cf. page 78), one can prove $(E_1x_2)(x_1 + x_2 = 0)$. Then introduce a new function letter f of one argument, abbreviate $f(t)$ by $(-t)$, and add the new axiom $x_1 + (-x_1) = 0$. By Proposition 2.29, we now cannot prove any wf of G which we could not prove before. Thus, the definition of $(-t)$ adds no really new power to the original theory.

2. In the elementary theory of fields F (cf. pp. 78–79), one can prove $(E_1x_2)((x_1 \neq 0 \wedge x_1 \cdot x_2 = 1) \vee (x_1 = 0 \wedge x_2 = 0))$. We then introduce a new function letter g of one argument, abbreviate $g(t)$ by t^{-1}, and introduce the axiom $(x_1 \neq 0 \wedge x_1 \cdot x_1^{-1} = 1) \vee (x_1 = 0 \wedge x_1^{-1} = 0)$, from which one can prove $x_1 \neq 0 \supset x_1 \cdot x_1^{-1} = 1$.

From Proposition 2.29, we can see that, in first-order theories with equality, only predicate letters are needed; function letters and individual constants are dispensable. If f_j^n is a function letter, we can replace it by a new predicate letter A_k^{n+1} if we add the axiom $(E_1u)A_k^{n+1}(y_1, \ldots, y_n, u)$. An individual constant is to be replaced by a new predicate letter A_k^1 if we add the axiom $(E_1u)A_k^1(u)$.

Example. In the elementary theory G of groups, we can replace + and 0 by predicates A_1^3 and A_1^1 if we add the axioms $(x_1)(x_2)(E_1x_3)A_1^3(x_1, x_2, x_3)$ and $(E_1x_1)A_1^1(x_1)$, and if we replace Axioms (a),(b),(c),(g) by

(a′) $A_1^3(x_2, x_3, y_1) \wedge A_1^3(x_1, y_1, y_2) \wedge A_1^3(x_1, x_2, y_3) \wedge A_1^3(y_3, x_3, y_4) \supset y_2 = y_4$

(b′) $A_1^1(y_1) \wedge A_1^3(x_1, y_1, y_2) \supset y_2 = x_1$

(c′) $(Ex_2)(y_1)(y_2)(A_1^1(y_1) \wedge A_1^3(x_1, x_2, y_2) \supset y_2 = y_1)$
(g′) $[x_1 = x_2 \wedge A_1^3(x_1, x_3, y_1) \wedge A_1^3(x_2, x_3, y_2) \wedge A_1^3(x_3, x_1, y_3) \wedge A_1^3(x_3, x_2, y_4)] \supset y_1 = y_2 \wedge y_3 = y_4$

Notice that the proof of Proposition 2.29 is highly non-constructive, since it uses semantical notions (model, truth) and is based upon Corollary 2.15(a), which was proved in a non-constructive way. Constructive, syntactical proofs have been given for Proposition 2.29 (cf. Kleene [1952], § 74), but, in general, they are quite complex.

Descriptive phrases of the kind "the u such that $\mathscr{A}(u, y_1, \ldots, y_n)$" are very common in ordinary language and in mathematics. Such phrases are called definite descriptions. We let $\iota u(\mathscr{A}(u, y_1, \ldots, y_n))$ denote the unique object u such that $\mathscr{A}(u, y_1, \ldots, y_n)$ if there is such a unique object. If there is no such unique object, we may either let $\iota u(\mathscr{A}(u, y_1, \ldots, y_n))$ stand for some fixed object, say 0, or we may consider it meaningless. (For example, we may say that the phrases "the present king of France" or "the smallest integer" are meaningless, or we may arbitrarily make the convention that they denote 0.) There are various ways of incorporating these ι-terms in formalized theories, but since in most cases the same results are obtained by using new function letters as above, and since they all lead to theorems similar to Proposition 2.29, we shall not discuss them any further here. For details, cf. Hilbert-Bernays [1934] and Rosser [1939a], [1953].

§ 10. Prenex Normal Forms

A wf $(Q_1 y_1) \ldots (Q_n y_n)\mathscr{A}$, where each $(Q_i y_i)$ is a universal or existential quantifier, $y_i \neq y_j$ for $i \neq j$, and $\mathscr{A}$ contains no quantifiers, is said to be in *prenex normal form*. (We include the case n = 0 when there are no quantifiers at all.) We shall prove that for every wf we can construct an equivalent wf in prenex normal form.

LEMMA 2.30. *In any first-order theory,*

(I) $\vdash ((x)\mathscr{C}(x) \supset \mathscr{D}) \equiv (Ey)(\mathscr{C}(y) \supset \mathscr{D})$, if y is not free in $\mathscr{C}(x)$ or $\mathscr{D}$

(II) $\vdash ((Ex)\mathscr{C}(x) \supset \mathscr{D}) \equiv (y)(\mathscr{C}(y) \supset \mathscr{D})$, if y is not free in $\mathscr{C}(x)$ or $\mathscr{D}$

(III) $\vdash \mathscr{D} \supset (x)\mathscr{C}(x) \equiv (y)(\mathscr{D} \supset \mathscr{C}(y))$, if y is not free in $\mathscr{C}(x)$ or $\mathscr{D}$

(IV) $\vdash \mathscr{D} \supset (Ex)\mathscr{C}(x) \equiv (Ey)(\mathscr{D} \supset \mathscr{C}(y))$, if y is not free in $\mathscr{C}(x)$ or $\mathscr{D}$

(V) $\vdash \sim(x)\mathscr{C} \equiv (Ex)\sim\mathscr{C}$

(VI) $\vdash \sim(Ex)\mathscr{C} \equiv (x)\sim\mathscr{C}$

PROOF. I(A)

1.	$(x)\mathscr{C}(x) \supset \mathscr{D}$	Hyp
2.	$\sim(Ey)(\mathscr{C}(y) \supset \mathscr{D})$	Hyp
3.	$\sim\sim(y)\sim(\mathscr{C}(y) \supset \mathscr{D})$	2, Abbreviation
4.	$(y)(\mathscr{C}(y) \wedge \sim\mathscr{D})$	3, Tautologies $\sim\sim A \supset A$, $\sim(A \supset B) \equiv (A \wedge \sim B)$, Corollary 2.21
5.	$\mathscr{C}(y) \wedge \sim\mathscr{D}$	4, Rule A4
6.	$\mathscr{C}(y)$	5, Tautology $(A \wedge B) \supset A$
7.	$(y)\mathscr{C}(y)$	6, Gen
8.	$(x)\mathscr{C}(x)$	7, Lemma 2.8
9.	$\mathscr{D}$	1,8, MP
10.	$\sim\mathscr{D}$	5, Tautology†
11.	$\mathscr{D} \wedge \sim\mathscr{D}$	9,10, Tautology
12.	$(x)\mathscr{C}(x) \supset \mathscr{D}, \sim(Ey)(\mathscr{C}(y) \supset \mathscr{D}) \vdash \mathscr{D} \wedge \sim\mathscr{D}$	1–11
13.	$(x)\mathscr{C}(x) \supset \mathscr{D} \vdash \sim(Ey)(\mathscr{C}(y) \supset \mathscr{D}) \supset \mathscr{D} \wedge \sim\mathscr{D}$	12, Prop. 2.4
14.	$(x)\mathscr{C}(x) \supset \mathscr{D} \vdash (Ey)(\mathscr{C}(y) \supset \mathscr{D})$	13, Tautology
15.	$\vdash ((x)\mathscr{C}(x) \supset \mathscr{D}) \supset (Ey)(\mathscr{C}(y) \supset \mathscr{D})$	14, Proposition 2.4

PROOF. I(B)

1.	$(Ey)(\mathscr{C}(y) \supset \mathscr{D})$	Hyp
2.	$(x)\mathscr{C}(x)$	Hyp
3.	$\mathscr{C}(b) \supset \mathscr{D}$	1, Rule C
4.	$\mathscr{C}(b)$	2, Rule A4
5.	$\mathscr{D}$	3,4, MP
6.	$(Ey)(\mathscr{C}(y) \supset \mathscr{D}), (x)\mathscr{C}(x) \vdash_C \mathscr{D}$	1–5
7.	$(Ey)(\mathscr{C}(y) \supset \mathscr{D}), (x)\mathscr{C}(x) \vdash \mathscr{D}$	6, Prop. 2.23
8.	$\vdash (Ey)(\mathscr{C}(y) \supset \mathscr{D}) \supset ((x)\mathscr{C}(x) \supset \mathscr{D})$	7, Prop. 2.4 twice

PROOF. I(C)

$\vdash ((x)\mathscr{C}(x) \supset \mathscr{D}) \equiv (Ey)(\mathscr{C}(y) \supset \mathscr{D})$ (A), (B), Tautology

Parts (II) through (VI) are proved easily and left as an exercise. (VI) is trivial, and (V) appeared in Exercise 1, page 72; (III) and (IV) follow easily from (II) and (I), respectively.)

Lemma 2.30 allows us to move interior quantifiers to the front of a wf. This is the essential process in the proof of the following theorem.

† From now on, application of obvious tautologies will merely be indicated by the word "Tautology".

PROPOSITION 2.31. *There is an effective procedure for transforming any* wf $\mathscr{A}$ *into a* wf $\mathscr{B}$ *in prenex normal form such that* $\vdash \mathscr{A} \equiv \mathscr{B}$.

PROOF. We describe the procedure by induction on the number k of connectives and quantifiers in $\mathscr{A}$. (By Proposition 2.18 (a)–(b), we can assume that the quantified variables in the prefix that we shall obtain are distinct.) If k = 0, $\mathscr{B}$ is $\mathscr{A}$ itself. Assume that we can find a corresponding $\mathscr{B}$ for all wfs with k < n. Assume $\mathscr{A}$ has n connectives and quantifiers.

Case 1. If $\mathscr{A}$ is $\sim \mathscr{C}$, then, by inductive hypothesis, we can construct a wf $\mathscr{D}$ in prenex normal form such that $\vdash \mathscr{C} \equiv \mathscr{D}$. Hence, $\vdash \sim \mathscr{C} \equiv \sim \mathscr{D}$, i.e., $\vdash \mathscr{A} \equiv \sim \mathscr{D}$; but, applying (V) and (VI) of Lemma 2.30 and Corollary 2.21, we can find a wf $\mathscr{B}$ in prenex normal form such that $\vdash \sim \mathscr{D} \equiv \mathscr{B}$. Hence, $\vdash \mathscr{A} \equiv \mathscr{B}$.

Case 2. If $\mathscr{A}$ is $\mathscr{C} \supset \mathscr{E}$, then by inductive hypothesis, we can find wfs $\mathscr{C}_1$ and $\mathscr{E}_1$ in prenex normal form such that $\vdash \mathscr{C} \equiv \mathscr{C}_1$ and $\vdash \mathscr{E} \equiv \mathscr{E}_1$. Hence, by a tautology, $\vdash (\mathscr{C} \supset \mathscr{E}) \equiv (\mathscr{C}_1 \supset \mathscr{E}_1)$, i.e., $\vdash \mathscr{A} \equiv (\mathscr{C}_1 \supset \mathscr{E}_1)$. Now, applying (I)–(IV) of Lemma 2.30 and Corollary 2.21, we can move the quantifiers in the prefixes of $\mathscr{C}_1$ and $\mathscr{E}_1$ to the front obtaining a wf $\mathscr{B}$ in prenex normal form with $\vdash \mathscr{A} \equiv \mathscr{B}$.

Case 3. $\mathscr{A}$ is $(x)\mathscr{C}$. By inductive hypothesis, there is a wf $\mathscr{C}_1$ in prenex normal form such that $\vdash \mathscr{C} \equiv \mathscr{C}_1$. Hence $\vdash (x)\mathscr{C} \equiv (x)\mathscr{C}_1$, i.e., $\vdash \mathscr{A} \equiv (x)\mathscr{C}_1$. But $(x)\mathscr{C}_1$ is in prenex normal form.

Examples.

1. Let $\mathscr{A}$ be $(x)(A_1^1(x) \supset (y)(A_2^2(x, y) \supset \sim(z)A_3^2(y, z)))$.

By (V) of Lemma 2.30: $(x)(A_1^1(x) \supset (y)(A_2^2(x, y) \supset (Ez) \sim A_3^2(y, z)))$.
By (IV): $(x)(A_1^1(x) \supset (y)(Eu)(A_2^2(x, y) \supset \sim A_3^2(y, u)))$.
By (III): $(x)(v)(A_1^1(x) \supset (Eu)(A_2^2(x, v) \supset \sim A_3^2(v, u)))$.
By (IV): $(x)(v)(Ew)(A_1^1(x) \supset (A_2^2(x, v) \supset \sim A_3^2(v, w)))$.
Changing bound variables (Corollary 2.22): $(x)(y)(Ez)(A_1^1(x) \supset (A_2^2(x, y) \supset \sim A_3^2(y, z)))$.

2. Let $\mathscr{A}$ be $A_1^2(x, y) \supset (Ey)[A_1^1(y) \supset (((Ex)A_1^1(x)) \supset A_2^1(y))]$.

By (II): $A_1^2(x, y) \supset (Ey)[A_1^1(y) \supset (u)(A_1^1(u) \supset A_2^1(y))]$.
By (III): $A_1^2(x, y) \supset (Ey)(v)(A_1^1(y) \supset (A_1^1(v) \supset A_2^1(y)))$.
By (IV): $(Ew)(A_1^2(x, y) \supset (v)(A_1^1(w) \supset (A_1^1(v) \supset A_2^1(w))))$.
By (III): $(Ew)(z)(A_1^2(x, y) \supset (A_1^1(w) \supset (A_1^1(z) \supset A_2^1(w))))$.

EXERCISES

Find a prenex normal form equivalent to the following wfs:

1. $[(x)(A_1^1(x) \supset A_1^2(x, y))] \supset ([(Ey)A_1^1(y)] \supset [(Ez)A_1^2(y, z)])$
2. $(Ex)A_1^2(x, y) \supset (A_1^1(x) \supset \sim(Eu)A_1^2(x, u))$

A first-order predicate calculus in which there are no function letters or individual constants and in which, for any positive integer n, there are infinitely many predicate letters with n arguments is called a *pure first-order predicate calculus.* For pure predicate calculi, we can find a very simple prenex normal form theorem. A wf in prenex normal form such that all existential quantifiers precede all universal quantifiers is said to be in *Skolem normal form.*

PROPOSITION 2.32. *In a pure first-order predicate calculus, there is an effective process assigning to each* wf $\mathscr{A}$ *another* wf $\mathscr{B}$ *in Skolem normal form such that* $\vdash \mathscr{A}$ *if and only if* $\vdash \mathscr{B}$ *(or, equivalently, by Gödel's Completeness Theorem* 2.14, *such that* $\mathscr{A}$ *is logically valid if and only if* $\mathscr{B}$ *is logically valid).*

PROOF. First we may assume that $\mathscr{A}$ is a closed wf, since a wf is provable if and only if its closure is provable. By Proposition 2.31, we may also assume that $\mathscr{A}$ is in prenex normal form. Let the *rank* r of $\mathscr{A}$ be the number of universal quantifiers in $\mathscr{A}$ which precede existential quantifiers. By induction on the rank, we shall describe the process for finding Skolem normal forms. Clearly, when the rank r = 0, we already have the Skolem normal form. Let us assume that we can construct Skolem normal forms when the rank is less than r, and let r be the rank of $\mathscr{A}$. $\mathscr{A}$ can be written as follows: $(Ey_1)\dots(Ey_n)(u)\mathscr{B}(y_1, \dots, y_n, u)$, where $\mathscr{B}(y_1, \dots, y_n, u)$ has only $y_1, \dots, y_n, u$ as its free variables. Let A_j^{n+1} be the first predicate letter of $n + 1$ arguments not occurring in $\mathscr{A}$. Construct the wf

$$(\mathscr{A}_1) \quad (Ey_1)\dots(Ey_n)([(u)(\mathscr{B}(y_1, \dots, y_n, u) \supset A_j^{n+1}(y_1, \dots, y_n, u))] \supset (u)A_j^{n+1}(y_1, \dots, y_n, u))$$

Let us show that $\vdash \mathscr{A}$ if and only if $\vdash \mathscr{A}_1$. Assume $\vdash \mathscr{A}_1$. In the proof of $\mathscr{A}_1$ replace all occurrences of $A_j^{n+1}(z_1, \dots, z_n, w)$ by $\mathscr{B}^\star(z_1, \dots, z_n, w)$, where $\mathscr{B}^\star$ is obtained from $\mathscr{B}$ by replacing all bound variables having free occurrences in the proof by new variables not occurring in the proof. The result is a proof of the wf:

$$(Ey_1)\dots(Ey_n)(((u)(\mathscr{B}^\star(y_1, \dots, y_n, u) \supset \mathscr{B}^\star(y_1, \dots, y_n, u))) \supset (u)\mathscr{B}^\star(y_1, \dots, y_n, u))$$

($\mathscr{B}$ was replaced by $\mathscr{B}^\star$ so that applications of Axiom (4) would remain applications of the same axiom.) Now, by changing the bound variables back again by Corollary 2.22, we see that

$$\vdash (Ey_1)\dots(Ey_n)[(u)(\mathscr{B}(y_1, \dots, y_n, u) \supset \mathscr{B}(y_1, \dots, y_n, u)) \supset (u)\mathscr{B}(y_1, \dots, y_n, u)]$$

Since $\vdash (u)(\mathscr{B}(y_1, \ldots, y_n, u) \supset \mathscr{B}(y_1, \ldots, y_n, u))$, we obtain by Corollary 2.21, $\vdash (Ey_1)\ldots(Ey_n)(u)\mathscr{B}(y_1, \ldots, y_n, u)$, i.e., $\vdash \mathscr{A}$. Conversely, assume $\vdash \mathscr{A}$. By Rule C, we obtain $(u)\mathscr{B}(b_1, \ldots, b_n, u)$. But $\vdash (u)\mathscr{D} \supset ((u)(\mathscr{D} \supset \mathscr{F}) \supset (u)\mathscr{F})$ (cf. Exercise 1, page 62), for any wfs $\mathscr{D}, \mathscr{F}$. Hence, $(u)(\mathscr{B}(b_1, \ldots, b_n, u) \supset A_j^{n+1}(b_1, \ldots, b_n, u)) \supset (u)A_j^{n+1}(b_1, \ldots, b_n, u)$. So, by Rule E4, $(Ey_1)\ldots(Ey_n)([(u)(\mathscr{B}(y_1, \ldots, y_n, u) \supset A_j^{n+1}(y_1, \ldots, y_n, u))] \supset (u)A_j^{n+1}(y_1, \ldots, y_n, u))$, i.e., $\vdash_C \mathscr{A}_1$. Now, by Proposition 2.23, $\vdash \mathscr{A}_1$. A prenex normal form of $\mathscr{A}_1$ has the form $\mathscr{A}_2$: $(Ey_1)\ldots(Ey_n)(Eu)(Q_1z_1)\ldots(Q_sz_s)\mathscr{G}$, where $\mathscr{G}$ has no quantifiers and $(Q_1z_1)\ldots(Q_sz_s)$ is the prefix of $\mathscr{B}$. (For, in deriving the prenex normal form, first, by Lemma 2.30(I), we pull out the first (u), which changes to (Eu); then we pull out of the first conditional the quantifiers in the prefix of $\mathscr{B}$. By Proposition 2.30(II), this changes existential and universal quantifiers, but then we again pull these out of the second conditional of $\mathscr{A}_1$, which brings the prefix back to its original form. Finally, by Proposition 2.30(III), we bring the second (u) out to the prefix, changing it to a new variable (v).) Clearly, $\mathscr{A}_2$ has rank one less than the rank of $\mathscr{A}$, and, by Proposition 2.31, $\vdash \mathscr{A}_1 \equiv \mathscr{A}_2$; but $\vdash \mathscr{A}$ if and only if $\vdash \mathscr{A}_1$. Hence, $\vdash \mathscr{A}$ if and only if $\vdash \mathscr{A}_2$. By inductive hypothesis, we can find a Skolem normal form for $\mathscr{A}_2$, which is also a Skolem normal form for $\mathscr{A}$.

Example. $\mathscr{A}$: $(x)(y)(Ez)\mathscr{C}(x, y, z)$, where $\mathscr{C}$ contains no quantifiers. $\mathscr{A}_1$: $(x)((y)(Ez)\mathscr{C}(x, y, z) \supset A_j^1(x)) \supset (x)A_j^1(x)$, where A_j^1 is not in $\mathscr{C}$. We obtain the prenex normal form of $\mathscr{A}_1$:

$$(Ex)([(y)(Ez)\mathscr{C}(x, y, z) \supset A_j^1(x)] \supset (x)A_j^1(x)) \qquad (2.30\text{I})$$
$$(Ex)((Ey)[(Ez)\mathscr{C}(x, y, z) \supset A_j^1(x)] \supset (x)A_j^1(x)) \qquad (2.30\text{I})$$
$$(Ex)((Ey)(z)(\mathscr{C}(x, y, z) \supset A_j^1(x)) \supset (x)A_j^1(x)) \qquad (2.30\text{II})$$
$$(Ex)(y)((z)(\mathscr{C}(x, y, z) \supset A_j^1(x)) \supset (x)A_j^1(x)) \qquad (2.30\text{II})$$
$$(Ex)(y)(Ez)(\mathscr{C}(x, y, z) \supset A_j^1(x)) \supset (x)A_j^1(x)) \qquad (2.30\text{I})$$
$$(Ex)(y)(Ez)(v)((\mathscr{C}(x, y, z) \supset A_j^1(x)) \supset A_j^1(v)) \qquad (2.30\text{III})$$

We repeat this process again: Let $\mathscr{D}(x, y, z, v)$ be $(\mathscr{C}(x, y, z) \supset A_j^1(x)) \supset A_j^1(v)$. Let A_k^2 not occur in $\mathscr{D}$. Form:

$$(Ex)[(y)[(Ez)(v)(\mathscr{D}(x, y, z, v)) \supset A_k^2(x, y))] \supset (y)A_k^2(x, y)]$$
$$(Ex)(Ey)[(Ez)(v)(\mathscr{D}(x, y, z, v)) \supset A_k^2(x, y))) \supset (y)A_k^2(x, y)] \quad (2.30(\text{I}))$$
$$(Ex)(Ey)(Ez)(v)([\mathscr{D}(x, y, z, v) \supset A_k^2(x, y)] \supset (y)A_k^2(x, y)) \quad (2.30(\text{I}),(\text{II}))$$
$$(Ex)(Ey)(Ez)(v)(w)([\mathscr{D}(x, y, z, v) \supset A_k^2(x, y)] \supset A_k^2(x, w)) \quad (2.30(\text{III}))$$

Thus, a Skolem normal form of $\mathscr{A}$ is

$$(Ex)(Ey)(Ez)(v)(w)([((\mathscr{C}(x, y, z) \supset A_j^1(x)) \supset A_j^1(v)) \supset A_k^2(x, y)] \supset A_k^2(x, w))$$

EXERCISES

1. Find Skolem normal forms for the wfs:

(a) $\sim(Ex)A_1^1(x) \supset (u)(Ey)(x)A_1^3(u, x, y)$
(b) $(x)(Ey)(u)(Ev)A_1^4(x, y, u, v)$

2. Show that there is an effective process which gives, for each wf $\mathscr{A}$ of a pure predicate calculus, another wf $\mathscr{B}$ of this calculus of the form $(y_1)\ldots(y_n)(Ez_1)\ldots(Ez_m)\mathscr{C}$, such that $\mathscr{C}$ is quantifier-free, n, m $\geqslant 0$, and $\mathscr{A}$ is satisfiable if and only if $\mathscr{B}$ is satisfiable. (Hint: apply Proposition 2.32 to $\sim\mathscr{A}$.)

3. Find a Skolem normal form $\mathscr{B}$ for $(x)(Ey)A_1^2(x, y)$, and show that not-$\vdash \mathscr{B} \equiv (x)(Ey)A_1^2(x, y)$. Hence a Skolem normal form for $\mathscr{A}$ is not necessarily logically equivalent to $\mathscr{A}$, in contradistinction to the prenex normal form given by Proposition 2.31.

§ 11. Isomorphism of Interpretations. Categoricity of Theories

We shall say that an interpretation M of the wfs of some first-order theory K is *isomorphic* with another interpretation M′ of K if and only if there is a 1–1 correspondence g (called an isomorphism) of the domain D of M with the domain D′ of M′ such that:

(i) If $(A_j^n)^\star$ and $(A_j^n)'$ are the interpretations in M and M′, respectively, of A_j^n, then, for any $b_1, \ldots, b_n$ in D, $(A_j^n)^\star(b_1, \ldots, b_n)$ if and only if $(A_j^n)'(g(b_1), \ldots, g(b_n))$.

(ii) If $(f_j^n)^\star$ and $(f_j^n)'$ are the interpretations of f_j^n in M and M′. respectively, then, for any $b_1, \ldots, b_n$ in D, $g((f_j^n)^\star(b_1, \ldots, b_n)) = (f_j^n)'(g(b_1), \ldots, g(b_n))$.

(iii) If $a_j{}^\star$ and $a_j{}'$ are the interpretations of the individual constant a_j in M and M′, respectively, then $g(a_j{}^\star) = a_j{}'$.

Notice that if M and M′ are isomorphic, their domains must be of the same cardinality.

PROPOSITION 2.33. *If g is an isomorphism of* M *with* M′ *then* (1) *for any* wf $\mathscr{A}$ *of* K, *any sequence* $s = (b_1, b_2, \ldots)$ *of elements of* D, *and the corresponding sequence* $g(s) = (g(b_1), g(b_2), \ldots)$, *s satisfies* $\mathscr{A}$ *if and only if g(s) satisfies* $\mathscr{A}$; (2) *hence*, $\mathscr{A}$ *is true in* M *if and only if* $\mathscr{A}$ *is true in* M′.

PROOF. (2) follows directly from (1). The proof of (1) is a simple induction on the number of connectives and quantifiers in $\mathscr{A}$, and is left as an exercise.

We see from Proposition 2.33 that isomorphic interpretations have the same "structure" and, thus, differ in no essential way.

EXERCISES

1. If M is an interpretation with domain D, and D′ is a set having the same cardinality as D, then one can define an interpretation M′ with domain D′ such that M is isomorphic with M′.

2. M is isomorphic with M. If M is isomorphic with M′, then M′ is isomorphic with M. If M is isomorphic with M′ and M′ is isomorphic with M″, then M is isomorphic with M″.

A first-order theory K with equality is said to be $\mathfrak{m}$-categorical, where $\mathfrak{m}$ is a cardinal number, if and only if (1) any two normal models of K of cardinality $\mathfrak{m}$ are isomorphic; (2) K has at least one normal model of cardinality $\mathfrak{m}$ (cf. Łoś [1954c]).

Examples

1. Let K^2 be the first-order theory of equality K_1 (cf. page 77) to which we have added the axiom (E2):

$$(Ex_1)(Ex_2)(x_1 \neq x_2 \wedge (x_3)(x_3 = x_1 \vee x_3 = x_2))$$

Then K^2 is 2-categorical. Moreover, every normal model of K^2 has exactly two elements. More generally, define (En) to be

$$(Ex_1)(Ex_2)\dots(Ex_n)(\bigwedge_{1 \leq i < j \leq n} x_i \neq x_j \wedge (x_{n+1})$$
$$(x_{n+1} = x_1 \vee x_{n+1} = x_2 \vee \dots \vee x_{n+1} = x_n))$$

where $\bigwedge_{1 \leq i < j \leq n} x_i \neq x_j$ is the conjunction of all wf $x_i \neq x_j$ with $1 \leqslant i < j \leqslant n$. Then, if K^n is obtained from K_1 by adding (En) as an axiom, K^n is n-categorical, and every normal model of K^n has exactly n elements.

2. The theory K_2 (cf. page 78) of densely-ordered sets with neither first nor last element is $\aleph_0$-categorical (cf. Kamke [1950], page 71: every denumerable normal model of K_2 is isomorphic with the model consisting of the set of rational numbers under their natural ordering). But one can prove that K_2 is not $\mathfrak{m}$-categorical for any $\mathfrak{m}$ different from $\aleph_0$.

EXERCISES

A1. Find a first-order theory with equality which is not $\aleph_0$-categorical, but is $\mathfrak{m}$-categorical for all $\mathfrak{m} > \aleph_0$. (Hint: consider the theory G_c of commutative groups (cf. page 78). For each integer n, let nx stand for the term $\underbrace{(x + x) + \dots + x}_{n\text{-times}}$. Add to G_c the new axioms ($\mathscr{B}_n$): $(x)(E_1 y)(ny = x)$ for all $n \geqslant 2$. The new theory is the theory of uniquely divisible commutative groups. Its normal models are essentially vector spaces over the field of rational numbers. However, any two vector spaces over the rationals of the same non-denumerable cardinality are isomorphic, and there are denumerable vector spaces over the rationals which are not isomorphic (cf. Bourbaki [1947]).)

[A]2. Find a first-order theory with equality which is $\mathfrak{m}$-categorical for all infinite cardinals $\mathfrak{m}$. (Hint: add to the theory G_c of commutative groups the axiom $(x_1)(2x_1 = 0)$. The normal models of the new theory are just the vector spaces over the field of integers modulo 2. Any two such vector spaces of the same cardinality are isomorphic (cf. Bourbaki [1947]).)

[A]3. Is there a first-order theory with equality which is $\mathfrak{m}$-categorical for some non-countable cardinal $\mathfrak{m}$ but not $\mathfrak{n}$-categorical for some other non-countable cardinal $\mathfrak{n}$? In Example 2 we found a theory which is only $\aleph_0$-categorical; in Exercise 1, we found a theory which is $\mathfrak{m}$-categorical for all infinite $\mathfrak{m} > \aleph_0$, but not $\aleph_0$-categorical; and in Exercise 2, a theory which is $\mathfrak{m}$-categorical for all infinite $\mathfrak{m}$. The elementary theory G of groups is not $\mathfrak{m}$-categorical for any infinite $\mathfrak{m}$. The problem is whether these four cases exhaust all the possibilities. (A proof that these cases do exhaust all the possibilities has been announced by M. D. Morley, *Notices Amer. Math. Soc.*, Vol. 9, No. 3 (1962), p. 218.)

4. Show that the theorems of the theory K^n in Example (a) above are precisely the set of all wfs of K^n which are true in all normal models of cardinality n.

[A]§ 12. Generalized First-Order Theories. Completeness and Decidability†

If, in the definition of the notion of first-order theory, we allow a noncountable number of predicate letters, function letters, and individual constants, and possibly a noncountable number of axioms, we arrive at the notion of a generalized first-order theory. First-order theories are special cases of generalized first-order theories. The reader may easily check that all the results for first-order theories, through Lemma 2.9, hold also for generalized first-order theories, without any changes in the proofs. Lemma 2.10 becomes Lemma 2.10′: if the set of symbols of a generalized first-order theory K can be well-ordered and has cardinality $\aleph_\alpha$, then the set of expressions of K also can be well-ordered and has cardinality $\aleph_\alpha$. (First, order the expressions by their length, which is some positive integer, and then stipulate that if e_1 and e_2 are two distinct expressions of the same length k, and j is the first

† Presupposed in this Section is a slender acquaintance with ordinal and cardinal numbers (cf. Chapter IV, or Kamke [1950], or Sierpinski [1958]).

place in which they differ, then e_1 "precedes" e_2 if the jth symbol of e_1 precedes the jth symbol of e_2 according to the given well-ordering of the symbols of K.) Now, under the same assumption as for Lemma 2.10′, Lindenbaum's Lemma 2.11′ can be proved for generalized first-order theories much as before, except that all the enumerations (of the wfs $\mathscr{B}_i$ and of the theories J_i) are transfinite, and the proof that J is consistent and complete uses transfinite induction. The analogue of Henkin's Theorem 2.12 runs as follows:

PROPOSITION 2.34. *If the set of symbols of a consistent generalized first-order theory K can be well-ordered and has cardinality $\aleph_\alpha$, then K has a model of cardinality $\aleph_\alpha$.*

PROOF. The original proof for Proposition 2.12 is modified in the following way. Add $\aleph_\alpha$ new individual constants $b_1, b_2, \ldots, b_\lambda, \ldots$. As before, the new theory K_0 is consistent. Let $F_1(x_{i_1}), \ldots, F_\lambda(x_{i_l}), \ldots$ $(\lambda < \omega_\alpha)$ be a sequence consisting of all wfs of K_0 with at most one free variable. Let (S_λ) be the wf $\sim(x_{i_\lambda})F_\lambda(x_{i_\lambda}) \supset \sim F_\lambda(b_{j_\lambda})$, where the sequence $b_{j_1}, b_{j_2}, \ldots, b_{j_\lambda}, \ldots$ of distinct constants is chosen so that b_{j_λ} does not occur in $F_\beta(x_{i_\beta})$ for $\beta \leqslant \lambda$. The new theory K_∞ obtained by adding all the wfs (S_λ) as axioms is consistent, by a transfinite induction analogous to that of Proposition 2.12. Now, by the extension 2.11′ of Lindenbaum's Lemma, there is a complete, consistent extension J of K_∞. The model is defined now as in Proposition 2.12, and its domain, the set of closed terms of K_0, has cardinality $\aleph_\alpha$.

COROLLARY 2.35. (1) *If the set of symbols of a consistent generalized first-order theory* K *with equality can be well-ordered and has cardinality $\aleph_\alpha$, then it has a normal model of cardinality $\leqslant \aleph_\alpha$.* (2) *If, in addition,* K *has an infinite normal model (or if* K *has arbitrarily large finite normal models), then* K *has a normal model of any cardinality $\aleph_\beta \geqslant \aleph_\alpha$.* (3) *In particular, if* K *is an ordinary first-order theory with equality* (i.e., $\aleph_\alpha = \aleph_0$), *and* K *has an infinite normal model (or if* K *has arbitrarily large finite normal models), then* K *has a normal model of any cardinality* $\aleph_\beta$ $(\beta \geqslant 0)$.

PROOF. (1) The model guaranteed by Proposition 2.34 can be contracted to a normal model (cf. page 80) consisting of equivalence classes in a set of cardinality $\aleph_\alpha$. Such a set of equivalence classes has cardinality $\leqslant \aleph_\alpha$. (2) Assume $\aleph_\beta \geqslant \aleph_\alpha$. Let $b_1, b_2, \ldots$ be a set of new individual constants of cardinality $\aleph_\beta$, and add the axioms $b_\lambda \neq b_\mu$ for $\lambda \neq \mu$. As in the proof of Corollary 2.28, this new theory is consistent, and so, by (1), has a normal model of cardinality $\leqslant \aleph_\beta$ (since the new theory has $\aleph_\beta$ symbols). But, because of the axioms $b_\lambda \neq b_\mu$, the normal model has exactly $\aleph_\beta$ elements. (3) is a special case of (2).

From Lemma 2.9′ and Corollary 2.35(1, 2), it follows easily that, if a generalized first-order theory K with equality has $\aleph_\alpha$ symbols, is $\aleph_\beta$-categorical for some $\beta \geqslant \alpha$, and has no finite models, then K is complete, in the sense that, for any closed wf $\mathscr{A}$, either $\vdash_K \mathscr{A}$ or $\vdash_K \sim\mathscr{A}$ (Vaught [1954]). For, if not-$\vdash_K \mathscr{A}$ and not-$\vdash_K \sim\mathscr{A}$, then the theories $K' = K + \{\sim\mathscr{A}\}$ and $K'' = K + \{\mathscr{A}\}$ are consistent by Lemma 2.9′, and so, by Corollary 2.35(1), there are normal models M_1 and M_2 of K′ and K″, respectively, of cardinality $\leqslant \aleph_\alpha$. Since K has no finite models, M_1 and M_2 are infinite. Hence, by Corollary 2.35(2), there are normal models N_1 and N_2 of K′ and K″, respectively, of cardinality $\aleph_\beta$. By the $\aleph_\beta$-categoricity of K, N_1 and N_2 must be isomorphic. But, since $\sim\mathscr{A}$ is true in N_1 and $\mathscr{A}$ is true in N_2, this is impossible. Therefore, either $\vdash_K \mathscr{A}$ or $\vdash_K \sim\mathscr{A}$.

In particular, if K is an ordinary first-order theory with equality which has no finite models and is $\aleph_\beta$-categorical for some $\beta \geqslant 0$, then K is complete. As an example, consider the theory K_2 of densely-ordered sets with neither first nor last element (cf. page 78, Example 2). K_2 has no finite models and is $\aleph_0$-categorical.

If an ordinary first-order theory K is axiomatic (i.e., one can effectively decide whether any wf is an axiom) and complete, then K is decidable, that is, there is an effective procedure to determine whether any given wf is a theorem. To see this, remember that if a theory is axiomatic, one can effectively enumerate the theorems. Any wf $\mathscr{A}$ is provable if and only if its closure is provable. Hence, we may confine our attention to closed wfs $\mathscr{A}$. Since K is complete, either $\mathscr{A}$ is a theorem or $\sim\mathscr{A}$ is a theorem, and, therefore, one or the other will eventually turn up in our enumeration of the theorems. This provides an effective test for theoremhood. Notice that if K is inconsistent, then every wf is a theorem, and there is an obvious decision procedure; if K is consistent, then not both $\mathscr{A}$ and $\sim\mathscr{A}$ can show up as theorems, and we need only wait till one or the other appears.

If an ordinary axiomatic first-order theory K with equality has no finite models and is $\aleph_\beta$-categorical for some $\beta \geqslant 0$, then, by what we have proved above, K is decidable. In particular, the theory K_2 mentioned above is decidable.

In certain cases, there is a more direct method of proving completeness or decidability. Let us take as an example the theory K_2 of densely-ordered sets with neither first nor last element. Langford [1927] has given the following procedure for K_2. Consider any closed wf $\mathscr{A}$. By Proposition 2.31, we can assume that $\mathscr{A}$ is in prenex normal form $(Qy_1)\ldots(Qy_n)\mathscr{B}$, where $\mathscr{B}$ contains no quantifiers. If (Qy_n) is (y_n), replace $(y_n)\mathscr{B}$ by $\sim(Ey_n)\sim\mathscr{B}$. In all cases, then, we have, at the right side of the wf, $(Ey_n)\mathscr{C}$, where $\mathscr{C}$ has no quantifiers. Any negation

$x \neq y$ can be replaced by $x < y \vee y < x$, and $x \not< y$ can be replaced by $x = y \vee y < x$. Hence, all negation signs may be eliminated from $\mathscr{C}$. We can now put $\mathscr{C}$ into disjunctive normal form, i.e., a disjunction of conjunctions of atomic wfs (cf. page 27, Exercise 2). Now, $(Ey_n)(\mathscr{C}_1 \vee \mathscr{C}_2 \vee \ldots \vee \mathscr{C}_k)$ is equivalent to $(Ey_n)\mathscr{C}_1 \vee (Ey_n)\mathscr{C}_2 \vee \ldots \vee (Ey_n)\mathscr{C}_k$. Consider each $(Ey_n)\mathscr{C}_i$ separately. $\mathscr{C}_i$ is a conjunction of atomic wfs of the form $t < s$ and $t = s$. If $\mathscr{C}_i$ does not contain y_n, just erase (Ey_n). Note that, if a wf $\mathscr{D}$ does not contain y_n, then $(Ey_n)(\mathscr{D} \wedge \mathscr{E})$ may be replaced by $\mathscr{D} \wedge (Ey_n)\mathscr{E}$. Hence, we are reduced to the consideration of $(Ey_n)\mathscr{F}$, where $\mathscr{F}$ is a conjunction of atomic wfs, each of which contains y_n. Now, if one of the conjuncts is $y_n = z$ for some z different from y_n, replace in $\mathscr{F}$ all occurrences of y_n by z and erase (Ey_n). If we have $y_n = y_n$ alone, then just erase (Ey_n). If we have $y_n = y_n$ as one conjunct among others, erase $y_n = y_n$. If $\mathscr{F}$ has a conjunct $y_n < y_n$, replace all of $(Ey_n)\mathscr{F}$ by $y_n < y_n$. If $\mathscr{F}$ consists of $y_n < z_1 \wedge \ldots \wedge y_n < z_j$, or if $\mathscr{F}$ consists of $u_1 < y_n \wedge \ldots \wedge u_m < y_n$, where $z_1, \ldots, z_j, u_1, \ldots, u_m$ are different from y_n, replace $(Ey_n)\mathscr{F}$ by $y_n = y_n$. If $\mathscr{F}$ consists of $y_n < z_1 \wedge \ldots \wedge y_n < z_j \wedge u_1 < y_n \wedge \ldots \wedge u_m < y_n$, replace $(Ey_n)\mathscr{F}$ by the conjunction of all the wfs $u_i < z_l$ for $1 \leqslant i \leqslant m$ and $1 \leqslant l \leqslant j$. This exhausts all possibilities, and, in every case, we have replaced $(Ey_n)\mathscr{C}$ by a wf $\mathscr{R}$ containing no quantifiers, i.e., we have eliminated the quantifier (Ey_n). We are left with $(Qy_1)\ldots(Qy_{n-1})\mathscr{S}$ where $\mathscr{S}$ contains no quantifiers. Now we apply the same procedure successively to $(Qy_{n-1}), \ldots, (Qy_1)$. Finally, we are left with a wf without quantifiers built up out of wfs of the form $x = x$ and $x < x$. Now, if we replace $x = x$ by $x = x \supset x = x$ and $x < x$ by $\sim(x = x \supset x = x)$, then the result is either an instance of a tautology or the negation of such an instance (Exercise). Hence, by Proposition 2.1, either the result or its negation is provable. Now, one can easily check that all the replacements we have made in this whole reduction process applied to $\mathscr{A}$ have been replacements of wfs $\mathscr{T}$ by other wfs $\mathscr{U}$ such that $\vdash_K \mathscr{T} \equiv \mathscr{U}$. Hence, by Corollary 2.21, if our final result is provable, then so is the original wf $\mathscr{A}$, and, if the negation of our result is provable, so is $\sim\mathscr{A}$. Thus, K_2 is complete and decidable.

The method employed in this proof, the successive elimination of existential quantifiers, has been applied to other theories. It yields a decision procedure (cf. Hilbert-Bernays [1934]I, § 5) for the elementary theory K_1 of equality (cf. page 77). It has been applied by Tarski [1951] to prove the completeness and decidability of elementary algebra (i.e., of the elementary theory of real-closed fields; cf. van der Waerden [1949]) and by Szmielew [1955] to prove the decidability of the elementary theory of abelian groups. (There is also a useful application of this method in Feferman-Vaught [1959].)

D EXERCISES

1. (Henkin [1955]). If an ordinary first-order theory K with equality is finitely axiomatizable and $\aleph_\alpha$-categorical for some α, then K is decidable. (Hint: extend K by adding the axioms (B_n), where (B_n) asserts that there are at least n elements. The new theory has no finite models.)

2. Prove the decidability of the elementary theory K_1 of equality (cf. page 77). (Hint: consider the wfs (B_n), where (B_n) asserts that there are at least n elements. In the elimination of existential quantifiers treat every (B_n) as an atomic wf.)

Mathematical Applications

(1) Let F be the elementary theory of fields (cf. page 78). We let n stand for the term $\underbrace{1 + 1 + \ldots + 1}_{n\text{-times}}$. Then the assertion that a field has characteristic p can be expressed by the wf $\mathscr{C}_{\mathrm{p}}$: $p = 0$. Then for any closed wf $\mathscr{A}$ of F which holds for all fields of characteristic zero, there is a prime number q such that $\mathscr{A}$ holds for all fields of characteristic $\geqslant$q. For, if F′ is obtained from F by adding as axioms $\sim\mathscr{C}_2$, $\sim\mathscr{C}_3, \ldots, \sim\mathscr{C}_p, \ldots$ (for all primes p), the normal models of F′ are the fields of characteristic zero. Hence, by Corollary 2.15(a), noting that if $\mathscr{A}$ holds in all normal models of F′ it holds in all models of F′, $\vdash_{\mathrm{F}'} \mathscr{A}$; but then, for some finite number of the new axioms $\sim\mathscr{C}_{\mathrm{q}_1}, \sim\mathscr{C}_{\mathrm{q}_2}, \ldots, \sim\mathscr{C}_{\mathrm{q}_n}$, we have $\sim\mathscr{C}_{\mathrm{q}_1}, \ldots, \sim\mathscr{C}_{\mathrm{q}_n} \vdash_{\mathrm{F}} \mathscr{A}$. Let q be a prime greater than all $\mathrm{q}_1, \ldots, \mathrm{q}_n$. In every field of characteristic $\geqslant$q, the wfs $\sim\mathscr{C}_{\mathrm{q}_1}, \sim\mathscr{C}_{\mathrm{q}_2}, \ldots, \sim\mathscr{C}_{\mathrm{q}_n}$ are true; hence, $\mathscr{A}$ is also true (A. Robinson [1951]).

(2) A *graph* may be considered as a set partially ordered by a symmetric binary relation R (i.e., the relation which holds between any two vertices if and only if they are connected by an edge). Call a graph k-colorable if and only if the graph can be divided into k disjoint (possibly empty) sets such that no two elements in the same set are in the relation R. (Intuitively, these k sets correspond to k colors, each color being painted on the points in the corresponding set, with the proviso that two points connected by an edge are painted different colors.) Notice that any subgraph of a k-colorable graph is also k-colorable. Now, we can show that if every finite subgraph of a graph $\mathscr{G}$ is k-colorable, and if $\mathscr{G}$ can be well-ordered, then the whole graph $\mathscr{G}$ is k-colorable. To prove this, construct the following generalized first-order theory K with equality (Beth [1953]). There are two binary predicate letters A_1^2 (=) and A_2^2 (corresponding to the relation R on $\mathscr{G}$); there are k monadic predicate letters $A_1^1, \ldots, A_k^1$ (corresponding to the

k subsets into which we hope to divide the graph), and there are individual constants a_c, one for each element c of the graph $\mathscr{G}$. We have as proper axioms, in addition to the usual assumptions (6)–(7) for equality, the following wfs:

(I) $\sim A_2^2(x, x)$ (irreflexivity of R)

(II) $A_2^2(x, y) \supset A_2^2(y, x)$ (symmetry of R)

(III) $(x)(A_1^1(x) \vee A_2^1(x) \vee \ldots \vee A_k^1(x))$ (division into k classes)

(IV) $(x) \sim (A_i^1(x) \wedge A_j^1(x))$ for $1 \leqslant i < j \leqslant k$ (disjointness of the k classes)

(V) For $1 \leqslant i \leqslant k$, $(x)(y)(A_i^1(x) \wedge A_i^1(y) \supset \sim A_2^2(x, y))$
(Two elements in the same class are not in the relation R.)

(VI) For any two distinct elements b, c of $\mathscr{G}$, $a_b \neq a_c$.

(VII) If R(b, c) holds in $\mathscr{G}$, $A_2^2(a_b, a_c)$.

Now, any finite set of these axioms involves only a finite number of the individual constants $a_{c_1}, \ldots, a_{c_n}$, and since the corresponding subgraph $\{c_1, \ldots, c_n\}$ is, by assumption, k-colorable, the given finite set of axioms has a model, and is, therefore, consistent. Since any finite set of axioms is consistent, K is consistent. By Corollary 2.35(1), K has a normal model of cardinality $\leqslant$ the cardinality of the graph $\mathscr{G}$. This model is a k-colorable graph, and, by (VI)–(VII), has $\mathscr{G}$ as a subgraph. Hence, $\mathscr{G}$ is also k-colorable. (Compare this proof with a standard mathematical proof of the same result by Bruijn and Erdos [1951]. Generally, use of the method above replaces complicated applications of Tychonoff's Theorem or König's Unendlichkeit's Lemma.)

EXERCISES

1. (Loś [1954b]). A group B is said to be orderable if there exists a binary relation R on B which totally orders B such that, if x R y, then (x + z) R (y + z) and (z + x) R (z + y). Show, by a method similar to that used in Example (2) above, that a group B is orderable if and only if every finitely-generated subgroup is orderable (if we assume that the set B can be well-ordered).

2. Set up a first-order theory for algebraically-closed fields of characteristic p ($\geqslant 0$) by adding to the theory F of fields the new axioms P_n, where P_n states that every non-constant polynomial of degree $\leqslant$ n has a root, as well as axioms to determine the characteristic. Show that every wf of F which holds for one algebraically closed field of characteristic zero holds for all of them. (Hint: this theory is $\aleph_\beta$-categorical for $\beta > 0$, axiomatizable, and has no finite models.) (Cf. A. Robinson [1952].)

3. By ordinary mathematical reasoning, solve the finite marriage problem: given a finite set M of m men and a set N of women such that each man knows only a finite number of women and, for $1 \leqslant k \leqslant m$, any subset of M having k elements is acquainted with at least k women of N (i.e., there are at least k women in N acquainted with at least one of the k given men). Then it is possible to marry (monogamously) all the men of M to women in N so that every man is married to a women with whom he is acquainted. (Hint—Halmos-Vaughn [1950]: $m = 1$ is trivial. For $m > 1$, use induction, considering the cases: (I) for all k with $1 \leqslant k < m$, every set of k men knows at least $k + 1$ women, and (II) for some k with $1 \leqslant k < m$, there is a set of k men knowing exactly k women.) Extend this result to the infinite case, i.e., when M is infinite and well-orderable and the assumptions above hold for all finite k. (Hint: construct an appropriate generalized first-order theory, analogous to that of Application (2) above, and use Corollary 2.35(1).)

4. For a solution of Hilbert's 17th Problem, using the method of this section, refer to A. Robinson [1955].

Let $\mathscr{A}$ be a wf in prenex normal form, and form its closure, say, $(Ey_1)(y_2)(y_3)(Ey_4)(Ey_5)(y_6)\mathscr{B}(y_1, y_2, y_3, y_4, y_5, y_6)$, where $\mathscr{B}$ contains no quantifiers. Erase (Ey_1) and replace y_1 in $\mathscr{B}$ by a new individual constant b_1: $(y_2)(y_3)(Ey_4)(Ey_5)(y_6)\mathscr{B}(b_1, y_2, y_3, y_4, y_5, y_6)$. Erase (y_2) and (y_3), obtaining $(Ey_4)(Ey_5)(y_6)\mathscr{B}(b_1, y_2, y_3, y_4, y_5, y_6)$. Now erase (Ey_4) and replace y_4 in $\mathscr{B}$ by a new function letter $g(y_2, y_3)$: $(Ey_5)(y_6)\mathscr{B}(b_1, y_2, y_3, g(y_2, y_3), y_5, y_6)$. Erase (Ey_5) and replace y_5 in $\mathscr{B}$ by a new function letter $h(y_2, y_3)$: $(y_6)\mathscr{B}(b_1, y_2, y_3, g(y_2, y_3), h(y_2, y_3), y_6)$. Finally, erase (y_6). The terminal wf $\mathscr{B}(b_1, y_2, y_3, g(y_2, y_3), h(y_2, y_3), y_6)$ contains no quantifiers, and is denoted by $\mathscr{A}^\star$. Thus, by introducing new function letters, we can eliminate the quantifiers from a wf.

Examples

1. If $\mathscr{A}$ is $(y_1)(Ey_2)(y_3)(y_4)(Ey_5)\mathscr{B}(y_1, y_2, y_3, y_4, y_5)$ where $\mathscr{B}$ contains no quantifiers, $\mathscr{A}^\star$ may be taken to be

$$\mathscr{B}(y_1, g(y_1), y_3, y_4, h(y_1, y_3, y_4))$$

2. If $\mathscr{A}$ is $(Ey_1)(Ey_2)(y_3)(y_4)(Ey_5)\mathscr{B}(y_1, y_2, y_3, y_4, y_5)$ where $\mathscr{B}$ contains no quantifiers, then $\mathscr{A}^\star$ is of the form $\mathscr{B}(b, c, y_3, y_4, g(y_3, y_4))$.

Notice that $\mathscr{A}^\star \vdash \mathscr{A}$, since we can put the quantifiers back on by several applications of Gen and Rule E4. (To be more precise, in the process of obtaining $\mathscr{A}^\star$, we drop all universal quantifiers and all existential quantifiers, and, for each existentially quantified variable y_i, we substitute a function letter $g(z_1, \ldots, z_k)$, where $z_1, \ldots, z_k$ are the variables which were universally quantified in the prefix preceding (Ey_i).)

PROPOSITION 2.36 (Second ε-Theorem. Rasiowa [1956], Hilbert-Bernays [1939]). *Let* K *be a first-order theory. Replace each axiom* $\mathscr{A}$ *of* K *by* $\mathscr{A}^\star$. *(The new function letters and individual constants introduced for* one *wf are to be different from those introduced for* another *wf.) Let* $K^\star$ *be the first-order theory with the proper axioms* $\mathscr{A}^\star$. *Then,* (a) *If* $\mathscr{C}$ *is a* wf *of* K *and* $\vdash_{K^\star} \mathscr{C}$, *then* $\vdash_K \mathscr{C}$; (b) K *is consistent if and only if* $K^\star$ *is consistent.*

PROOF

(1) Let $\mathscr{C}$ be a wf of K such that $\vdash_{K^\star} \mathscr{C}$. Assume that M is a denumerable model of K. Clearly, we may assume that the domain of M is the set P of positive integers (cf. page 91, Exercise 1). Let $\mathscr{A}$ be any axiom of K; say, $\mathscr{A}$ is $(Ey_1)(y_2)(y_3)(Ey_4)\mathscr{B}(y_1, y_2, y_3, y_4)$, where $\mathscr{B}$ contains no quantifiers. $\mathscr{A}^\star$ has the form $\mathscr{B}(b, y_2, y_3, g(y_2, y_3))$. Extend the model M step by step as follows (note that the domain always remains the set P): since $\mathscr{A}$ is true in M, $(Ey_1)(y_2)(y_3)(Ey_4)\mathscr{B}(y_1, y_2, y_3, y_4)$ is true in M. Let the interpretation $b^\star$ of b be the least positive integer y_1 such that $(y_2)(y_3)(Ey_4)\mathscr{B}(y_1, y_2, y_3, y_4)$ is true in the model. Hence, $(Ey_4)\mathscr{B}(b, y_2, y_3, y_4)$ is true in this extended model. For any positive integers y_2, y_3 let the interpretation of $g(y_2, y_3)$ be the least positive integer y_4 such that $\mathscr{B}(b, y_2, y_3, y_4)$ is true in the extended model. Hence, $\mathscr{B}(b, y_2, y_3, g(y_2, y_3))$ is true in the extended model. If we do this for all the axioms $\mathscr{A}$ of K, we obtain a model $M^\star$ of $K^\star$. Since $\vdash_{K^\star} \mathscr{C}$, $\mathscr{C}$ is true in $M^\star$. Since $M^\star$ differs from M only in having interpretations of the new individual constants and function letters, and since $\mathscr{C}$ does not contain any of these constants or function letters, $\mathscr{C}$ is true in M. Thus, $\mathscr{C}$ is true in every denumerable model of K. Hence, $\vdash_K \mathscr{C}$ by Corollary 2.15(a). (For a constructive proof of an equivalent result, compare Hilbert-Bernays [1939].)

(2) Clearly, $K^\star$ is an extension of K, since $\mathscr{A}^\star \vdash \mathscr{A}$. Hence, if $K^\star$ is consistent, so is K. Conversely, assume K consistent. Let $\mathscr{C}$ be any wf of K. If $K^\star$ is inconsistent, $\vdash_{K^\star} \mathscr{C} \wedge \sim\mathscr{C}$. By Part (1), $\vdash_K \mathscr{C} \wedge \sim\mathscr{C}$, contradicting the consistency of K.

Let us use the term *Generalized Completeness Theorem* for the proposition that every consistent generalized first-order theory has a model. Clearly, if we assume that every set can be well-ordered (or, equivalently, the axiom of choice), then the Generalized Completeness Theorem is a consequence of Proposition 2.34.

By the Maximal Ideal Theorem (M.I.), we mean the proposition that every Boolean algebra has a maximal ideal. This is equivalent to the Boolean Representation Theorem, which states that every Boolean algebra is isomorphic to a Boolean algebra of sets. (Compare Stone

[1936]. For the theory of Boolean algebras, see Sikorski [1960].) The only known proof of the M.I. Theorem uses the axiom of choice, but it is a remarkable fact that the M.I. Theorem is equivalent to the Generalized Completeness Theorem, and this equivalence can be proved without use of the axiom of choice.

PROPOSITION 2.37 (Loś [1954a], Rasiowa-Sikorski [1951–2]). *The Generalized Completeness Theorem is equivalent to the Maximal Ideal Theorem.*

PROOF

(1) Assume the Generalized Completeness Theorem. Let B be a Boolean algebra. Construct a generalized first-order theory K with equality having the binary function letters $\cup$ and $\cap$, the singulary function letter f_1^1 (we denote $f_1^1(t)$ by $\bar{t}$), predicate letters $=$ and A_1^1, and, for each element b in B, an individual constant a_b. As axioms, we take the usual axioms for a Boolean algebra (cf. Sikorski [1960]), the axioms (6)–(7) for equality, a complete description of B (i.e., if b, c, d, e, b_1 are in B, the axioms $a_b \neq a_c$ if $b \neq c$; $a_b \cup a_c = a_d$ if $b \cup c = d$ in B; $a_b \cap a_c = a_e$ if $b \cap c = e$ in B; $\bar{a}_b = a_{b_1}$, if $\bar{b} = b_1$ in B, where $\bar{b}$ denotes the complement of b), and axioms asserting that A_1^1 determines a maximal ideal (i.e., $A_1^1(x \cap \bar{x})$, $A_1^1(x) \wedge A_1^1(y) \supset A_1^1(x \cup y)$; $A_1^1(x) \supset A_1^1(x \cap y)$; $A_1^1(x) \vee A_1^1(\bar{x})$; $\sim A_1^1(x \cup \bar{x})$). Now K is consistent, for, if there is a proof in K of a contradiction, this proof contains only a finite number of the symbols $a_b, a_c, \ldots$, say $a_{b_1}, \ldots, a_{b_n}$. The elements $b_1, \ldots, b_n$ generate a finite subalgebra B′ of B. Every finite Boolean algebra clearly has a maximal ideal. Hence, B′ is a model for the wfs occurring in the proof of the contradiction, and therefore the contradiction is true in B′, which is impossible. Thus, K is consistent, and, by the Generalized Completeness Theorem, K has a model, which is a Boolean algebra A with a maximal ideal I. But B is a subalgebra of A and $I \cap B$ is a maximal ideal in B.

(2) Assume the Maximal Ideal Theorem. Let K be a consistent generalized first-order theory. For each axiom $\mathscr{A}$ of K, form the wf $\mathscr{A}^\star$ obtained by constructing a prenex normal form for $\mathscr{A}$ and then eliminating the quantifiers through the addition of new individual constants and function letters. Let K′ be a new theory having the wfs $\mathscr{A}^\star$, plus all instances of tautologies, as its axioms, such that its wfs contain no quantifiers and its rules of inference are modus ponens and a rule of substitution for variables (viz., substitution of terms for variables). Now K′ is consistent, since the theorems of K′ are also theorems of the consistent theory K* of Proposition 2.36. Let B be the Lindenbaum algebra determined by K′ (i.e., for any wfs $\mathscr{A}$ and $\mathscr{B}$,

let $\mathscr{A}$ Eq $\mathscr{B}$ mean that $\vdash_{K'} \mathscr{A} \equiv \mathscr{B}$; Eq is an equivalence relation; let $[\mathscr{A}]$ be the equivalence class of $\mathscr{A}$; define $[\mathscr{A}] \cup [\mathscr{B}] = [\mathscr{A} \vee \mathscr{B}]$, $[\mathscr{A}] \cap [\mathscr{B}] = [\mathscr{A} \wedge \mathscr{B}]$, $\overline{[\mathscr{A}]} = [\sim \mathscr{A}]$; under these operations, the set of equivalence classes is a Boolean algebra, called the Lindenbaum algebra of K'). By the Maximal Ideal Theorem, let I be a maximal ideal in B. Define a model M of K' having the set of terms of K' as its domain; the individual constants and function letters are their own interpretations, and, for any predicate letter A_j^n, we say that $A_j^n(t_1, \ldots, t_n)$ is true in M if and only if $[A_j^n(t_1, \ldots, t_n)]$ is not in I. One can show easily that a wf $\mathscr{A}$ of K' is true in M if and only if $[\mathscr{A}]$ is not in I. But, for any theorem $\mathscr{B}$ of K', $[\mathscr{B}] = 1$, which is not in I. Hence, M is a model for K'. For any axiom $\mathscr{A}$ of K, every substitution instance of $\mathscr{A}^\star(y_1, \ldots, y_n)$ is a theorem in K'; therefore, $\mathscr{A}^\star(y_1, \ldots, y_n)$ is true for all $y_1, \ldots, y_n$ in the model. It follows easily, by reversing the process through which $\mathscr{A}^\star$ arose from $\mathscr{A}$, that $\mathscr{A}$ is true in the model. Hence, M is a model for K.

Is the Generalized Completeness Theorem strictly weaker than or equivalent to the axiom of choice? For some partial results, refer to Łoś-Ryll-Nardzewski [1954], Henkin [1954]. A proof that they are not equivalent has been announced by J. D. Halpern (*Notices Amer. Math. Soc.*, Vol. 9, No. 4 (1962), p. 315).

EXERCISES

1. Show that the Generalized Completeness Theorem implies that every set can be totally ordered (and, therefore, that the axiom of choice holds for any set of non-empty disjoint finite sets).

2. In the proof of Proposition 2.37(2), show that if K is an ordinary first-order theory, then the Lindenbaum algebra B is countable and the Maximal Ideal Theorem need not be assumed in the proof.

The natural algebraic structures corresponding to the propositional calculus are Boolean algebras (cf. page 43, Exercise 3, and Rosenbloom [1950], Chapters 1–2). For first-order theories, the presence of quantifiers introduces more algebraic structure. For example, if K is a first-order theory, then, in the corresponding Lindenbaum algebra B, $[(Ex)\,\mathscr{A}(x)] = \sum_t [\mathscr{A}(t)]$ where $\sum_t$ indicates the least upper bound in B, and t ranges over all terms of K which are free for x in $\mathscr{A}(x)$. Two types of algebraic structures have been proposed to serve as algebraic counterparts of quantification theory. The first, cylindrical algebras, have been studied extensively by Tarski, Thompson, Henkin, and others (cf. Henkin-Tarski [1961]). The other approach is the theory of polyadic algebras, invented and developed by Halmos [1962].

CHAPTER 3

FORMAL NUMBER THEORY

§1. An Axiom System

Together with geometry, the theory of numbers is the most immediately intuitive of all branches of mathematics. It is not surprising then that attempts to formalize mathematics and to establish a rigorous foundation for mathematics should begin with number theory. The first semi-axiomatic presentation of this subject was given by Dedekind [1901] and has come to be known as Peano's Postulates.† It can be formulated as follows:

(P1) 0 is a natural number.

(P2) If x is a natural number, there is another natural number denoted by x′ (and called the *successor* of x).

(P3) $0 \neq x'$ for any natural number x.

(P4) If $x' = y'$, then $x = y$.

(P5) If Q is a property which may or may not hold of natural numbers, and if (I) 0 has the property Q, and (II) whenever a natural number x has the property Q, then x′ has the property Q, then all natural numbers have the property Q (Principle of Induction).

These axioms, together with a certain amount of set theory, can be used to develop not only number theory but also the theory of rational, real, and complex numbers (cf. Landau [1951]). However, the axioms involve certain intuitive notions, such as "property", which prevent this system from being a rigorous formalization. We therefore shall build a first-order theory S that is based upon Peano's Postulates and seems to be adequate for the proofs of all the basic results of elementary number theory.

The first-order theory S has a single predicate letter A_1^2 (as usual, we write $t = s$ for $A_1^2(t, s)$); it has one individual constant a_1 (written, as usual, 0); it has three function letters f_1^1, f_1^2, f_2^2. We shall write t'

† For historical information, see Wang [1957a].

instead of $f_1^1(t)$; $t + s$ instead of $f_1^2(t, s)$; and $t \cdot s$ instead of $f_2^2(t, s)$. The proper axioms of S are:

(S1) $x_1 = x_2 \supset (x_1 = x_3 \supset x_2 = x_3)$
(S2) $x_1 = x_2 \supset x_1{}' = x_2{}'$
(S3) $0 \neq (x_1)'$
(S4) $(x_1)' = (x_2)' \supset x_1 = x_2$
(S5) $x_1 + 0 = x_1$
(S6) $x_1 + x_2{}' = (x_1 + x_2)'$
(S7) $x_1 \cdot 0 = 0$
(S8) $x_1 \cdot (x_2{}') = (x_1 \cdot x_2) + x_1$
(S9) For any wf $\mathscr{A}(x)$ of S, $\mathscr{A}(0) \supset ((x)(\mathscr{A}(x) \supset \mathscr{A}(x')) \supset (x)\mathscr{A}(x))$

Notice that Axioms (S1)–(S8) are particular wfs while (S9) is an axiom schema providing an infinite number of axioms. However, (S9), which we shall call the *Principle of Mathematical Induction*, cannot fully correspond to Peano's Postulate (P5), since the latter refers intuitively to the $2^{\aleph_0}$ properties of natural numbers, while (S9) can only take care of the denumerable number of properties defined by wfs of S.

Axioms (S3) and (S4) correspond to the Peano Postulates (P3) and (P4), respectively. Peano's axioms (P1) and (P2) are taken care of by the presence of 0 as an individual constant and f_1^1 as a function letter. Our axioms (S1)–(S2) furnish some needed properties of equality; they would have been assumed as intuitively obvious by Dedekind and Peano. Axioms (S5)–(S8) are the recursion equations for addition and multiplication. Dedekind and Peano didn't have to assume them because they allowed the use of intuitive set theory, from which the existence of operations + and · satisfying (S5)–(S8) is deducible (cf. Landau [1951], Theorems 4 and 28).

From (S9), by MP, we can obtain the *Induction Rule*: from $\mathscr{A}(0)$ and $(x)(\mathscr{A}(x) \supset \mathscr{A}(x'))$, we can derive $(x)\mathscr{A}(x)$.

It will be our immediate aim to establish the usual rules of equality, i.e., we shall show that the properties (6) and (7) of equality (cf. page 75) are derivable in S, and hence that S is a first-order theory with equality.

First, for convenience and brevity in carrying out proofs, we cite some immediate, trivial consequences of the axioms.

LEMMA 3.1. *For any terms t, s, r of S, the following* wfs *are theorems.*

(S1′) $t = r \supset (t = s \supset r = s)$
(S2′) $t = r \supset t' = r'$
(S3′) $0 \neq t'$
(S4′) $t' = r' \supset t = r$

(S5′) $t + 0 = t$
(S6′) $t + r' = (t + r)'$
(S7′) $t \cdot 0 = 0$
(S8′) $t \cdot r' = (t \cdot r) + t$

PROOF. (S1′)–(S8′) follow from (S1)–(S8) respectively by first forming the closure by means of Gen, and then applying rule A4 with the appropriate terms t, r, s.

PROPOSITION 3.2. *For any terms* t, r, s *the following* wfs *are theorems of* S.

(a) $t = t$
(b) $t = r \supset r = t$
(c) $t = r \supset (r = s \supset t = s)$
(d) $r = t \supset (s = t \supset r = s)$
(e) $t = r \supset t + s = r + s$
(f) $t = 0 + t$
(g) $t' + r = (t + r)'$
(h) $t + r = r + t$
(i) $t = r \supset s + t = s + r$
(j) $(t + r) + s = t + (r + s)$
(k) $t = r \supset t \cdot s = r \cdot s$
(l) $0 \cdot t = 0$
(m) $t' \cdot r = t \cdot r + r$
(n) $t \cdot r = r \cdot t$
(o) $t = r \supset s \cdot t = s \cdot r$

PROOF

(a)	1.	$t + 0 = t$	(S5′)
	2.	$(t + 0 = t) \supset (t + 0 = t \supset t = t)$	(S1′)
	3.	$t + 0 = t \supset t = t$	1, 2, MP
	4.	$t = t$	1, 3, MP
(b)	1.	$t = r \supset (t = t \supset r = t)$	(S1′)
	2.	$t = t \supset (t = r \supset r = t)$	1, Tautology
	3.	$t = r \supset r = t$	2, Part (a), MP
(c)	1.	$r = t \supset (r = s \supset t = s)$	(S1′)
	2.	$t = r \supset r = t$	Part (b)
	3.	$t = r \supset (r = s \supset t = s)$	1, 2, Tautology
(d)	1.	$r = t \supset (t = s \supset r = s)$	Part (c)
	2.	$t = s \supset (r = t \supset r = s)$	1, Tautology
	3.	$s = t \supset t = s$	Part (b)
	4.	$s = t \supset (r = t \supset r = s)$	2, 3, Tautology
	5.	$r = t \supset (s = t \supset r = s)$	4, Tautology

(e) Apply the Induction Rule to $\mathscr{A}(z)$: $x = y \supset (x + z = y + z)$.

(i) 1.	$x + 0 = x$	(S5′)
2.	$y + 0 = y$	(S5′)
3.	$x = y$	Hyp
4.	$x + 0 = y$	1, 3, Part (c)
5.	$x + 0 = y + 0$	2, 4, Part (d)
6.	$x = y \supset x + 0 = y + 0$	1–5, Deduction Theorem
	i.e., $\vdash \mathscr{A}(0)$.	
(ii) 1.	$x = y \supset x + z = y + z$	Hyp
2.	$x = y$	Hyp
3.	$x + z' = (x + z)'$	(S6′)
4.	$y + z' = (y + z)'$	(S6′)
5.	$x + z = y + z$	1, 2, MP
6.	$(x + z)' = (y + z)'$	5, (S2′)
7.	$x + z' = (y + z)'$	3, 6, Part (c)
8.	$x + z' = y + z'$	4, 7, Part (d)
9.	$(x = y \supset (x + z = y + z)) \supset (x = y \supset (x + z' = y + z'))$	1–8, Deduction Theorem
	i.e., $\vdash \mathscr{A}(z) \supset \mathscr{A}(z')$.	

Hence, $\vdash (z)\mathscr{A}(z)$ by the Induction Rule, from (i) and (ii). Therefore, by Gen and Rule A4, $\vdash t = r \supset t + s = r + s$.

(f) Let $\mathscr{A}(x)$ be $x = 0 + x$.

(i) $0 = 0 + 0$, by (S5′) and Part (b); i.e., $\vdash \mathscr{A}(0)$.

(ii) 1.	$x = 0 + x$	Hyp
2.	$(0 + x') = (0 + x)'$	(S6′)
3.	$x' = (0 + x)'$	1, (S2′)
4.	$x' = 0 + x'$	2, 3, Part (d)
5.	$x = 0 + x \supset x' = 0 + x'$	1–4, Deduction Theorem
	i.e., $\vdash \mathscr{A}(x) \supset \mathscr{A}(x')$.	

By (i)–(ii) and the Induction Rule, $\vdash (x)(x = 0 + x)$. So, by Rule A4, $\vdash t = 0 + t$.

(g) Let $\mathscr{A}(y)$ be $x' + y = (x + y)'$.

(i) 1.	$x' + 0 = x'$	(S5′)
2.	$x + 0 = x$	(S5′)
3.	$(x + 0)' = x'$	2, (S2′)
4.	$x' + 0 = (x + 0)'$	1, 3, Part (d)
	i.e., $\vdash \mathscr{A}(0)$.	
(ii) 1.	$x' + y = (x + y)'$	Hyp
2.	$x' + y' = (x' + y)'$	(S6′)
3.	$(x' + y)' = (x + y)''$	1, (S2′)
4.	$x' + y' = (x + y)''$	2, 3, Part (c)

5. $(x + y') = (x + y)'$ (S6′)
6. $(x + y')' = (x + y)''$ 5, (S2′)
7. $x' + y' = (x + y')'$ 4, 6, Part (d)
8. $x' + y = (x + y)' \supset x' + y' = (x + y')'$ 1–7, Deduction Theorem

i.e., $\vdash \mathscr{A}(y) \supset \mathscr{A}(y')$.

So, by (i), (ii), and the Induction Rule, $\vdash (y)(x' + y = (x + y)')$, and, then by Gen and Rule A4, $\vdash t' + r = (t + r)'$.

(h) Let $\mathscr{A}(y)$ be $x + y = y + x$.

(i) 1. $x + 0 = x$ (S5′)
2. $x = 0 + x$ Part (f)
3. $x + 0 = 0 + x$ 1, 2, Part (c)

i.e., $\vdash \mathscr{A}(0)$.

(ii) 1. $x + y = y + x$ Hyp
2. $x + y' = (x + y)'$ (S6′)
3. $y' + x = (y + x)'$ Part (g)
4. $(x + y)' = (y + x)'$ 1, (S2′)
5. $x + y' = (y + x)'$ 2, 4, Part (c)
6. $x + y' = y' + x$ 3, 5, Part (d)
7. $x + y = y + x \supset x + y' = y' + x$ 1–6, Deduction Theorem

i.e., $\vdash \mathscr{A}(y) \supset \mathscr{A}(y')$.

So, by (i), (ii), and the Induction Rule, $\vdash (y)(x + y = y + x)$, and, then by Gen and Rule A4, $\vdash t + r = r + t$.

(i) 1. $t = r \supset t + s = r + s$ Part (e)
2. $t + s = s + t$ Part (h)
3. $r + s = s + r$ Part (h)
4. $t = r$ Hyp
5. $t + s = r + s$ 1, 4, MP
6. $s + t = r + s$ 2, 5, (S1′)
7. $s + t = s + r$ 3, 6, Part (c)
8. $t = r \supset s + t = s + r$ 1–7, Deduction Theorem

(j) Let $\mathscr{A}(z)$ be $(x + y) + z = x + (y + z)$.

(i) 1. $(x + y) + 0 = x + y$ (S5′)
2. $y + 0 = y$ (S5′)
3. $x + (y + 0) = x + y$ 2, Part (i)
4. $(x + y) + 0 = x + (y + 0)$ 1, 3, Part (d)

i.e., $\vdash \mathscr{A}(0)$.

(ii) 1. $(x + y) + z = x + (y + z)$ Hyp
2. $(x + y) + z' = ((x + y) + z)'$ (S6′)
3. $((x + y) + z)' = (x + (y + z))'$ 1, (S2′)

4.	$(x + y) + z' = (x + (y + z))'$	2, 3, Part (c)
5.	$y + z' = (y + z)'$	(S6′)
6.	$x + (y + z') = x + (y + z)'$	5, Part (i)
7.	$x + (y + z)' = (x + (y + z))'$	(S6′)
8.	$x + (y + z') = (x + (y + z))'$	6, 7, Part (d)
9.	$(x + y) + z' = x + (y + z')$	4, 8, Part (d)
10.	$(x + y) + z = x + (y + z) \supset (x + y) + z' = x + (y + z')$	1–9, Deduction Theorem

i.e., $\vdash \mathscr{A}(z) \supset \mathscr{A}(z')$.

By (i), (ii), and the Induction Rule, $\vdash (z)((x + y) + z = x + (y + z))$, and then, by Gen and Rule A4, $\vdash (t + r) + s = t + (r + s)$.

Parts (k)–(o) are left as exercises for the reader.

COROLLARY 3.3. *S is a first-order theory with equality, i.e., we have* (6): $\vdash x_1 = x_1$, *and* (7): $\vdash x = y \supset \mathscr{A}(x, x) \supset \mathscr{A}(x, y)$, *where* $\mathscr{A}(x, y)$ *comes from* $\mathscr{A}(x, x)$ *by replacing one or more occurrences of* x *by* y, *with the proviso that* y *is free for those occurrences of* x (cf. page 75).

PROOF. By Proposition 2.26, this reduces to Proposition 3.2 (a)–(e), (i), (k), (o), and (S2′).

Notice that the interpretation in which

(a) the set of non-negative integers is the domain,
(b) the integer 0 is the interpretation of the symbol 0,
(c) the successor operation (addition of 1) is the interpretation of the ′ function (i.e., of f_1^1),
(d) ordinary addition and multiplication are the interpretations of + and ·,
(e) the interpretation of the predicate letter = is the identity relation,

is a normal model for S. This model is called the *standard model* for S. Any normal model for S which is not isomorphic to the standard model will be called a non-standard model for S.

If we recognize the standard interpretation to be a model for S, then of course, S is consistent. However, semantic methods, involving as they do a certain amount of set-theoretic reasoning, are regarded by some as too precarious to serve as a basis for consistency proofs; likewise, we have not proved in a rigorous way that the axioms of S are true under the standard interpretation, but have taken it as intuitively obvious. For these and other reasons, when the consistency of S enters into the argument of a proof, it is common practice to take the statement of the consistency of S as an explicit, unproved assumption. (A "proof" of the consistency is given in the Appendix.)

Some important additional properties of addition and multiplication are covered by the following result.

PROPOSITION 3.4. *For any terms t, r, s the following* wfs *are theorems of* S.

(a) $t\cdot(r + s) = (t\cdot r) + (t\cdot s)$ (Distributivity)
(b) $(r + s)\cdot t = (r\cdot t) + (s\cdot t)$ (Distributivity)
(c) $(t\cdot r)\cdot s = t\cdot(r\cdot s)$ (Associativity of $\cdot$)
(d) $t + s = r + s \supset t = r$ (Cancellation Law for $+$)

PROOF

(a) Prove $\vdash x\cdot(y + z) = (x\cdot y) + (x\cdot z)$ by induction on z.
(b) From (a) by Proposition 3.2(n).
(c) Prove $\vdash (x\cdot y)\cdot z = x\cdot(y\cdot z)$ by induction on z.
(d) Prove $\vdash x + z = y + z \supset x = y$ by induction on z. This requires, for the first time, use of (S4′).

The terms $0, 0', 0'', 0''', \ldots$ we shall call *numerals*, and denote by $0, \overline{1}, \overline{2}, \overline{3}, \ldots$ in the usual way. In general, if n is a non-negative integer, we shall let $\overline{\mathrm{n}}$ stand for the corresponding numeral $0'''\cdots'$, i.e., for 0 followed by n strokes. We can define the numerals recursively by stating that 0 is a numeral and, if u is a numeral, then u' is also a numeral.

PROPOSITION 3.5

(a) $\vdash t + \overline{1} = t'$
(b) $\vdash t\cdot\overline{1} = t$
(c) $\vdash t\cdot\overline{2} = t + t$ (etc., for 3, 4, ...)
(d) $\vdash t + s = 0 \supset t = 0 \wedge s = 0$
(e) $\vdash t \neq 0 \supset (s\cdot t = 0 \supset s = 0)$
(f) $\vdash t + s = \overline{1} \supset (t = 0 \wedge s = \overline{1}) \vee (t = \overline{1} \wedge s = 0)$
(g) $\vdash t\cdot s = \overline{1} \supset (t = \overline{1} \wedge s = \overline{1})$
(h) $\vdash t \neq 0 \supset (Ey)(t = y')$
(i) $\vdash s \neq 0 \supset (t\cdot s = r\cdot s \supset t = r)$
(j) $\vdash t \neq 0 \supset (t \neq \overline{1} \supset (Ey)(t = y''))$

PROOF

(a) 1.	$t + 0' = (t + 0)'$	(S6′)
2.	$t + 0 = t$	(S5′)
3.	$(t + 0)' = t'$	2, (S2′)
4.	$t + 0' = t'$	1, 3, Proposition 3.2(c)
5.	$t + \overline{1} = t'$	4, Abbreviation
(b) 1.	$t\cdot 0' = t\cdot 0 + t$	(S8′)
2.	$t\cdot 0 = 0$	(S7′)
3.	$(t\cdot 0) + t = 0 + t$	2, Proposition 3.2(e)
4.	$t\cdot 0' = 0 + t$	1, 3, Proposition 3.2(c)
5.	$0 + t = t$	Proposition 3.2(f), (b)

6.	$t \cdot 0' = t$	4, 5, Proposition 3.2(c)
7.	$t \cdot \overline{1} = t$	6, Abbreviation
(c) 1.	$t \cdot \overline{1}' = (t \cdot \overline{1}) + t$	(S8′)
2.	$t \cdot \overline{1} = t$	Part (b)
3.	$(t \cdot \overline{1}) + t = t + t$	2, Proposition 3.2(e)
4.	$t \cdot \overline{1}' = t + t$	1, 3, Proposition 3.2(c)
5.	$t \cdot \overline{2} = t + t$	4, Abbreviation

(d) Let $\mathscr{A}(y)$ be $x + y = 0 \supset x = 0 \wedge y = 0$. It is easy to prove that $\vdash \mathscr{A}(0)$. Also, since $\vdash (x + y)' \neq 0$ by (S3′), then, by (S6′), it follows that $\vdash x + y' \neq 0$. Hence, $\vdash \mathscr{A}(y')$ by the tautology $\sim A \supset (A \supset B)$. So, $\vdash \mathscr{A}(y) \supset \mathscr{A}(y')$ by the tautology $A \supset (B \supset A)$. Thus, by the Induction Rule, $\vdash (y)\mathscr{A}(y)$, and then, by Gen and Rule A4, we obtain Part (d).

(e) The proof is similar to that for (d) and is left as an exercise.

(f) By induction on y in $x + y = \overline{1} \supset ((x = 0 \wedge y = \overline{1}) \vee (x = \overline{1} \wedge y = 0))$.

(g) By induction on y in $x \cdot y = \overline{1} \supset (x = \overline{1} \wedge y = \overline{1})$.

(h) Perform induction in x in $x \neq 0 \supset (Ew)(x = w')$.

(i) Let $\mathscr{A}(y)$ be $(x)(z \neq 0 \supset (x \cdot z = y \cdot z \supset x = y))$.

(i) 1.	$z \neq 0$	Hyp
2.	$x \cdot z = 0 \cdot z$	Hyp
3.	$0 \cdot z = 0$	Proposition 3.2(l)
4.	$x \cdot z = 0$	2, 3, Proposition 3.2(c)
5.	$x = 0$	1, 4, Part (e) above
6.	$z \neq 0 \supset (x \cdot z = 0 \cdot z \supset x = 0)$	1–5, Deduction Theorem
7.	$(x)(z \neq 0 \supset (x \cdot z = 0 \cdot z \supset x = 0))$	6, Gen

i.e., $\vdash \mathscr{A}(0)$.

(ii) 1.	$(x)(z \neq 0 \supset (x \cdot z = y \cdot z \supset x = y))$	Hyp ($\mathscr{A}(y)$)
2.	$z \neq 0$	Hyp
3.	$x \cdot z = y' \cdot z$	Hyp
4.	$y' \neq 0$	(S3′), Proposition 3.2(b)
5.	$y' \cdot z \neq 0$	2, 4, Part (e) and a tautology
6.	$x \cdot z \neq 0$	3, 5, (S1′) and tautologies
7.	$x \neq 0$	6, (S7′), Proposition 3.2(o), (e), and tautologies
8.	$(Ew)(x = w')$	7, (h) above
9.	$x = w'$	8, Rule C
10.	$w' \cdot z = y' \cdot z$	3, 9, Equality law (7)
11.	$w \cdot z + z = y \cdot z + z$	10, Proposition 3.2(m), (d)
12.	$w \cdot z = y \cdot z$	11, Proposition 3.4(d)

13. $z \neq 0 \supset ((w \cdot z = y \cdot z) \supset (w = y))$ — 1, Rule A4
14. $w \cdot z = y \cdot z \supset w = y$ — 2, 13, MP
15. $w = y$ — 12, 14, MP
16. $w' = y'$ — 15, (S2′)
17. $x = y'$ — 9, 16, Proposition 3.2(c)
18. $\mathscr{A}(y), z \neq 0, x \cdot z = y' \cdot z \vdash x = y'$ — 1–17, Proposition 2.23
19. $\mathscr{A}(y) \vdash z \neq 0 \supset (x \cdot z = y' \cdot z \supset x = y')$ — 19, Deduction Theorem twice
20. $\mathscr{A}(y) \vdash (x)(z \neq 0 \supset (x \cdot z = y' \cdot z \supset x = y')$ — 19, Gen
21. $\vdash \mathscr{A}(y) \supset \mathscr{A}(y')$ — 20, Deduction Theorem

Hence, by (i) and (ii) and the Induction Rule, we obtain $\vdash (y)\mathscr{A}(y)$, and then, by Gen and Rule A4, we have the desired result.
(j) Exercise for the reader.

PROPOSITION 3.6. (a) *For any natural numbers* m, n, *if* $m \neq n$, *then* $\vdash \overline{m} \neq \overline{n}$. *Also,* $\vdash \overline{m + n} = \overline{m} + \overline{n}$ *and* $\vdash \overline{m \cdot n} = \overline{m} \cdot \overline{n}$, *for any* m *and* n. (b) *Any model for* S *is infinite.* (c) *For any cardinal number* $\aleph_\beta$, S *has a normal model of cardinality* $\aleph_\beta$.

PROOF

(a) Assume $m \neq n$. Now, either $m < n$ or $n < m$; say, $m < n$.

1. $\overline{m} = \overline{n}$ — Hyp
2. $\underbrace{0''\cdots'}_{\text{m times}} = \underbrace{0'''\cdots'}_{\text{n times}}$ — 1 is an abbreviation of 2
3. Apply (S4′) m times in a row. Then $0 = \underbrace{0''\cdots'}_{(n-m)\text{ times}}$. Let t be $\overline{(n\text{-}m\text{-}1)}$. Since $n > m$, $n\text{-}m\text{-}1 \geqslant 0$. Thus, $0 = t'$.
4. $0 \neq t'$ — (S3′)
5. $0 = t' \wedge 0 \neq t'$ — 3, 4, Tautology
6. $\vdash \overline{m} = \overline{n} \supset (0 = t' \wedge 0 \neq t')$ — 1–5, Deduction Theorem
7. $\vdash \overline{m} \neq \overline{n}$ — 6, Tautology

A similar proof holds in the case when $n < m$. Now, we can prove $\vdash \overline{m + n} = \overline{m} + \overline{n}$ by induction in the metalanguage on n. First, $\overline{m + 0}$ is $\overline{m}$. Hence, $\vdash \overline{m + 0} = \overline{m} + \overline{0}$ by (S5′). Assume $\vdash \overline{m + n} = \overline{m} + \overline{n}$. Therefore, $\vdash (\overline{m + n})' = \overline{m} + (\overline{n}')$ by (S2′) and (S6′). But $\overline{m + (n + 1)}$ is $(\overline{m + n})'$ and $\overline{n + 1}$ is $(\overline{n})'$. Hence, $\vdash \overline{m + (n + 1)} = \overline{m} + \overline{n + 1}$. Similarly, we can prove $\vdash \overline{m \cdot n} = \overline{m} \cdot \overline{n}$ by induction in the metalanguage on n.

(b) By Proposition 3.6(a), in a model for S, the objects corresponding to the numerals must be distinct. But there are denumerably many numerals.

(c) This follows from Corollary 2.35(3) and the fact that the standard model is an infinite normal model.

An order relation can be introduced by definition in S.

DEFINITIONS

$t < s$ for $(Ew)(w \neq 0 \wedge t + w = s)$
$t \leqslant s$ for $t < s \vee t = s$
$t > s$ for $s < t$
$t \geqslant s$ for $s \leqslant t$
$t \nless s$ for $\sim(t < s)$, etc.

In the first definition, to be precise, we can choose w to be the first variable not in t or s.

PROPOSITION 3.7. *For any terms t, r, s the following* wfs *are theorems.*

(a) $t \nless t$
(b) $t < s \supset (s < r \supset t < r)$
(c) $t < s \supset s \nless t$
(d) $t < s \equiv t + r < s + r$
(e) $t \leqslant t$
(f) $t \leqslant s \supset (s \leqslant r \supset t \leqslant r)$
(g) $t \leqslant s \equiv (t + r \leqslant s + r)$
(h) $t \leqslant s \supset (s < r \supset t < r)$
(i) $0 \leqslant t$
(j) $0 < t'$
(k) $t < r \equiv t' \leqslant r$
(l) $t \leqslant r \equiv t < r'$
(m) $t < t'$
(n) $(0 < \bar{1}) \wedge (\bar{1} < \bar{2}) \wedge (\bar{2} < \bar{3}) \wedge \ldots$
(o) $t \neq r \supset (t < r \vee r < t)$
(o′) $t = r \vee t < r \vee r < t$
(p) $t \leqslant r \vee r \leqslant t$
(q) $t + r \geqslant t$
(r) $r \neq 0 \supset t + r > t$
(s) $r \neq 0 \supset t \cdot r \geqslant t$
(t) $r \neq 0 \equiv r > 0$
(u) $r > 0 \supset (t > 0 \supset r \cdot t > 0)$
(v) $r \neq 0 \supset (t > \bar{1} \supset t \cdot r > r)$
(w) $r \neq 0 \supset (t < s \equiv t \cdot r < s \cdot r)$
(x) $r \neq 0 \supset (t \leqslant s \equiv t \cdot r \leqslant s \cdot r)$
(y) $t \nless 0$
(z) $t \leqslant r \wedge r \leqslant t \supset t = r$

PROOF

(a) By Proposition 3.4(d).

(b)

1.	$t < s$	Hyp
2.	$s < r$	Hyp
3.	$(Ew)(w \neq 0 \wedge t + w = s)$	1, Definition
4.	$(Ev)(v \neq 0 \wedge s + v = r)$	2, Definition, and, possibly, a change of bound variables
5.	$w \neq 0 \wedge t + w = s$	3, Rule C
6.	$v \neq 0 \wedge s + v = r$	5, Rule C
7.	$t + w = s$	5, Tautology
8.	$s + v = r$	6, Tautology
9.	$(t + w) + v = r$	7, 8, Proposition 3.2(e)

10.	$t + (w + v) = r$	9, Proposition 3.2(j)
11.	$w \neq 0$	5, Tautology
12.	$v \neq 0$	6, Tautology
13.	$w + v \neq 0$	11, 12, Proposition 3.5(d), Tautology
14.	$w + v \neq 0 \wedge t + (w + v) = r$	10, 13, Tautology
15.	$(Eu)(u \neq 0 \wedge t + u = r)$	14, Rule E4
16.	$t < r$	15, Definition
17.	$\vdash t < s \supset (s < r \supset t < r)$	1–16, Deduction Theorem, Proposition 2.23

Parts (c)–(z) are left as exercises. These theorems are not arranged in any special order, though, generally, they can be proved more or less directly from preceding ones in the list.

PROPOSITION 3.8. (a) *For any natural number* k,

$$\vdash x = 0 \vee \ldots \vee x = \bar{k} \equiv x \leqslant \bar{k}.$$

(a′) *For any natural number* k *and any* wf $\mathscr{A}$,

$$\vdash \mathscr{A}(0) \wedge \mathscr{A}(\bar{1}) \wedge \ldots \wedge \mathscr{A}(\bar{k}) \equiv (x)(x \leqslant \bar{k} \supset \mathscr{A}(x))$$

(b) *For any natural number* k > 0, $\vdash x = 0 \vee \ldots \vee x = \overline{(k-1)} \equiv x < \bar{k}$.

(b′) *For any natural number* k > 0, *and any* wf $\mathscr{A}$,

$$\vdash \mathscr{A}(0) \wedge \mathscr{A}(\bar{1}) \wedge \ldots \wedge \mathscr{A}(\overline{k-1}) \equiv (x)(x < \bar{k} \supset \mathscr{A}(x))$$

(c) $\vdash ((x)(x < y \supset \mathscr{A}(x)) \wedge (x)(x \geqslant y \supset \mathscr{B}(x))) \supset (x)(\mathscr{A}(x) \vee \mathscr{B}(x))$.

PROOF. (a) We prove $\vdash x = 0 \vee \ldots \vee x = \bar{k} \equiv x \leqslant \bar{k}$ by induction in the metalanguage on k. The case for k = 0, $\vdash x = 0 \equiv x \leqslant 0$ is obvious from the definitions and Proposition 3.7. Assume $\vdash x = 0 \vee \ldots \vee x = \bar{k} \equiv x \leqslant \bar{k}$. Now, assume $x = 0 \vee \ldots \vee x = \bar{k} \vee x = \overline{k+1}$; but, $x = \overline{k+1} \supset x \leqslant \overline{k+1}$; also, $x = 0 \vee \ldots \vee x = \bar{k} \supset x \leqslant \bar{k}$, and $x \leqslant \bar{k} \supset x \leqslant \overline{k+1}$. Hence, $x = 0 \vee \ldots \vee x = \overline{k+1} \supset x \leqslant \overline{k+1}$. On the other hand, assume $x \leqslant \overline{k+1}$. Then $x = \overline{k+1} \vee x < \overline{k+1}$. If $x = \overline{k+1}$, then $x = 0 \vee \ldots \vee x = \overline{k+1}$. If $x < \overline{k+1}$, then, since $\overline{k+1}$ is $(\bar{k})'$, we have $x \leqslant \bar{k}$, by Proposition 3.7(l). By inductive hypothesis, $x = 0 \vee \ldots \vee x = \bar{k}$, and so, $x = 0 \vee \ldots \vee x = \overline{k+1}$. (This proof has been given in an informal manner that we shall generally use from now on. In particular, the Deduction Theorem, the eliminability of Rule C, and the Replacement Theorem (Corollary 2.21) will be tacitly applied, and tautologies used will not be explicitly mentioned.)

Parts (a′), (b), (b′) follow easily from (a). Part (c) follows almost immediately from Proposition 3.7(o), using obvious tautologies.

There are several stronger forms of the induction principle which we can prove at this point.

PROPOSITION 3.9

(a) (Complete Induction)

$$\vdash (x)((z)(z < x \supset \mathscr{A}(z)) \supset \mathscr{A}(x)) \supset (x)\mathscr{A}(x)$$

(Given a property P *such that, for any* x, *if it holds for all natural numbers less than* x, *then it holds for* x *also. Then* P *holds for all natural numbers.)*

(b) (Least-number Principle)

$$\vdash \mathscr{A}(x) \supset ((Ey)(\mathscr{A}(y) \wedge (z)(z < y \supset \sim\mathscr{A}(z))))$$

(If a property P *holds for some natural number, then there is a least number satisfying* P.)

PROOF

(a) Let $\mathscr{B}(x)$ be $(z)(z \leqslant x \supset \mathscr{A}(z))$.

(i)
1. $(x)((z)(z < x \supset \mathscr{A}(z)) \supset \mathscr{A}(x))$ — Hyp
2. $(z)(z < 0 \supset \mathscr{A}(z)) \supset \mathscr{A}(0)$ — 1, Rule A4
3. $z \nless 0$ — Proposition 3.7(y)
4. $(z)(z < 0 \supset \mathscr{A}(z))$ — 3, Tautology, Gen
5. $\mathscr{A}(0)$ — 2, 4, Gen
6. $(z)(z \leqslant 0 \supset \mathscr{A}(z))$ i.e., $\mathscr{B}(0)$ — 5, Proposition 3.8(a′)
7. $(x)((z)(z < x \supset \mathscr{A}(z)) \supset \mathscr{A}(x)) \vdash \mathscr{B}(0)$ — 1–6

(ii)
1. $(x)((z)(z < x \supset \mathscr{A}(z)) \supset \mathscr{A}(x))$ — Hyp
2. $\mathscr{B}(x)$, i.e., $(z)(z \leqslant x \supset \mathscr{A}(z))$ — Hyp
3. $(z)(z < x' \supset \mathscr{A}(z))$ — 2, Proposition 3.7(l)
4. $(z)(z < x' \supset \mathscr{A}(z)) \supset \mathscr{A}(x')$ — 1, Rule A4
5. $\mathscr{A}(x')$ — 3, 4, MP
6. $z \leqslant x' \supset z < x' \vee z = x'$ — Definition, Tautology
7. $z < x' \supset \mathscr{A}(z)$ — 3, Rule A4
8. $z = x' \supset \mathscr{A}(z)$ — 5, Equality Axiom (7)
9. $(z)(z \leqslant x' \supset \mathscr{A}(z))$ i.e., $\mathscr{B}(x')$ — 6, 7, 8, Tautology, Gen
10. $(x)((z)(z < x \supset \mathscr{A}(z)) \supset \mathscr{A}(x)) \vdash (x)(\mathscr{B}(x) \supset \mathscr{B}(x'))$ — 1–9, Deduction Theorem, Gen

From (i), (ii), and the Induction Rule, we obtain $\mathscr{C} \vdash (x)\mathscr{B}(x)$, i.e., $\mathscr{C} \vdash (x)(z)(z \leqslant x \supset \mathscr{A}(z))$, where $\mathscr{C}$ is $(x)((z)(z < x \supset \mathscr{A}(z)) \supset \mathscr{A}(x))$.

Hence, by Rule A4 twice, $\mathscr{C} \vdash x \leqslant x \supset \mathscr{A}(x)$; but, $\vdash x \leqslant x$. So, $\mathscr{C} \vdash \mathscr{A}(x)$, and, by Gen and the Deduction Theorem, $\vdash \mathscr{C} \supset (x)\mathscr{A}(x)$.

(b)

1.	$\sim(Ey)(\mathscr{A}(y) \wedge (z)(z < y \supset \sim\mathscr{A}(z)))$	Hyp
2.	$(y)\sim(\mathscr{A}(y) \wedge (z)(z < y \supset \sim\mathscr{A}(z)))$	1, Tautology
3.	$(y)((z)(z < y \supset \sim\mathscr{A}(z)) \supset \sim\mathscr{A}(y))$	2, Tautology
4.	$(y)\sim\mathscr{A}(y)$	3, Part (a) with $\sim\mathscr{A}$ instead of $\mathscr{A}$
5.	$\sim\mathscr{A}(x)$	4, Rule A4
6.	$\sim(Ey)(\mathscr{A}(y) \wedge (z)(z < y \supset \sim\mathscr{A}(z))) \supset \sim\mathscr{A}(x)$	1–5, Deduction Theorem
7.	$\mathscr{A}(x) \supset (Ey)(\mathscr{A}(y) \supset (z)(z < y \supset \sim\mathscr{A}(z)))$	6, Tautology

EXERCISE. Show that

$$\vdash (x)(\mathscr{A}(x) \supset (Ey)(y < x \wedge \mathscr{A}(y))) \supset (x)\sim\mathscr{A}(x)$$

(Method of Infinite Descent).

Another important notion in number theory is divisibility, which we now define.

DEFINITION. $t \mid s$ for $(Ez)(s = t \cdot z)$, where z is the first variable not in t or s.

PROPOSITION 3.10. *The following* wfs *are theorems.*

(a) $t \mid t$
(b) $\bar{1} \mid t$
(c) $t \mid 0$
(d) $t \mid s \wedge s \mid r \supset t \mid r$
(e) $s \neq 0 \wedge t \mid s \supset t \leqslant s$
(f) $t \mid s \wedge s \mid t \supset s = t$
(g) $t \mid s \supset t \mid r \cdot s$
(h) $t \mid s \wedge t \mid r \supset t \mid (s + r)$

PROOF. (a) $t = t \cdot \bar{1}$. Hence $t \mid t$. (b) $t = \bar{1} \cdot t$. Hence $\bar{1} \mid t$. (c) $0 = t \cdot 0$. Hence, $t \mid 0$. (d) If $s = t \cdot z$ and $r = s \cdot w$, then $r = t \cdot (z \cdot w)$. (e) If $s \neq 0$ and $t \mid s$, then $s = t \cdot z$ for some z. If $z = 0$, then $s = 0$. Hence, $z \neq 0$. So, $z = u'$ for some u. $s = t \cdot (u') = t \cdot u + t \geqslant t$. (f)–(h) are left as exercises.

EXERCISES

Prove the following:

1. $\vdash t \mid \bar{1} \supset t = \bar{1}$
2. $\vdash (t \mid s \wedge t \mid s') \supset t = \bar{1}$

It will be useful, for later purposes, to prove the existence of a unique quotient and remainder upon division of one number by another.

PROPOSITION 3.11. $\vdash y \neq 0 \supset (E_1u)(E_1v)(x = y \cdot u + v \wedge v < y)$.

PROOF. Let $\mathscr{A}(x)$ be $y \neq 0 \supset (Eu)(Ev)(x = y \cdot u + v \wedge v < y)$.

(i) 1. $y \neq 0$ — Hyp
2. $0 = y \cdot 0 + 0$ — (S5′), (S7′)
3. $0 < y$ — 1, Proposition 3.7(t)
4. $0 = y \cdot 0 + 0 \wedge 0 < y$ — 2, 3, Tautology
5. $(Eu)(Ev)(0 = y \cdot u + v \wedge v < y)$ — 4, Rule E4
6. $y \neq 0 \supset (Eu)(Ev)(0 = y \cdot u + v \wedge v < y)$ — 1–5, Deduction Theorem

(ii) 1. $\mathscr{A}(x)$, i.e., $y \neq 0 \supset (Eu)(Ev)(x = y \cdot u + v \wedge v < y)$ — Hyp
2. $y \neq 0$ — Hyp
3. $(Eu)(Ev)(x = y \cdot u + v \wedge v < y)$ — 1, 2, MP
4. $x = y \cdot a + b \wedge b < y$ — 3, Rule C twice
5. $b < y$ — 4, Tautology
6. $b' \leqslant y$ — 5, Proposition 3.7(k)
7. $b' < y \vee b' = y$ — 6, Definition
8. $b' < y \supset (x' = y \cdot a + b' \wedge b' < y)$ — 4, (S6′)
9. $b' < y \supset (Eu)(Ev)(x' = y \cdot u + v \wedge v < y)$ — 8, Rule E4, Deduction Theorem
10. $b' = y \supset x' = y \cdot a + y \cdot \bar{1}$ — 4, (S6′), Proposition 3.5(b)
11. $b' = y \supset (x' = y \cdot (a + \bar{1}) + 0 \wedge 0 < y)$ — 10, Proposition 3.4, 2, Proposition 3.7(t), (S5′)
12. $b' = y \supset (Eu)(Ev)(x' = y \cdot u + v \wedge v < y)$ — 11, Deduction Theorem, Rule E4
13. $(Eu)(Ev)(x' = y \cdot u + v \wedge v < y)$ — 7, 9, 12, Tautology
14. $\mathscr{A}(x) \supset (y \neq 0 \supset (Eu)(Ev)(x' = y \cdot u + v \wedge v < y))$ — 1–13, Deduction Theorem

i.e., $\mathscr{A}(x) \supset \mathscr{A}(x')$

By (i), (ii), and the Induction Rule, $\vdash (x)\mathscr{A}(x)$. This establishes the existence of a quotient u and a remainder v. To prove uniqueness, proceed as follows. Assume $y \neq 0$. Assume $x = y \cdot u_1 + v_1 \wedge v_1 < y$ and $x = y \cdot u_2 + v_2 \wedge v_2 < y$. Now, $u_1 = u_2$ or $u_1 < u_2$ or $u_2 < u_1$. If $u_1 = u_2$, then $v_1 = v_2$ by Proposition 3.4(d). If $u_1 < u_2$, then $u_2 = u_1 + w$ for some $w \neq 0$. Then $y \cdot u_1 + v_1 = y \cdot (u_1 + w) + v_2 = y \cdot u_1 + y \cdot w + v_2$. Hence, $v_1 = y \cdot w + v_2$; but $w \neq 0$. Hence, $y \cdot w \geqslant y$. So, $v_1 = y \cdot w + v_2 \geqslant y$, contradicting $v_1 < y$. Hence, $u_1 \nless u_2$. Similarly, $u_1 \ngtr u_2$. Hence, $u_1 = u_2$, and so, $v_1 = v_2$.

From this point on, one can generally translate into S and prove the results from any text on elementary number theory (e.g., Vinogradov [1954]). There are certain number-theoretic functions, such as x^y and x!, which we have to be able to define in S, and this we shall do later in this chapter. (In most cases, by suitable paraphrasing, one can get along without explicitly defining these functions, but, after a short time, this leads to unwieldy complications.) Some standard results of number theory, such as Dirichlet's Theorem, are proved with the aid of the theory of complex variables, and it is often not known whether elementary proofs (or proofs in S) can be given for such theorems. The statement of some results in number theory, such as the Prime Number Theorem, involve non-elementary concepts, such as the logarithmic function, and, except in cases where an equivalent elementary formula can be obtained, cannot even be formulated in S. More information about the strength and expressive powers of S will be revealed in the sequel. For example it will be shown later that there are closed wfs which are neither provable nor disprovable in S, if S is consistent; hence there is a wf which is true under the standard interpretation but is not provable in S. We shall also see that this incompleteness of S cannot be attributed to omission of some essential axiom, but has deeper underlying causes which apply to other theories as well.

EXERCISES

1. Show that the Induction Principle (S9) is independent of the other axioms of S. (Hint: consider the interpretation having as its domain the set of polynomials with integral coefficients such that the leading coefficient is non-negative. The usual operations of addition and multiplication are the interpretations of + and $\cdot$. Verify that (S1)–(S8) hold, but that Theorem 3.11 is false (substituting the polynomial x for x and 2 for y).

^{D}2. There exist non-standard models for S of any cardinality $\aleph_\alpha$. (Hint: form a new theory S′ by adding to S a new individual constant b and the axioms $b \neq 0, b \neq \overline{1}, b \neq \overline{2}, \ldots, b \neq \overline{n}, \ldots$. Show that S′ is consistent and apply Proposition 2.27 and Corollary 2.35(c).) Ehrenfeucht [1958] has shown the existence of at least $2^{\aleph_0}$ non-isomorphic models of cardinality $\aleph_\alpha$.

^{D}3. Give a standard mathematical proof of the categoricity of Peano's Postulates, in the sense that any two "models" are isomorphic. Explain why this proof does not apply to the first-order theory S.

^{D}4. (Presburger [1929]) If we eliminate from S the function letter f_2^2 for multiplication and the axioms (S7)–(S8), then the new system S_+ is complete and decidable. (Hint: use a reduction procedure similar to that given for the theory K_2 on pp. 94–95. For any number k, define $k \cdot t$ by induction: $0 \cdot t$ is 0 and $(k + 1) \cdot t$ is $(k \cdot t) + t$; thus $k \cdot t$ is the sum of t taken k times. Also, for any given k, let $t \equiv s$ (mod k) stand for $(Ex)(t = s + k \cdot x \vee s = t + k \cdot x)$. In the reduction procedure, consider all such wfs $t \equiv s$ (mod k), as well as the wfs $t < s$, as atomic wfs, although they actually are not. Given any wf of S_+, we may assume by Proposition 2.31 that it is in prenex normal form. Describe a method which, given a wf $(Ey)(\mathscr{C})$ where $\mathscr{C}$ contains no quantifiers (remembering the convention that $t \equiv s$ (mod k) and $t < s$ are considered atomic), finds an equivalent wf without quantifiers (again remembering our convention). For help on details, cf. Hilbert-Bernays [1934] I, pp. 359–366.)

5. (a) Every closed atomic wf of S, $t = s$, is decidable, i.e., either $\vdash_S t = s$ or $\vdash_S t \neq s$. (b) Every closed wf of S without quantifiers is decidable.

§ 2. Number-Theoretic Functions and Relations

A number-theoretic function is one whose arguments and values are natural numbers, and a number-theoretic relation is a relation whose arguments are natural numbers. For example, multiplication is a number-theoretic function of two arguments, and the expression $x + y < z$ determines a number-theoretic relation of three arguments. Number-theoretic functions and relations are intuitive and are not bound up with any formal system.

A number-theoretic relation $R(x_1, \ldots, x_n)$ is said to be *expressible* in S if and only if there is a wf $\mathscr{A}(x_1, \ldots, x_n)$ of S with n free variables such that: for any natural numbers $k_1, \ldots, k_n$,

(1) if $R(k_1, \ldots, k_n)$ is true, then $\vdash_S \mathscr{A}(\overline{k_1}, \ldots, \overline{k_n})$.

(2) if $R(k_1, \ldots, k_n)$ is false, then $\vdash_S \sim\mathscr{A}(\overline{k_1}, \ldots, \overline{k_n})$.

For example, the number-theoretic relation of equality is expressed in S by the wf $x_1 = x_2$. In fact, if $k_1 = k_2$, then $\overline{k_1}$ is the same term as $\overline{k_2}$, and so, by Proposition 3.2(a), $\vdash_S \overline{k_1} = \overline{k_2}$. Also, if $k_1 \neq k_2$, then, by Proposition 3.6(a), $\vdash_S \overline{k_1} \neq \overline{k_2}$.

Likewise, the relation "less than" is expressed in S by the wf $x_1 < x_2$. For, if $k_1 < k_2$, then there is some non-zero number n such that $k_2 = k_1 + n$. Now, by Proposition 3.6(a), $\vdash_S \overline{k_2} = \overline{k_1} + \overline{n}$. Also, by (S3′), since $n \neq 0$, $\vdash \overline{n} \neq 0$. Hence, one can prove in S the wf $(Ew)(\overline{k_2} = \overline{k_1} + w \wedge w \neq 0)$, i.e., $\overline{k_1} < \overline{k_2}$. Now, if $k_1 \nless k_2$, then $k_2 < k_1$ or $k_2 = k_1$. If $k_2 < k_1$, then, as we have just seen, $\vdash \overline{k_2} < \overline{k_1}$. If $k_2 = k_1$, then $\vdash \overline{k_2} = \overline{k_1}$. In either case, $\vdash \overline{k_2} \leqslant \overline{k_1}$, and then by Proposition 3.7(a),(c), $\vdash \overline{k_1} \nless \overline{k_2}$.

EXERCISES

1. Show that the negation, conjunction, and disjunction of expressible relations are also expressible (in S).

2. Show that the relation $x + y = z$ is expressible in S.

A number-theoretic function $f(x_1, \ldots, x_n)$ is said to be *representable* in S if and only if there is a wf $\mathscr{A}(x_1, \ldots, x_{n+1})$ of S with the free variables $x_1, \ldots, x_{n+1}$ such that, for any numbers $k_1, \ldots, k_{n+1}$:

(1) if $f(k_1, \ldots, k_n) = k_{n+1}$, then $\vdash_S \mathscr{A}(\overline{k_1}, \ldots, \overline{k_n}, \overline{k_{n+1}})$;

(2) $\vdash_S (E_1 x_{n+1})\mathscr{A}(\overline{k_1}, \ldots, \overline{k_n}, x_{n+1})$.

If, in this definition, we change (2) to (2′), $\vdash_S (E_1 x_{n+1})\mathscr{A}(x_1, \ldots, x_n, x_{n+1})$, then the function f is said to be *strongly representable* in S. Notice that (2′) implies (2), by Gen and Rule A4. Hence, every strongly representable function is also representable. (For the converse, cf. Exercise 3 on p. 135.)

Examples

(a) The zero function, $Z(x) = 0$, is strongly representable in S by the wf $x_1 = x_1 \wedge x_2 = 0$. For any k_1, if $Z(k_1) = k_2$, then $k_2 = 0$, and $\vdash \overline{k_1} = \overline{k_1} \wedge 0 = 0$, i.e., (1) holds. Also, $\vdash (E_1 x_2)(x_1 = x_1 \wedge x_2 = 0)$. Thus, (2′) holds.

(b) The successor function, $N(x) = x + 1$, is strongly representable in S by the wf $x_2 = (x_1)'$. For any k_1, if $N(k_1) = k_2$, then $k_2 = k_1 + 1$; hence, $\overline{k_2}$ is $(\overline{k_1})'$. Then $\vdash \overline{k_2} = (\overline{k_1})'$. Also, $\vdash (E_1 x_2)(x_2 = (x_1)')$.

(c) The projection function, $U_i^n(x_1, \ldots, x_n) = x_i$, is strongly representable in S by the wf $x_1 = x_1 \wedge x_2 = x_2 \wedge \ldots \wedge x_n = x_n \wedge x_{n+1} = x_i$. If $U_i^n(k_1, \ldots, k_n) = k_{n+1}$, then $k_{n+1} = k_i$, and $\overline{k_{n+1}}$ is $\overline{k_i}$. Hence, $\vdash \overline{k_1} = \overline{k_1} \wedge \overline{k_2} = \overline{k_2} \wedge \ldots \wedge \overline{k_n} = \overline{k_n} \wedge \overline{k_{n+1}} = \overline{k_i}$. Thus, (1) holds. In addition, $\vdash (E_1 x_{n+1})(x_1 = x_1 \wedge x_2 = x_2 \wedge \ldots \wedge x_n = x_n \wedge x_{n+1} = x_i)$, i.e., (2′) holds.

(d) Assume that the functions $g(x_1, \ldots, x_m)$, $h_1(x_1, \ldots, x_n), \ldots, h_m(x_1, \ldots, x_n)$ are (strongly) representable in S, by the wfs $\mathscr{B}(x_1, \ldots, x_m, x_{m+1})$, $\mathscr{A}_1(x_1, \ldots, x_{n+1}), \ldots, \mathscr{A}_m(x_1, \ldots, x_{n+1})$, respectively. Define a new function f by the equation $f(x_1, \ldots, x_n) = g(h_1(x_1, \ldots, x_n), \ldots, h_m(x_1, \ldots, x_n))$. f is said to be obtained from $g, h_1, \ldots, h_m$ by substitution. Then f is also (strongly) representable in S, by the wf $\mathscr{A}(x_1, \ldots, x_{n+1})$:

$$(Ey_1)\ldots(Ey_m)(\mathscr{A}_1(x_1, \ldots, x_n, y_1) \wedge \ldots \wedge \mathscr{A}_m(x_1, \ldots, x_n, y_m) \wedge \mathscr{B}(y_1, \ldots, y_m, x_{n+1}))$$

To prove (1), let $f(k_1, \ldots, k_n) = k_{n+1}$. Let $h_i(k_1, \ldots, k_n) = r_i$ for $1 \leqslant i \leqslant m$; then $g(r_1, \ldots, r_m) = k_{n+1}$. By our assumption that $\mathscr{B}$,

$\mathscr{A}_1, \ldots, \mathscr{A}_m$ (strongly) represent g, $h_1, \ldots, h_m$, respectively, we have $\vdash \mathscr{A}_i(\overline{k_1}, \ldots, \overline{k_n}, \overline{r_i})$ for $1 \leqslant i \leqslant m$, and $\vdash \mathscr{B}(\overline{r_1}, \ldots, \overline{r_m}, \overline{k_{n+1}})$. Hence,

$$\vdash \mathscr{A}_1(\overline{k_1}, \ldots, \overline{k_n}, \overline{r_1}) \wedge \ldots \wedge \mathscr{A}_m(\overline{k_1}, \ldots, \overline{k_n}, \overline{r_m}) \wedge \mathscr{B}(\overline{r_1}, \ldots, \overline{r_m}, \overline{k_{n+1}})$$

By Rule E4, $\vdash \mathscr{A}(\overline{k_1}, \ldots, \overline{k_n}, \overline{k_{n+1}})$, i.e., (1) holds. We shall prove (2′) in the case of strong representability; the proof of (2) in the case of representability is similar. Assume

$$(\maltese)\ (Ey_1)(Ey_2)\ldots(Ey_m)(\mathscr{A}_1(x_1, \ldots, x_n, y_1) \wedge \ldots \wedge \mathscr{A}_m(x_1, \ldots, x_n, y_m) \wedge \mathscr{B}(y_1, \ldots, y_m, u))$$

and

$$(\maltese\maltese)\ (Ey_1)(Ey_2)\ldots(Ey_m)(\mathscr{A}_1(x_1, \ldots, x_n, y_1) \wedge \ldots \wedge \mathscr{A}_m(x_1, \ldots, x_n, y_m) \wedge \mathscr{B}(y_1, \ldots, y_m, v))$$

By (✠), using Rule C m times,

$$\mathscr{A}_1(x_1, \ldots, x_n, b_1) \wedge \ldots \wedge \mathscr{A}_m(x_1, \ldots, x_n, b_m) \wedge \mathscr{B}(y_1, \ldots, y_m, u)$$

By (✠✠), using Rule C again,

$$\mathscr{A}_1(x_1, \ldots, x_n, c_1) \wedge \ldots \wedge \mathscr{A}_m(x_1, \ldots, x_n, c_m) \wedge \mathscr{B}(c_1, \ldots, c_m, v))$$

Since $\vdash (E_1x_{n+1})\mathscr{A}_i(x_1, \ldots, x_n, x_{n+1})$, we obtain, from $\mathscr{A}_i(x_1, \ldots, x_n, b_i)$ and $\mathscr{A}_i(x_1, \ldots, x_n, c_i)$, that $b_i = c_i$. From $\mathscr{B}(b_1, \ldots, b_m, u)$ and $b_1 = c_1, \ldots, b_m = c_m$, we have $\mathscr{B}(c_1, \ldots, c_m, u)$. Hence, from $\vdash (E_1x_{n+1})\mathscr{B}(x_1, \ldots, x_{n+1})$ and $\mathscr{B}(c_1, \ldots, c_m, v)$, we obtain $u = v$. We have shown $\vdash \mathscr{A}(x_1, \ldots, x_n, u) \wedge \mathscr{A}(x_1, \ldots, x_n, v) \supset u = v$. It is also easy to show that $\vdash (Ex_{n+1})\mathscr{A}(x_1, \ldots, x_{n+1})$ (Exercise). From this, we have $\vdash (E_1x_{n+1})\mathscr{A}(x_1, \ldots, x_n, x_{n+1})$, i.e., (2′).

EXERCISES

Show that the following functions are strongly representable in S.

1. $Z_n(x_1, \ldots, x_n) = 0$ (Hint: $Z_n(x_1, \ldots, x_n) = Z(U_1^n(x_1, \ldots, x_n))$. Use (a), (c), (d).)
2. For any given k, $C_k^n(x_1, \ldots, x_n) = k$ (Hint: by 1, we have C_0^n; assume C_k^n is strongly representable. Then $C_{k+1}^n(x_1, \ldots, x_n) = N(C_k^n(x_1, \ldots, x_n))$; use (b), (d).)
3. Addition.
4. Multiplication.

If $R(x_1, \ldots, x_n)$ is a relation, then the characteristic function $C_R(x_1, \ldots, x_n)$ is defined as follows:

$$C_R(x_1, \ldots, x_n) = \begin{cases} 0 & \text{if } R(x_1, \ldots, x_n) \text{ is true} \\ 1 & \text{if } R(x_1, \ldots, x_n) \text{ is false} \end{cases}$$

PROPOSITION 3.12. *$R(x_1, \ldots, x_n)$ is expressible in S if and only if $C_R(x_1, \ldots, x_n)$ is (strongly) representable in S.*

PROOF. If $R(x_1, \ldots, x_n)$ is expressible in S by a wf $\mathscr{A}(x_1, \ldots, x_n)$, then it is easy to verify that $C_R(x_1, \ldots, x_n)$ is strongly representable in S by the wf $(\mathscr{A}(x_1, \ldots, x_n) \wedge x_{n+1} = 0) \vee (\sim\mathscr{A}(x_1, \ldots, x_n) \wedge x_{n+1} = 1)$. Conversely, if $C_R(x_1, \ldots, x_n)$ is representable in S by a wf $\mathscr{B}(x_1, \ldots, x_n, x_{n+1})$, then $R(x_1, \ldots, x_n)$ is expressible in S by the wf $\mathscr{B}(x_1, \ldots, x_n, 0)$.

EXERCISES

1. The *representing relation* (or *graph*) of a function $f(x_1, \ldots, x_n)$ is the relation $f(x_1, \ldots, x_n) = x_{n+1}$. Show that if $f(x_1, \ldots, x_n)$ is representable in S, then its representing relation is expressible in S.

2. If R_1 and R_2 are relations of n arguments, then $C_{\text{not-}R_1} = 1 - C_{R_1}$, $C_{(R_1 \text{ or } R_2)} = C_{R_1} \cdot C_{R_2}$ and $C_{(R_1 \text{ and } R_2)} = C_{R_1} + C_{R_2} - C_{R_1} \cdot C_{R_2}$.

§ 3. Primitive Recursive and Recursive Functions

The study of representability of functions in S leads to a class of number-theoretic functions which turn out to be of great importance in mathematical logic.

DEFINITION

(1) The following functions are called *initial functions.*

(I) The zero function: $Z(x) = 0$ for all x.

(II) The successor function: $N(x) = x + 1$ for all x.

(III) The projection functions: $U_i^n(x_1, \ldots, x_n) = x_i$ for all $x_1, \ldots, x_n$.

(2) The following are rules for obtaining new functions from given functions.

(IV) Substitution:

$$f(x_1, \ldots, x_n) = g(h_1(x_1, \ldots, x_n), \ldots, h_m(x_1, \ldots, x_n))$$

f is said to be obtained by substitution from the functions $g(y_1, \ldots, y_m), h_1(x_1, \ldots, x_n), \ldots, h_m(x_1, \ldots, x_n)$.

(V) Recursion:

$$f(x_1, \ldots, x_n, 0) = g(x_1, \ldots, x_n)$$

$$f(x_1, \ldots, x_n, y + 1) = h(x_1, \ldots, x_n, y, f(x_1, \ldots, x_n, y))$$

Here, we allow $n = 0$, in which case we have

$$f(0) = k \quad \text{(where k is a fixed integer)}$$

$$f(y + 1) = h(y, f(y)).$$

We shall say that f is obtained from g and h (or, in the case $n = 0$, from h alone) by recursion. The *parameters* of the recursion are $x_1, \ldots, x_n$. Notice that f is well-defined: the value of $f(x_1, \ldots, x_n, 0)$ is given by the first equation, and if we already know the value $f(x_1, \ldots, x_n, y)$, then we can obtain $f(x_1, \ldots, x_n, y + 1)$ by the second equation.

(VI) μ-Operator: assume that $g(x_1, \ldots, x_n, y)$ is a function such that for any $x_1, \ldots, x_n$ there is at least one y such that $g(x_1, \ldots, x_n, y) = 0$. We denote by $\mu y(g(x_1, \ldots, x_n, y) = 0)$ the least number y such that $g(x_1, \ldots, x_n, y) = 0$. In general, for any relation $R(x_1, \ldots, x_n, y)$, we denote by $\mu y R(x_1, \ldots, x_n, y)$ the least y such that $R(x_1, \ldots, x_n, y)$ is true, if there is any y at all such that $R(x_1, \ldots, x_n, y)$ holds. Let $f(x_1, \ldots, x_n) = \mu y(g(x_1, \ldots, x_n, y) = 0)$. Then f is said to be obtained from g by means of the μ-operator, if the given assumption about g holds: for any $x_1, \ldots, x_n$, there is at least one y such that $g(x_1, \ldots, x_n, y) = 0$.

(3) A function f is said to be *primitive recursive* if and only if it can be obtained from the initial functions by any finite number of substitutions (IV) and recursions (V), i.e., if there is a finite sequence of functions $f_0, \ldots, f_n$ such that $f_n = f$, and, for $0 \leqslant i \leqslant n$, either f_i is an initial function or f_i comes from preceding functions in the sequence by an application of Rule (IV) (Substitution) or Rule (V) (Recursion).

(4) A function f is said to be *recursive* if and only if it can be obtained from the initial functions by any finite number of applications of Substitution (IV), Recursion (V), and the μ-operator (VI). This differs from the definition above of primitive recursive functions only in the addition of possible applications of the μ-operator (Rule VI). Hence, every primitive recursive function is recursive. We shall see later that the converse is false.

We shall show that the class of recursive functions is identical with the class of functions representable in S. (In the literature, the phrase "general recursive" is sometimes used instead of "recursive".)

First, let us prove that we can add dummy variables to and also permute and identify variables in any primitive recursive or recursive function, obtaining a function of the same type.

PROPOSITION 3.13. *Let* $g(y_1, \ldots, y_k)$ *be primitive recursive (or recursive). Let* $x_1, \ldots, x_n$ *be distinct variables, and, for* $1 \leqslant i \leqslant k$, *let* z_i *be one of the* $x_1, \ldots, x_n$. *Then the function* $f(x_1, \ldots, x_n) = g(z_1, \ldots, z_k)$ *is primitive recursive (or recursive).*

PROOF. Let $z_i = x_{j_i}$ (where $1 \leqslant j_i \leqslant n$). Then $z_i = U^n_{j_i}(x_1, \ldots, x_n)$. Then

$$f(x_1, \ldots, x_n) = g(U^n_{j_1}(x_1, \ldots, x_n), U^n_{j_2}(x_1, \ldots, x_n), \ldots, U^n_{j_k}(x_1, \ldots, x_n))$$

and therefore f is primitive recursive (or recursive), since it arises from g, $U^n_{j_1}, \dots, U^n_{j_k}$ by substitution.

Examples

1. (Adding dummy variables.) If $g(x_1, x_3)$ is primitive recursive and if $f(x_1, x_2, x_3) = g(x_1, x_3)$, then $f(x_1, x_2, x_3)$ is also primitive recursive. In Proposition 3.13, let $z_1 = x_1$ and $z_2 = x_3$.

2. (Permuting variables.) If $g(x_1, x_2)$ is primitive recursive and if $f(x_1, x_2) = g(x_2, x_1)$, then $f(x_1, x_2)$ is also primitive recursive. In Proposition 3.13, let $z_1 = x_2$ and $z_2 = x_1$.

3. (Identifying variables.) If $g(x_1, x_2, x_3)$ is primitive recursive and if $f(x_1, x_2) = g(x_1, x_2, x_1)$, then $f(x_1, x_2)$ is primitive recursive. In Proposition 3.13, let $n = 2$ and let $z_1 = x_1$, $z_2 = x_2$, and $z_3 = x_1$.

COROLLARY 3.14. (a) *The zero function* $Z_n(x_1, \dots, x_n) = 0$ *is primitive recursive.* (b) *The constant function* $C^n_k(x_1, \dots, x_n) = k$, *where* k *is some fixed integer, is primitive recursive.* (c) *The Substitution Rule* (IV) *can be extended to the case where each* h_i *may be a function of some but not all of the variables. Likewise, in the Recursion Rule* (V), *the function* g *may not involve all of the variables* $x_1, \dots, x_n$; *and* h *may not involve all of the variables* $x_1, \dots, x_n, y$, *or* $f(x_1, \dots, x_n, y)$.

PROOF. (a) In Proposition 3.13, let g be the zero function Z; then $k = 1$. Take z_1 to be x_1. (b) For $k = 0$, this is part (a). Assume true for k. Then $C^n_{k+1}(x_1, \dots, x_n) = N(C^n_k(x_1, \dots, x_n))$. (c) By Proposition 3.13, any variables among $x_1, \dots, x_n$ not present in a function can be added as "dummy variables". For example, if $h(x_1, x_3)$ is given as primitive recursive (or recursive), then $h\#(x_1, x_2, x_3) = h(x_1, x_3) = h(U^3_1(x_1, x_2, x_3), U^3_3(x_1, x_2, x_3))$ is also primitive recursive (or recursive).

PROPOSITION 3.15. *The following functions are primitive recursive.*

(a) $x + y$; (b) $x \cdot y$; (c) x^y; (d) $\delta(x) = \begin{cases} x - 1 & \text{if } x > 0 \\ 0 & \text{if } x = 0 \end{cases}$;

(e) $x \dot{-} y = \begin{cases} x - y & \text{if } x \geqslant y \\ 0 & \text{if } x < y \end{cases}$; (f) $|x - y| = \begin{cases} x - y & \text{if } x \geqslant y \\ y - x & \text{if } x < y \end{cases}$;

(g) $sg(x) = \begin{cases} 0 & \text{if } x = 0 \\ 1 & \text{if } x \neq 0 \end{cases}$; (h) $\overline{sg}(x) = \begin{cases} 1 & \text{if } x = 0 \\ 0 & \text{if } x \neq 0 \end{cases}$;

(i) $x!$; (j) $\min(x, y) =$ *minimum of* x *and* y; (k) $\min(x_1, \dots, x_n)$;
(l) $\max(x, y) =$ *maximum of* x *and* y; (m) $\max(x_1, \dots, x_n)$;
(n) $rm(x, y) =$ *remainder upon division of* y *by* x;
(o) $qt(x, y) =$ *quotient upon division of* y *by* x.

PROOF

(a) Recursion Rule (V).

$$x + 0 = x \qquad \text{i.e.,} \qquad f(x, 0) = U_1^1(x)$$
$$x + (y + 1) = N(x + y) \qquad f(x, y + 1) = N(f(x, y))$$

(b)
$$x \cdot 0 = 0 \qquad \text{i.e.,} \qquad g(x, 0) = Z(x)$$
$$x \cdot (y + 1) = (x \cdot y) + x \qquad g(x, y + 1) = f(g(x, y), x),$$
where f is the addition function

(c)
$$x^0 = 1$$
$$x^{y+1} = (x^y) \cdot x$$

(d)
$$\delta(0) = 0$$
$$\delta(y + 1) = y$$

(e)
$$x \dot{-} 0 = x$$
$$x \dot{-} (y + 1) = \delta(x \dot{-} y)$$

(f)
$$|x - y| = (x \dot{-} y) + (y \dot{-} x) \qquad \text{(Substitution)}$$

(g)
$$sg(0) = 0$$
$$sg(y + 1) = 1$$

(h)
$$\overline{sg}(x) = 1 \dot{-} sg(x)$$

(i)
$$0! = 1$$
$$(y + 1)! = (y!) \cdot (y + 1)$$

(j)
$$\min(x, y) = x \dot{-} (x \dot{-} y)$$

(k) Assume $\min(x_1, \ldots, x_n)$ already shown primitive recursive.
$$\min(x_1, \ldots, x_n, x_{n+1}) = \min(\min(x_1, \ldots, x_n), x_{n+1})$$

(l)
$$\max(x, y) = y + (x \dot{-} y)$$

(m)
$$\max(x_1, \ldots, x_{n+1}) = \max(\max(x_1, \ldots, x_n), x_{n+1})$$

(n)
$$rm(x, 0) = 0$$
$$rm(x, y + 1) = N(rm(x, y)) \cdot sg(|x - N(rm(x, y))|)$$

(o)
$$qt(x, 0) = 0$$
$$qt(x, y + 1) = qt(x, y) + \overline{sg}(|x - N(rm(x, y))|)$$

DEFINITIONS

$$\sum_{y<z} f(x_1, \ldots, x_n, y) = \begin{cases} 0 & \text{if } z = 0 \\ f(x_1, \ldots, x_n, 0) + \ldots + f(x_1, \ldots, x_n, z - 1) & \text{if } z > 0 \end{cases}$$

$$\sum_{y \leqslant z} f(x_1, \ldots, x_n, y) = \sum_{y<z+1} f(x_1, \ldots, x_n, y)$$

$$\prod_{y<z} f(x_1, \ldots, x_n, y) = \begin{cases} 1 & \text{if } z = 0 \\ f(x_1, \ldots, x_n, 0) \cdot \ldots \cdot f(x_1, \ldots, x_n, z - 1) & \text{if } z > 0 \end{cases}$$

$$\prod_{y \leqslant z} f(x_1, \ldots, x_n, y) = \prod_{y<z+1} f(x_1, \ldots, x_n, y)$$

These *bounded* sums and products are functions of $x_1, \ldots, x_n, z$. We can also define doubly bounded sums and products in terms of the ones already given, e.g.,

$$\sum_{u<y<v} f(x_1, \ldots, x_n, y) = f(x_1, \ldots, x_n, u+1) + \ldots + f(x_1, \ldots, x_n, v-1)$$
$$= \sum_{y<(v \dot{-} u) \dot{-} 1} f(x_1, \ldots, x_n, y+u+1)$$

PROPOSITION 3.16. *If* $f(x_1, \ldots, x_n, y)$ *is primitive recursive* (*or recursive*), *then all the bounded sums and products defined above are also primitive recursive* (*or recursive*).

PROOF. Let $g(x_1, \ldots, x_n, z) = \sum_{y<z} f(x_1, \ldots, x_n, y)$. Then, we have the following recursion.

$$g(x_1, \ldots, x_n, 0) = 0$$
$$g(x_1, \ldots, x_n, z+1) = g(x_1, \ldots, x_n, z) + f(x_1, \ldots, x_n, z)$$

If $h(x_1, \ldots, x_n, z) = \sum_{y \leqslant z} f(x_1, \ldots, x_n, y)$, then $h(x_1, \ldots, x_n, z) = g(x_1, \ldots, x_n, z+1)$ (Substitution). The proofs for bounded products and doubly bounded sums and products are left as exercises.

Example. Let $D(x)$ be the number of divisors of x, if $x > 0$; let $D(0) = 1$. Then $D(x)$ is primitive recursive, since

$$D(x) = \sum_{y \leqslant x} \overline{sg}(rm(y, x)).$$

Given number-theoretic relations, we can apply the connectives of the propositional calculus to them to obtain new relations. We shall use the same symbols ($\sim$, $\wedge$, $\vee$, $\supset$, $\equiv$) for them here, except where confusion may arise between these symbols as they occur in our intuitive metalanguage and as they occur in first-order theories. For example, if $R_1(x_1, \ldots, x_n)$ and $R_2(x_1, \ldots, x_n)$ are relations, then $R_1(x_1, \ldots, x_n) \vee R_2(x_1, \ldots, x_n)$ is a new relation which holds for $x_1, \ldots, x_n$ when and only when $R_1(x_1, \ldots, x_n)$ holds or $R_2(x_1, \ldots, x_n)$ holds. We shall use $(y)_{y<z}R(x_1, \ldots, x_n, y)$ to express the relation: for all y, if y is less than z, then $R(x_1, \ldots, x_n, y)$ holds. We shall use $(y)_{y \leqslant z}$, $(Ey)_{y<z}$, $(Ey)_{y \leqslant z}$ in an analogous way, e.g., $(Ey)_{y<z}R(x_1, \ldots, x_n, y)$ means that there is some $y < z$ such that $R(x_1, \ldots, x_n, y)$ holds. We shall call $(y)_{y<z}$, $(y)_{y \leqslant z}$, $(Ey)_{y<z}$, $(Ey)_{y \leqslant z}$ *bounded quantifiers.* In addition, we define a *bounded μ-operator*:

$$\mu y_{y<z} R(x_1, \ldots, x_n, y) = \begin{cases} \text{the least } y < z \text{ for which } R(x_1, \ldots, x_n) \\ \qquad \text{holds if there is such a } y; \\ z \text{ otherwise} \end{cases}$$

(The value z is chosen in the second case because it is more convenient in later proofs; this choice has no intuitive significance.)

A relation $R(x_1, \ldots, x_n)$ is said to be primitive recursive (or recursive) if and only if its characteristic function $C_R(x_1, \ldots, x_n)$ is primitive recursive (or recursive). In particular, a set A of natural numbers is primitive recursive (or recursive) if and only if its characteristic function $C_A(x)$ is primitive recursive (or recursive).

Examples

(1) The relation $x_1 = x_2$ is primitive recursive. Its characteristic function is $sg(|x_1 - x_2|)$, which is primitive recursive, by Proposition 3.15(f), (g).

(2) The relation $x_1 < x_2$ is primitive recursive, since its characteristic function is $\overline{sg}(x_2 \dot{-} x_1)$, which is primitive recursive, by Proposition 3.15(e), (h).

(3) The relation $x_1 \mid x_2$ is primitive recursive, since its characteristic function is $sg(rm(x_1, x_2))$.

(4) The relation $Pr(x)$, x is a prime, is primitive recursive, since $C_{Pr}(x) = sg((D(x) \dot{-} 2) + \overline{sg}(|x - 1|) + \overline{sg}(|x - 0|))$. Remember that x is a prime if and only if it has exactly two divisors and is not equal to 0 or 1.

PROPOSITION 3.17. *Relations obtained from primitive recursive (or recursive) relations by means of the propositional connectives and the bounded quantifiers are also primitive recursive (or recursive). Also, application of the bounded μ-operators* $\mu y_{y<z}$ *or* $\mu y_{y \leq z}$ *leads from primitive recursive (or recursive) relations to primitive recursive (or recursive) functions.*

PROOF. Assume $R_1(x_1, \ldots, x_n)$ and $R_2(x_1, \ldots, x_n)$ primitive recursive (or recursive) relations. Then the characteristic functions C_{R_1} and C_{R_2} are primitive recursive (or recursive). But $C_{\sim R_1}(x_1, \ldots, x_n) = 1 - C_{R_1}(x_1, \ldots, x_n)$; hence $\sim R_1$ is primitive recursive (or recursive). Also, $C_{R_1 \vee R_2}(x_1, \ldots, x_n) = C_{R_1}(x_1, \ldots, x_n) \cdot C_{R_2}(x_1, \ldots, x_n)$; so, $R_1 \vee R_2$ is primitive recursive (or recursive). Since all the propositional connectives are definable in terms of $\sim$ and $\vee$, this takes care of them. Now, assume $R(x_1, \ldots, x_n, y)$ primitive recursive (or recursive). If $Q(x_1, \ldots, x_n, z)$ is the relation $(Ey)_{y<z}R(x_1, \ldots, x_n, y)$, then it is easy to verify that $C_Q(x_1, \ldots, x_n, z) = \prod_{y<z} C_R(x_1, \ldots, x_n, y)$, which, by Proposition 3.16, is primitive recursive (or recursive). The bounded quantifier $(Ey)_{y \leq z}$ is equivalent to $(Ey)_{y<z+1}$, which is obtainable from $(Ey)_{y<z}$ by substitution. Also, $(y)_{y<z}$ is equivalent to $\sim (Ey)_{y<z} \sim$, and $(y)_{y \leq z}$ is equivalent to $\sim (Ey)_{y \leq z} \sim$. Doubly bounded quantifiers, such as $(Ey)_{u<y<v}$ can be defined by substitution in the bounded

quantifiers already mentioned. Finally, $\prod_{u \leqslant y} C_R(x_1, \ldots, x_n, u)$ has the value 1 for all y such that $R(x_1, \ldots, x_n, u)$ is false for all $u \leqslant y$; it has the value 0 as soon as there is some $u \leqslant y$ such that $R(x_1, \ldots, x_n, u)$ holds. Hence, $\sum_{y<z} (\prod_{u \leqslant y} C_R(x_1, \ldots, x_n, u))$ counts the number of integers from 0 up to but not including the first $y < z$ such that $R(x_1, \ldots, x_n, y)$ holds and is z if there is no such y; thus, it is equal to $\mu y_{y<z} R(x_1, \ldots, x_n, y)$ and so the latter function is primitive recursive (or recursive), by Proposition 3.16.

Examples

(1) Let p(x) be the xth prime number in ascending order, with $p(0) = 2$. We shall write p_x instead of p(x). Then p_x is a primitive recursive function. For

$$p_0 = 2$$

$$p_{x+1} = \mu_{y \leqslant (p_x)!+1}(p_x < y \wedge Pr(y))$$

Notice that the relation $u < y \wedge Pr(y)$ is primitive recursive. Hence, by Proposition 3.17, the function $\mu y_{y \leqslant v}(u < y \wedge Pr(y))$ is a primitive recursive function g(u, v). If we substitute the primitive recursive functions z and $(z)! + 1$ for u and v respectively in g(u, v), we obtain the primitive recursive function

$$h(z) = \mu_{y \leqslant z!+1}(z < y \wedge Pr(y))$$

and the right-hand side of the second equation is $h(p_x)$; hence we have an application of the Recursion Rule (V). The bound $(p_x)! + 1$ on the first prime after p_x is given by Euclid's proof of the infinitude of primes (cf. Vinogradov [1954], page 14).

(2) Every positive integer x has a unique factorization into prime powers: $x = p_0^{a_0} p_1^{a_1} \ldots p_k^{a_k}$. Let us denote by $(x)_i$ the exponent a_i in this factorization. If $x = 1$, $(x)_i$ is 0 for all i. If $x = 0$, we arbitrarily let $(x)_i = 0$. Then the function $(x)_i$ is primitive recursive, since $(x)_i = \mu y_{y<x}(p_i^y | x \wedge \sim(p_i^{y+1} | x))$.

(3) Let lh(x) be the number of non-zero exponents in the factorization of x into powers of primes. Let $lh(0) = 0$. Then lh is primitive recursive. For, let R(x, y) be the primitive recursive predicate $Pr(y) \wedge y | x \wedge x \neq 0$. Then $lh(x) = \sum_{y \leqslant x} \overline{sg}(C_R(x, y))$.

(4) If $x = 2^{a_0} 3^{a_1} \ldots p_k^{a_k}$ "represents" the sequence of positive integers $a_0, a_1, \ldots, a_k$, and $y = 2^{b_0} 3^{b_1} \ldots p_m^{b_m}$ "represents" the sequence $b_0, b_1, \ldots, b_m$, then the number $x * y = 2^{a_0} 3^{a_1} \ldots p_k^{a_k} p_{k+1}^{b_0} p_{k+2}^{b_1} \ldots p_{k+1+m}^{b_m}$ "represents" the new sequence $a_0, a_1, \ldots a_k, b_0, b_1, \ldots, b_m$ obtained by juxtaposing the two sequences. But,

$k + 1 = lh(x)$, $m + 1 = lh(y)$, and $b_j = (y)_j$. Hence, $x * y = x \cdot \prod_{j < lh(y)} (p_{lh(x)+j})^{(y)_j}$, and thus $*$ is a primitive recursive function. We can omit parentheses in writing two or more applications of $*$, since $x * (y * z) = (x * y) * z$.

(5) Let

$$f^*(x_1, \ldots, x_n, 0) = f(x_1, \ldots, x_n, 0)$$

$$f^*(x_1, \ldots, x_n, y + 1) = f^*(x_1, \ldots, x_n, y) * f(x_1, \ldots, x_n, y + 1)$$

Thus,

$$f^*(x_1, \ldots, x_n, z) = f(x_1, \ldots, x_n, 0) * f(x_1, \ldots, x_n, 1) * \ldots * f(x_1, \ldots, x_n, z)$$

and if f is primitive recursive (or recursive), then so is f^*.

EXERCISES

1. Using Proposition 3.17, prove that, if $R(x_1, \ldots, x_n, y)$ is a primitive recursive (or recursive) relation, then $(Ey)_{u<y<v}R(x_1, \ldots, x_n, y)$, $(Ey)_{u \leqslant y \leqslant v}R(x_1, \ldots, x_n, y)$, $(Ey)_{u \leqslant y < v}R(x_1, \ldots, x_n, y)$, and $(Ey)_{u<y \leqslant v} R(x_1, \ldots, x_n, y)$ are primitive recursive (or recursive) relations, and $(\mu y)_{u<y<v}R(x_1, \ldots, x_n, y)$, $(\mu y)_{u \leqslant y \leqslant v}R(x_1, \ldots, x_n, y)$, $(\mu y)_{u \leqslant y<v} R(x_1, \ldots, x_n, y)$, and $(\mu y)_{u<y \leqslant v}R(x_1, \ldots, x_n, y)$ are primitive recursive (or recursive) functions.

2. Show that the intersection, union, and complement of primitive recursive (or recursive) sets are also primitive recursive (or recursive). Prove that every finite set is primitive recursive.

3.(a) $[\sqrt{n}]$ = the greatest integer $\leqslant \sqrt{n}$. (b) $\Pi(n)$ = the number of primes $\leqslant n$. Show that $[\sqrt{n}]$ and $\Pi(n)$ are primitive recursive.

^A4. Let e be the base of the natural logarithms. Show that $[ne]$ = the greatest integer $\leqslant ne$ is primitive recursive. (Hint: let $S(0) = 1$ and $S(n + 1) = (n + 1)S(n) + 1$.)

^A5. Let $RP(y, z)$ hold if and only if y, z are relatively prime. Let $\varphi(n)$ be the number of positive integers $\leqslant n$ which are relatively prime to n. Prove that RP and φ are primitive recursive.

For use in the further study of recursive functions, we prove the following theorem on definition by cases.

PROPOSITION 3.18. *Let*

$$f(x_1, \ldots, x_n) = \begin{cases} g_1(x_1, \ldots, x_n) & \text{if } R_1(x_1, \ldots, x_n) \text{ holds} \\ g_2(x_1, \ldots, x_n) & \text{if } R_2(x_1, \ldots, x_n) \text{ holds} \\ \ldots & \\ \ldots & \\ g_k(x_1, \ldots, x_n) & \text{if } R_k(x_1, \ldots, x_n) \text{ holds.} \end{cases}$$

If the functions $g_1, \ldots, g_k$ *and the relations* $R_1, \ldots, R_k$ *are primitive recursive (or recursive), and if, for any* $x_1, \ldots, x_n$, *exactly one of the relations* $R_1(x_1, \ldots, x_n), \ldots, R_k(x_1, \ldots, x_n)$ *is true, then* f *is primitive recursive (or recursive).*

PROOF. $f(x_1, \ldots, x_n) = g_1(x_1, \ldots, x_n)\cdot\overline{sg}(C_{R_1}(x_1, \ldots, x_n)) + \ldots + g_k(x_1, \ldots, x_n)\cdot\overline{sg}(C_{R_k}(x_1, \ldots, x_n))$.

EXERCISES

1. Show that in Proposition 3.18 it is not necessary to assume that R_k is primitive recursive (or recursive).
2. Let

$$f(x) = \begin{cases} x^2 & \text{if x is even} \\ x + 1 & \text{if x is odd} \end{cases}$$

Prove that f is primitive recursive.

3. Let

$$h(x) = \begin{cases} 2 & \text{if Fermat's Last Theorem is true} \\ 1 & \text{if Fermat's Last Theorem is false} \end{cases}$$

Is h primitive recursive?

It is often important to have available a primitive recursive one-one correspondence between the set of ordered pairs of natural numbers and the set of natural numbers. We shall enumerate the pairs as follows:

$$\overbrace{(0, 0)},\quad \overbrace{(0, 1), (1, 0), (1, 1)}\quad \overbrace{(0, 2), (2, 0), (1, 2), (2, 1), (2, 2)}, \ldots.$$

After we have enumerated all the pairs having components $\leqslant k$, we then add a new group of all the new pairs involving components $\leqslant k + 1$ in the following order: $(0, k + 1), (k + 1, 0), (1, k + 1), (k + 1, 1), \ldots, (k, k + 1), (k + 1, k), (k + 1, k + 1)$. Now, if $x < y$, then (x, y) occurs before (y, x) and both are in the $(y + 1)^{th}$ group. (Note that we start from one in counting groups.) The first y groups contain y^2 pairs, and (x, y) is the $(2x + 1)^{th}$ pair in the $(y + 1)^{th}$ group. Hence, (x, y) is the $(y^2 + 2x + 1)^{th}$ pair in the ordering, and (y, x) is the $(y^2 + 2x + 2)^{th}$ pair. On the other hand, if $x = y$, (x, y) is the $((x + 1)^2)^{th}$ pair. This justifies the following definition, in which $\sigma^2(x, y)$ denotes the place of the pair (x, y) in the above enumeration, with $(0, 0)$ considered to be in the 0th place.

$$\sigma^2(x, y) = (sg(x \dot{-} y))\cdot(x^2 + 2y + 1) + (\overline{sg}(x \dot{-} y))\cdot(y^2 + 2x)$$

Clearly σ^2 is primitive recursive.

Let us define inverse functions σ_1^2 and σ_2^2 such that $\sigma_1^2(\sigma^2(x, y)) = x$, $\sigma_2^2(\sigma^2(x, y)) = y$, and $\sigma^2(\sigma_1^2(z), \sigma_2^2(z)) = z$. Thus, $\sigma_1^2(z)$ and $\sigma_2^2(z)$ are the first and second components, respectively, of the zth ordered pair in the given enumeration. Note first that $\sigma_1^2(0) = 0$, $\sigma_2^2(0) = 0$,

$$\sigma_1^2(n+1) = \begin{cases} \sigma_2^2(n) & \text{if } \sigma_1^2(n) < \sigma_2^2(n) \\ \sigma_2^2(n) + 1 & \text{if } \sigma_1^2(n) > \sigma_2^2(n) \\ 0 & \text{if } \sigma_1^2(n) = \sigma_2^2(n) \end{cases}$$

and

$$\sigma_2^2(n+1) = \begin{cases} \sigma_1^2(n) & \text{if } \sigma_1^2(n) \neq \sigma_2^2(n) \\ \sigma_1^2(n) + 1 & \text{if } \sigma_1^2(n) = \sigma_2^2(n) \end{cases}$$

Hence,

$$\begin{aligned} \sigma_1^2(n+1) &= \sigma_2^2(n)\cdot(\mathrm{sg}(\sigma_2^2(n) \dot{-} \sigma_1^2(n))) + (\sigma_2^2(n) + 1)\cdot(\mathrm{sg}(\sigma_1^2(n) \dot{-} \sigma_2^2(n))) \\ &= \varphi(\sigma_1^2(n), \sigma_2^2(n)) \end{aligned}$$

$$\begin{aligned} \sigma_2^2(n+1) &= \mathrm{sg}(|\sigma_1^2(n) - \sigma_2^2(n)|)\cdot\sigma_1^2(n) + \overline{\mathrm{sg}}(|\sigma_1^2(n) \dot{-} \sigma_2^2(n)|)\cdot(\sigma_1^2(n) + 1) \\ &= \psi(\sigma_1^2(n), \sigma_2^2(n) \end{aligned}$$

where φ and ψ are primitive recursive functions. Thus, σ_1^2 and σ_2^2 are defined recursively at the same time. We can show that σ_1^2 and σ_2^2 are primitive recursive in the following devious way. Let $\tau(u) = 2^{\sigma_1^2(u)}3^{\sigma_2^2(u)}$. Now, τ is primitive recursive, since $\tau(0) = 2^{\sigma_1^2(0)}3^{\sigma_2^2(0)} = 2^0\cdot 3^0 = 1$, and $\tau(n+1) = 2^{\sigma_1^2(n+1)}\cdot 3^{\sigma_2^2(n+1)} = 2^{\varphi(\sigma_1^2(n),\sigma_2^2(n))}3^{\psi(\sigma_1^2(n),\sigma_2^2(n))} = 2^{\varphi((\tau(n))_0,(\tau(n))_1)}3^{\psi((\tau(n))_0,(\tau(n))_1)}$. Remembering that the function $(x)_i$ is primitive recursive (cf. Example 2, page 126), we conclude by Recursion Rule (V) that τ is primitive recursive. But $\sigma_1^2(x) = (\tau(x))_0$ and $\sigma_2^2(x) = (\tau(x))_1$; by substitution, σ_1^2 and σ_2^2 are primitive recursive.

One-one primitive recursive correspondences between all n-tuples of natural numbers and all natural numbers can be defined step by step, using induction on n. For $n = 2$, it has already been established. Assume that, for $n = k$, we have primitive recursive functions $\sigma^k(x_1, \ldots, x_k)$, $\sigma_1^k(x), \ldots, \sigma_k^k(x)$ such that $\sigma_i^k(\sigma^k(x_1, \ldots, x_k)) = x_i$ for $1 \leqslant i \leqslant k$, and $\sigma^k(\sigma_1^k(x), \ldots, \sigma_k^k(x)) = x$. Now, for $n = k + 1$, define $\sigma^{k+1}(x_1, \ldots, x_k, x_{k+1}) = \sigma^2(\sigma^k(x_1, \ldots, x_k), x_{k+1})$, $\sigma_i^{k+1}(x) = \sigma_i^k(\sigma_1^2(x))$ for $1 \leqslant i \leqslant k$, and $\sigma_{k+1}^{k+1}(x) = \sigma_2^2(x)$. Then $\sigma^{k+1}, \sigma_1^{k+1}, \ldots, \sigma_{k+1}^{k+1}$ are all primitive recursive, and we leave it as an exercise to verify that $\sigma_i^{k+1}(\sigma^{k+1}(x_1, \ldots, x_{k+1})) = x_i$, for $1 \leqslant i \leqslant k+1$, and $\sigma^{k+1}(\sigma_1^{k+1}(x), \ldots, \sigma_{k+1}^{k+1}(x)) = x$.

It is often convenient to define functions by a recursion in which the value of $f(x_1, \ldots, x_n, y+1)$ depends not only upon $f(x_1, \ldots, x_n, y)$ but also upon several or all values of $f(x_1, \ldots, x_n, u)$ with $u \leqslant y$. This type of recursion is called a course-of-values recursion. Let $f\#(x_1, \ldots, x_n, y) = \prod_{u<y} p_u^{f(x_1,\ldots,x_n,u)}$. Note that f can be obtained from f# as follows: $f(x_1, \ldots, x_n, y) = (f\#(x_1, \ldots, x_n, y+1))_y$.

PROPOSITION 3.19. *If* $h(x_1, \ldots, x_n, y, z)$ *is primitive recursive (or recursive), and* $f(x_1, \ldots, x_n, y) = h(x_1, \ldots, x_n, y, f\#(x_1, \ldots, x_n, y))$, *then* f *is primitive recursive (or recursive).*

PROOF

$$f\#(x_1, \ldots, x_n, 0) = 1$$

$$f\#(x_1, \ldots, x_n, y + 1) = f\#(x_1, \ldots, x_n, y) \cdot p_y^{f(x_1, x_2, \ldots, x_n, y)}$$

$$= f\#(x_1, \ldots, x_n, y) \cdot (p_y)^{h(x_1, \ldots, x_n, y, f\#(x_1, \ldots, x_n, y))}$$

Thus, by the Recursion Rule (V), $f\#$ is primitive recursive (or recursive); but $f(x_1, \ldots, x_n, y) = (f\#(x_1, \ldots, x_n, y + 1))_y$.

Example. The Fibonacci sequence is defined as follows: $f(0) = 1$, $f(1) = 2$, $f(k + 2) = f(k) + f(k + 1)$ for $k \geqslant 0$. Then f is primitive recursive, since

$$f(k) = \overline{sg}(k) + 2 \cdot \overline{sg}(|k - 1|) + ((f\#(k))_{k \dot{-} 1} + (f\#(k))_{k \dot{-} 2}) \cdot sg(k \dot{-} 1),$$

the function

$$h(y, z) = \overline{sg}(y) + 2 \cdot \overline{sg}(|y - 1|) + ((z)_{y \dot{-} 1} + (z)_{y \dot{-} 2}) \cdot sg(y \dot{-} 1)$$

is primitive recursive, and

$$f(k) = h(k, f\#(k))$$

EXERCISE. Let $g(0) = 2$, $g(1) = 4$, and $g(k + 2) = 3g(k + 1) \dot{-} (2g(k) + 1)$. Show that g is primitive recursive.

COROLLARY 3.20. *If* $H(x_1, \ldots, x_n, y, z)$ *is a primitive recursive (or recursive) relation, and* $R(x_1, \ldots, x_n, y)$ *holds if and only if* $H(x_1, \ldots, x_n, y, (C_R)\#(x_1, \ldots, x_n, y))$, *where* C_R *is the characteristic function of* R, *then* R *is primitive recursive (or recursive).*

PROOF. $C_R(x_1, \ldots, x_n, y) = C_H(x_1, \ldots, x_n, y, (C_R)\#(x_1, \ldots, x_n, y))$, where the characteristic function C_H of H is primitive recursive (or recursive). Hence, by Proposition 3.19, C_R is primitive recursive (or recursive), and, therefore, so is the relation R.

Proposition 3.19 and Corollary 3.20 will be drawn upon heavily in the sequel. They are applicable whenever the value of a function or relation for y is defined in terms of values for arguments less than y. Notice in this connection that $R(x_1, \ldots, x_n, u)$ is equivalent to $C_R(x_1, \ldots, x_n, u) = 0$, which, in turn, for $u < y$, is equivalent to $((C_R)\#(x_1, \ldots, x_n, y))_u = 0$.

EXERCISES

1. Prove that the set of general recursive functions is denumerable.
2. If $f_1, f_2, \ldots$ is an enumeration of all primitive recursive functions

(or all recursive functions) of one variable, prove that the function $f_x(y)$ is not primitive recursive (or recursive).

PROPOSITION 3.21 (Gödel's β-Function). *Let* $\beta(x_1, x_2, x_3) = \mathrm{rm}(1 + (x_3 + 1)\cdot x_2, x_1)$. *Then* β *is primitive recursive, by Proposition* 3.15(n). *Also,* $\beta(x_1, x_2, x_3)$ *is strongly representable in* S *by the* wf $Bt(x_1, x_2, x_3, x_4)$:

$$(Ew)(x_1 = (1 + (x_3 + 1)\cdot x_2)\cdot w + x_4 \wedge x_4 < 1 + (x_3 + 1)\cdot x_2)$$

PROOF. By Proposition 3.11, $\vdash (E_1 x_4) Bt(x_1, x_2, x_3, x_4)$. Assume $\beta(k_1, k_2, k_3) = k_4$. Then $k_1 = (1 + (k_3 + 1)\cdot k_2)\cdot k + k_4$ for some k, and $k_4 < 1 + (k_3 + 1)\cdot k_2$. So, $\vdash \overline{k_1} = (\overline{1} + (\overline{k_3} + \overline{1})\cdot \overline{k_2})\cdot \overline{k} + \overline{k_4}$, by Proposition 3.6(a); and $\vdash \overline{k_4} < \overline{1} + (\overline{k_3} + \overline{1})\cdot \overline{k_2}$ by the expressibility of < and Proposition 3.6(a). Hence, $\vdash \overline{k_1} = (\overline{1} + (\overline{k_3} + \overline{1})\cdot \overline{k_2})\cdot \overline{k} + \overline{k_4} \wedge \overline{k_4} < \overline{1} + (\overline{k_3} + \overline{1})\overline{k_2}$ from which, by Rule E4, $\vdash Bt(\overline{k_1}, \overline{k_2}, \overline{k_3}, \overline{k_4})$. Thus, Bt strongly represents β in S.

PROPOSITION 3.22. *For any sequence of natural numbers* $k_0, k_1, \ldots, k_n$, *there exist natural numbers* b, c *such that* $\beta(b, c, i) = k_i$ *for* $0 \leqslant i \leqslant n$.

PROOF. Let $j = \max(n, k_0, k_1, \ldots, k_n)$ and let $c = j!$. Consider the numbers $u_i = 1 + (i + 1)c$ for $0 \leqslant i \leqslant n$; they have no factors in common other than one. For, if p were a prime dividing both $1 + (i + 1)c$ and $1 + (m + 1)c$ with $0 \leqslant i < m \leqslant n$, then p would divide their difference $(m - i)c$; now, p does not divide c, since, in that case, p would divide both $(i + 1)c$ and $1 + (i + 1)c$, and so would divide 1, which is impossible. Hence, p also does not divide $(m - i)$; for $m - i \leqslant n \leqslant j$, and so, $m - i$ divides $j! = c$; if p divided $m - i$, then p would divide c. Hence, p does not divide $(m - i)c$, which yields a contradiction. Thus, the numbers u_i, $0 \leqslant i \leqslant n$, are relatively prime in pairs. Also, for $0 \leqslant i \leqslant n$, $k_i \leqslant j \leqslant j! = c < 1 + (i + 1)c = u_i$, i.e., $k_i < u_i$. Now, by the Chinese Remainder Theorem (cf. Dickson [1929], or Exercise 1, page 135), there is a number $b < u_0 u_1 \ldots u_n$ such that $\mathrm{rm}(u_i, b) = k_i$ for $0 \leqslant i \leqslant n$. But $\beta(b, c, i) = \mathrm{rm}(1 + (i + 1)c, b) = \mathrm{rm}(u_i, b) = k_i$.

Propositions 3.21 and 3.22 enable us to express within S assertions about finite sequences of natural numbers and this ability is crucial in part of the proof of the following fundamental theorem.

PROPOSITION 3.23. *Every recursive function is representable in* S.

PROOF. The initial functions Z, N, U_i^n are representable in S, by Examples (a)–(c) on page 118. The Substitution Rule (IV) does not lead out of the class of representable functions, by Example (d) on page 118.

The Recursion Rule (V): assume that $g(x_1, \ldots, x_n)$ and $h(x_1, \ldots, x_n, y, z)$ are representable in S by wfs $\mathscr{A}(x_1, \ldots, x_{n+1})$ and $\mathscr{B}(x_1, \ldots, x_{n+3})$, respectively, and let

$$\text{(I)}\begin{cases} f(x_1, \ldots, x_n, 0) = g(x_1, \ldots, x_n) \\ f(x_1, \ldots, x_n, y + 1) = h(x_1, \ldots, x_n, y, f(x_1, \ldots, x_n, y)) \end{cases}$$

Now, $f(x_1, \ldots, x_n, y) = z$ if and only if there is a finite sequence of numbers $b_0, \ldots, b_y$ such that $b_0 = g(x_1, \ldots, x_n)$, $b_{w+1} = h(x_1, \ldots, x_n, w, b_w)$ for $w + 1 \leqslant y$, and $b_y = z$; but, by Proposition 3.22, reference to finite sequences can be paraphrased in terms of the function β, and, by Proposition 3.21, β is representable in S.

We shall show that $f(x_1, \ldots, x_n, x_{n+1})$ is representable in S by the wf $\mathscr{C}(x_1, \ldots, x_{n+2})$: $(Eu)(Ev)[((Ew)(Bt(u, v, 0, w) \wedge \mathscr{A}(x_1, \ldots, x_n, w))) \wedge Bt(u, v, x_{n+1}, x_{n+2}) \wedge (w)(w < x_{n+1} \supset (Ey)(Ez)(Bt(u, v, w, y) \wedge Bt(u, v, w', z) \wedge \mathscr{B}(x_1, \ldots, x_n, w, y, z))]$.

(i) First, assume that $f(k_1, \ldots, k_n, p) = m$. We wish to show that $\vdash \mathscr{C}(\overline{k_1}, \ldots, \overline{k_n}, \overline{p}, \overline{m})$. If $p = 0$, then $m = g(k_1, \ldots, k_n)$. Consider the sequence consisting of m alone. By Proposition 3.22, there exist b, c such that $\beta(b, c, 0) = m$. Hence, $\vdash Bt(\overline{b}, \overline{c}, 0, \overline{m})$, by Proposition 3.21. Also, $\vdash \mathscr{A}(\overline{k_1}, \ldots, \overline{k_n}, \overline{m})$ since $m = g(k_1, \ldots, k_n)$. Hence, by Rule E4, (✠) $\vdash (Ew)(Bt(\overline{b}, \overline{c}, 0, w) \wedge \mathscr{A}(\overline{k_1}, \ldots, \overline{k_n}, w)$. We previously obtained (✠✠) $\vdash Bt(\overline{b}, \overline{c}, 0, \overline{m})$. By a tautology, the last conjunction (✠✠✠) of $\mathscr{C}(\overline{k_1}, \ldots, \overline{k_n}, 0, m)$ is provable, since $\vdash \sim(w < 0)$. Applying Rule E4 to the conjunction of (✠), (✠✠), (✠✠✠), we obtain $\vdash \mathscr{C}(\overline{k_1}, \ldots, \overline{k_n}, 0, \overline{m})$. Now, for $p > 0$, $f(k_1, \ldots, k_n, p)$ is calculated from the equations (I) in $p + 1$ steps. Let $r_i = f(k_1, \ldots, k_n, i)$. For the sequence of numbers $r_0, r_1, \ldots, r_p$, there are, by Proposition 3.22, numbers b, c such that $\beta(b, c, i) = r_i$ for $0 \leqslant i \leqslant p$. Hence, by Proposition 3.21, $\vdash Bt(\overline{b}, \overline{c}, \overline{i}, \overline{r_i})$. In particular, $\beta(b, c, 0) = r_0 = f(k_1, \ldots, k_n, 0) = g(k_1, \ldots, k_n)$. Therefore, $\vdash Bt(\overline{b}, \overline{c}, 0, \overline{r_0}) \wedge \mathscr{A}(\overline{k_1}, \ldots, \overline{k_n}, \overline{r_0})$, and by Rule E4, (1) $\vdash (Ew)(Bt(\overline{b}, \overline{c}, 0, w) \wedge \mathscr{A}(\overline{k_1}, \ldots, \overline{k_n}, w))$. Since $r_p = f(k_1, \ldots, k_n, p) = m$, $\beta(b, c, p) = m$; hence, (2) $\vdash Bt(\overline{b}, \overline{c}, \overline{p}, \overline{m})$. For $0 \leqslant i \leqslant p - 1$, $\beta(b, c, i) = \overline{r_i} = f(k_1, \ldots, k_n, i)$; $\beta(b, c, i + 1) = r_{i+1} = f(k_1, \ldots, k_n, i + 1) = h(k_1, \ldots, k_n, i, f(k_1, \ldots, k_n, i)) = h(k_1, \ldots, k_n, i, r_i)$. Hence, $\vdash Bt(\overline{b}, \overline{c}, \overline{i}, \overline{r_i}) \wedge Bt(\overline{b}, \overline{c}, \overline{i}', \overline{r_{i+1}}) \wedge \mathscr{B}(\overline{k_1}, \ldots, \overline{k_n}, \overline{i}, \overline{r_i}, \overline{r_{i+1}})$. By Rule E4, $\vdash (Ey)(Ez)(Bt(\overline{b}, \overline{c}, \overline{i}, y) \wedge Bt(\overline{b}, \overline{c}, \overline{i}', z) \wedge \mathscr{B}(\overline{k_1}, \ldots, \overline{k_n}, \overline{i}, y, z))$. Hence, by Proposition 3.8(b′), we have (3) $\vdash (w)(w < \overline{p} \supset (Ey)(Ez)(Bt(\overline{b}, \overline{c}, \overline{i}, y) \wedge Bt(\overline{b}, \overline{c}, \overline{i}', z) \wedge \mathscr{B}(\overline{k_1}, \ldots, \overline{k_n}, \overline{i}, y, z)))$. Then, applying Rule E4 twice to the conjunction of (1), (2), and (3), we obtain $\vdash \mathscr{C}(\overline{k_1}, \ldots, \overline{k_n}, \overline{p}, \overline{m})$. Thus, we have verified clause (1) of the definition of representability in S (cf. page 118).

(ii) We must show that $\vdash (E_1 x_{n+2})\mathscr{C}(\overline{k_1}, \ldots, \overline{k_n}, \overline{p}, x_{n+2})$. The proof is by induction on p in the metalanguage. Notice that, by what we have proved above, it suffices to prove only uniqueness. The case for $p = 0$ is easy and is left as an exercise. Now, assume $\vdash (E_1 x_{n+2})\mathscr{C}(\overline{k_1}, \ldots, \overline{k_n}, \overline{p}, x_{n+2})$. Let $\alpha = g(k_1, \ldots, k_n)$, $\beta = f(k_1, \ldots, k_n, p)$, and $\gamma = f(k_1, \ldots, k_n, p + 1) = h(k_1, \ldots, k_n, p, \beta)$. Then,

(1) $\vdash \mathscr{B}(\overline{k_1}, \ldots, \overline{k_n}, \overline{p}, \bar{\beta}, \bar{\gamma})$

(2) $\vdash \mathscr{A}(\overline{k_1}, \ldots, \overline{k_n}, \bar{\alpha})$

(3) $\vdash \mathscr{C}(\overline{k_1}, \ldots, \overline{k_n}, \overline{p}, \bar{\beta})$

(4) $\vdash \mathscr{C}(\overline{k_1}, \ldots, \overline{k_n}, \overline{p + 1}, \bar{\gamma})$

(5) $\vdash (E_1 x_{n+2})\mathscr{C}(\overline{k_1}, \ldots, \overline{k_n}, \overline{p}, x_{n+2})$.

Assume

(6) $\mathscr{C}(\overline{k_1}, \ldots, \overline{k_n}, \overline{p + 1}, x_{n+2})$

We must prove $x_{n+2} = \bar{\gamma}$. Now from (6) by Rule C,

(a) $(Ew)(Bt(b, c, 0, w) \wedge \mathscr{A}(\overline{k_1}, \ldots, \overline{k_n}, w))$

(b) $Bt(b, c, \overline{p + 1}, x_{n+2})$

(c) $(w)(w < \overline{p + 1} \supset (Ey)(Ez)(Bt(b, c, w, y) \wedge Bt(b, c, w', z) \wedge \mathscr{B}(\overline{k_1}, \ldots, \overline{k_n}, w, y, z))$

From (c),

(d) $(w)(w < \overline{p} \supset (Ey)(Ez)(Bt(b, c, w, y) \wedge Bt(b, c, w', z) \wedge \mathscr{B}(\overline{k_1}, \ldots, \overline{k_n}, w, y, z))$

From (c) by Rule C,

(e) $Bt(b, c, \overline{p}, d) \wedge Bt(b, c, \overline{p + 1}, e) \wedge \mathscr{B}(\overline{k_1}, \ldots, \overline{k_n}, \overline{p}, d, e)$

From (a), (d), (e),

(f) $\mathscr{C}(\overline{k_1}, \ldots, \overline{k_n}, \overline{p}, d)$

From (f) and (5),

(g) $d = \bar{\beta}$

From (e), (g),

(h) $\mathscr{B}(\overline{k_1}, \ldots, \overline{k_n}, \overline{p}, \bar{\beta}, e)$

By the theorem for $\mathscr{B}$ and (1),

(i) $\bar{\gamma} = e$

From (e), (i),

(j) $Bt(b, c, \overline{p + 1}, \bar{\gamma})$

From (b), (j), and Proposition 3.21,

(k) $x_{n+2} = \bar{\gamma}$.

This completes the induction.

The μ-operator (VI). Let us assume that, for any $x_1, \ldots, x_n$, there is some y such that $g(x_1, \ldots, x_n, y) = 0$, and let us assume g is representable in S by a wf $\mathscr{D}(x_1, \ldots, x_{n+2})$. Let $f(x_1, \ldots, x_n) = \mu y(g(x_1, \ldots, x_n, y) = 0)$. Then f is representable in S by the wf $\mathscr{E}(x_1, \ldots, x_{n+1})$:

$$\mathscr{D}(x_1, \ldots, x_{n+1}, 0) \wedge (y)(y < x_{n+1} \supset \sim \mathscr{D}(x_1, \ldots, x_n, y, 0))$$

First, assume $f(k_1, \ldots, k_n) = m$. Then $g(k_1, \ldots, k_n, m) = 0$ and, for $k < m$, $g(k_1, \ldots, k_n, k) \neq 0$. So, $\vdash \mathscr{D}(\overline{k_1}, \ldots, \overline{k_n}, \overline{m}, 0)$ and, for $k < m$, $\vdash \sim \mathscr{D}(\overline{k_1}, \ldots, \overline{k_n}, \overline{k}, 0)$. By Proposition 3.8(b′), $\vdash (y)(y < \overline{m} \supset \sim \mathscr{D}(\overline{k_1}, \ldots, \overline{k_n}, y, 0))$. Hence, $\vdash \mathscr{E}(\overline{k_1}, \ldots, \overline{k_n}, \overline{m})$. We must also show: $\vdash (E_1 x_{n+1})\mathscr{E}(\overline{k_1}, \ldots, \overline{k_n}, x_{n+1})$. It suffices, by what we have already shown, to prove the uniqueness. If $\mathscr{D}(\overline{k_1}, \ldots, \overline{k_n}, u, 0) \wedge (y)(y < u \supset \sim \mathscr{D}(\overline{k_1}, \ldots, \overline{k_n}, y, 0))$, and if $\mathscr{D}(\overline{k_1}, \ldots, \overline{k_n}, v, 0) \wedge (y)(y < v \supset \sim \mathscr{D}(\overline{k_1}, \ldots, \overline{k_n}, y, 0))$, then it follows that if $v < u$ we obtain a contradiction $\mathscr{D}(\overline{k_1}, \ldots, \overline{k_n}, v, 0) \wedge \sim \mathscr{D}(\overline{k_1}, \ldots, \overline{k_n}, v, 0)$, and if $u < v$, then we obtain a contradiction $\mathscr{D}(\overline{k_1}, \ldots, \overline{k_n}, u, 0) \wedge \sim \mathscr{D}(\overline{k_1}, \ldots, \overline{k_n}, u, 0)$. Hence, since $\vdash (u = v) \vee (u < v) \vee (v < u)$, we conclude $u = v$. This shows the uniqueness.

Thus, we have shown that all recursive functions are representable in S.

COROLLARY 3.24. *Every recursive relation is expressible in* S.

PROOF. Let $R(x_1, \ldots, x_n)$ be a recursive predicate.† Then its characteristic function C_R is recursive. By Proposition 3.23, C_R is representable in S and, therefore, by Proposition 3.12, R is expressible in S.

† "Predicate" is often used as a synonym for "relation."

EXERCISES

A1. (a) Show that, if a and b are relatively prime natural numbers, then there is a natural number c such that $ac \equiv 1 \pmod{b}$. (In general, $x \equiv y \pmod{z}$ means that x and y leave the same remainder upon division by z, or, equivalently, that $x - y$ is divisible by z. This exercise amounts to showing that there exist integers u and v such that $1 = au + bv$.)

(b) Prove the Chinese Remainder Theorem: If $x_1, \ldots, x_k$ are relatively prime in pairs, and $y_1, \ldots, y_k$ are any natural numbers, there is a natural number z such that $z \equiv y_1 \pmod{x_1}, \ldots, z \equiv y_k \pmod{x_k}$. Any two such z's differ by a multiple of $x_1 \ldots x_k$. (Hint: let $x = x_1 \ldots x_k$ and let $x = w_1x_1 = w_2x_2 = \ldots = w_kx_k$. Then, for $1 \leqslant i \leqslant k$, w_i is relatively prime to x_i, and so, by part (a), there is some z_i such that $w_iz_i \equiv 1 \pmod{x_i}$. Now, let $z = w_1z_1y_1 + w_2z_2y_2 + \ldots + w_kz_ky_k$. Then $z \equiv w_iz_iy_i \equiv y_i \pmod{x_i}$. In addition, the difference between any two such solutions is divisible by $x_1, \ldots, x_k$, and hence by $x_1x_2 \ldots x_k$.)

2. (a) Call a predicate $R(x_1, \ldots, x_n)$ *arithmetical* if it is the interpretation of some wf $\mathscr{A}(x_1, \ldots, x_n)$ of S with respect to the standard model. Show that every recursive predicate is arithmetical. (Hint: use Corollary 3.24.)

(b) If $f(x_1, \ldots, x_n)$ is a recursive function, show that its representing predicate $f(x_1, \ldots, x_n) = y$ is recursive. (Hint: the characteristic function of the representing predicate is $sg(|f(x_1, \ldots, x_n) - y|)$.

(c) If $f(x_1, \ldots, x_n)$ is recursive, then its representing predicate is arithmetical.

3. Prove that representability implies strong representability, and hence that every recursive function is strongly representable in S (V. H. Dyson).

§ 4. Arithmetization. Gödel Numbers.

For an arbitrary first-order theory K, we correlate with each symbol *u* of K a positive integer $g(u)$, called the Gödel number of *u*, in the following way.

$$g(\,(\,) = 3;\ g(\,)\,) = 5;\ g(\,,\,) = 7;\ g(\sim) = 9;\ g(\supset) = 11$$
$$g(x_k) = 5 + 8k \quad \text{for } k = 1, 2, \ldots$$
$$g(a_k) = 7 + 8k \quad \text{for } k = 1, 2, \ldots$$
$$g(f_k^n) = 9 + 8(2^n3^k) \quad \text{for } k, n \geqslant 1$$
$$g(A_k^n) = 11 + 8(2^n3^k) \quad \text{for } k, n \geqslant 1$$

Thus, different symbols have different Gödel numbers, and every Gödel number is an odd positive integer.†

† The same numbering was used on page 64, Lemma 2.10.

Examples. $g(x_2) = 21$, $g(a_4) = 39$, $g(f_1^2) = 105$, $g(A_2^1) = 155$.

Given an expression $u_1u_2 \ldots u_r$, we define its Gödel number to be $g(u_1u_2 \ldots u_r) = 2^{g(u_1)}3^{g(u_2)} \ldots p_r^{g(u_r)}$, where p_i is the ith prime and $p_0 = 2$. For example, $g(A_1^2(x_1, x_2)) = 2^{g(A_1^2)} \cdot 3^{g(\,(\,)} \cdot 5^{g(x_1)} \cdot 7^{g(\,,\,)} \cdot 11^{g(x_2)} \cdot 13^{g(\,)\,)} = 2^{107}3^3 5^{13}7^7 11^{21}13^5$. Observe that different expressions have different Gödel numbers, by the uniqueness of the factorization of integers into primes. In addition, expressions and symbols have different Gödel numbers, since the former have even Gödel numbers and the latter odd Gödel numbers. (A single symbol, considered as an expression, has a different number from its number as a symbol. This situation should cause no confusion.)

If we have an arbitrary finite sequence of expressions $e_1, e_2, \ldots, e_r$, we can assign a Gödel number to this sequence by setting $g(e_1, e_2, \ldots, e_r) = 2^{g(e_1)} \cdot 3^{g(e_2)} \ldots p_r^{g(e_r)}$. Different sequences of expressions have different Gödel numbers. Since a Gödel number of a sequence of expressions is even and the exponent of 2 in its prime factorization is also even, it differs from Gödel numbers of symbols and expressions.

Thus, g is a one-one function from the set of symbols of K, expressions of K, and finite sequences of expressions of K, into the set of positive integers. The range of g is not the whole set of positive integers; for example, 9 is not a Gödel number.

EXERCISES

1. Determine the objects which have the following Gödel numbers: 1944, 47.
2. Show that if n is odd, 4n is not a Gödel number.
3. Find the Gödel numbers of the expressions (a) $f_1^1(a_1)$; (b) $(\sim(A_1^3(a_1, x_3, x_5))) \supset (A_1^1(x_2))$.

This correlation of numbers with symbols, expressions, and sequences of expressions was originally devised by Gödel [1931] in order to *arithmetize* metamathematics,† i.e., to replace assertions about a formal system by equivalent number-theoretic statements, and then to express these statements within the formal system. This idea turned out to be the key to a great number of significant problems in mathematical logic.

The assignment of Gödel numbers given here is in no way unique.

† An *arithmetization* of a first-order theory K is a one-one function g from the set of symbols of K, expressions of K, and finite sequences of expressions of K into the set of positive integers. The following conditions are to be satisfied by the function g: (i) g is effectively computable; (ii) there is an effective procedure which determines whether any given positive integer m is in the range of g, and, if m is in the range of g, the procedure finds the object x such that $g(x) = m$.

Other methods may be found in Kleene [1952, Chap. X] and in Smullyan [1961, Chap. I, § 6].

PROPOSITION 3.25. *Let* K *be a first-order theory about which we make the assumption that the following relations are primitive recursive* (*or recursive*): (a) IC(x): x *is the Gödel number of an individual constant of* K; (b) FL(x): x *is the Gödel number of a function letter of* K; (c) PL(x): x *is the Gödel number of a predicate letter of* K. *Then the following relations and functions are primitive recursive* (*or recursive*). (In (1)–(4), we do not need the assumptions (a)–(c).)

(1) EVbl(x): x is the Gödel number of an expression consisting of a variable. $(Ez)_{z<x}(1 \leqslant z \wedge x = 2^{5+8z})$. By Proposition 3.17, this is primitive recursive.

(2) $Arg_T(x) = (qt(8, x \dot{-} 9))_0$: If x is the Gödel number of a function letter f_j^n, then $Arg_T(x) = n$.

$Arg_P(x) = (qt(8, x \dot{-} 11))_0$: If x is the Gödel number of a predicate letter A_j^n, then $Arg_P(x) = n$.

(3) MP(x, y, z): The expression with Gödel number z is a direct consequence of the expressions with Gödel numbers x and y by modus ponens. $y = 2^3 * x * 2^{11} * z * 2^5$.†

(4) Gen(x, y): The expression with Gödel number y comes from the expression with Gödel number x by the Generalization Rule.

$$(Ev)_{v<y}(EVbl(v) \wedge y = 2^3 * 2^3 * v * 2^5 * x * 2^5).$$

(5) EIC(x): x is the Gödel number of an expression consisting of an individual constant. $(Ey)_{y<x}(IC(y) \wedge x = 2^y)$. (Proposition 3.17.)

EFL(x): x is the Gödel number of an expression consisting of a function letter. $(Ey)_{y<x}(FL(y) \wedge x = 2^y)$. (Proposition 3.17.)

EPL(x): x is the Gödel number of an expression consisting of a predicate letter. $(Ey)_{y<x}(PL(y) \wedge x = 2^y)$. (Proposition 3.17.)

(6) Trm(x): x is the Gödel number of a term of K. This holds when and only when either x is the Gödel number of an expression consisting of a variable or an individual constant or there is a function letter f_k^n and terms $t_1, \ldots, t_n$ such that x is the Gödel number of $f_k^n(t_1, \ldots, t_n)$. The latter holds if and only if there is a sequence of expressions f_k^n $f_k^n($ $f_k^n(t_1,$ $f_k^n(t_1, t_2,$ $\ldots,$ $f_k^n(t_1, t_2, \ldots, t_{n-1},$ $f_k^n(t_1, \ldots, t_{n-1}, t_n,$ $f_k^n(t_1, \ldots, t_{n-1}, t_n)$. This sequence of (n + 3) expressions can be represented by its Gödel number y. Clearly $y < p_{n+2}{}^x < p_x{}^x$. Note also that $n = Arg_T((x)_0)$, since $(x)_0$ is the Gödel number of f_k^n. Hence, Trm(x) is equivalent to the following relation.

† Remember the definition of the juxtaposition function * on p. 126, Example (4).

$\mathrm{EVbl(x)} \vee \mathrm{EIC(x)} \vee (\mathrm{Ey})_{\mathrm{y} < (\mathrm{p_x})^{\mathrm{x}}}[\mathrm{x} = (\mathrm{y})_{\mathrm{lh(y)} \dot{-} 1} \wedge \mathrm{FL}((\mathrm{y})_0) \wedge \mathrm{lh(y)} = \mathrm{Arg_T}((\mathrm{x})_0) + 3 \wedge (\mathrm{y})_1 = 3 \wedge (\mathrm{u})_{\mathrm{u} < \mathrm{lh(y)}}(\mathrm{u} > 1 \wedge \mathrm{u} \leqslant \mathrm{Arg_T}((\mathrm{x})_0) \supset (\mathrm{Ev})_{\mathrm{v} < \mathrm{x}}((\mathrm{y})_\mathrm{u} = (\mathrm{y})_{\mathrm{u} \dot{-} 1} * \mathrm{v} * 2^7 \wedge \mathrm{Trm(v)})) \wedge (\mathrm{Ev})_{\mathrm{v} < \mathrm{y}}((\mathrm{y})_{\mathrm{lh(y)} \dot{-} 2} = (\mathrm{y})_{\mathrm{lh(y)} \dot{-} 3} * \mathrm{v} \wedge \mathrm{Trm(v)}) \wedge (\mathrm{y})_{\mathrm{lh(y)} \dot{-} 1} = (\mathrm{y})_{\mathrm{lh(y)} \dot{-} 2} * 2^5]$

Thus, Trm(x) is primitive recursive (or recursive), by Corollary 3.20, since the formula above involves Trm(v) only for $\mathrm{v} < \mathrm{x}$.†

(7) Atfml(x): x is the Gödel number of an atomic wf of K. This holds if and only if there are terms $t_1, \ldots, t_n$ and a predicate letter A_k^n such that x is the Gödel number of $A_k^n(t_1, \ldots, t_n)$. The latter holds if and only if there is a sequence of expressions A_k^n $A_k^n($ $A_k^n(t_1,$ $A_k^n(t_1, t_2,$ $\ldots,$ $A_k^n(t_1, t_2, \ldots, t_{n-1},$ $A_k^n(t_1, t_2, \ldots, t_{n-1}, t_n$ $A_k^n(t_1, \ldots, t_{n-1}, t_n)$. This sequence of (n + 3) expressions can be represented by its Gödel number y. Clearly $\mathrm{y} < \mathrm{p_x}^{\mathrm{x}}$ and $\mathrm{n} = \mathrm{Arg_P}((\mathrm{x})_0)$. Hence, Atfml(x) is equivalent to the following relation.

$(\mathrm{Ey})_{\mathrm{y} < (\mathrm{p_x})^{\mathrm{x}}}[\mathrm{x} = (\mathrm{y})_{\mathrm{lh(y)} \dot{-} 1} \wedge \mathrm{PL}((\mathrm{y})_0) \wedge \mathrm{lh(y)} = \mathrm{Arg_P}((\mathrm{x})_0) + 3 \wedge (\mathrm{y})_1 = 1 \wedge (\mathrm{u})_{\mathrm{u} < \mathrm{lh(y)}}(\mathrm{u} > 1 \wedge \mathrm{u} \leqslant \mathrm{Arg_P}((\mathrm{x})_0) \supset (\mathrm{Ev})_{\mathrm{v} < \mathrm{y}}((\mathrm{y})_\mathrm{u} = (\mathrm{y})_{\mathrm{u} \dot{-} 1} * \mathrm{v} * 2^7 \wedge \mathrm{Trm(v)})) \wedge (\mathrm{Ev})_{\mathrm{v} < \mathrm{y}}((\mathrm{y})_{\mathrm{lh(y)} \dot{-} 2} = (\mathrm{y})_{\mathrm{lh(y)} \dot{-} 3} * \mathrm{v} \wedge \mathrm{Trm(v)}) \wedge (\mathrm{y})_{\mathrm{lh(y)} \dot{-} 1} = (\mathrm{y})_{\mathrm{lh(y)} \dot{-} 2} * 2^5]$

Hence, by Proposition 3.17, Atfml(x) is primitive recursive (or recursive).

(8) Fml(y): y is the Gödel number of a wf of K.

$\mathrm{Atfml(y)} \vee (\mathrm{Ez})_{\mathrm{z} < \mathrm{y}}[(\mathrm{Fml(z)} \wedge \mathrm{y} = 2^3 * 2^9 * \mathrm{z} * 2^5) \vee (\mathrm{Fml}((\mathrm{z})_0) \wedge \mathrm{Fml}((\mathrm{z})_1) \wedge \mathrm{y} = 2^3 * (\mathrm{z})_0 * 2^{11} * (\mathrm{z})_1 * 2^5) \vee (\mathrm{Fml}((\mathrm{z})_0) \wedge \mathrm{EVbl}((\mathrm{z})_1) \wedge \mathrm{y} = 2^3 * 2^3 * (\mathrm{z})_1 * 2^5 * (\mathrm{z})_0 * 2^5)]$

Corollary 3.20 (Course-of-Values Recursion) is applicable now. (Exercise.)

(9) (a) $\mathrm{Subst}_1(\gamma, \mathrm{u}, \mathrm{v})$: $(\gamma)_0$ is the Gödel number of the result of substituting in the expression with Gödel number $(\gamma)_1$ the term with Gödel number u for all free occurrences of the variable with Gödel number v.

$$\begin{aligned}
&\mathrm{Trm(u)} \wedge \mathrm{EVbl(v)} \wedge (((\gamma)_1 = \mathrm{v} \wedge (\gamma)_0 = \mathrm{u}) \vee \\
&((\mathrm{Ew})_{\mathrm{w} < (\gamma)_1}((\gamma)_1 = 2^{\mathrm{w}} \wedge (\gamma)_1 \neq \mathrm{v} \wedge (\gamma)_0 = (\gamma)_1)) \vee \\
&((\mathrm{Ew})_{\mathrm{w} < (\gamma)_1}(1 < \mathrm{w} \wedge (\gamma)_1 = 2^3 * 2^3 * \mathrm{v} * 2^5 * \mathrm{w} \wedge (\gamma)_1 = (\gamma)_0)) \vee \\
&((\sim (\mathrm{Ew})_{\mathrm{w} < (\gamma)_1}(1 < \mathrm{w} \wedge (\gamma)_1 = 2^3 * 2^3 * \mathrm{v} * 2^5 * \mathrm{w})) \wedge \\
&(\mathrm{E}\alpha)_{\alpha < (\gamma)_0}(\mathrm{E}\beta)_{\beta < (\gamma)_0}(\mathrm{Ez})_{\mathrm{z} < (\gamma)_1}(1 < \mathrm{z} \wedge (\gamma)_1 = ((\gamma)_1)_0 * \mathrm{z} \wedge \\
&(\gamma)_0 = \alpha * \beta \wedge \mathrm{Subst}_1(2^{\alpha} 3^{((\gamma)_1)_0}, \mathrm{u}, \mathrm{v}) \wedge \mathrm{Subst}_1(2^{\beta} 3^{\mathrm{z}}, \mathrm{u}, \mathrm{v}))))
\end{aligned}$$

† If we replace both occurrences of Trm(v) in the formula above by $(\mathrm{z})_\mathrm{v} = 0$, then the new formula defines a primitive recursive (or recursive) predicate H(x, z), and $\mathrm{Trm(x)} \equiv \mathrm{H}(\mathrm{x}, (\mathrm{C_{Trm}})\#(\mathrm{x}))$; Corollary 3.20 is therefore applicable.

By Course-of-Values Recursion (Corollary 3.20), $Subst_1$ is primitive recursive (or recursive). (Verify the applicability of Corollary 3.20.)

(b) Subst(x, y, u, v): x is the Gödel number of the result of substituting the term with Gödel number u for all free occurrences of the variable with Gödel number v in the expression with Gödel number y. This is equivalent to $Subst_1(2^x 3^y, u, v)$.

(c) Let Sub(y, u, v) be the Gödel number of the result of substituting the term with Gödel number u for all free occurrences in the expression with Gödel number y of the variable with Gödel number v. Then $Sub(y, u, v) = \mu x_{x < uy^{lh(y)}}\ Subst(x, y, u, v)$. Hence, Sub is primitive recursive (or recursive) by Proposition 3.17.

(10) (a) Fr(u, x): u is the Gödel number of a wf or a term of K which contains the variable with Gödel number x free.

$$(Fml(u) \vee Trm(u)) \wedge EVbl(x) \wedge \sim Subst(u, u, 2^{5+8u}, x)$$

(i.e., substitution in the wf with Gödel number u of a variable different from that with Gödel number x for all free occurrences of the variable with Gödel number x yields a different expression).

(b) $Fr_1(u, v, w)$: u is the Gödel number of a term which is free for the variable with Gödel number v in the wf with Gödel number w.

$$Trm(u) \wedge EVbl(v) \wedge Fml(w) \wedge [Atfml(w) \vee (Ey)_{y<w}(w = 2^3 * 3^9 * y * 2^5 \wedge Fr_1(u, v, y)) \vee (Ey_{y<w}(Ez)_{z<w}(w = 2^3 * y * 2^{11} * z * 2^5 \wedge Fr_1(u, v, y) \wedge Fr_1(u, v, z)) \vee (Ey)_{y<w}(Ez)_{z<w}(w = 2^3 * 2^3 * z * 2^5 * y * 2^5 \wedge EVbl(z) \wedge (z \neq v \supset Fr_1(u, v, y))).$$

Use Course-of-Values Recursion (Corollary 3.20).

(11) (a) $Ax_1(x)$: x is the Gödel number of an instance of Axiom Schema (1).

$$(Eu)_{u<x}(Ev)_{v<x}(Fml(u) \wedge Fml(v) \wedge x = 2^3 * u * 2^{11} * 2^3 * v * 2^{11} * u * 2^5 * 2^5)$$

(b) $Ax_2(x)$: x is the Gödel number of an instance of Axiom Schema (2).

$$(Eu)_{u<x}(Ev)_{v<x}(Ew)_{w<x}(Fml(u) \wedge Fml(v) \wedge Fml(w) \wedge x = 2^3 * 2^3 * u * 2^{11} * 2^3 * v * 2^{11} * w * 2^5 * 2^5 * 2^{11} * 2^3 * 2^3 * u * 2^{11} * v * 2^5 * 2^{11} * 2^3 * u * 2^{11} * w * 2^5 * 2^5 * 2^5)$$

(c) $Ax_3(x)$: x is the Gödel number of an instance of Axiom Schema (3).

$$(Eu)_{u<x}(Ev)_{v<x}(Fml(u) \wedge Fml(v) \wedge x = 2^3 * 2^3 * 2^3 * 2^9 * v * 2^5 * 2^{11} * 2^3 * 2^9 * u * 2^5 * 2^5 * 2^{11} * 2^3 * 2^3 * 2^3 * 2^9 * v * 2^5 * 2^{11} * u * 2^5 * 2^{11} * v * 2^5 * 2^5)$$

(d) $Ax_4(x)$: x is the Gödel number of an instance of Axiom Schema (4).

$$(Eu)_{u<x}(Ev)_{v<x}(Ew)_{w<x}(Fml(u) \wedge Trm(v) \wedge EVbl(w) \wedge Fr_1(v, w, u) \wedge x = 2^3 * 2^3 * 2^3 * w * 2^5 * u * 2^5 * 2^{11} * Sub(u, v, w) * 2^5)$$

(e) $Ax_5(x)$: x is the Gödel number of an instance of Axiom Schema (5).

$$(Eu)_{u<x}(Ev)_{v<x}(Ew)_{w<x}(Fml(u) \wedge Fml(v) \wedge EVbl(w) \wedge \sim Fr(u, w) \wedge x = 2^3 * 2^3 * 2^3 * w * 2^5 * 2^3 * u * 2^{11} * v * 2^5 * 2^5 * 2^{11} * 2^3 * u * 2^{11} * 2^3 * 2^3 * w * 2^5 * v * 2^5 * 2^5 * 2^5)$$

(f) LAx(y): y is the Gödel number of a logical axiom.

$$Ax_1(y) \vee Ax_2(y) \vee Ax_3(y) \vee Ax_4(y) \vee Ax_5(y)$$

(11′) Gd(x): x is the Gödel number of an expression of K.

$$EVbl(x) \vee EIC(x) \vee EFL(x) \vee EPL(x) \vee x = 2^3 \vee x = 2^5 \vee x = 2^7 \vee x = 2^9 \vee x = 2^{11} \vee (Eu)_{u<x}(Ev)_{v<x}(x = u * v \wedge Gd(u) \wedge Gd(v))$$

(Corollary 3.20.)

Remark. The assumptions (a)–(c) of Proposition 3.25 hold for a first-order theory K which has only a finite number of individual constants, function letters, and predicate letters, since, in that case, IC(x), FL(x), and PL(x) are primitive recursive. For example, if the individual constants of K are $a_{j_1}, a_{j_2}, \ldots, a_{j_n}$, then IC(x) if and only if $x = 7 + 8j_1 \vee x = 7 + 8j_2 \vee \ldots \vee x = 7 + 8j_n$. In particular, the assumptions (a)–(c) hold for S.

PROPOSITION 3.26. *If a first-order theory* K *not only satisfies assumptions* (a)–(c) *of Proposition* 3.25, *but also the following assumption*:

(d) *the property* PrAx(y), y *is the Gödel number of a proper axiom of* K, *is primitive recursive* (*or recursive*)

then the following relations are primitive recursive (*or recursive*).

(12) Ax(y): y is the Gödel number of an axiom of K. $LAx(y) \vee PrAx(y)$.

(13) (a) Prf(y): y is the Gödel number of a proof in K. By Course-of-Values Recursion (Corollary 3.20),

$$(Ew)_{w<y}(y = 2^w \wedge Ax(w)) \vee (Eu)_{u<y}(Ew)_{w<y}(Ev)_{v<y}(Prf(u) \wedge y = u * (p_{lh(u)})^v \wedge Gen(v, (u)_w)) \vee (Ez)_{z<y}(Ew)_{w<y}(Eu)_{u<y}(Ev)_{v<y}(Prf(u) \wedge y = u * (p_{lh(u)})^v \wedge MP((u)_z, (u)_w, v))$$

which is equivalent to Prf(y), is primitive recursive (or recursive).

(b) Pf(y, x): y is the Gödel number of a proof of the wf with Gödel number x. Pf(y, x) is equivalent to $\mathrm{Prf(y)} \wedge \mathrm{x} = (\mathrm{y})_{\mathrm{lh(y)} \dot{-} 1}$.

(Notice that S satisfies assumption (d). Let $a_1, a_2, \ldots, a_8$ be the Gödel numbers of Axioms (S1)–(S8); also, u is the Gödel number of an instance of Axiom Schema (S9) if and only if $(\mathrm{Ev})_{\mathrm{v}<\mathrm{u}}(\mathrm{Ey})_{\mathrm{y}<\mathrm{u}}(\mathrm{EVbl(v)} \wedge \mathrm{Fml(y)} \wedge \mathrm{u} = 2^3 * \mathrm{Sub}(\mathrm{y}, 2^{15}, \mathrm{v}) * 2^{11} * 2^3 * 2^3 * 2^3 * \mathrm{v} * 2^3 * \mathrm{y} * 2^{11} * \mathrm{Sub}(\mathrm{y}, 2^{57} * 2^3 * \mathrm{v} * 2^5, \mathrm{v}) * 2^5 * 2^5 * 2^{11} * 2^3 * \mathrm{v} * 2^5 * \mathrm{y} * 2^5 * 2^5)$. If we denote this last formula by $A_9(u)$, then x is a proper axiom of S if and only if $\mathrm{x} = a_1 \vee \mathrm{x} = a_2 \vee \ldots \vee \mathrm{x} = a_8 \vee A_9(\mathrm{x})$.)

PROPOSITION 3.27. *For first-order number theory* S, *in addition to the relations and functions* (a)–(d), *and* (1)–(13), *the following are also primitive recursive.*

(14) (a) Nu(y): y is the Gödel number of a numeral of S.

$\mathrm{y} = 2^{15} \vee (\mathrm{Ex})_{\mathrm{x}<\mathrm{y}}(\mathrm{Nu(x)} \wedge \mathrm{y} = 2^{57} * 2^3 * \mathrm{x} * 2^5)$. Use Corollary 3.20.

(b) Num(y) = the Gödel number of $\overline{\mathrm{y}}$.

$$\mathrm{Num}(0) = 2^{15}$$
$$\mathrm{Num}(\mathrm{y}+1) = 2^{57} * 2^3 * \mathrm{Num(y)} * 2^5$$

(15) Bw(u, v, x, y): u is the Gödel number of a wf $\mathscr{A}$, v is the Gödel number of a variable free in $\mathscr{A}$, and y is a Gödel number of a proof in S of the wf obtained from $\mathscr{A}$ by substituting the numeral $\overline{\mathrm{x}}$ for the free occurrences of the variable with Gödel number v.

$$\mathrm{Fml(u)} \wedge \mathrm{EVbl(v)} \wedge \mathrm{Fr(u, v)} \wedge \mathrm{Pf(y, Subst(u, Num(x), v))}$$

(16) Let $\mathscr{A}(x_1, \ldots, x_n)$ be a fixed wf of S containing $x_1, \ldots, x_n$ as its only free variables, and let m be the Gödel number of $\mathscr{A}(x_1, \ldots, x_n)$. Let $\mathrm{Bw}_{\mathscr{A}}(u_1, \ldots, u_n, y)$ mean: y is the Gödel number of a proof in S of $\mathscr{A}(\overline{u}_1, \ldots, \overline{u}_n)$. Then $\mathrm{Bw}_{\mathscr{A}}(u_1, \ldots, u_n, y)$ is equivalent to

$$\mathrm{Pf}(\mathrm{y}, \mathrm{Sub}\ldots(\mathrm{Sub}(\mathrm{Sub}(\mathrm{m}, \mathrm{Num}(u_1), 2^{5+8}), \mathrm{Num}(u_2), 2^{5+16})\ldots).$$

(17) (a) $W_1(u, y)$: u is the Gödel number of a wf $\mathscr{A}(x_1)$ containing the free variable x_1, and y is the Gödel number of a proof of $\mathscr{A}(\overline{u})$. This is equivalent to

$$\mathrm{Fml(u)} \wedge \mathrm{Fr}(\mathrm{u}, 2^{13}) \wedge \mathrm{Pf}(\mathrm{y}, \mathrm{Sub}(\mathrm{u}, \mathrm{Num(u)}, 2^{13})).$$

(b) $W_2(u, y)$: u is the Gödel number of a wf $\mathscr{A}(x_1)$ containing the free variable x_1, and y is the Gödel number of a proof of $\sim\mathscr{A}(\overline{u})$. This is equivalent to

$$\mathrm{Fml(u)} \wedge \mathrm{Fr}(\mathrm{u}, 2^{13}) \wedge \mathrm{Pf}(\mathrm{y}, \mathrm{Sub}(2^3 * 2^9 * \mathrm{u} * 2^5, \mathrm{Num(u)}, 2^{13}).$$

(18) We wish to define a function D(u) such that, if u is the Gödel number of a wf $\mathscr{A}(x_1)$ with free variable x_1, then D(u) is the Gödel number of $\mathscr{A}(\overline{u})$. Let $D(u) = Sub(u, Num(u), 2^{13})$.

The relations and functions of Propositions 3.25–3.27 which relate to the system S should have the subscript "S" attached to the corresponding signs to indicate the dependence upon S. If we were considering another first-order theory S′ with the same symbols as S, then, in general, we would obtain different relations and functions in Propositions 3.25–3.27.

PROPOSITION 3.28. *Any function* $f(x_1, \ldots, x_n)$ *which is representable in* S *is recursive.*

PROOF. Let $\mathscr{A}(x_1, \ldots, x_n, z)$ be a wf of S representing f. Consider natural numbers $k_1, \ldots, k_n$. Let $f(k_1, \ldots, k_n) = m$. Then $\vdash_S \mathscr{A}(\overline{k_1}, \ldots, \overline{k_n}, \overline{m})$. Let j be the Gödel number of a proof in S of $\mathscr{A}(\overline{k_1}, \ldots, \overline{k_n}, \overline{m})$. Then $Bw_{\mathscr{A}}(k_1, \ldots, k_n, m, j)$ (cf. Proposition 3.27(16)). So, for any $x_1, \ldots, x_n$, there is some y such that $Bw_{\mathscr{A}}(x_1, \ldots, x_n, (y)_0, (y)_1)$. Then $f(x_1, \ldots, x_n) = (\mu y(Bw_{\mathscr{A}}(x_1, \ldots, x_n, (y)_0, (y)_1))_0$. By Proposition 3.27(16), $Bw_{\mathscr{A}}$ is primitive recursive. Hence, by the μ-operator Rule (VI), $\mu y(Bw_{\mathscr{A}}(x_1, \ldots, x_n, (y)_0, (y)_1))$ is recursive, and, therefore, so is f.

Proposition 3.28, together with Proposition 3.23, shows that the class of recursive functions is identical with the class of functions representable in S. In Chapter V, it will be made plausible that the notion of recursive function is a precise mathematical equivalent of the intuitive idea of effectively computable function.

COROLLARY 3.29. *A number-theoretic relation* $R(x_1, \ldots, x_n)$ *is recursive if and only if* $R(x_1, \ldots, x_n)$ *is expressible in* S.

PROOF. R is recursive if and only if C_R is recursive, by definition. R is expressible in S if and only if C_R is representable in S, by Proposition 3.12.

§5. Gödel's Theorem for S

Let K be any first-order theory with the same symbols as S. Then K is said to be *ω-consistent* if and only if, for every wf $\mathscr{A}(x)$ of K, if $\vdash_K \mathscr{A}(\overline{n})$ for every natural number n, then it is not the case that $\vdash_K (Ex) \sim \mathscr{A}(x)$. If we accept the standard interpretation as a model of S, then S is ω-consistent, but we shall always explicitly state the assumption that S is ω-consistent whenever it is used in a proof (compare the remarks about consistency on page 107).

PROPOSITION 3.30. *If* K *is ω-consistent, then* K *is consistent.*

PROOF. Assume K ω-consistent. Consider any wf $\mathscr{A}(x)$ which is provable in K, e.g., $x = x \supset x = x$. In particular, $\vdash_K \overline{n} = \overline{n} \supset \overline{n} = \overline{n}$ for all natural numbers n. Hence, $(Ex) \sim (x = x \supset x = x)$ is not provable in K. Therefore, K is consistent (since, by the tautology $\sim A \supset (A \supset B)$, if K were inconsistent, every wf would be provable in K).

By Proposition 3.27, (17a), the relation $W_1(u, y)$ is primitive recursive and so, by Corollary 3.24, W_1 is expressible in S by a wf $\mathscr{W}_1(x_1, x_2)$ with two free variables x_1, x_2, i.e., if $W_1(k_1, k_2)$, then $\vdash_S \mathscr{W}_1(\overline{k_1}, \overline{k_2})$, and, if not-$W_1(k_1, k_2)$, then $\vdash_S \sim \mathscr{W}_1(\overline{k_1}, \overline{k_2})$. Let us consider the wf

(✠) $(x_2) \sim \mathscr{W}_1(x_1, x_2)$

Let m be the Gödel number of the wf (✠). Substitute $\overline{m}$ for x_1 in (✠) to obtain the closed wf

(✠✠) $(x_2) \sim \mathscr{W}_1(\overline{m}, x_2)$

Remember that $W_1(u, y)$ holds if and only if u is the Gödel number of a wf $\mathscr{A}(x_1)$ containing the free variable x_1, and y is the Gödel number of a proof in S of $\mathscr{A}(\overline{u})$. Now, m is the Gödel number of (✠), and (✠✠) comes from (✠) by substituting $\overline{m}$ for the variable x_1. Hence,

(I) $W_1(m, y)$ holds if and only if y is the Gödel number of a proof in S of (✠✠).

PROPOSITION 3.31 (Gödel's Theorem for S [1931]).

(1) *If* S *is consistent, then the* wf (✠✠) *is not provable in* S.

(2) *If* S *is ω-consistent, then the* wf $\sim$(✠✠) *is not provable in* S.

(*Hence, by Proposition* 3.30, *if* S *is ω-consistent, the closed* wf (✠✠) *is neither provable nor disprovable in* S. *Such a closed* wf *is said to be an* undecidable sentence *of* S.)

PROOF

(1) Assume S consistent, and assume that $\vdash_S (x_2) \sim \mathscr{W}_1(\overline{m}, x_2)$. Let k be the Gödel number of a proof in S of this wf. By (I) above, $W_1(m, k)$. Since $\mathscr{W}_1$ expresses W_1 in S, we have $\vdash_S \mathscr{W}_1(\overline{m}, \overline{k})$. From $(x_2) \sim \mathscr{W}_1(\overline{m}, x_2)$, by Rule A4, we deduce $\sim \mathscr{W}_1(\overline{m}, \overline{k})$. Thus, $\mathscr{W}_1(\overline{m}, \overline{k})$ and $\sim \mathscr{W}_1(\overline{m}, \overline{k})$ are provable in S, contradicting the consistency of S.

(2) Assume S ω-consistent, and assume that $\vdash_S \sim (x_2) \sim \mathscr{W}_1(\overline{m}, x_2)$, i.e., $\vdash_S \sim$(✠✠). By Proposition 3.30, S is consistent, so that not-$\vdash_S$ (✠✠). Therefore, for every natural number n, n is not the Gödel number of a proof in S of (✠✠), i.e., by (I), for every n, $W_1(m, n)$ is false. So, for every n, $\vdash_S \sim \mathscr{W}_1(\overline{m}, \overline{n})$. If we let $\mathscr{A}(x_2)$ be

$\sim \mathscr{W}_1(\overline{m}, x_2)$, then, by the ω-consistency of S, it follows that not-$\vdash_S (Ex_2) \sim \sim \mathscr{W}_1(\overline{m}, x_2)$; hence, not-$\vdash_S (Ex_2)\mathscr{W}_1(\overline{m}, x_2)$. But this contradicts our assumption that $\vdash_S (Ex_2)\mathscr{W}_1(\overline{m}, x_2)$.

The standard interpretation of the undecidable sentence (✠✠): $(x_2) \sim \mathscr{W}_1(\overline{m}, x_2)$ is rather remarkable. Since $\mathscr{W}_1$ expresses the relation W_1 in S, (✠✠) states, according to the standard interpretation, that $W_1(m, x_2)$ is false for every natural number x_2. Now, by (I), this means that there is no proof in S of (✠✠). In other words, (✠✠) affirms its own unprovability in S.† Now, by Gödel's Theorem, if S is consistent, then (✠✠) is, in fact, unprovable in S, and so, (✠✠) is true under the standard interpretation. Thus, (✠✠) is true for the natural numbers according to the usual interpretation, but is unprovable in S. This might lead us to believe that Gödel's Theorem holds only because the axiom system S that we initially chose just happens to be too weak and that, if we strengthen S by adding new axioms, then the new system might be complete. For example, we might add the true wf (✠✠) to S to obtain a stronger axiom system S_1. However, every recursive function, being representable in S, is also representable in S_1; likewise, Propositions 3.25–3.27 obviously hold when S_1 is substituted everywhere for S. But this is all we need for the derivation of Gödel's result; hence, if S_1 is ω-consistent, then S_1 also has an undecidable statement $\mathscr{B}$. ($\mathscr{B}$ is of the form $(x_2) \sim (\mathscr{W}_1)_{S_1}(\overline{k}, x_2)$, but, of course, $\mathscr{B}$ will be different from (✠✠), since the relation W_1 for S_1 is different from the relation W_1 for S, and hence the wf $(\mathscr{W}_1)_{S_1}$ and the numeral $\overline{k}$ entering into $\mathscr{B}$ are different from $\mathscr{W}_1$ and the numeral $\overline{m}$ of (✠✠).)

EXERCISES

1. Let S_g be the extension of S obtained by adding $\sim$(✠✠) as a new axiom. Show that, if S is consistent, then S_g is consistent and ω-inconsistent.

2. A theory K having the same symbols as S is ω-incomplete if there is a wf $\mathscr{A}(x)$ such that $\vdash_K \mathscr{A}(\overline{n})$ for all non-negative n, but not-$\vdash (x)\mathscr{A}(x)$. Show that, if S is consistent, then S is ω-incomplete. (Hint: consider the wf $\sim \mathscr{W}_1(\overline{m}, x_2)$ and use Proposition 3.31.)

3. Prove that ω-inconsistency implies ω-incompleteness for consistent theories.

Gödel's Theorem involves the assumption of ω-consistency, but, as Rosser [1936b] has shown, at the cost of complicating the argument, we need only assume consistency.

† Thus, (✠✠) is an analogue of various semantical paradoxes, especially those of Richard and Berry, and the liar paradox (cf. Wang [1955]).

In Proposition 3.27, (17b), the relation $W_2(u, y)$ was shown to be primitive recursive, and so, by Corollary 3.24, W_2 is expressible in S by a wf $\mathscr{W}_2(x_1, x_2)$. Now, consider the wf

(¶) $(x_2)(\mathscr{W}_1(x_1, x_2) \supset (Ex_3)(x_3 \leqslant x_2 \wedge \mathscr{W}_2(x_1, x_3)))$

Let n be the Gödel number of (¶). Substitute $\bar{n}$ for x_1 in (¶) to obtain the closed wf

(¶¶) $(x_2)(\mathscr{W}_1(\bar{n}, x_2) \supset (Ex_3)(x_3 \leqslant x_2 \wedge \mathscr{W}_2(\bar{n}, x_3)))$

Notice that $W_1(u, y)$ (respectively, $W_2(u, y)$) holds if and only if u is the Gödel number of a wf $\mathscr{A}(x_1)$ containing the free variable x_1, and y is the Gödel number of a proof in S of $\mathscr{A}(\bar{u})$ (respectively, $\sim\mathscr{A}(\bar{u})$). Since n is the Gödel number of (¶), we have:

(II) $W_1(n, y)$ holds if and only if y is the Gödel number of a proof in S of (¶¶).

(III) $W_2(n, y)$ holds if and only if y is the Gödel number of a proof in S of $\sim$(¶¶).

PROPOSITION 3.32 (Gödel-Rosser Theorem [1936b]). *If* S *is consistent, then* (¶¶) *and* $\sim$(¶¶) *are both unprovable in* S; *hence,* S *contains an undecidable sentence.*

PROOF

(1) Assume S consistent. Assume (¶¶) provable in S, i.e., $\vdash_S (x_2)(\mathscr{W}_1(\bar{n}, x_2) \supset (Ex_3)(x_3 \leqslant x_2 \wedge \mathscr{W}_2(\bar{n}, x_3)))$. Let k be the Gödel number of a proof in S of (¶¶). By (II), $W_1(n, k)$. Since $\mathscr{W}_1$ expresses W_1 in S, $\vdash_S \mathscr{W}_1(\bar{n}, \bar{k})$. But, from (¶¶), we obtain by Rule A4, $\vdash_S \mathscr{W}_1(\bar{n}, \bar{k}) \supset (Ex_3)(x_3 \leqslant \bar{k} \wedge \mathscr{W}_2(\bar{n}, x_3))$, and then by MP, $\vdash_S (Ex_3)(x_3 \leqslant \bar{k} \wedge \mathscr{W}_2(\bar{n}, x_3))$. Now, since S is consistent, and $\vdash_S$ (¶¶), it follows that there is no proof in S of $\sim$(¶¶). So, by (III), $W_2(n, y)$ is false for all natural numbers y. Since $\mathscr{W}_2$ expresses W_2 in S, $\vdash_S \sim\mathscr{W}_2(\bar{n}, \bar{j})$ for every natural number j. In particular, we deduce $\vdash_S \sim\mathscr{W}_2(\bar{n}, 0) \wedge \sim\mathscr{W}_2(\bar{n}, \bar{1}) \wedge \ldots \wedge \sim\mathscr{W}_2(\bar{n}, \bar{k})$. Hence, by Proposition 3.8(a′), $\vdash_S (x_3)(x_3 \leqslant \bar{k} \supset \sim\mathscr{W}_2(\bar{n}, x_3))$, and so, $\vdash_S \sim(Ex_3)(x_3 \leqslant \bar{k} \wedge \mathscr{W}_2(\bar{n}, x_3))$ by the Replacement Theorem (Corollary 2.21). But this is the negation of a wf we have already derived above, contradicting the consistency of S.

(2) Assume $\vdash_S \sim$(¶¶), i.e., $\vdash_S \sim(x_2)(\mathscr{W}_1(\bar{n}, x_2) \supset (Ex_3)(x_3 \leqslant x_2 \wedge \mathscr{W}_2(\bar{n}, x_3)))$. Let r be the Gödel number of a proof of $\sim$(¶¶). By (III), $W_2(n, r)$; therefore, $\vdash_S \mathscr{W}_2(\bar{n}, \bar{r})$. Since S is consistent, there is no proof in S of (¶¶), i.e., by (II), $W_1(n, y)$ is false for all natural numbers y. Hence, $\vdash_S \sim\mathscr{W}_1(\bar{n}, \bar{j})$ for all natural numbers j. In particular,

$$\vdash_S \sim\mathscr{W}_1(\bar{n}, 0) \wedge \sim\mathscr{W}_1(\bar{n}, \bar{1}) \wedge \ldots \wedge \sim\mathscr{W}_1(\bar{n}, \bar{r})$$

Then, by Proposition 3.8(a′),

(i) $\vdash_S x_2 \leqslant \bar{r} \supset \sim \mathscr{W}_1(\bar{n}, x_2)$. On the other hand, consider the following deduction.

(1)	$\bar{r} \leqslant x_2$	Hyp
(2)	$\mathscr{W}_2(\bar{n}, \bar{r})$	Already proved above
(3)	$\bar{r} \leqslant x_2 \wedge \mathscr{W}_2(\bar{n}, \bar{r})$	(1), (2), Tautology
(4)	$(Ex_3)(x_3 \leqslant x_2 \wedge \mathscr{W}_2(\bar{n}, x_3))$	(3), Rule E4

From (1)–(4), by the Deduction Theorem, we obtain

(ii) $\vdash_S \bar{r} \leqslant x_2 \supset (Ex_3)(x_3 \leqslant x_2 \wedge \mathscr{W}_2(\bar{n}, x_2))$

But, by Proposition 3.7(p),

(iii) $\vdash_S x_2 \leqslant \bar{r} \vee \bar{r} \leqslant x_2$

Now, from (i)–(iii), we obtain, by the appropriate tautology,

$$\vdash_S \sim \mathscr{W}_1(\bar{n}, x_2) \vee (Ex_3)(x_3 \leqslant x_2 \wedge \mathscr{W}_2(\bar{n}, x_2))$$

and then by a tautology, MP and Gen,

$$\vdash_S (x_2)(\mathscr{W}_1(\bar{n}, x_2) \supset (Ex_3)(x_3 \leqslant x_2 \wedge \mathscr{W}_2(\bar{n}, x_2)))$$

Thus, $\vdash_S$ (¶¶). But, since $\vdash_S \sim$(¶¶) has been assumed, this contradicts the consistency of S.

Rosser's undecidable sentence (¶¶) also has an interesting standard interpretation. By (II) and (III), $W_1(n, x_2)$ means that x_2 is the Gödel number of a proof in S of (¶¶), and $W_2(n, x_3)$ means that x_3 is the Gödel number of a proof in S of $\sim$(¶¶). Thus, (¶¶) asserts that, if there is a proof in S of (¶¶), then there is a proof in S, with even a smaller Gödel number, of $\sim$(¶¶). Now, Proposition 3.32 shows that, if S is consistent, then (¶¶) is not provable; therefore, if S is consistent, (¶¶) is true under the standard interpretation.

The application of the Gödel-Rosser Theorem is not limited to S. Let K be any first-order theory with the same symbols as S. If we analyze the proof above, we obtain the following sufficient conditions for the applicability of the Gödel-Rosser Theorem to K.

(a) The relations W_1 and W_2 (cf. Proposition 3.27(17); replace S everywhere by K in the definitions) should be expressible in K.

(b) There is a wf $u \leqslant v$ such that

(i) for any wf $\mathscr{A}(x)$ and any natural number k,

$$\vdash_K \mathscr{A}(0) \wedge \mathscr{A}(\bar{1}) \wedge \ldots \wedge \mathscr{A}(\bar{k}) \supset (x)(x \leqslant \bar{k} \supset \mathscr{A}(x))$$

(ii) and for any natural number k,

$$\vdash_K x \leqslant \bar{k} \vee \bar{k} \leqslant x$$

Notice that, if K is a first-order theory with equality, then (i) may be replaced by (i′): $\vdash_K x \leqslant \bar{k} \supset (x = 0 \vee x = \bar{1} \vee \ldots \vee x = \bar{k})$.

The condition (a) that W_1 and W_2 be expressible in K will be satisfied if W_1 and W_2 are recursive and every recursive relation is expressible in K. From the proofs of Proposition 3.25–3.27, it is obvious that W_1 and W_2 will be recursive if the assumption (d) of Proposition 3.26 holds for K, i.e., if the property $PrAx_K$ of being a Gödel number of a proper axiom of K is recursive (or, in other words, if the set of Gödel numbers of proper axioms of K is recursive). Thus, we have the following result.

PROPOSITION 3.33. *Let* K *be a first-order theory having the same symbols as* S. *Assume also that the following conditions hold for* K.

(1) *Every recursive relation is expressible in* K.
(2) *The set* $PrAx_K$ *of Gödel numbers of proper axioms of* K *is recursive.*
(3) *Conditions* (b), (i)–(ii) *above, hold.*

Then the Gödel-Rosser Theorem holds for K. *i.e., if* K *is consistent, then* K *has an undecidable sentence.* (Observe that (1) holds if every recursive function is representable in K, by Proposition 3.12; condition (i) of (3) can be replaced by (i′) above if K is a first-order theory with equality.)

Let us call a theory K *recursively axiomatizable* if and only if there is a theory K′ having the same theorems as K such that the set $PrAx_{K'}$ of Gödel numbers of proper axioms of K′ is recursive.

COROLLARY 3.34. *Every consistent recursively axiomatizable extension of* S *is subject to the Gödel-Rosser Theorem, and therefore has an undecidable sentence.*

PROOF. Since all recursive relations are expressible in S, they are also expressible in any extension of S. Likewise, since conditions (i)–(ii) hold in S, they also hold in any extension of S. So, by Proposition 3.33, the Gödel-Rosser Theorem applies to any consistent recursively axiomatizable extension of S.

It will appear plausible after Chapter V that the precise notion of a "recursive" set corresponds to the intuitive idea of an effectively decidable set. This hypothesis is known as Church's Thesis.† If we accept this thesis, then Corollary 3.34 asserts that S is *essentially incomplete*, i.e., that every consistent axiomatic extension of S has an

† Later on (p. 227), Church's Thesis will be taken in the form: A number-theoretic function is effectively computable if and only if it is recursive. We leave it as an exercise to show that this is equivalent to the definition given above.

undecidable sentence. (Remember that a theory is said to be axiomatic if there is an effective procedure for determining whether any given wf is an axiom of the theory.)

EXERCISES

1. Prove that the set Tr of Gödel numbers of all wfs of S which are true in the standard model is not recursive. (Hint: let K be the first-order extension of S having Tr as its set of axioms, and apply Corollary 3.34.)

2. From Corollary 3.34, prove that there is no recursively axiomatizable theory having Tr as the set of Gödel numbers of its theorems.

Let $\mathrm{Neg}(x) = 2^3 * 2^9 * x * 2^5$. Then if x is the Gödel number of a wf $\mathscr{A}$, Neg(x) is the Gödel number of $(\sim \mathscr{A})$. Clearly Neg is recursive, and, hence, is representable in S by a wf $\mathscr{N}g(x_1, x_2)$. Remember that Pf(y, x) is the relation which holds when and only when x is the Gödel number of a wf $\mathscr{A}$ of S and y is the Gödel number of a proof in S of $\mathscr{A}$. By Proposition 3.26, Pf is primitive recursive; hence, by Corollary 3.24, Pf is expressible in S by some wf $\mathscr{P}f(x_1, x_2)$.

Let Con_S be the wf: $(x_1)(x_2)(x_3)(x_4) \sim (\mathscr{P}f(x_1, x_3) \wedge \mathscr{P}f(x_2, x_4) \wedge \mathscr{N}g(x_3, x_4))$. Intuitively, according to the standard interpretation, Con_S asserts that there is no proof in S of any wf and its negation, and this is true if and only if S is consistent. Thus, Con_S can be interpreted as asserting the consistency of S. Now, Gödel's undecidable sentence (✠✠) (cf. page 143) means, according to the standard interpretation, that (✠✠) is not provable in S. Hence, the wf $Con_S \supset$ (✠✠) asserts that if S is consistent, then (✠✠) is not provable in S. But this is just the first half of Gödel's Theorem. The metamathematical reasoning used in Gödel's Theorem can be expressed and carried through within S itself, so that one obtains a proof in S of $Con_S \supset$ (✠✠). (For a proof of this assertion, see Hilbert-Bernays [1939], pages 285–328; Feferman [1960]; Feferman-Montague [196].) Thus, $\vdash_S Con_S \supset$ (✠✠). But, by Gödel's Theorem, if S is consistent, then (✠✠) is unprovable in S. Therefore, if S is consistent, then Con_S is unprovable in S, i.e., if S is consistent, a wf which asserts the consistency of S is unprovable in S. This is *Gödel's Second Theorem* [1931]. One can very roughly paraphrase it by stating that if S is consistent, the consistency of S cannot be proved within S; or, equivalently, a consistency proof of S must use ideas and methods which go beyond those available in S. In fact, the consistency proofs for S given by Gentzen [1936, 1938b] and Schütte [1951] (see Appendix) do employ notions and methods (e.g., a portion of the theory of denumerable ordinal numbers) that apparently are not formalizable in S.

We can state Gödel's Second Theorem approximately as follows:

If Con_K is an arithmetization of the statement that the first-order theory K is consistent (where K is a theory possessing the individual constants of S), then, if K is sufficiently strong and consistent, Con_K is not provable in K. Actually, the theorem applies to much more general theories (not necessarily first-order). Aside from the vagueness due to the phrase "sufficiently strong" (which can be made precise without much difficulty), the way in which Con_K is constructed also adds an element of ambiguity. This ambiguity is dangerous, because, as Feferman has shown (Feferman [1960], Corollary 5.10), there is a reasonable way of defining Con_S so that $\vdash_S Con_S$. Therefore, it is necessary to make the statement of the theorem more precise. This has been done by Feferman [1960] (for details, cf. Feferman-Montague [196]), roughly in the following way. For any primitive recursive function $f(x_1, \ldots, x_n)$, we showed in the proof of Proposition 3.23 (pages 131–134) how to find a wf $\mathscr{A}(x_1, \ldots, x_n, y)$ representing f in S. The wfs $\mathscr{A}(x_1, \ldots, x_n, 0)$ obtained in this way are called *PR-formulas*. A wf $\mathscr{B}$ is said to be an *RE-formula* if, and only if, for some PR-formula $\mathscr{A}$, $\mathscr{B}$ is of the form $(Ey_1)\ldots(Ey_k)\mathscr{A}$ (with $k \geqslant 0$). In particular, every PR-formula is an RE-formula. If we think of a given wf $\mathscr{A}(x)$ as representing the theory K, the axioms of which are those wfs whose Gödel numbers satisfy $\mathscr{A}$, then we can construct a proof predicate for K as follows: $\mathrm{Prf}_{\mathscr{A}}(x, y)$ is the wf obtained from $x = (y)_{\mathrm{lh}(y)-1} \wedge y > 1 \wedge (z)(z < \mathrm{lh}(y) \supset (\mathrm{Fml}((y)_z)) \wedge (\mathrm{LAx}((y)_z) \vee \mathscr{A}((y)_z) \vee (Ev)(Ew)(v < z \wedge w < z \wedge (\mathrm{MP}((y)_v, (y)_w, (y)_z) \vee \mathrm{Gen}((y)_v, (y)_z)))))$, by replacing all the primitive recursive functions and predicates by the wfs which represent or express them. (For example, if $\mathscr{C}(u, v)$ represents lh(y), then $z < \mathrm{lh}(y)$ is replaced by $(Ev)(\mathscr{C}(y, v) \wedge z < v)$.) The wf $\mathrm{Prf}_{\mathscr{A}}(x, y)$ expresses in S the relation that y is the Gödel number of a proof in the theory K of a wf having Gödel number x. (See pages 126, 137 for definitions of the relations and functions Fml, lh, $(y)_v$, Gen, MP appearing in the formula above.) We now can construct a wf corresponding to the notion of a theorem of K: Let $\mathrm{Pr}_{\mathscr{A}}(x)$ stand for $(Ey)\mathrm{Prf}_{\mathscr{A}}(x, y)$. We then can construct a wf expressing the consistency of K: $Con_{\mathscr{A}}$ for $(x)(\mathrm{Fml}(x) \supset \sim \mathrm{Pr}_{\mathscr{A}}(x) \vee (Ey)(\mathscr{N}g(x, y) \wedge \sim \mathrm{Pr}_{\mathscr{A}}(y)))$. One of the consequences of Feferman's work [1960] is the following precise version of Gödel's Second Theorem: Let K be a consistent extension of S. Let K_1 be any theory such that K is an extension of K_1 and K_1 is an extension of Robinson's system Q. (In particular, K_1 may be S or K itself.) Let T_K be the set of Gödel numbers of theorems of K, and assume that $\mathscr{A}(x)$ is an RE-formula which expresses T_K in K_1. Then not-$\vdash_K Con_{\mathscr{A}}$. (The assumption that $\mathscr{A}(x)$ is an RE-formula is shown to be necessary by Feferman's proof ([1960], Corollary 5.10) that there is a wf $\mathscr{B}(x)$ which expresses T_S in S such that $\vdash_S Con_{\mathscr{B}}$.)

§6. Recursive Undecidability. Tarski's Theorem. Robinson's System.

Let K be a first-order theory with equality having the same symbols as S. If u is the Gödel number of wf $\mathscr{A}(x_1)$ with free variable x_1, then the function D(u), as defined in Proposition 3.27(18), has as its value the Gödel number of the wf $\mathscr{A}(\overline{u})$. Since $D(u) = \text{Sub}(u, \text{Num}(u), 2^{13})$, it is clear that D is primitive recursive.

Let T_K be the set of Gödel numbers of theorems of K.

PROPOSITION 3.35. *If* K *is consistent and the function* D *is representable in* K, *then* T_K *is not expressible in* K.

PROOF. Assume D representable in K and T_K expressible in K. Then there are wfs $\mathscr{D}(x_1, x_2)$ and $\mathscr{T}(x_2)$ such that

(1) If $D(k) = j$, then $\vdash_K \mathscr{D}(\overline{k}, \overline{j})$
(2) $\vdash (E_1x_2)\mathscr{D}(\overline{k}, x_2)$
(3) If k is in T_K, then $\vdash_K \mathscr{T}(\overline{k})$
(4) If k is not in T_K, then $\vdash_K \sim\mathscr{T}(\overline{k})$.

Consider the wf $\mathscr{A}(x_1)$: $(x_2)(\mathscr{D}(x_1, x_2) \supset \sim\mathscr{T}(x_2))$. Let p be the Gödel number of this wf. Construct the wf $\mathscr{A}(\overline{p})$:

$$(x_2)(\mathscr{D}(\overline{p}, x_2) \supset \sim\mathscr{T}(x_2)).$$

Let q be the Gödel number of $\mathscr{A}(\overline{p})$. Hence, $D(p) = q$. Therefore, by (1), $\vdash_K \mathscr{D}(\overline{p}, \overline{q})$. Now, either $\vdash_K \mathscr{A}(\overline{p})$ or not-$\vdash_K \mathscr{A}(\overline{p})$. If not-$\vdash_K \mathscr{A}(\overline{p})$, then q is not in T_K, and so, by (4), $\vdash_K \sim\mathscr{T}(q)$. On the other hand, if $\vdash_K \mathscr{A}(\overline{p})$, then $\vdash_K (x_2)(\mathscr{D}(\overline{p}, x_2) \supset \sim\mathscr{T}(x_2))$. Hence, by Rule A4, $\vdash_K \mathscr{D}(\overline{p}, \overline{q}) \supset \sim\mathscr{T}(\overline{q})$; but $\vdash_K \mathscr{D}(\overline{p}, \overline{q})$. Hence, $\vdash_K \sim\mathscr{T}(\overline{q})$. Thus, in both cases, $\vdash_K \sim\mathscr{T}(\overline{q})$. Now, from $\vdash_K \mathscr{D}(\overline{p}, \overline{q})$ and (2), $\vdash_K \mathscr{D}(\overline{p}, x_2) \supset x_2 = \overline{q}$. But, since $\vdash_K \sim\mathscr{T}(\overline{q})$, $\vdash_K x_2 = \overline{q} \supset \sim\mathscr{T}(x_2)$. Hence, $\vdash_K \mathscr{D}(\overline{p}, x_2) \supset \sim\mathscr{T}(x_2)$, and, by Gen, $\vdash_K (x_2)(\mathscr{D}(\overline{p}, x_2) \supset \sim\mathscr{T}(x_2))$, i.e., $\vdash_K \mathscr{A}(\overline{p})$. Therefore, q is in T_K, and, by (3), $\vdash_K \mathscr{T}(\overline{q})$. Since we also have $\vdash_K \sim\mathscr{T}(\overline{q})$, K is inconsistent.

COROLLARY 3.36. *If* K *is consistent and every recursive function is representable in* K, *then* T_K *is not expressible in* K. *Hence,* T_K *is not recursive.*

PROOF. D is primitive recursive, and, therefore, would be representable in K. By Proposition 3.35, T_K is not expressible in K. By the proof of Proposition 3.12, the characteristic function C_{T_K} is not representable in K. Hence C_{T_K} is not recursive, and so, T_K is not recursive.

We shall say that K is *recursively undecidable* if and only if T_K is not recursive; and K is called *essentially recursively undecidable* if and only if K and every consistent extension of K is recursively undecidable. (If we accept Church's Thesis, then recursive undecidability is equivalent to effective undecidability, i.e., non-existence of a mechanical decision procedure for theoremhood. The non-existence of such a mechanical procedure means that ingenuity is required for determining whether any given wf is a theorem.)

COROLLARY 3.37. *If* S *is consistent, then* S *is essentially recursively undecidable.*

PROOF. If K is any consistent extension of S (possibly S itself), then, since every recursive function is representable in S, the same holds true for K, and, therefore, by Corollary 3.36, T_K is not recursive.

COROLLARY 3.38 (Tarski's Theorem [1936]). *The set* Tr *of Gödel numbers of* wfs *of* S *which are true in the standard model is not arithmetical, i.e., there is no* wf $\mathscr{A}(x)$ *of* S *such that* Tr *is the set of numbers k for which* $\mathscr{A}(\bar{k})$ *is true in the standard model.*

PROOF. Let K be the extension of S having as its axioms all those wfs which are true in the standard model. Then $T_K = \text{Tr}$. We assume that K is consistent, since it has the standard model. By Corollary 3.36, since every recursive function is representable in K, Tr is not expressible in K. But a relation is expressible in K if and only if it is the standard interpretation of some wf of S. Hence Tr is not arithmetical. (This result can be roughly paraphrased by saying that the notion of arithmetical truth is not arithmetically definable.)

EXERCISES

1. (a) If n is the Gödel number of a wf $\mathscr{A}$, let Cl(n) be the Gödel number of the closure of $\mathscr{A}$; otherwise, let Cl(n) = n. Using Proposition 3.25, show that Cl is primitive recursive.

(b) Show that if the first-order theory K is recursively axiomatizable and complete, then K is recursively decidable, i.e., the set T_K is recursive; or, equivalently, if K is recursively axiomatizable and recursively undecidable, then K is incomplete. Hint: if n is the Gödel number of a wf $\mathscr{A}$, then there is a proof either of the closure of $\mathscr{A}$ or of the negation of the closure of $\mathscr{A}$, i.e., $(Ey)(\text{Pf}(y, \text{Cl}(n)) \vee \text{Pf}(y, 2^3 * 2^9 * \text{Cl}(n) * 2^5) \vee \sim \text{Fml}(n))$. Abbreviating this last formula by $(Ey)\mathscr{B}(y, n)$, we know, by the μ-operator Rule (VI), that $\mu y(\mathscr{B}(y, n))$ is a recursive function. Therefore, $\text{Pf}(\mu y(\mathscr{B}(y, n)), \text{Cl}(n))$ is recursive, but it is equivalent to Cl(n) being in T_K, which, in turn, is equivalent to n being in T_K. The same proof also shows that if the first-order theory K is axiomatic and complete, then K is effectively decidable, i.e., there is an effective procedure to determine whether any given wf is a theorem.

(c) If K is consistent and recursively axiomatizable and every recursive function is representable in K, then K has an undecidable sentence.

2. Show that, if K is not recursively axiomatizable, then it is recursively undecidable.

Robinson's System: Consider the first-order theory with the same symbols as S and having the following finite number of axioms.

(1) $x_1 = x_1$
(2) $x_1 = x_2 \supset x_2 = x_1$
(3) $x_1 = x_2 \supset (x_2 = x_3 \supset x_1 = x_3)$
(4) $x_1 = x_2 \supset x_1{}' = x_2{}'$
(5) $x_1 = x_2 \supset (x_1 + x_3 = x_2 + x_3 \wedge x_3 + x_1 = x_3 + x_2)$
(6) $x_1 = x_2 \supset (x_1 \cdot x_3 = x_2 \cdot x_3 \wedge x_3 \cdot x_1 = x_3 \cdot x_2)$
(7) $x_1{}' = x_2{}' \supset x_1 = x_2$
(8) $0 \neq (x_1)'$
(9) $x_1 \neq 0 \supset (Ex_2)(x_1 = x_2{}')$
(10) $x_1 + 0 = x_1$
(11) $x_1 + (x_2)' = (x_1 + x_2)'$
(12) $x_1 \cdot 0 = 0$
(13) $x_1 \cdot (x_2)' = (x_1 \cdot x_2) + x_1$
(14) $(x_2 = x_1 \cdot x_3 + x_4 \wedge x_4 < x_1 \wedge x_2 = x_1 \cdot x_6 + x_5 \wedge x_5 < x_1) \supset x_4 = x_5$

(Uniqueness of remainder)

We shall call this theory RR. (The system Q of Axioms (1)–(13) is due to Raphael Robinson [1950]. Axiom (14) has been added to make one of the proofs below easier.) Clearly, RR is a subtheory of S, since all the axioms of RR are theorems of S. In addition, it follows from Proposition 2.26 and Axioms (1)–(6) that RR is a first-order theory with equality.

PROPOSITION 3.39. *In* RR, *the following are theorems.*

(a) $\overline{n} + \overline{m} = \overline{n + m}$ *for any natural numbers* m *and* n.
(b) $\overline{n} \cdot \overline{m} = \overline{n \cdot m}$ *for any natural numbers* m *and* n.
(c) $\overline{n} \neq \overline{m}$ *if* $n \neq m$, *for any natural numbers* n *and* m.
(d) $x \leqslant \overline{n} \supset x = 0 \vee x = \overline{1} \vee \ldots \vee x = \overline{n}$ *for any natural number* n.
(e) $x \leqslant \overline{n} \vee \overline{n} \leqslant x$, *for any natural number* n.

PROOF. Parts (a)–(c) are proved just as in Proposition 3.6(a). Parts (d) and (e) are proved by induction on n in the metalanguage, making strong use of Axiom (9). (Remember that, by definition, $x \leqslant y$ stands for $x = y \vee (Ez)(z \neq 0 \wedge x + z = y)$.) The proofs are left as exercises.

EXERCISES

1. Show that RR is a proper subtheory of S. (Hint: take as a normal model for RR, but not for S, the set of polynomials with integral coefficients such that the leading coefficient is non-negative. Note that $(Ey)(x = y + y \vee x = y + y + 1)$ is false in this model but is provable in S.) Remark: not only is S different from RR, but it is not finitely axiomatizable at all (i.e., there is no theory K having only a finite number of proper axioms, whose theorems are the same as those of S). This has been proved by Ryll-Nardzewski [1953] and Rabin [1961].

2. Show that Axiom (14) is not provable from Axioms (1)–(13). (Hint: let ∞ be an object which is not a natural number. Let $\infty' = \infty$, $\infty + x = x + \infty = \infty$ for all x, $\infty \cdot 0 = 0 \cdot \infty = 0$, and $\infty \cdot x = x \cdot \infty = \infty$ for all $x \neq 0$.)

PROPOSITION 3.40. *Every recursive function is representable in* RR.

PROOF. For the initial functions and the rules of substitution and the μ-operator, essentially the same proof holds as was given for S in Proposition 3.23. For the recursion rule, inspection of the proof given for Proposition 3.23 shows that it is still valid for RR if we note that, for the wf Bt defined in Proposition 3.21, if $\beta(\mathrm{k}_1, \mathrm{k}_2, \mathrm{k}_3) = \mathrm{m}$, then $\vdash_{\mathrm{RR}} Bt(\overline{\mathrm{k}_1}, \overline{\mathrm{k}_2}, \overline{\mathrm{k}_3}, \overline{\mathrm{m}})$, and also, by Axiom (14), $\vdash_{\mathrm{RR}} Bt(u, v, x, y) \wedge Bt(u, v, x, z) \supset y = z$.

EXERCISE. Carry through the details of the proof of Proposition 3.40.

We shall take for granted that RR is consistent, since it has the standard interpretation as a model. However, more constructive consistency proofs can be given along the same lines as the proofs in Beth [1959, § 84] or Kleene [1952, § 79].

PROPOSITION 3.41

(a) RR *is essentially recursively undecidable.*
(b) RR *is essentially recursively incomplete.*

PROOF. (a) By Corollary 3.36 and Proposition 3.40. (b) By Propositions 3.33 and 3.40 (or, from (a), by Exercise 1(b), page 151).

Of course, we already had these results for the theory S. The reason that we have gone to the trouble of obtaining them again for RR is that RR is finitely axiomatizable. It can be shown that Proposition 3.40, and therefore also Proposition 3.41, holds for Robinson's system Q (Axioms (1)–(13)). However, the proof for Proposition 3.40 is more complex (cf. Tarski-Mostowski-Robinson [1953], pages 56–59) than the one given above for RR.

Let K_1 and K_2 be any two first-order theories having the same symbols. K_2 is called a *finite extension* of K_1 if and only if there is a set A of wfs and a finite set B of wfs such that (1) the theorems of K_1 are precisely the wfs derivable from A; (2) the theorems of K_2 are precisely the wfs derivable from $A \cup B$.

We say that K_1 and K_2 are *compatible* if and only if the theory $K_1 \cup K_2$, the set of axioms of which is the union of the set of axioms of K_1 and the set of axioms of K_2, is consistent.

PROPOSITION 3.42. *Let* K_1 *and* K_2 *be first-order theories having the same symbols as* S. *If* K_2 *is a finite extension of* K_1 *and if* K_2 *is recursively undecidable, then* K_1 *is also recursively undecidable.*

PROOF. Let A be a set of axioms of K_1, and $A \cup \{\mathscr{A}_1, \ldots, \mathscr{A}_n\}$ a set of axioms for K_2. We may assume that $\mathscr{A}_1, \ldots, \mathscr{A}_n$ are closed wfs. Then, by the Deduction Theorem, a wf $\mathscr{B}$ is provable in K_2 if and only if $(\mathscr{A}_1 \wedge \ldots \wedge \mathscr{A}_n) \supset \mathscr{B}$ is provable in K_1. Let c be a Gödel number of $(\mathscr{A}_1 \wedge \ldots \wedge \mathscr{A}_n)$. Then b is a Gödel number of a theorem of K_2 when and only when $2^3 * c * 2^{11} * b * 2^5$ is a Gödel number of a theorem of K_1, i.e., b is in T_{K_2} if and only if $2^3 * c * 2^{11} * b * 2^5$ is in T_{K_1}. Hence, if T_{K_1} were recursive, then, by substitution, T_{K_2} would also be recursive, contradicting the recursive undecidability of K_2.

PROPOSITION 3.43. *Let* K *be a first-order theory having the same symbols as* S. *If* K *is compatible with* RR, *then* K *is recursively undecidable.*

PROOF. Since K is compatible with RR, the theory $K \cup RR$ is a consistent extension of RR. Therefore, by Proposition 3.41(a), $K \cup RR$ is recursively undecidable. But $K \cup RR$ is a finite extension of K. Hence, by Proposition 3.42, K is recursively undecidable.

COROLLARY 3.44. *Let* K *be a first-order theory with the same symbols as* S *such that all the axioms of* K *are true in the standard model. Then* K *is recursively undecidable.*

PROOF. $K \cup RR$ has the standard interpretation as a model, and is, therefore, consistent, i.e., K is compatible with RR. Now apply Proposition 3.43.

COROLLARY 3.45. *Let* P_S *be the predicate calculus having the same symbols as* S. *Then* P_S *is recursively undecidable.*

PROOF. $P_S \cup RR = RR$. Hence, P_S is compatible with RR, and, therefore, by Proposition 3.43, recursively undecidable.

By PF we mean the full first-order predicate calculus containing all predicate letters A_j^n, function letters f_j^n, and individual constants a_j. Let PP be the pure first-order predicate calculus containing all predicate letters, but no function letters or individual constants.

LEMMA 3.46. *There is a recursive function h such that, for any* wf $\mathscr{A}$ *of* PF *having Gödel number u, there is a* wf $\mathscr{A}'$ *of* PP *having Gödel number h(u) such that* $\mathscr{A}$ *is provable in* PF *if and only if* $\mathscr{A}'$ *is provable in* PP.

PROOF. Let $\mathscr{A}$ be a wf of PF. With the distinct function letters f_j^n in $\mathscr{A}$, associate distinct predicate letters A_r^{n+1} not occurring in $\mathscr{A}$, and with the distinct individual constants a_j in $\mathscr{A}$, associate distinct predicate letters A_k^1 not occurring in $\mathscr{A}$. Find the first individual constant a_j in $\mathscr{A}$; let z be the first variable not in $\mathscr{A}$; and let $\mathscr{A}^\star$ result from $\mathscr{A}$ by replacing all occurrences of a_j in $\mathscr{A}$ by z. Form the wf $\mathscr{A}_1$: $(Ez)A_k^1(z) \supset (Ez)(A_k^1(z) \wedge \mathscr{A}^\star)$, where A_k^1 is the predicate letter associated with a_j. It is easy to check (cf. proof of Proposition 2.29) that $\mathscr{A}$ is logically valid if and only if $\mathscr{A}_1$ is logically valid. Keep on performing similar transformations until a wf $\mathscr{B}$ is reached without individual constants such that $\mathscr{A}$ is logically valid if and only if $\mathscr{B}$ is logically valid. Take the left-most term $f_l^n(t_1, \ldots, t_n)$ in $\mathscr{B}$, where $t_1, \ldots, t_n$ do not contain function letters. Let w be the first variable not in $\mathscr{B}$, let $\mathscr{B}^\star$ result from $\mathscr{B}$ by replacing $f_l^n(t_1, \ldots, t_n)$ by w, and let $\mathscr{B}_1$ be the wf $(Ew)A_r^{n+1}(w, t_1, \ldots, t_n) \supset (Ew)(A_r^{n+1}(w, t_1, \ldots, t_n) \wedge \mathscr{B}^\star)$, where A_r^{n+1} is the predicate letter corresponding to f_l^n. It is easy to verify that $\mathscr{B}$ is logically valid if and only if $\mathscr{B}_1$ is logically valid. Repeat the same transformation on $\mathscr{B}_1$, etc., until a wf $\mathscr{A}'$ is reached which contains no function letters. Then $\mathscr{A}'$ is a wf of PP and $\mathscr{A}'$ is logically valid if and only if $\mathscr{A}$ is logically valid. By Gödel's Completeness Theorem (Corollary 2.14), $\mathscr{A}$ is logically valid if and only if $\vdash_{PF} \mathscr{A}$, and $\mathscr{A}'$ is logically valid if and only if $\vdash_{PP} \mathscr{A}'$. Hence, $\vdash_{PF} \mathscr{A}$ if and only if $\vdash_{PP} \mathscr{A}'$. In addition, if u is not the Gödel number of a wf of PF, we define h(u) to be 0; if u is the Gödel number of a wf $\mathscr{A}$ of PF, we let h(u) be the Gödel number of $\mathscr{A}'$. Clearly, h is effectively computable, and we leave it as an exercise for the diligent reader to show that h is recursive.

PROPOSITION 3.47 (Church's Theorem [1936a]). PF *and* PP *are recursively undecidable.*

PROOF

(1) By Gödel's Completeness Theorem, a wf $\mathscr{A}$ of P_S is provable in

P_S if and only if $\mathscr{A}$ is logically valid, and $\mathscr{A}$ is provable in PF if and only if $\mathscr{A}$ is logically valid. Hence, $\vdash_{P_S} \mathscr{A}$ if and only if $\vdash_{PF} \mathscr{A}$. However, the set Fml_{P_S} of Gödel numbers of wfs of P_S is recursive. Then, $T_{P_S} = T_{PF} \cap Fml_{P_S}$, where T_{P_S} and T_{PF} are, respectively, the sets of Gödel numbers of the theorems of P_S and PF; and, if T_{PF} were recursive, T_{P_S} would be recursive, contradicting Corollary 3.45. Therefore, PF is recursively undecidable.

(2) By Lemma 3.46, u is in T_{PF} if and only if h(u) is in T_{PP}. Since h is recursive, the recursiveness of T_{PP} would imply the recursiveness of T_{PF}, contradicting (1). Thus, T_{PP} is not recursive, i.e., PP is recursively undecidable.

If we accept Church's Thesis, then "recursively undecidable" can be replaced everywhere by "effectively undecidable". In particular, Proposition 3.47 asserts that there is no decision procedure for the pure predicate calculus PP, nor for the full predicate calculus PF. This implies that there is no effective method for determining whether any given wf is logically valid.

EXERCISE

Show that, in contrast to Church's Theorem, the pure monadic predicate calculus is effectively decidable. The pure monadic predicate calculus consists of those wfs of the pure predicate calculus which contain only predicate letters of one argument.

Hint: let $B_1, \ldots, B_k$ be the distinct predicate letters in a wf $\mathscr{A}$. Then $\mathscr{A}$ is valid if and only if $\mathscr{A}$ is true in every interpretation with at most 2^k elements. For, assume $\mathscr{A}$ true in every interpretation with at most 2^k elements, and let M be any interpretation. For any elements b, c of the domain D of M, call b and c equivalent if the truth values of $B_1(b), B_2(b), \ldots, B_k(b)$ in M are respectively the same as $B_1(c), B_2(c), \ldots, B_k(c)$. This defines an equivalence relation in D, and the corresponding set of equivalence classes has $\leqslant 2^k$ members and can be made the domain of an interpretation M′ of $\mathscr{A}$ by defining interpretations of $B_1, \ldots, B_k$, in the obvious way, on the equivalence classes. By induction, one can show that $\mathscr{A}$ is true in M if and only if it is true in M′. Since $\mathscr{A}$ is true in M′, it is also true in M. Hence, $\mathscr{A}$ is true in every interpretation, and is, therefore, by Corollary 2.14, provable. Note also that whether $\mathscr{A}$ is true in every interpretation having at most 2^k elements can be effectively determined.

The result in this exercise is, in a sense, the best possible. For, by a theorem of Kalmar [1936], there is an effective procedure producing, for each wf $\mathscr{A}$ of the pure predicate calculus, another wf $\mathscr{A}^\star$ of the pure predicate calculus such that $\mathscr{A}^\star$ contains only one predicate letter, a binary one, and such that $\mathscr{A}$ is valid if and only if $\mathscr{A}^\star$ is valid. (For another proof, cf. Church [1956, § 47].) Hence, by Church's Theorem, there is no decision procedure for validity (or provability) of wfs containing only binary predicate letters.

[D]EXERCISES

(TARSKI-MOSTOWSKI-ROBINSON [1953], I)

1. If a first-order theory $K^\star$ is consistent, if every theorem of an essentially recursively undecidable theory K_1 is a theorem of $K^\star$, and if the notion $\mathrm{Fml}_{K_1}(x)$ is recursive, then $K^\star$ is essentially recursively undecidable.

2. Let K be a first-order theory with equality. If a predicate letter A_j^n, a function letter f_j^n, and an individual constant a_j are not symbols of K, then by *possible definitions* of A_j^n, f_j^n, and a_j in K we mean, respectively, expressions of the form

(a) $(x_1)\ldots(x_n)(A_j^n(x_1, \ldots, x_n) \equiv \mathscr{A}(x_1, \ldots, x_n))$,
(b) $(x_1)\ldots(x_n)(y)(f_j^n(x_1, \ldots, x_n) = y \equiv \mathscr{B}(x_1, \ldots, x_n, y))$,
(c) $(y)(a_j = y \equiv \mathscr{C}(y))$,

where $\mathscr{A}$, $\mathscr{B}$, $\mathscr{C}$ are wfs of K, and, in case (b), $\vdash_K (x_1)\ldots(x_n)(E_1y)\mathscr{B}(x_1, \ldots, x_n, y)$, and, in case (c), $\vdash_K (E_1y)\mathscr{C}(y)$. If K is consistent, then the addition of any possible definitions to K as new axioms yields a consistent theory K′, and K′ is recursively undecidable if and only if K is. (Use Proposition 2.29.)

3. By a *non-logical constant*, we mean a predicate letter, function letter, or individual constant. Let K_1 be a first-order theory with equality having a finite number of non-logical constants. Then K_1 is said to be *interpretable* in a first-order theory with equality K if we can associate with each non-logical constant of K_1 which is not a non-logical constant of K a possible definition in K such that, if $K^\star$ is the theory obtained from K by adding these possible definitions as axioms, then every axiom (and hence every theorem) of K_1 is a theorem of $K^\star$. Notice that if K_1 is interpretable in K, then it is interpretable in every extension of K. If K_1 is interpretable in K and K is consistent, and if K_1 is essentially recursively undecidable, then so is K. (Hint: by 2., $K^\star$ is consistent; so, by 1., $K^\star$ is essentially recursively undecidable. Hence, by 2., K is recursively undecidable.)

4. Let K be a first-order theory with equality, and A_j^1 a monadic predicate letter not in K. Given a closed wf $\mathscr{A}$, let $\mathscr{A}^{(A_j^1)}$ (called the relativization of $\mathscr{A}$ with respect to A_j^1) be the wf obtained from $\mathscr{A}$ by replacing every subformula (starting from the smallest subformulas) of

the form $(x)\mathscr{B}(x)$ by $(x)(A_j^1(x) \supset \mathscr{B}(x))$. Let the axioms of a new theory $K^{A_j^1}$ be the set of relativizations with respect to A_j^1 of the closures of all proper axioms of K. (a) $K^{A_j^1}$ is interpretable in K. (Hint: take $(x)(A_j^1(x) \equiv x = x)$ as a possible definition of A_j^1.) (b) $K^{A_j^1}$ is consistent if and only if K is consistent. (c) $K^{A_j^1}$ is essentially recursively undecidable if and only if K is. (Tarski-Mostowski-Robinson [1953], page 28.)

5. K is said to be *relatively interpretable* in K′ if there is some predicate letter A_j^1 not in K such that $K^{A_j^1}$ is interpretable in K′. Hence, if K is relatively interpretable in K′ and K is essentially recursively undecidable, then so is K′. (Use 3. and 4.)

6. Call a first-order theory K in which RR is relatively interpretable *sufficiently strong*. Prove that any sufficiently strong consistent theory K is essentially recursively undecidable, and if, in addition, K is recursively axiomatizable, then K is incomplete. (Use Proposition 3.41(a), page 153, and Exercise 1(b), page 151.) Roughly speaking, K is sufficiently strong if the notions of natural number, 0, 1, addition, and multiplication are "definable" in K so that the axioms of RR (relativized to "natural numbers" of K) are provable. Clearly, any theory adequate for present-day mathematics will be sufficiently strong, and so, if it is consistent, it will be recursively undecidable, and, if it is recursively axiomatizable, it will be incomplete. If we accept Church's Thesis, this implies that any consistent sufficiently strong theory will be effectively undecidable, and, if it is axiomatic, it will be incomplete. (Similar results also hold for higher-order theories; for example, cf. Gödel [1931], Scholz-Hasenjaeger [1961], §§ 237–238.) This seems to destroy all hope for a consistent and complete axiomatization of mathematics.

CHAPTER 4

AXIOMATIC SET THEORY

§ 1. An Axiom System

A prime reason for the increase in importance of mathematical logic in this century was the discovery of the paradoxes of set theory and the need for a revision of intuitive (and contradictory) set theory. Many different axiomatic theories have been proposed to serve as a foundation for set theory, but, no matter how they differ at the fringes, they all have as a common core the fundamental theorems which mathematicians need in their daily work. A choice among the available theories is primarily a matter of taste, and we make no claim about the system we shall use except that it is an adequate basis for present-day mathematics.

We shall describe a first-order theory NBG, which is basically a system of the same type as one originally proposed by von Neumann [1925, 1928] and later thoroughly revised and simplified by R. Robinson [1937], Bernays [1937–1954], and Gödel [1940]. (We shall follow Gödel's monograph to a great extent, though there will be some important differences.) NBG has a single predicate letter A_2^2, but no function letters or individual constants. In order to conform to the notation in Bernays [1937–1954] and Gödel [1940], we shall use capital Latin letters $X_1, X_2, X_3, \ldots$ as variables, instead of $x_1, x_2, x_3, \ldots$. (As usual, we shall use $X, Y, Z, \ldots$ to represent arbitrary variables.) We shall abbreviate $A_2^2(X, Y)$ by $X \in Y$, and $\sim A_2^2(X, Y)$ by $X \notin Y$; intuitively, $\in$ is thought of as the membership relation.

Let us define equality in the following way.

Definition. $X = Y$ for $(Z)(Z \in X \equiv Z \in Y)$

Thus, two objects are equal when and only when they have the same members.

Definition. $X \subseteq Y$ for $(Z)(Z \in X \supset Z \in Y)$ (Inclusion)

Definition. $X \subset Y$ for $X \subseteq Y \wedge X \neq Y$ (Proper inclusion)

As easy consequences of these definitions, we have the following.

PROPOSITION 4.1

(a) $\vdash X = Y \equiv (X \subseteq Y \wedge Y \subseteq X)$
(b) $\vdash X = X$
(c) $\vdash X = Y \supset Y = X$
(d) $\vdash X = Y \supset (Y = Z \supset X = Z)$
(e) $\vdash X = Y \supset (Z \in X \equiv Z \in Y)$

We shall now present the proper axioms of NBG, interspersing among the statement of the axioms some additional definitions and various consequences of the axioms. First, however, notice that in the "interpretation" we have in mind the variables take classes as values. Classes are the totalities corresponding to some, but not necessarily all, properties.† (This "interpretation" is as imprecise as the notions of "totality", "property", etc.)

We define a class to be a *set* if it is a member of some class, whereas those classes which are not sets are called *proper classes*.

DEFINITION. $M(X)$ for $(EY)(X \in Y)$. (X is a set.)

DEFINITION. $Pr(X)$ for $\sim M(X)$. (X is a proper class.)

It will be seen later that the usual derivation of the paradoxes now no longer leads to a contradiction, but only yields the result that various classes are proper classes, not sets. The sets are intended to be those safe, comfortable classes which are used by mathematicians in their daily life and work, whereas proper classes are thought of as monstrously large collections which, if permitted to be sets (i.e., allowed to belong to other classes), would engender contradictions.

EXERCISE. $\vdash Y \in X \supset M(Y)$

The system NBG is designed to handle classes, not individuals. The reason for this is that mathematics has no need for non-classes, like cows or molecules; all mathematical objects and relations can be formulated in terms of classes alone. If non-classes are required for applications to other sciences, then the system NBG can be modified slightly so as to apply to both classes and non-classes alike (cf. Mostowski [1939]).

† Those properties which actually do determine classes will be partially specified in the axioms. These axioms provide us with the classes we need in mathematics and appear (we hope) modest enough so that contradictions are not derivable from them.

Let us introduce small letters $x_1, x_2, \ldots$ as special, restricted variables for sets. In other words, $(x_i)\mathscr{A}(x_i)$ stands for $(X)(M(X) \supset \mathscr{A}(X))$, i.e., $\mathscr{A}$ holds for all sets; $(Ex_i)\mathscr{A}(x_i)$ stands for $(EX)(M(X) \wedge \mathscr{A}(X))$, i.e., $\mathscr{A}$ holds for some set. Note that the variable X used in this definition should be one which does not occur in $\mathscr{A}(x_i)$. (As usual, we use $x, y, z, \ldots$ to stand for arbitrary set variables.)

Example. $(X)(x)(Ey)(EZ)\mathscr{A}(X, x, y, Z)$ stands for

$$(X)(X_j)(M(X_j) \supset (EY)(M(Y) \wedge (EZ)\mathscr{A}(X, X_j, Y, Z)))$$

EXERCISE. $\vdash X = Y \equiv (z)(z \in X \equiv z \in Y)$

AXIOM T (Axiom of Extensionality). $X = Y \supset (X \in Z \equiv Y \in Z)$

PROPOSITION 4.2. NBG *is a first-order theory with equality.*

PROOF. By Proposition 4.1 and Axiom T, and the Remark on page 79.

EXERCISE. $\vdash M(Z) \wedge Z = Y \supset M(Y)$

AXIOM P (Pairing Axiom). $(x)(y)(Ez)(u)(u \in z \equiv u = x \vee u = y)$, i.e., for any sets x, y there is a set z such that z has x and y as its only members.

EXERCISES

1. $\vdash (x)(y)(E_1z)(u)(u \in z \equiv u = x \vee u = y)$, i.e., there is a unique set z, called the *unordered pair* of x and y, such that z has x and y as its only members. This follows easily from Axiom P and the definition of equality.

2. $\vdash (X)(M(X) \equiv (Ey)(X \in y))$

AXIOM N (Null Set). $(Ex)(y)(y \notin x)$, *i.e., there is a set which has no elements.*

Obviously, from Axiom N and the Axiom of Extensionality, there is a unique set which has no members, i.e., $\vdash (E_1x)(y)(y \notin x)$. Therefore, we can introduce a new individual constant 0 by means of the following condition.

DEFINITION. $(y)(y \notin 0)$

Since we have the uniqueness condition for the unordered pair, we can introduce a new function letter $g(x, y)$ to designate the unordered pair of x and y. We shall write $\{x, y\}$ for $g(x, y)$. Notice that we have to define a unique value for $\{X, Y\}$ for any classes X and Y, not only for sets x and y. We shall let $\{X, Y\} = 0$ whenever X is not a set or

Y is not a set. One can prove: $\vdash_{\text{NBG}} (E_1 Z)((M(X) \wedge M(Y) \wedge (u)(u \in Z \equiv u = X \vee u = Y)) \vee ((\sim M(X) \vee \sim M(Y)) \wedge Z = 0))$. This justifies the introduction of $\{X, Y\}$:

DEFINITION. $(M(X) \wedge M(Y) \wedge (u)(u \in \{X, Y\} \equiv u = X \vee u = Y)) \vee ((\sim M(X) \vee \sim M(Y)) \wedge \{X, Y\} = 0)$.

One can then prove: $\vdash_{\text{NBG}} (x)(y)(u)(u \in \{x, y\} \equiv u = x \vee u = y)$ and $\vdash_{\text{NBG}} (x)(y)(M(\{x, y\}))$.

In connection with these definitions, the reader should review § 9 of Chapter II, and, in particular, Proposition 2.29, which assures us that the introduction of new individual constants and function letters, such as 0 and $\{X, Y\}$, adds nothing essentially new to the theory NBG.

EXERCISES

1. $\vdash \{X, Y\} = \{Y, X\}$. (The subscript NBG will be omitted from $\vdash_{\text{NBG}}$ in the rest of this chapter.)
2. Define: $\{X\}$ for $\{X, X\}$. Then $\vdash (x)(y)(\{x\} = \{y\} \supset x = y)$.

DEFINITION. $\langle X, Y \rangle = \{\{X\}, \{X, Y\}\}$

$\langle X, Y \rangle$ is called the *ordered pair* of X and Y.

The definition of $\langle X, Y \rangle$ does not have any intrinsic intuitive meaning. It is just a convenient way (discovered by Kuratowski) to define ordered pairs so that one can prove the characteristic property of ordered pairs expressed in the following proposition.

PROPOSITION 4.3. $\vdash (x)(y)(u)(v)(\langle x, y \rangle = \langle u, v \rangle \supset x = u \wedge y = v)$.

PROOF. Assume $\langle x, y \rangle = \langle u, v \rangle$. Then $\{\{x\}, \{x, y\}\} = \{\{u\}, \{u, v\}\}$. Since $\{x\} \in \{\{x\}, \{x, y\}\}$, $\{x\} \in \{\{u\}, \{u, v\}\}$. Hence, $\{x\} = \{u\}$ or $\{x\} = \{u, v\}$. In both cases, $x = u$. Now, $\{u, v\} \in \{\{u\}, \{u, v\}\}$; so, $\{u, v\} \in \{\{x\}, \{x, y\}\}$. Then $\{u, v\} = \{x\}$ or $\{u, v\} = \{x, y\}$. Similarly, $\{x, y\} = \{u\}$ or $\{x, y\} = \{u, v\}$. If $\{u, v\} = \{x\}$ and $\{x, y\} = \{u\}$, then $x = u = y = v$; if not, $\{u, v\} = \{x, y\}$. Hence, $\{u, v\} = \{u, y\}$. So, if $v \neq u$, then $y = v$; if $v = u$, then $y = v$. Thus, in all cases, $y = v$.

We now extend the definition of ordered pairs to ordered n-tuples.

DEFINITION

$$\langle X \rangle = X$$

$$\langle X_1, \ldots, X_{n+1} \rangle = \langle \langle X_1, \ldots, X_n \rangle, X_{n+1} \rangle$$

Thus,

$$\langle X, Y, Z \rangle = \langle \langle X, Y \rangle, Z \rangle, \text{ and } \langle X, Y, Z, U \rangle = \langle \langle \langle X, Y \rangle, Z \rangle, U \rangle$$

One can easily establish the following generalization of Proposition 4.3:

$$\vdash (x_1)\ldots(x_n)(y_1)\ldots(y_n)(\langle x_1, \ldots, x_n\rangle = \langle y_1, \ldots, y_n\rangle \supset x_1 = y_1 \wedge \ldots \wedge x_n = y_n)$$

Axioms of Class Existence. These axioms state that, for certain properties expressed by wfs, there are corresponding classes of all those sets satisfying the property.

AXIOM B1. $(EX)(u)(v)(\langle u, v\rangle \in X \equiv (u \in v))$ ($\in$-relation)
AXIOM B2. $(X)(Y)(EZ)(u)(u \in Z \equiv u \in X \wedge u \in Y)$ (Intersection)
AXIOM B3. $(X)(EZ)(u)(u \in Z \equiv u \notin X)$ (Complement)
AXIOM B4. $(X)(EZ)(u)(u \in Z \equiv (Ev)(\langle u, v\rangle \in X))$ (Domain)
AXIOM B5. $(X)(EZ)(u)(v)(\langle u, v\rangle \in Z \equiv u \in X)$
AXIOM B6. $(X)(EZ)(u)(v)(w)(\langle u, v, w\rangle \in Z \equiv \langle v, w, u\rangle \in X)$
AXIOM B7. $(X)(EZ)(u)(v)(w)(\langle u, v, w\rangle \in Z \equiv \langle u, w, v\rangle \in X)$

From Axioms B2–B4 and the Axiom of Extensionality,

$$\vdash (X)(Y)(E_1Z)(u)(u \in Z \equiv u \in X \wedge u \in Y)$$
$$\vdash (X)(E_1Z)(u)(u \in Z \equiv u \notin X)$$
$$\vdash (X)(E_1Z)(u)(u \in Z \equiv (Ev)(\langle u, v\rangle \in X))$$

These results justify the introduction of new function letters: $\cap$, $\bar{\ }$, $\mathscr{D}$.

DEFINITIONS

$(u)(u \in X \cap Y \equiv u \in X \wedge u \in Y)$ (Intersection of X and Y)
$(u)(u \in \bar{X} \equiv u \notin X)$ (Complement of X)
$(u)(u \in \mathscr{D}(X) \equiv (Ev)(\langle u, v\rangle \in X))$ (Domain of X)
$X \cup Y = \overline{(\bar{X} \cap \bar{Y})}$ (Union of X and Y)
$V = \bar{0}$ (Universal Class)
$X - Y = X \cap \bar{Y}$

EXERCISES

1. $\vdash (u)(u \in X \cup Y \equiv u \in X \vee u \in Y)$
   $\vdash (u)(u \in V)$
2. $\vdash X \cap Y = Y \cap X$ — $\vdash X \cup Y = Y \cup X$
   $\vdash (X \cap Y) \cap Z = X \cap (Y \cap Z)$ — $\vdash (X \cup Y) \cup Z = X \cup (Y \cup Z)$
   $\vdash X \cap X = X$ — $\vdash X \cup X = X$
   $\vdash X \cap 0 = 0$ — $\vdash X \cup 0 = X$
   $\vdash X \cap V = X$ — $\vdash X \cup V = V$
   $\vdash X \cap (Y \cup Z) = (X \cap Y) \cup (X \cap Z)$ — $\vdash X \cup (Y \cap Z) = (X \cup Y) \cap (X \cup Z)$

$\vdash \overline{X \cup Y} = \overline{X} \cap \overline{Y}$ $\quad\quad$ $\vdash \overline{X \cap Y} = \overline{X} \cup \overline{Y}$
$\vdash X - X = 0$ $\quad\quad$ $\vdash V - X = \overline{X}$
$\vdash \overline{\overline{X}} = X$ $\quad\quad$ $\vdash \overline{V} = 0$

3. (a) $\vdash (X)(EZ)(u)(v)(\langle u, v\rangle \in Z \equiv \langle v, u\rangle \in X)$. (Hint: apply successively B5, B7, B6, B4.)

(b) $\vdash (X)(EZ)(u)(v)(w)(\langle u, v, w\rangle \in Z \equiv \langle u, w\rangle \in X)$. (Hint: use B5 and B7.)

(c) $\vdash (X)(EZ)(v)(x_1)\ldots(x_n)(\langle x_1, \ldots, x_n, v\rangle \in Z \equiv \langle x_1, \ldots, x_n\rangle \in X)$. (Hint: use B5.)

(d) $\vdash (X)(EZ)(v_1)\ldots(v_m)(x_1)\ldots(x_n)(\langle x_1, \ldots, x_n, v_1, \ldots, v_m\rangle \in Z \equiv \langle x_1, \ldots, x_n\rangle \in X)$. (Hint: by iteration of (c).)

(e) $\vdash (X)(EZ)(v_1)\ldots(v_m)(x_1)\ldots(x_n)(\langle x_1, \ldots, x_{n-1}, v_1, \ldots, v_m, x_n\rangle \in Z \equiv \langle x_1, \ldots, x_n\rangle \in X)$. (Hint: for m = 1, from (b), substituting $\langle x_1, \ldots, x_{n-1}\rangle$ for u and x_n for w; the general case then follows by iteration.)

(f) $\vdash (X)(EZ)(x)(v_1)\ldots(v_m)(\langle v_1, \ldots, v_m, x\rangle \in Z \equiv x \in X)$. (Hint: from B5 and Part (a) above.)

(g) $\vdash (X)(EZ)(x_1)\ldots(x_n)(\langle x_1, \ldots, x_n\rangle \in Z \equiv (Ey)(\langle x_1, \ldots, x_n, y\rangle \in X))$. (Hint: from B4, substituting $\langle x_1, \ldots, x_n\rangle$ for u, and y for v.)

(h) $\vdash (X)(EZ)(u)(v)(w)(\langle v, u, w\rangle \in Z \equiv \langle u, w\rangle \in X)$. (Hint: substitute $\langle u, w\rangle$ for u in Axiom B5, and apply Axiom B6.)

(i) $\vdash (X)(EZ)(v_1)\ldots(v_k)(u)(w)(\langle v_1, \ldots, v_k, u, w\rangle \in Z \equiv \langle u, w\rangle \in X)$. (Hint: substitute $\langle v_1, \ldots, v_k\rangle$ for v in (h).)

Now we can derive a general class existence theorem.

PROPOSITION 4.4. *Let* $\varphi(X_1, \ldots, X_n, Y_1, \ldots, Y_m)$ *be a* wf *the variables of which occur among* $X_1, \ldots, X_n, Y_1, \ldots, Y_m$ *and in which only set variables are quantified (i.e.,* φ *can be abbreviated in such a way that only set variables are quantified). We call such a* wf predicative. *Then,*

$$\vdash (EZ)(x_1)\ldots(x_n)(\langle x_1, \ldots, x_n\rangle \in Z \equiv \varphi(x_1, \ldots, x_n, Y_1, \ldots, Y_m))$$

PROOF. We shall consider only wfs φ in which no wf of the form $Y_i \in W$ occurs, since $Y_i \in W$ can be replaced by $(Ex)(x = Y_i \wedge x \in W)$, which is equivalent to $(Ex)((z)(z \in x \equiv z \in Y_i) \wedge x \in W)$. Also, we may assume that φ contains no wf of the form $X \in X$, since this may be replaced by $(Eu)(u = X \wedge u \in X)$, which is equivalent to $(Eu)((z)(z \in u \equiv z \in X) \wedge u \in X)$. We shall proceed now by induction on the number k of connectives and quantifiers in φ (written with restricted set variables).

Case 1. k = 0. Then φ has the form $x_i \in x_j$ or $x_j \in x_i$ or $x_i \in Y_l$, where $1 \leqslant i < j \leqslant n$. For $x_i \in x_j$, there is, by Axiom B1, some W_1 such that $(x_i)(x_j)(\langle x_i, x_j\rangle \in W_1 \equiv x_i \in x_j)$. For $x_j \in x_i$, there is, by

Axiom B1, some W_2 such that $(x_i)(x_j)(\langle x_j, x_i\rangle \in W_2 \equiv x_j \in x_i)$, and then, by Exercise 3(a), there is some W_3 such that $(x_i)(x_j)(\langle x_i, x_j\rangle \in W_3 \equiv x_j \in x_i)$. So, in both cases, there is some W such that $(x_i)(x_j)(\langle x_i, x_j\rangle \in W \equiv \varphi(x_1, \ldots, x_n, Y_1, \ldots, Y_m))$. Then, by Exercise 3(i) with $W = X$, there is some Z_1 such that

$$(x_1)\ldots(x_{i-1})(x_i)(x_j)(\langle x_1, \ldots, x_{i-1}, x_i, x_j\rangle \in Z_1 \equiv \varphi(x_1, \ldots, x_n, Y_1, \ldots, Y_m)).$$

Hence, by Exercise 3(e) with $Z_1 = X$, there is some Z_2 such that

$$(x_1)\ldots(x_i)(x_{i+1})\ldots(x_j)(\langle x_1, \ldots, x_j\rangle \in Z_2 \equiv \varphi(x_1, \ldots, x_n, Y_1, \ldots, Y_m)).$$

Then, by Exercise 3(d) with $Z_2 = X$, there is some Z such that

$$(x_1)\ldots(x_n)(\langle x_1, \ldots, x_n\rangle \in Z \equiv \varphi(x_1, \ldots, x_n, Y_1, \ldots, Y_m)).$$

In the remaining case, $x_i \in Y_l$, the theorem follows by application of Exercise 3(f) and 3(d).

Case 2. Let the theorem be provable for all k < m, and assume that φ has m connectives and quantifiers.

(a) φ is $\sim\psi$. By inductive hypothesis, there is some W such that

$$(x_1)\ldots(x_n)(\langle x_1, \ldots, x_n\rangle \in W \equiv \psi(x_1, \ldots, x_n, Y_1, \ldots, Y_m))$$

Let $Z = \overline{W}$.

(b) φ is $\psi \supset \theta$. By inductive hypothesis, there are classes Z_1 and Z_2 such that

$$(x_1)\ldots(x_n)(\langle x_1, \ldots, x_n\rangle \in Z_1 \equiv \psi(x_1, \ldots, x_n, Y_1, \ldots, Y_m))$$

and

$$(x_1)\ldots(x_n)(\langle x_1, \ldots, x_n\rangle \in Z_2 \equiv \theta(x_1, \ldots, x_n, Y_1, \ldots, Y_m))$$

Let $Z = \overline{(Z_1 \cap \bar{Z}_2)}$.

(c) φ is $(x)\psi$. By inductive hypothesis, there is some W such that

$$(x_1)\ldots(x_n)(x)(\langle x_1, \ldots, x_n, x\rangle \in W \equiv \psi(x_1, \ldots, x_n, x, Y_1, \ldots, Y_m))$$

Apply Exercise 3(g) with $X = \overline{W}$ to obtain a class Z_1 such that

$$(x_1)\ldots(x_n)(\langle x_1, \ldots, x_n\rangle \in Z_1 \equiv (Ex)\sim\psi(x_1, \ldots, x_n, x, Y_1, \ldots, Y_m))$$

Now, let $Z = \bar{Z}_1$, noting that $(x)\psi$ is equivalent to $\sim(Ex)\sim\psi$.

Examples. 1. Let $\varphi(X, Y_1, Y_2)$ be $(Eu)(Ev)(X = \langle u, v\rangle \wedge u \in Y_1 \wedge v \in Y_2)$. The only quantifiers in φ involve set variables. Hence, by the Class Existence Theorem, $\vdash (EZ)(x)(x \in Z \equiv (Eu)(Ev)(x = \langle u, v\rangle \wedge$

$u \in Y_1 \wedge v \in Y_2)$. By the Axiom of Extensionality, $\vdash (E_1Z)(x)(x \in Z \equiv (Eu)(Ev)(x = \langle u, v\rangle \wedge u \in Y_1 \wedge v \in Y_2))$. So, we can introduce a new function letter $\times$:

DEFINITION. $(x)(x \in Y_1 \times Y_2 \equiv (Eu)(Ev)(x = \langle u, v\rangle \wedge u \in Y_1 \wedge v \in Y_2)$
(*Cartesian Product* of Y_1 and Y_2)

DEFINITIONS

X^2 for $X \times X$, (In particular, V^2 is the class of all ordered pairs.)
$\vdots$
X^n for $X^{n-1} \times X$, (Thus, V^n is the class of all ordered n-tuples.)
$Rel(X)$ for $X \subseteq V^2$ (X is a relation).

2. Let $\varphi(X, Y)$ be $X \subseteq Y$.

By the Class Existence Theorem and the Axiom of Extensionality, $\vdash (E_1Z)(x)(x \in Z \equiv x \subseteq Y)$. Thus, there is a class Z which has as its members all subsets of Y.

DEFINITION. $(x)(x \in \mathscr{P}(Y) \equiv x \subseteq Y)$. ($\mathscr{P}(Y)$: the *power class* of Y.)

3. Let $\varphi(X, Y)$ be $(Ev)(X \in v \wedge v \in Y)$.

By the Class Existence Theorem and the Axiom of Extensionality, $\vdash (E_1Z)(x)(x \in Z \equiv (Ev)(x \in v \wedge v \in Y))$. Thus, there is a class Z which contains all the elements of the elements of Y.

DEFINITION. $(x)(x \in \bigcup(Y) \equiv (Ev)(x \in v \wedge v \in Y))$. ($\bigcup(Y)$: the *sum class* of Y.)

4. Let $\varphi(X)$ be $(Eu)(x = \langle u, u\rangle)$.

By the Class Existence Theorem and the Axiom of Extensionality, there is a unique class Z such that $(x)(x \in Z \equiv (Eu)(x = \langle u, u\rangle))$.

DEFINITION. $(x)(x \in I \equiv (Eu)(x = \langle u, u\rangle)$ (Identity Relation.)

COROLLARY 4.5. *Given a predicative* wf $\varphi(X_1, \ldots, X_n, Y_1, \ldots, Y_m)$. *Then*

$$\vdash (E_1W)(W \subseteq V^n \wedge (x_1)\ldots(x_n)(\langle x_1, \ldots, x_n\rangle \in W \equiv \varphi(x_1, \ldots, x_n, Y_1, \ldots, Y_m)))$$

PROOF. By Proposition 4.4, there is some Z such that

$$(x_1)\ldots(x_n)(\langle x_1, \ldots, x_n\rangle \in Z \equiv \varphi(x_1, \ldots, x_n, Y_1, \ldots, Y_m))$$

Clearly, $W = Z \cap V^n$ satisfies the corollary, and the uniqueness follows from the Axiom of Extensionality.

DEFINITION. Given any predicative wf $\varphi(X_1, \ldots, X_n, Y_1, \ldots, Y_m)$, we shall use $\hat{x}_1\hat{x}_2\ldots\hat{x}_n\varphi(x_1, \ldots, x_n, Y_1, \ldots, Y_m)$ to denote the class of all n-tuples $\langle x_1, \ldots, x_n\rangle$ satisfying $\varphi(x_1, \ldots, x_n, Y_1, \ldots, Y_m)$, i.e., $(u)(u \in \hat{x}_1\ldots\hat{x}_n\varphi(x_1, \ldots, x_n, Y_1, \ldots, Y_m) \equiv (Ex_1)\ldots(Ex_n)(u = \langle x_1, \ldots, x_n\rangle \wedge \varphi(x_1, \ldots, x_n, Y_1, \ldots, Y_m))$. This definition is justified by Corollary 4.5. In particular, when n = 1, $\vdash (u)(u \in \hat{x}\varphi(x, Y_1, \ldots, Y_m) \equiv \varphi(u, Y_1, \ldots, Y_m))$.†

Examples

1. Take φ to be $\langle x_2, x_1\rangle \in Y$. Let $\breve{Y}$ be an abbreviation for $\hat{x}_1\hat{x}_2(\langle x_2, x_1\rangle \in Y)$. Hence, $\breve{Y} \subseteq V^2 \wedge (x_1)(x_2)(\langle x_1, x_2\rangle \in \breve{Y} \equiv \langle x_2, x_1\rangle \in Y)$. Call $\breve{Y}$ the *inverse relation* of Y.

2. Take φ to be $(Ev)(\langle v, x\rangle \in Y)$. Let $\mathscr{R}(Y)$ stand for $\hat{x}((Ev)(\langle v, x\rangle \in Y))$. Then $\vdash (u)(u \in \mathscr{R}(Y) \equiv (Ev)(\langle v, u\rangle \in Y))$. $\mathscr{R}(Y)$ is called the *range* of Y. Clearly, $\vdash \mathscr{R}(Y) = \mathscr{D}(\breve{Y})$.

Notice that Axioms B1–B7 are special cases of the Class Existence Theorem, Proposition 4.4. Thus, instead of having to assume Proposition 4.4 as an axiom schema, we need only take a finite number of instances of that schema. Until now, although we can prove, via Proposition 4.4, the existence of a great many classes, the existence of only a few sets, such as 0, {0}, {0, {0}}, {{0}}, etc., is known to us. To guarantee the existence of sets of greater complexity, we require more axioms.

AXIOM U (Sum Set). $(x)(Ey)(u)(u \in y \equiv (Ev)(u \in v \wedge v \in x))$.

This axiom asserts that the sum class $\bigcup(x)$ of a set x (cf. Example 3, page 166) is also a set, which we shall call the *sum set* of x, i.e., $\vdash (x)(M(\bigcup(x)))$. The sum set $\bigcup(x)$ is usually referred to as the union of all the sets in the set x, and is often denoted $\bigcup_{v \in x} v$.

EXERCISES

1. Show that $\vdash (x)(y)(\bigcup(\{x, y\}) = x \cup y)$. Hence, $\vdash (x)(y)(M(x \cup y))$.

2. (a) $\vdash \bigcup(0) = 0$. (b) $\vdash \bigcup(\{0\}) = 0$. (c) $\vdash (x)(\bigcup(\{x\}) = x)$. (d) $\vdash (x)(y)(\bigcup(\langle x, y\rangle) = \{x, y\})$.

3. We can define by induction, $\{x_1, \ldots, x_n\}$ for $\{x_1, \ldots, x_{n-1}\} \cup \{x_n\}$. Then $\vdash (x_1)(x_2)\ldots(x_n)(u)(u \in \{x_1, \ldots, x_n\} \equiv u = x_1 \vee u = x_2 \vee \ldots \vee u = x_n)$. Thus, for any given sets $x_1, \ldots, x_n$, there is a set which has $x_1, \ldots, x_n$ as its only members.

† Sometimes, instead of $\hat{x}_1, \hat{x}_2, \ldots, \hat{x}_n\varphi(x_1, \ldots, x_n, Y_1, \ldots, Y_m)$, one uses $\{\langle x_1, x_2, \ldots, x_n\rangle \mid \varphi(x_1, \ldots, x_n, Y_1, \ldots, Y_m)\}$.

Another means of generating new sets from old is the formation of the set of all subsets of a given set.

AXIOM W (Power Set). $(x)(Ey)(u)(u \in y \equiv u \subseteq x)$.

This axiom asserts that the power class $\mathscr{P}(x)$ of a set x (cf. Example 2, page 166) is also a set, called the *power set* of x, i.e., $\vdash (x)(M(\mathscr{P}(x)))$.

Examples. $\vdash \mathscr{P}(0) = \{0\}$
$\vdash \mathscr{P}(\{0\}) = \{0, \{0\}\}$
$\vdash \mathscr{P}(\{0, \{0\}\}) = \{0, \{0\}, \{0, \{0\}\}, \{\{0\}\}\}$

A much more general way to produce sets is the following *Axiom of Subsets*.

AXIOM S. $(x)(Y)(Ez)(u)(u \in z \equiv u \in x \wedge u \in Y)$.

Thus, for any set x and class Y, there is a set consisting of the common elements of x and Y. Hence, $\vdash (x)(Y)(M(x \cap Y))$, i.e., the intersection of a set and a class is a set.

PROPOSITION 4.6. $\vdash (x)(Y)(Y \subseteq x \supset M(Y))$ (i.e., any subclass of a set is a set).

PROOF. $\vdash (x)(Y \subseteq x \supset Y \cap x = Y)$, and $\vdash (x)M(Y \cap x)$.

Since any predicative wf $\mathscr{A}(y)$ generates a corresponding class (cf. Proposition 4.4), Axiom S implies that, given any set x, the class of all elements of x which satisfy $\mathscr{A}(y)$ is a set.

A stronger axiom than the Axiom of Subsets (S) will be necessary for the full development of set theory. First, we introduce a few definitions.

DEFINITIONS

$Un(X)$ for $(x)(y)(z)(\langle x, y\rangle \in X \wedge \langle x, z\rangle \in X \supset y = z)$ (X is univocal.)

$Fnc(X)$ for $X \subseteq V^2 \wedge Un(X)$. ($X$ is a function.)

$Y \upharpoonright X$ for $X \cap (Y \times V)$. (Restriction of X to the domain Y.)

$Un_1(X)$ for $Un(X) \wedge Un(\check{X})$. ($X$ is one-one.)

$$X \text{`} Y = \begin{cases} z & \text{if } (u)(\langle Y, u\rangle \in X \equiv u = z), \\ 0 & \text{otherwise.} \end{cases}$$

If there is a unique z such that $\langle y, z\rangle \in X$, then $z = X \text{`} y$; otherwise, $X \text{`} y = 0$. If X is a function and y is a set in its domain, $X \text{`} y$ is the value of the function applied to y.†

† From here on, we shall introduce new function letters or individual constants wherever it is made clear that the definition is based upon a uniqueness theorem. In this case, we have introduced a new function letter $h(X, Y)$ abbreviated $X \text{`} Y$.

$X \text{ ``} Y = \mathscr{R}(Y \upharpoonright X)$ (If $X$ is a function, $X \text{ ``} Y$ is the range of X restricted to Y.)

AXIOM R (Replacement).

$$(x)(Un(X) \supset (Ey)(u)(u \in y \equiv (Ev)(\langle v, u\rangle \in X \wedge v \in x)))$$

Axiom R asserts that if X is univocal, then the class of second components of ordered pairs in X whose first components are in x is a set (or, equivalently, $M(\mathscr{R}(x \upharpoonright X))$). When X is a function, this implies that the range of the restriction of the function X to a domain which is a set is also a set.

EXERCISES

1. Show that the Axiom of Replacement (R) implies the Axiom of Subsets (S). (Hint: let $X = \hat{y}_1\hat{y}_2(y_1 = y_2 \wedge y_1 \in Y)$, i.e., X is the class of all ordered pairs $\langle u, u\rangle$ where $u \in Y$. Clearly, $Un(X)$ and $((Ev)(\langle v, u\rangle \in X \wedge v \in x)) \equiv u \in Y \cap x)$.
2. $\vdash (x)(M(\mathscr{D}(x)) \wedge M(\mathscr{R}(x)))$. (Suggestion: show that $\mathscr{D}(x) \subseteq \bigcup(\bigcup(x))$ and $\mathscr{R}(x) \subseteq \bigcup(\bigcup(x))$; apply Proposition 4.6 and Axiom U.)
3. $\vdash (x)(y)(M(x \times y))$. (Hint: show that $x \times y \subseteq \mathscr{P}(\mathscr{P}(x \cup y))$. Apply Proposition 4.6 and Axiom P.)
4. (a) $\vdash M(\mathscr{D}(X)) \wedge M(\mathscr{R}(X)) \wedge Rel(X) \supset M(X)$. (Hint: $X \subseteq \mathscr{D}(X) \times \mathscr{R}(X)$.)
   (b) $\vdash (y)(Fnc(X) \supset M(y \upharpoonright X))$. (Hint: $Fnc(y \upharpoonright X) \wedge \mathscr{D}(y \upharpoonright X) \subseteq y$. By Axiom R, $M(X \text{ ``} y)$.)

To insure the existence of an infinite set, we add the following axiom.

AXIOM I (Axiom of Infinity).

$$(Ex)(0 \in x \wedge (u)(u \in x \supset u \cup \{u\} \in x))$$

Axiom I states that there is a set x which contains 0 and such that, whenever $u \in x$, then $u \cup \{u\}$ also belongs to x. Clearly, for such a set x, $\{0\} \in x$, $\{0, \{0\}\} \in x$, $\{0, \{0\}, \{0, \{0\}\}\} \in x$, etc. Intuitively, if we let 1 stand for $\{0\}$, 2 for $\{0, 1\}$, 3 for $\{0, 1, 2\}$, ..., n for $\{0, 1, 2, \ldots, n-1\}$, ..., then, for all integers $n \geqslant 0$, $n \in x$; and $0 \neq 1$, $0 \neq 2$, $1 \neq 2$, $0 \neq 3$, $1 \neq 3$, $2 \neq 3$, ...

EXERCISE. Prove that Axiom I implies Axiom N†. Also prove that any formula which implies $(EX)(M(X))$ would also, together with Axiom S, imply Axiom N.

† In Axiom I, replace "$0 \in x$" by "$(Ey)(y \in x \wedge (u)(u \notin y))$", so that we do not presuppose Axiom N in the formulation of Axiom I.

This completes the list of axioms of NBG, and we see that NBG has only a finite number of axioms: namely, Axiom T (Extensionality), Axiom P (Pairing), Axiom N (Null Set), Axiom S (Subsets), Axiom U (Sum Set), Axiom W (Power Set), Axiom R (Replacement), Axiom I (Infinity), and the seven class existence axioms B1–B7. We have also seen that Axioms N and S are provable from the other axioms; however, they have been included here because they are of interest in the study of certain weaker subtheories of NBG.

Let us verify now that Russell's Paradox is not derivable in NBG. Let $Y = \hat{x}(x \notin x)$. Hence, $(x)(x \in Y \equiv x \notin x)$. (Such a class Y exists by the Class Existence Theorem, Proposition 4.4, since $x \notin x$ is a predicative wf.) This, in unabbreviated notation, is $(X)(M(X) \supset (X \in Y \equiv X \notin X))$. Assume $M(Y)$. Then $Y \in Y \equiv Y \notin Y$, which by the tautology $(A \equiv \sim A) \supset (A \wedge \sim A)$, implies $Y \in Y \wedge Y \notin Y$. Hence, by the Deduction Theorem, $\vdash M(Y) \supset (Y \in Y \wedge Y \notin Y)$, and so, by the tautology $(B \supset (A \wedge \sim A)) \supset \sim B$, $\vdash \sim M(Y)$. Thus, in NBG, the argument for Russell's Paradox merely shows that Russell's class Y is a proper class, not a set. This is typical of the way NBG avoids the usual paradoxes (Cantor, Burali-Forti).

EXERCISE. $\vdash \sim M(V)$. (The universal class is not a set.) (Hint: $V = \hat{x}(x = x)$. Now, for Russell's class $Y = \hat{x}(x \notin x)$, we have shown that $\sim M(Y)$. But $Y \subseteq V$. Apply Proposition 4.6.)

§2. Ordinal Numbers

Let us first define some familiar notions concerning relations.

DEFINITIONS

$X\ Irr\ Y$ for $(y)(y \in Y \supset \langle y, y\rangle \notin X) \wedge Rel(X)$. ($X$ is an *irreflexive* relation on Y.)

$X\ Tr\ Y$ for $Rel(X) \wedge (u)(v)(w)(u \in Y \wedge v \in Y \wedge w \in Y \wedge \langle u, v\rangle \in X \wedge \langle v, w\rangle \in X \supset \langle u, w\rangle \in X)$. ($X$ is a *transitive* relation on Y.)

$X\ Part\ Y$ for $(X\ Irr\ Y) \wedge (X\ Tr\ Y)$. ($X$ *partially orders* Y.)

$X\ Con\ Y$ for $Rel(X) \wedge (u)(v)(u \in Y \wedge v \in Y \wedge u \neq v \supset \langle u, v\rangle \in X \vee \langle v, u\rangle \in X)$. ($X$ is a *connected* relation on Y.)

$X\ Tot\ Y$ for $(X\ Irr\ Y) \wedge (X\ Tr\ Y) \wedge (X\ Con\ Y)$. ($X$ *totally orders* Y.)

$X \; We \; Y$ for $Rel(X) \wedge (X \; Irr \; Y) \wedge (Z)(Z \subseteq Y \wedge Z \neq 0 \supset (Ey)(y \in Z \wedge (v)(v \in Z \wedge v \neq y \supset \langle y, v \rangle \in X \wedge \langle v, y \rangle \notin X))$.
(X *well-orders* Y, i.e., the relation X is irreflexive on Y and every non-empty subclass of Y has a least element with respect to X.)

EXERCISES

1. $\vdash (X \; We \; Y) \supset (X \; Tot \; Y)$. (Hint: to show $X \; Con \; Y$, let $x, y \in Y$ with $x \neq y$. Then $\{x, y\}$ has a least element, say x. Then $\langle x, y \rangle \in X$. To show $X \; Tr \; Y$, let $x, y, z \in Y$ with $\langle x, y \rangle \subset X \wedge \langle y, z \rangle \in X$. Then $\{x, y, z\}$ has a least element, which must be x.)
2. $\vdash (X \; We \; Y) \wedge (Z \subseteq Y) \supset (X \; We \; Z)$.

Examples (from intuitive set theory).

1. The relation $<$ on the set of positive integers P well-orders P.
2. The relation $<$ on the set of all integers totally orders, but does not well-order, this set.
3. The relation $\subset$ on the set W of all subsets of the set of integers partially orders W, but does not totally order W. (For example, $\{1\} \not\subset \{2\}$ and $\{2\} \not\subset \{1\}$.)

DEFINITION. $Sim(Z, W_1, W_2)$ for $(Ex_1)(Ex_2)(Er_1)(Er_2)(Rel(r_1) \wedge Rel(r_2) \wedge W_1 = \langle r_1, x_1 \rangle \wedge W_2 = \langle r_2, x_2 \rangle \wedge Fnc(Z) \wedge Un_1(Z) \wedge \mathscr{D}(Z) = x_1 \wedge \mathscr{R}(Z) = x_2 \wedge (u)(v)(u \in x_1 \wedge v \in x_1 \supset (\langle u, v \rangle \in r_1 \equiv \langle Z \text{ ` } u, Z \text{ ` } v \rangle \in r_2))$. ($Z$ is a *similarity mapping* of the relation r_1 on x_1 onto the relation r_2 on x_2.)

DEFINITION. $Sim(W_1, W_2)$ for $(Ez)Sim(z, W_1, W_2)$. (W_1 and W_2 are *similar ordered structures*.)

Example. Let r_1 be the relation $<$ on the set of non-negative integers Nn, and let r_2 be the relation $<$ on the set of positive integers P. Let z be the set of all ordered pairs $\langle x, x + 1 \rangle$ for $x \in \text{Nn}$. Then z is a similarity mapping of $\langle r_1, \text{Nn} \rangle$ onto $\langle r_2, \text{P} \rangle$.

EXERCISES

1. $\vdash Sim(Z, X, Y) \supset Sim(\check{Z}, Y, X)$
2. $\vdash Sim(Z, X, Y) \supset M(Z) \wedge M(X) \wedge M(Y)$

DEFINITIONS

$Fld(X)$	for	$\mathscr{D}(X) \cup \mathscr{R}(X)$.	(The *field* of X.)
$TOR(X)$	for	$Rel(X) \wedge (X\ Tot\ (Fld(X)))$.	(X is a total order.)
$WOR(X)$	for	$Rel(X) \wedge (X\ We\ (Fld(X)))$.	(X is a well-ordering relation.)

EXERCISES

1. $\vdash (Sim(X, Y) \supset Sim(Y, X)) \wedge (Sim(X, Y) \wedge Sim(Y, U) \supset Sim(X, U))$
2. $\vdash Sim(\langle X, Fld(X)\rangle, \langle Y, Fld(Y)\rangle) \supset (TOR(X) \equiv TOR(Y)) \wedge (WOR(X) \equiv WOR(Y))$

If x is a total-order, then, the class of all total orders similar to x is called the order type of x. We are especially interested in the order types of well-ordering relations, but, since, in NBG, it turns out that all order types are proper classes (except the order type $\{0\}$ of 0), it is convenient to find a class W of well-ordered structures such that every well-ordering is similar to a unique element of W. This leads us to the study of ordinal numbers.

DEFINITIONS

E	for	$\hat{x}\hat{y}(x \in y)$. (The membership relation.)
$Trans(X)$	for	$(u)(u \in X \supset u \subseteq X)$. ($X$ is transitive.)
$Sect_Y(X, Z)$	for	$Z \subseteq X \wedge (u)(v)(u \in X \wedge v \in Z \wedge \langle u, v\rangle \in Y \supset u \in Z)$. ($Z$ is a Y-section of X.)

$Seg_Y(X, U) = \hat{x}(x \in X \wedge \langle x, U\rangle \in Y.)$
(The Y-segment of X determined by U.)

EXERCISES

1. $\vdash Trans(X) \equiv \bigcup(X) \subseteq X$
2. $\vdash Trans(X) \wedge Trans(Y) \supset Trans(X \cup Y) \wedge Trans(X \cap Y)$
3. $\vdash Seg_E(X, u) = \hat{x}(x \in X \wedge x \in u) \wedge Seg_E(Y, u) \subseteq Y \cap u \wedge M(Seg_E(Y, u))$
4. $\vdash Trans(X) \equiv (u)(u \in X \supset Seg_E(X, u) = u)$
5. $\vdash (E\ We\ X) \wedge Sect_E(X, Z) \wedge Z \neq X \supset (Eu)(u \in X \wedge Z = Seg_E(X, u)$ (Hint: let u be the least $\in$-element of $X - Z$.)

DEFINITIONS

$Ord(X)$ for $(E\ We\ X) \wedge Trans(X)$
(X is an *ordinal class* if and only if the $\in$-relation well-orders X and any member of X is a subset of X.)

On for $\hat{x}(Ord(x))$ (i.e., $\vdash (x)(x \in On \equiv Ord(x))$)

An ordinal class which is a set is called an *ordinal number*. *On* is the class of all ordinal numbers. Notice that a wf $x \in On$ is equivalent to a predicative wf, namely the conjunction of the wfs

(a) $(u)(u \in x \supset u \notin u)$; (b) $(u)(u \subseteq x \wedge u \neq 0 \supset (Ev)(v \in u \wedge (w)(w \in u \wedge w \neq v \supset v \in w \wedge w \notin v)))$; (c) $(u)(u \in x \supset u \subseteq x)$.

(The first conjunct is equivalent to $(E\ Irr\ x)$, the second to $(E\ We\ x)$, and the third to $Trans(x)$.) Hence any wf which is predicative except for the presence of "*On*" is equivalent to a predicative wf, and, therefore, can be used in connection with the Class Existence Theorem. (Any wf $On \in Y$ can be replaced by $(Ey)(y \in Y \wedge (z)(z \in y \equiv z \in On))$.)

Examples

1. $\vdash 0 \in On$.
2. Let 1 stand for $\{0\}$. Then $\vdash 1 \in On$.

We shall use small Greek letters $\alpha, \beta, \gamma, \delta, \tau, \ldots$ as restricted variables for ordinal numbers. Thus, $(\alpha)\mathscr{A}(\alpha)$ stands for $(x)(x \in On \supset \mathscr{A}(x))$, and $(E\alpha)\mathscr{A}(\alpha)$ stands for $(Ex)(x \in On \wedge \mathscr{A}(x))$.

PROPOSITION 4.7

(1) $\vdash Ord(X) \supset (X \notin X \wedge (u)(u \in X \supset u \notin u))$
(2) $\vdash Ord(X) \wedge Y \subset X \wedge Trans(Y) \supset Y \in X$
(3) $\vdash (Ord(X) \wedge Ord(Y)) \supset (Y \subset X \equiv Y \in X)$
(4) $\vdash Ord(X) \wedge Ord(Y) \supset (X \in Y \vee X = Y \vee Y \in X) \wedge \sim(X \in Y \wedge Y \in X) \wedge \sim(X \in Y \wedge X = Y)$
(5) $\vdash Ord(X) \wedge Y \in X \supset Y \in On$
(6) $\vdash E\ We\ On$
(7) $\vdash Ord(On)$
(8) $\vdash \sim M(On)$
(9) $\vdash Ord(X) \supset X = On \vee X \in On$

PROOF

(1) If $Ord(X)$, then E is irreflexive on X; so, $(u)(u \in X \supset u \notin u)$; and if $X \in X$, $X \notin X$. Hence, $X \notin X$.

(2) Assume $Ord(X) \wedge Y \subset X \wedge Trans(Y)$. It is easy to see that Y is a proper E-section of X. Hence, by Exercises 4–5 (page 172), $Y \in X$.

(3) Assume $Ord(X) \wedge Ord(Y)$. If $Y \in X$, then $Y \subseteq X$, since X is transitive; but $Y \neq X$ by (1); so, $Y \subset X$. Conversely, if $Y \subset X$, then, since Y is transitive, we have $Y \in X$, by (2).

(4) Assume $Ord(X) \wedge Ord(Y) \wedge X \neq Y$. Now, $X \cap Y \subseteq X$ and $X \cap Y \subseteq Y$. Since X and Y are transitive, so is $X \cap Y$. If $X \cap Y \subset X$ and $X \cap Y \subset Y$, then, by (2), $X \cap Y \in X$ and $X \cap Y \in Y$; hence, $X \cap Y \in X \cap Y$, contradicting the irreflexivity of E on X. Hence, either $X \cap Y = X$ or $X \cap Y = Y$, i.e., $X \subseteq Y$ or $Y \subseteq X$.

But $X \neq Y$. Hence, by (3), $X \in Y$ or $Y \in X$. Also, if $X \in Y$ and $Y \in X$, then, by (3), $X \subset Y$ and $Y \subset X$, which is impossible. Clearly, $X \in Y \wedge X = Y$ is impossible, by (1).

(5) Assume $Ord(X) \wedge Y \in X$. We must show: $E\ We\ Y$ and $Trans(Y)$. Since $Y \in X$ and $Trans(X)$, $Y \subset X$. Hence, since $E\ We\ X$, $E\ We\ Y$. Moreover, if $u \in Y$ and $v \in u$, then, by $Trans(X)$, $v \in X$. Since $E\ Con\ X$ and $Y \in X \wedge v \in X$, then $v \in Y$ or $v = Y$ or $Y \in v$. If either $v = Y$ or $Y \in v$, then, since $E\ Tr\ X$ and $u \in Y \wedge v \in u$, we would have $u \notin u$, contradicting (1). Hence, $v \in Y$. So, if $u \in Y$, then $u \subseteq Y$, i.e., $Trans(Y)$.

(6) By (1), $E\ Irr\ On$. Now, assume $X \subseteq On \wedge X \neq 0$. Let $\alpha \in X$. If α is the least element of X, we are done. (By *least element* of X, we mean an element $v \in X$ such that $(u)(u \in X \wedge u \neq v \supset v \in u)$.) If not, then $E\ We\ \alpha$, and $X \cap \alpha \neq 0$; let β be the least element of $X \cap \alpha$. It is obvious, using (4), that β is the least element of X.

(7) We must show $E\ We\ On$ and $Trans(On)$. The first part is (6). For the second, if $u \in On$ and $v \in u$, then, by (5), $v \in On$. Hence, $Trans(On)$.

(8) If $M(On)$, then, by (7), $On \in On$, contradicting (1).

(9) Assume $Ord(X)$. Then $X \subseteq On$. If $X \neq On$, then, by (3), $X \in On$.

We see, from Proposition 4.7(9), that the only ordinal class which is not an ordinal number is the class On itself.

DEFINITION. $x <_0 y$ for $x \in On \wedge y \in On \wedge x \in y$
$x \leqslant_0 y$ for $y \in On \wedge (x = y \vee x <_0 y)$

Thus, for ordinals, $<_0$ is the same as $\in$; so, $<_0$ well-orders On. In particular, from Proposition 4.7(5), we see that any ordinal x is equal to the set of smaller ordinals.

PROPOSITION 4.8 (Transfinite Induction)

$$\vdash (\beta)((\alpha)(\alpha \in \beta \supset \alpha \in X) \supset \beta \in X) \supset On \subseteq X$$

(If, for any β, whenever all ordinals $<_0 \beta$ are in X, then β is in X, then all ordinals are in X.)

PROOF. Assume that $(\beta)((\alpha)(\alpha \in \beta \supset \alpha \in X) \supset \beta \in X)$. Assume there is an ordinal in $On - X$. Then, since On is well-ordered by E, there is a least ordinal β in $On - X$. Hence all ordinals $<_0 \beta$ are in X. So, by our hypothesis, β is in X, which is a contradiction.

Proposition 4.8 is used to prove that all ordinals have a given property $P(\alpha)$. We let $X = \hat{x}(P(x) \wedge x \in On)$ and show that $(\beta)((\alpha)(\alpha \in \beta \supset P(\alpha)) \supset P(\beta))$.

DEFINITION. x' for $x \cup \{x\}$

PROPOSITION 4.9

(1) $\vdash (x)(x \in On \equiv x' \in On)$
(2) $\vdash (\alpha) \sim (E\beta)(\alpha <_0 \beta <_0 \alpha')$
(3) $\vdash (\alpha)(\beta)(\alpha' = \beta' \supset \alpha = \beta)$

PROOF

(1) $x \in x'$. Hence, if $x' \in On$, then $x \in On$, by Proposition 4.7(5). Conversely, assume $x \in On$. We must prove $E\ We\ (x \cup \{x\})$ and $Trans(x \cup \{x\})$. Since $E\ We\ x$ and $x \notin x$, $E\ Irr\ (\hat{x} \cup \{x\})$. Also, if $y \neq 0 \wedge y \subseteq (x \cup \{x\})$, then either $y = \{x\}$, in which case the least element of y is x, or $y \cap x \neq 0$; the least element of $y \cap x$ is then the least element of y. Hence, $E\ We\ (x \cup \{x\})$. Also, if $y \in x \cup \{x\}$ and $u \in y$, then $u \in x$. Thus, $Trans(x \cup \{x\})$.

(2) Assume $\alpha <_0 \beta <_0 \alpha'$. Then $\alpha \in \beta \wedge \beta \in \alpha'$. Since $\alpha \in \beta$, $\beta \notin \alpha$, and $\beta \neq \alpha$, by Proposition 4.7(4), contradicting $\beta \in \alpha'$.

(3) Assume $\alpha' = \beta'$. Then $\beta <_0 \alpha'$, and, by Part (2), $\beta \leqslant_0 \alpha$. Similarly, $\alpha \leqslant_0 \beta$. Hence, $\alpha = \beta$.

DEFINITION. $Suc(X)$ for $X \in On \wedge (E\alpha)(X = \alpha')$. ($X$ is a successor ordinal)

DEFINITION. K_I for $\hat{x}(x = 0 \vee Suc(x))$. (The class of ordinals of the first kind)

DEFINITION. ω for $\hat{x}(x \in K_I \wedge (u)(u \in x \supset u \in K_I))$

ω is the class of all ordinals α of the first kind such that all ordinals $<_0 \alpha$ are also of the first kind

Examples. $0 \in \omega$. $1 = \{0\} \in \omega$.

PROPOSITION 4.10

(1) $M(\omega)$
(2) $(\alpha)(\alpha \in \omega \equiv \alpha' \in \omega)$
(3) $0 \in X \wedge (u)(u \in X \supset u' \in X) \supset \omega \subseteq X$
(4) $(\alpha)(\alpha \in \omega \wedge \beta <_0 \alpha \supset \beta \in \omega)$

PROOF

(1) By the Axiom of Infinity I, there is a set x such that $0 \in x$ and $(u)(u \in x \supset u' \in x)$. We shall prove $\omega \subseteq x$. Assume not. Let α be the least ordinal in $\omega - x$. Clearly, $\alpha \neq 0$, since $0 \in x$. Hence, $Suc(\alpha)$. So, $(E\beta)(\alpha = \beta')$. Let δ be an ordinal such that $\alpha = \delta'$. Then $\delta <_0 \alpha$. Therefore, $\delta \in x$. Hence, $\delta' \in x$. But $\alpha = \delta'$. Therefore, $\alpha \in x$, which yields a contradiction. Thus, $\omega \subseteq x$. So, $M(\omega)$, by Proposition 4.6.

(2) Assume $\alpha \in \omega$. Now, $Suc(\alpha')$. Hence $\alpha' \in K_{\mathrm{I}}$. Also, if $\beta \in \alpha'$, then $\beta \in \alpha$ or $\beta = \alpha$. Hence, $\beta \in K_{\mathrm{I}}$. Thus, $\alpha' \in \omega$. Conversely, if $\alpha' \in \omega$, then, since $\alpha \in \alpha'$, and $(\beta)(\beta \in \alpha \supset \beta \in \alpha')$, it follows that $\alpha \in \omega$.

(3) Is proved by the procedure used in Part (1), and (4) is an easy exercise.

The elements of ω are called *finite ordinals*. We shall use the standard notation: 1 for $0'$; 2 for $1'$; 3 for $2'$, etc. Thus, $0 \in \omega$, $1 \in \omega$, $2 \in \omega$, $3 \in \omega, \ldots$.

The non-zero ordinals which are not successor ordinals are called *limit ordinals*, or ordinals of the second kind.

DEFINITION. $Lim(x)$ for $x \in On \wedge x \notin K_{\mathrm{I}}$.

EXERCISE. $\vdash Lim(\omega)$.

PROPOSITION 4.11

(1) $\vdash (x)(x \subseteq On \supset (\bigcup(x) \in On \wedge (\alpha)(\alpha \in x \supset \alpha \leqslant_0 \bigcup(x)) \wedge (\beta)((\alpha)(\alpha \in x \supset \alpha \leqslant_0 \beta) \supset \bigcup(x) \leqslant_0 \beta)))$. (If x is a set of ordinals, then $\bigcup(x)$ is an ordinal which is the least upper bound of x.)

(2) $\vdash (x)(x \subseteq On \wedge x \neq 0 \wedge (\alpha)(\alpha \in x \supset (E\beta)(\beta \in x \wedge \alpha <_0 \beta)) \supset \mathrm{Lim}(\bigcup(x)))$. (If x is a non-empty set of ordinals without a maximum, then $\bigcup(x)$ is a limit ordinal.)

PROOF

(1) Assume $x \subseteq On$. $\bigcup(x)$, as a set of ordinals, is well-ordered by E. Also, if $\alpha \in \bigcup(x) \wedge \beta \in \alpha$, then there is some γ with $\gamma \in x \wedge \alpha \in \gamma$. Then $\beta \in \alpha$ and $\alpha \in \gamma$; since every ordinal is transitive, $\beta \in \gamma$. So, $\beta \in \bigcup(x)$. Hence, $\bigcup(x)$ is transitive, and therefore $\bigcup(x) \in On$. In addition, if $\alpha \in x$, then $\alpha \subseteq \bigcup(x)$; so, $\alpha \leqslant_0 \bigcup(x)$, by Proposition 4.7(3). Assume now that $(\alpha)(\alpha \in x \supset \alpha \leqslant_0 \beta)$. Clearly, if $\delta \in \bigcup(x)$, then there is some γ such that $\delta \in \gamma \wedge \gamma \in x$. Hence, $\gamma \leqslant_0 \beta$ and so, $\delta \leqslant_0 \beta$. Therefore, $\bigcup(x) \subseteq \beta$, and, by Proposition 4.7(3), $\bigcup(x) \leqslant_0 \beta$.

(2) Assume $x \neq 0 \wedge x \subseteq On \wedge (\alpha)(\alpha \in x \supset (E\beta)(\beta \in x \wedge \alpha <_0 \beta))$. If $\bigcup(x) = 0$, then, $\alpha \in x$ implies $\alpha = 0$. So, $x = 0$ or $x = 1$, which contradicts our assumption. Hence, $\bigcup(x) \neq 0$. Assume that $Suc(\bigcup(x))$. Then $\bigcup(x) = \gamma'$ for some γ. Since $\bigcup(x)$ is a least upper bound of x, by Part (1), γ is not an upper bound of x; and since x has no maximum, there is some $\delta \in x$ with $\gamma <_0 \delta$. But then $\delta = \bigcup(x)$, since $\bigcup(x)$ is an upper bound of x. Thus, $\bigcup(x)$ is a maximum element of x, contradicting our hypothesis. Hence $\sim Suc(\bigcup(x))$, and $Lim(x)$ is the only possibility left.

EXERCISE. $\vdash (\alpha)((Suc(\alpha) \supset (\bigcup(\alpha))' = \alpha) \wedge (Lim(\alpha) \supset \bigcup(\alpha) = \alpha))$

We can now state and prove another form of transfinite induction.

PROPOSITION 4.12 (Transfinite Induction: Second Form)

(1) $\vdash 0 \in X \wedge (\alpha)(\alpha \in X \supset \alpha' \in X) \wedge (\alpha)(Lim(\alpha) \wedge (\beta)(\beta <_0 \alpha \supset \beta \in X) \supset \alpha \in X) \supset On \subseteq X$

(2) (Induction up to δ) $\vdash 0 \in X \wedge (\alpha)(\alpha' <_0 \delta \wedge \alpha \in X \supset \alpha' \in X) \wedge (\alpha)(\alpha <_0 \delta \wedge Lim(\alpha) \wedge (\beta)(\beta <_0 \alpha \supset \beta \in X) \supset \alpha \in X) \supset \delta \subseteq X$

PROOF

(1) Assume the antecedent of the proposition. Let $Y = \hat{x}(x \in On \wedge (\alpha)(\alpha \leqslant_0 x \supset \alpha \in X))$. It is then easy to prove that $(\alpha)(\alpha <_0 \gamma \supset \alpha \in Y) \supset \gamma \in Y$. Hence, by Proposition 4.8, $On \subseteq Y$. But $Y \subseteq X$. Hence, $On \subseteq X$.

(2) is left as an exercise.

Set theory depends heavily upon definitions by transfinite induction, which are justified by the following theorems.

PROPOSITION 4.13

(1) $\vdash (X)(E_1 Y)(Fnc(Y) \wedge \mathscr{D}(Y) = On \wedge (\alpha)(Y \text{`} \alpha = X \text{`} (\alpha \upharpoonright Y)))$. (Given X, there is a unique function Y defined on all ordinals such that the value of Y at α is the value of X applied to the restriction of Y to the set of ordinals $<_0 \alpha$.)

(2) $\vdash (x)(X_1)(X_2)(E_1 Y)(Fnc(Y) \wedge \mathscr{D}(Y) = On \wedge Y \text{`} 0 = x \wedge (\alpha)(Y \text{`} (\alpha') = X_1 \text{`} (Y \text{`} \alpha)) \wedge (\alpha)(Lim(\alpha) \supset Y \text{`} \alpha = X_2 \text{`} (\alpha \upharpoonright Y)))$.

(3) (Induction up to δ) $\vdash (x)(X_1)(X_2)(E_1 Y)(Fnc(Y) \wedge \mathscr{D}(Y) = \delta \wedge Y \text{`} 0 = x \wedge (\alpha)(\alpha' <_0 \delta \supset Y \text{`} (\alpha') = X_1 \text{`} (Y \text{`} \alpha)) \wedge (\alpha)(Lim(\alpha) \wedge \alpha <_0 \delta \supset Y \text{`} \alpha = X_2 \text{`} (\alpha \upharpoonright Y)))$.

PROOF. (1) Let $Y_1 = \hat{u}(Fnc(u) \wedge \mathscr{D}(u) \in On \wedge (\alpha)(\alpha \in \mathscr{D}(u) \supset u \text{`} \alpha = X \text{`} (\alpha \upharpoonright u)))$. Now, if $u_1 \in Y_1$ and $u_2 \in Y_1$, then $u_1 \subseteq u_2$ or $u_2 \subseteq u_1$. For, let $\gamma_1 = \mathscr{D}(u_1)$ and $\gamma_2 = \mathscr{D}(u_2)$. Either $\gamma_1 \leqslant_0 \gamma_2$ or $\gamma_2 \leqslant_0 \gamma_1$, say $\gamma_1 \leqslant_0 \gamma_2$. Let w be the set of all ordinals $\alpha <_0 \gamma_1$ such that $u_1 \text{`} \alpha \neq u_2 \text{`} \alpha$; assume $w \neq 0$, and let η be the least ordinal in w. Then for all $\beta <_0 \eta$, $u_1 \text{`} \beta = u_2 \text{`} \beta$. Hence, $\eta \upharpoonright u_1 = \eta \upharpoonright u_2$. But $u_1 \text{`} \eta = X \text{`} (\eta \upharpoonright u_1)$ and $u_2 \text{`} \eta = X \text{`} (\eta \upharpoonright u_2)$; and so, $u_1 \text{`} \eta = u_2 \text{`} \eta$, contradicting our assumption. Therefore $w = 0$, i.e., for all $\alpha <_0 \gamma_1$, $u_1 \text{`} \alpha = u_2 \text{`} \alpha$. Hence, $u_1 = \gamma_1 \upharpoonright u_1 = \gamma_1 \upharpoonright u_2 \subseteq u_2$. Thus, any two functions in Y_1 agree in their common domain. Let $Y = \bigcup(Y_1)$. We leave it to the reader to prove that Y is a function the domain of which is either an ordinal or the class On, and $(\alpha)(Y \text{`} \alpha = X \text{`} (\alpha \upharpoonright Y))$. That $\mathscr{D}(Y) = On$ follows easily from the observation that if $\mathscr{D}(Y) = \delta$ and if we let $W = Y \cup \{\langle \delta, X \text{`} Y \rangle\}$, then $W \in Y_1$; so, $W \subseteq Y$ and $\delta \in \mathscr{D}(Y) = \delta$, which contradicts the fact that $\delta \notin \delta$. The uniqueness of Y follows by a simple transfinite induction (Proposition 4.12). The proof of (2) is similar to that of (1), and (3) follows from (2).

Using Proposition 4.13, one can introduce new function letters by transfinite induction.

Examples

1. Ordinal addition. In Proposition 4.13(2), take $x = \beta$, $X_1 = \hat{u}\hat{v}(v = u')$, $X_2 = \hat{u}\hat{v}(v = \bigcup(\mathscr{R}(u)))$. Hence, for each ordinal β, there is a unique function Y_β such that $Y_\beta \text{ ‘ } 0 = \beta \wedge (\alpha)(Y_\beta \text{ ‘ } (\alpha') = (Y_\beta \text{ ‘ } \alpha)') \wedge (\alpha)(Lim(\alpha) \supset Y_\beta \text{ ‘ } \alpha = \bigcup(Y_\beta \text{ “ } \alpha)))$. Hence, there is a unique binary function $+_0$ with domain On^2 such that, for any ordinals β and γ, $+_0(\beta, \gamma) = Y_\beta \text{ ‘ } \gamma$. As usual, we write $\beta +_0 \gamma$ instead of $+_0(\beta, \gamma)$. Notice that

$$\beta +_0 0 = \beta$$
$$\beta +_0 (\gamma') = (\beta +_0 \gamma)'$$
$$Lim(\alpha) \supset \beta +_0 \alpha = \bigcup_{\tau <_0 \alpha} (\beta +_0 \tau).$$

In particular,

$$\beta +_0 1 = \beta +_0 (0') = (\beta +_0 0)' = \beta'.$$

2. Ordinal multiplication. In Proposition 4.13(2), take $x = 0$, $X_1 = \hat{u}\hat{v}(v = u +_0 \beta)$; $X_2 = \hat{u}\hat{v}(v = \bigcup(\mathscr{R}(u)))$. Then, as in Example 1, one obtains a function $\beta \times_0 \gamma$ with the properties

$$\beta \times_0 0 = 0$$
$$\beta \times_0 (\gamma') = (\beta \times_0 \gamma) +_0 \beta$$
$$Lim(\alpha) \supset \beta \times_0 \alpha = \bigcup_{\tau <_0 \alpha} (\beta \times_0 \tau)$$

EXERCISE

Justify the definition of ordinal exponentiation:

$$\beta^0 = 1$$
$$\beta^{(\gamma')} = (\beta^\gamma) \times_0 \beta$$
$$Lim(\alpha) \supset \beta^\alpha = \bigcup_{0 <_0 \tau <_0 \alpha} (\beta^\tau)$$

For any set X, let E_X be the membership relation restricted to X, i.e., $E_X = \hat{x}\hat{y}(x \in y \wedge x \in X \wedge y \in X)$.

PROPOSITION 4.14.† *Let R be a well-ordering relation on a set x, i.e.,*

† From this point on we shall express many theorems of NBG in English by using the corresponding informal English translations. This is done to avoid writing mile-long wfs which are difficult to decipher, and only in cases where the reader can easily produce from the English version the precise wf of NBG.

$R\ We\ x$. Let f be a function from x into x such that, for any u, v in x, if $\langle u, v\rangle \in R$, then $\langle f\text{ `} u, f\text{ `} v\rangle \in R$. Then, for all u in x, $u = f\text{ `} u \vee \langle u, f\text{ `} u\rangle \in R$.

PROOF. Let $X = \hat{u}(\langle f\text{ `} u, u\rangle \in R)$. We wish to show that $X = 0$. Assume $X \neq 0$. Since $X \subseteq x$ and $R$ well-orders $x$, there is an $R$-least element $u_0$ of $X$. Hence, $\langle f\text{ `} u_0, u_0\rangle \in R$. Therefore, $\langle f\text{ `}(f\text{ `} u_0), f\text{ `} u_0\rangle \in R$. Thus, $f\text{ `} u_0 \in X$, but $f\text{ `} u_0$ is R-smaller than u_0, contradicting the definition of u_0.

COROLLARY 4.15. *Let $\alpha \in \beta$ and $y \subseteq \alpha$, i.e., let y be a subset of a segment of β. Then $\langle E_\beta, \beta\rangle$ is not similar to $\langle E_y, y\rangle$.*

PROOF. Assume f is a function from β onto y such that, for u, v in β, if $u \in v$, then $f\text{ `} u \in f\text{ `} v$. Since the range of f is y, $f\text{ `}\alpha \in y$. But $y \subseteq \alpha$. Hence $f\text{ `}\alpha \in \alpha$. But, by Proposition 4.14 (taking $\beta = x$), $f\text{ `}\alpha = \alpha$ or $\alpha \in f\text{ `}\alpha$, which yields a contradiction.

COROLLARY 4.16. (1) *For $\alpha \neq \beta$, $\langle E_\alpha, \alpha\rangle$ and $\langle E_\beta, \beta\rangle$ are not similar.* (2) *For any α, if f is a similarity mapping of $\langle E_\alpha, \alpha\rangle$ with $\langle E_\alpha, \alpha\rangle$, then f is the identity mapping, i.e., $f\text{ `}\beta = \beta$ for all $\beta <_0 \alpha$.*

PROOF. (1) By Corollary 4.15. (2) By Proposition 4.14, $f\text{ `}\beta \geqslant_0 \beta$ for all $\beta <_0 \alpha$. But, also by Proposition 4.14, $(\breve{f})\text{ `}\beta \geqslant_0 \beta$ for all $\beta <_0 \alpha$. Hence, $\beta = (\breve{f})\text{ `}(f\text{ `}\beta) \geqslant_0 f\text{ `}\beta \geqslant_0 \beta$, and, therefore, $f\text{ `}\beta = \beta$.

PROPOSITION 4.17. *Assume that R is a well-ordering of a non-empty set u, i.e., $R\ We\ u \wedge u = Fld(R) \wedge u \neq 0$. Then there is a unique ordinal γ and a unique similarity mapping of $\langle E_\gamma, \gamma\rangle$ with $\langle R, u\rangle$, i.e., every well-ordered set is similar to a unique ordinal.*

PROOF. Let $Z = \hat{v}\hat{w}(w \in u - v \wedge (z)(z \in u - v \supset \sim\langle z, w\rangle \in R))$. Z is a function such that if v is a subset of u and $u - v \neq 0$, then $Z\text{ `} v$ is the $R$-least element of $u - v$. Let $X = \hat{v}\hat{w}(\langle \mathscr{R}(v), w\rangle \in Z)$. Now, we use a definition by transfinite induction (Proposition 4.13) to obtain a function $Y$ with $On$ as its domain such that $(\alpha)(Y\text{ `}\alpha = X\text{ `}(\alpha \upharpoonright Y))$. Let $W = \hat{\alpha}(Y\text{ ``}\alpha \subseteq u \wedge u - Y\text{ ``}\alpha \neq 0)$. Clearly, if $\alpha \in W$ and $\beta \in \alpha$, then $\beta \in W$. Hence, either $W = On$ or W is some ordinal γ. (For, if $W \neq On$, let γ be the least ordinal in $On - W$.) If $\alpha \in W$, then $Y\text{ `}\alpha = X\text{ `}(\alpha \upharpoonright Y)$ is the R-least element of $u - Y\text{ ``}\alpha$; so, $Y\text{ `}\alpha \in u$ and, if $\beta \in \alpha$, then $Y\text{ `}\alpha \neq Y\text{ `}\beta$. Thus, Y is a one-one function on W and the range of Y restricted to W is a subset of u. Now, let $f = \breve{(W \upharpoonright Y)}$, i.e., let f be the converse of Y restricted to W. Then f is a one-one function with domain a subset of u and range W. So, by the Replacement Axiom R (cf. page 169), W is a set. Hence, W is some ordinal γ. Let $g = \gamma \upharpoonright Y$; g is a one-one function with domain γ and range a subset u_1 of u. We must show that $u_1 = u$ and that, if α and β are in γ and $\beta \in \alpha$, then $\langle g \text{ ‘ } \beta, g \text{ ‘ } \alpha \rangle \in R$. Assume α and β are in γ and $\beta \in \alpha$. Since $g \text{ ‘ } \beta$ is the R-least element of $u - g \text{ “ } \beta$, $\beta \in \alpha$ and g is one-one, $g \text{ ‘ } \alpha \in u - g \text{ “ } \beta$. Hence, $\langle g \text{ ‘ } \beta, g \text{ ‘ } \alpha \rangle \in R$. It remains to prove that $u_1 = u$. Now, $u_1 = Y \text{ “ } \gamma$. Assume $u - u_1 \neq 0$. Then $\gamma \in W$. But $W = \gamma$, which yields a contradiction. Hence $u = u_1$. That γ is unique follows from Corollary 4.16.

PROPOSITION 4.18. *Let R be a well-ordering of a proper class X such that, for each $y \in X$, the class of all R-predecessors of y in X (i.e., the R-segment in X determined by y) is a set. Then R is similar to E_{On} i.e., there is a one-one mapping h of On onto X such that $\alpha \in \beta$ implies $\langle h \text{ ‘ } \alpha, h \text{ ‘ } \beta \rangle \in R$.*

PROOF. Proceed as in the proof of Proposition 4.17. Here, however, $W = On$; also, one proves that $\mathscr{R}(Y) = X$ by using the hypothesis that every R-segment of X is a set. (If $X - \mathscr{R}(Y) \neq 0$, then, if w is the R-least element of $X - \mathscr{R}(Y)$, On is the range of $\check{Y}$, while the domain of $\check{Y}$ is the R-segment of X determined by w, contradicting the Replacement Axiom.)

§ 3. Equinumerosity. Finite and Denumerable Sets

We say that two classes X and Y are *equinumerous* if and only if there is a one-one function F with domain X and range Y. We shall denote this by $X \simeq Y$.

DEFINITIONS

$X \underset{F}{\simeq} Y$ for $(Fnc(F) \wedge Un_1(F) \wedge \mathscr{D}(F) = X \wedge \mathscr{R}(F) = Y)$

$X \simeq Y$ for $(EF)(X \underset{F}{\simeq} Y)$

Notice that $\vdash (x)(y)(x \simeq y \equiv (Ez)(x \underset{z}{\simeq} y))$. Hence, a wf $x \simeq y$ is predicative (i.e., is equivalent to a wf using only set quantifiers).

Clearly, if $X \underset{F}{\simeq} Y$, then $Y \underset{\check{F}}{\simeq} X$; and if $X \underset{F}{\simeq} Y$ and $Y \underset{G}{\simeq} Z$, then $X \underset{H}{\simeq} Z$, where H is the *composition* of F and G (i.e., $H = \hat{x}\hat{y}((Ez)(\langle x, z \rangle \in F \wedge \langle z, y \rangle \in G))$. Hence, we have the following theorem.

PROPOSITION 4.19. (1) $X \simeq X$. (2) $X \simeq Y \supset Y \simeq X$. (3) $X \simeq Y \wedge Y \simeq Z \supset X \simeq Z$.

PROPOSITION 4.20. (1) $(X \simeq Y \wedge X_1 \simeq Y_1 \wedge X \cap X_1 = 0 \wedge Y \cap Y_1 = 0) \supset X \cup X_1 \simeq Y \cup Y_1$.
(2) $(X \simeq Y \wedge X_1 \simeq Y_1) \supset X \times X_1 \simeq Y \times Y_1$. (3) $X \times \{y\} \simeq X$.
(4) $X \times Y \simeq Y \times X$. (5) $(X \times Y) \times Z \simeq X \times (Y \times Z)$.

PROOF

(1) Let $X \underset{F}{\simeq} Y$ and $X_1 \underset{G}{\simeq} Y_1$. Then $X \cup X_1 \underset{F \cup G}{\simeq} Y \cup Y_1$.

(2) Let $X \underset{F}{\simeq} Y$ and $X_1 \underset{G}{\simeq} Y_1$. Let $W = \hat{u}\hat{v}((Ex)(Ey)(x \in X \wedge y \in X_1 \wedge u = \langle x, y\rangle \wedge v = \langle F \text{‘} x, G \text{‘} y\rangle)$. Then $X \times X_1 \underset{W}{\simeq} Y \times Y_1$.

(3) Let $F = \hat{u}\hat{v}(u \in X \wedge v = \langle u, y\rangle)$. Then $X \underset{F}{\simeq} X \times \{y\}$.

(4) Let $F = \hat{u}\hat{v}((Ex)(Ey)(x \in X \wedge y \in Y \wedge u = \langle x, y\rangle \wedge v = \langle y, x\rangle)$. Then $X \times Y \underset{F}{\simeq} Y \times X$.

(5) Let $F = \hat{u}\hat{v}((Ex)(Ey)(Ez)(x \in X \wedge y \in Y \wedge z \in Z \wedge u = \langle\langle x, y\rangle, z\rangle \wedge v = \langle x, \langle y, z\rangle\rangle)$. Then $(X \times Y) \times Z \underset{F}{\simeq} X \times (Y \times Z)$.

EXERCISE. Prove: $\vdash (X)(Y)(EX_1)(EY_1)(X \simeq X_1 \wedge Y \simeq Y_1 \wedge X_1 \cap Y_1 = 0)$.

DEFINITION. $X^Y = \hat{u}(Fnc(u) \wedge \mathscr{D}(u) = Y \wedge \mathscr{R}(u) \subseteq X)$.

X^Y is the class of all sets which are functions from Y into X. Remember that $2 = \{0, 1\}$. Hence, for any set x, $\mathscr{P}(x) \simeq 2^x$. (For any $u \subseteq x$, the characteristic function C_u is the function with domain x such that $C_u \text{‘} y = 0$ if $y \in u$ and $C_u \text{‘} y = 1$ if $y \notin u$. Let F be the function on $\mathscr{P}(x)$ mapping u into C_u. Then $\mathscr{P}(x) \underset{F}{\simeq} 2^x$.)

EXERCISES

1. $\vdash \sim M(Y) \supset X^Y = 0$
2. $\vdash (x)(y)M(x^y)$ (Hint: $u \in x^y \supset u \subseteq y \times x$)
3. $\vdash X^0 = \{0\} = 1$
4. $\vdash Y \neq 0 \supset 0^Y = 0$
5. $\vdash X \simeq Y \wedge Z \simeq Z_1 \supset X^Z \simeq Y^{Z_1}$
6. $\vdash X \cap Y = 0 \supset Z^{X \cup Y} \simeq Z^X \times Z^Y$
7. $\vdash (X^Y)^Z \simeq X^{Y \times Z}$ (Hint: let $F = \hat{u}\hat{v}(Fnc(u) \wedge \mathscr{D}(u) = Z \wedge \mathscr{R}(u) \subseteq X^Y \wedge Fnc(v) \wedge \mathscr{D}(v) = Y \times Z \wedge \mathscr{R}(v) \subseteq X \wedge (y)(z)(y \in Y \wedge z \in Z \supset v \text{‘} \langle y, z\rangle = (u \text{‘} z) \text{‘} y)$.)

One can define a partial order $\preceq$ on classes such that, intuitively, $X \preceq Y$ if X has the same number or fewer elements than Y.

DEFINITION. $X \preceq Y$ for $(EZ)(Z \subseteq Y \wedge X \simeq Z)$ (i.e., X is equinumerous with a subclass of Y).

DEFINITION. $X \prec Y$ for $X \preceq Y \wedge \sim(X \simeq Y)$

Hence, $\vdash X \preceq Y \equiv (X \prec Y \vee X \simeq Y)$.

EXERCISE. $\vdash X \preceq Y \wedge \sim M(X) \supset \sim M(Y)$

PROPOSITION 4.21

(1) $\vdash X \preceq X \wedge \sim(X \prec X)$
(2) $\vdash X \subseteq Y \supset X \preceq Y$
(3) $\vdash X \preceq Y \wedge Y \preceq Z \supset X \preceq Z$
(4) (Schröder-Bernstein) $\vdash X \preceq Y \wedge Y \preceq X \supset X \simeq Y$

PROOF

(3) Assume $X \underset{F}{\simeq} Y_1 \wedge Y_1 \subseteq Y \wedge Y \underset{G}{\simeq} Z_1 \wedge Z_1 \subseteq Z$. Let H be the composition of F and G. Then $\mathscr{R}(H) \subseteq Z \wedge X \underset{H}{\simeq} \mathscr{R}(H)$.

(4) There are many proofs of this non-trivial theorem. The following is a new one devised by Hellman [1961]. Lemma: Assume $X \cap Y = 0$, $X \cap Z = 0$, $Y \cap Z = 0$, and let $X \underset{F}{\simeq} X \cup Y \cup Z$. Then there is a G such that $X \underset{G}{\simeq} X \cup Y$. (Proof. Define a function H with domain $X \times \omega$ as follows: $\langle\langle u, k\rangle, v\rangle \in H$ if and only if $u \in X$ and $k \in \omega$ and there is a function f with domain k' such that $f\text{‘}0 = F\text{‘}u$ and, if $j \in k$, then $f\text{‘}j \in X \wedge f\text{‘}(j') = F\text{‘}(f\text{‘}j) \wedge f\text{‘}k = v$. Thus, $H\text{‘}(\langle u, 0\rangle) = F\text{‘}u$, $H\text{‘}(\langle u, 1\rangle) = F\text{‘}(F\text{‘}u)$ if $F\text{‘}u \in X$, and $H\text{‘}(\langle u, 2\rangle) = F\text{‘}(F\text{‘}(F\text{‘}u))$ if $F\text{‘}u$ and $F\text{‘}(F\text{‘}u)$ are in X, etc. Let $X^\star$ be the class of all $u \in X$ such that $(Ey)(y \in \omega \wedge \langle u, y\rangle \in \mathscr{D}(H) \wedge H\text{‘}(\langle u, y\rangle) \in Z)$. Let $Y^\star$ be the class of all $u \in X$ such that $(y)(y \in \omega \wedge \langle u, y\rangle \in \mathscr{D}(H) \supset H\text{‘}(\langle u, y\rangle) \notin Z)$. Then $X = X^\star \cup Y^\star$. Now define G as follows: $\mathscr{D}(G) = X$, and, if $u \in X^\star$, then $G\text{‘}u = u$, whereas if $u \in Y^\star$, then $G\text{‘}u = F\text{‘}u$. Then $X \underset{G}{\simeq} X \cup Y$ (Exercise).) Now, to prove the Schröder-Bernstein Theorem: assume $X \underset{F}{\simeq} Y_1 \wedge Y_1 \subseteq Y \wedge Y \underset{G}{\simeq} X_1 \wedge X_1 \subseteq X$. Let $A = G\text{“}Y_1 \subseteq X_1 \subseteq X$. But $A \cap (X_1 - A) = 0$, $A \cap (X - X_1) = 0$, and $(X - X_1) \cap (X_1 - A) = 0$. Also, $X = (X - X_1) \cup (X_1 - A) \cup A$, and the composition H of F and G is a one-one function with domain X and range A. Hence, $A \underset{\breve{H}}{\simeq} X$. So, by the Lemma, there is a one-one function D such that $A \underset{D}{\simeq} X_1$ (since $(X_1 - A) \cup A = X_1$). Let T be the composition of the functions H, D, $\breve{G}$, i.e., let $T\text{‘}u = (\breve{G})\text{‘}(D\text{‘}(H\text{‘}u))$. Then $X \underset{T}{\simeq} Y$, since $X \underset{H}{\simeq} A$ and $A \underset{D}{\simeq} X_1$ and $X_1 \underset{\breve{G}}{\simeq} Y$.

EXERCISE

Carry out the details of the following proof (due to J. Whitaker) of the Schröder-Bernstein Theorem in the case where X and Y are sets. Let $X \underset{F}{\simeq} Y_1 \wedge Y_1 \subseteq Y \wedge Y \underset{G}{\simeq} X_1 \wedge X_1 \subseteq X$. We wish to find a set $Z \subseteq X$ such that G, restricted to $Y - F\text{“}Z$, is a one-one function of $Y - F\text{“}Z$ onto $X - Z$. (If we have such a set Z, let $H = (Z \rceil F) \cup$

$((X - Z) \mathbin{1} \breve{G})$, i.e., $H\text{`}x = F\text{`}x$ for $x \in Z$ and $H\text{`}x = G\text{`}x$ for $x \in X - Z$. Then $X \underset{H}{\simeq} Y$.) Let $Z = \hat{x}((Eu)(u \subseteq X \land x \in u \land G\text{``}(Y - F\text{``}u) \subseteq X - u))$. Notice that this proof does not presuppose the definition of ω nor any other part of the theory of ordinals. For still another proof, cf. Kleene [1952, § 4].

PROPOSITION 4.22. *Assume* $X \preceq Y$ *and* $A \preceq B$. *Then,*

(1) $Y \cap B = 0 \supset X \cup A \preceq Y \cup B$
(2) $X \times A \preceq Y \times B$
(3) $X^A \preceq Y^B$

PROOF. (1) Assume $X \underset{F}{\simeq} Y_1 \subseteq Y$ and $A \underset{G}{\simeq} B_1 \subseteq B$. Let H be a function with domain $X \cup A$ such that $H\text{`}x = F\text{`}x$ if $x \in X$ and $H\text{`}x = G\text{`}x$ if $x \in A - X$. Then $X \cup A \underset{H}{\simeq} H\text{``}(X \cup A) \subseteq Y \cup B$. (2) and (3) are left as exercises.

EXERCISES

1. $\vdash X \preceq X \cup Y$
2. $\vdash X \prec Y \supset \sim(Y \preceq X)$
3. $\vdash X \prec Y \land Y \preceq Z \supset X \prec Z$

PROPOSITION 4.23 (Cantor's Theorem). $\vdash (x)(x \prec \mathscr{P}(x))$. *Hence,* $\vdash (x)(x \prec 2^x)$.

PROOF

(1) Let F be a function with domain x such that $F\text{`}u = \{u\}$ for any $u \in x$. Then $F\text{``}x \subseteq \mathscr{P}(x)$ and F is one-one. Hence, $x \preceq \mathscr{P}(x)$.

(2) We must prove that $\sim(x \simeq \mathscr{P}(x))$. Assume that $x \underset{G}{\simeq} \mathscr{P}(x)$. Let $y = \hat{u}(u \in x \land u \notin G\text{`}u)$. Then $y \in \mathscr{P}(x)$. Hence, there is a unique $z$ in $x$ such that $G\text{`}z = y$. Now, $(u)(u \in y \equiv u \in x \land u \notin G\text{`}u))$. Hence, $(u)(u \in G\text{`}z \equiv u \in x \land u \notin G\text{`}u)$. Therefore, by Rule A4, $z \in G\text{`}z \equiv z \in x \land z \notin G\text{`}z$. Since $z \in x$, we have $z \in G\text{`}z \equiv z \notin G\text{`}z$, which yields a contradiction.

Observe that we have not proved $\vdash (x)(y)(x \preceq y \lor y \preceq x)$. This proposition is, in fact, not yet provable, since it turns out to be equivalent to the Axiom of Choice.

EXERCISE

Notice that, if NBG is consistent, then it has a denumerable model (Proposition 2.12). Explain why this does not contradict Cantor's Theorem, which implies that there exist non-denumerable infinite sets (e.g., 2^ω). (This apparent, but not real, contradiction is sometimes called Skolem's Paradox.)

The equinumerosity relation $\simeq$ has all the properties of an equivalence relation. We are inclined, therefore, to partition the class of all sets into equivalence classes under this relation. The equivalence class of a set x would be the class of all sets equinumerous with x. The equivalence classes are called *cardinal numbers*. For example, if u is a set, and $x = \{u\}$, then the equivalence class of x is the class of all unit sets $\{v\}$ and is called the cardinal number 1_c. Likewise, if $u \neq v$, and $y = \{u, v\}$, then the equivalence class of y is the class of all sets containing exactly two elements, and is called the cardinal number 2_c, i.e., $2_c = \hat{z}((Ex_1)(Ey_1)(x_1 \neq y_1 \wedge z = \{x_1, y_1\}))$. Now, notice that all the cardinal numbers, except the cardinal number of 0 (which is $\{0\}$), are proper classes. For example, $V \simeq 1_c$, where V is the universal class. (Let $F\text{ʻ}\, x = \{x\}$ for each $x \in V$. Then $V \underset{F}{\simeq} 1_c$.) But $\sim M(V)$; hence, by the Replacement Axiom R, $\sim M(1_c)$.

EXERCISE. $\vdash \sim M(2_c)$

Because the cardinal numbers are proper classes, we cannot talk about classes of cardinal numbers, and it is difficult or impossible to say and prove many interesting things about them. For this reason, we shall not discuss them any further at this point. Most assertions one should like to make about cardinal numbers can be paraphrased by suitable use of $\simeq$ and $\precsim$. In addition, we shall see later that, given certain additional plausible axioms, there are other ways of defining a notion which does the same job as that of cardinal number.

EXERCISE. Prove: $\vdash (x)(R)(R\ We\ x \supset (E\alpha)(x \simeq \alpha))$. (Every well-ordered set is equinumerous with some ordinal. Hint: use Proposition 4.17.)

Finite Sets: Remember (cf. page 175) that ω is the set of all ordinals α such that α and all smaller ordinals are of the first kind (i.e., are successor ordinals or 0). The elements of ω are the *finite ordinals*. A set will be called *finite* if and only if it is equinumerous with a finite ordinal.

DEFINITION. $Fin(X) \equiv (E\alpha)(\alpha \in \omega \wedge X \simeq \alpha)$

Clearly, by the Replacement Axiom R, $\vdash Fin(X) \supset M(X)$. Trivially, all finite ordinals are finite sets, and $\vdash Fin(X) \wedge X \simeq Y \supset Fin(Y)$.

PROPOSITION 4.24

(1) $\vdash (\alpha)(\alpha \in On - \omega \supset \alpha \simeq \alpha')$

(2) $\vdash (\alpha)(\beta)(\alpha \in \omega \land \alpha \neq \beta \supset \sim \alpha \simeq \beta)$. (*No finite ordinal is equinumerous with any other ordinal. Hence, a finite set is equinumerous with exactly one finite ordinal, and a non-finite ordinal* (*i.e.*, *a member of On-*ω) *is not finite.*)

(3) $\vdash (\alpha)(x)(\alpha \in \omega \land x \subset \alpha \supset \sim \alpha \simeq x)$. (No finite ordinal is equinumerous with a proper subset of itself.)

PROOF

(1) Assume $\alpha \in On\text{-}\omega$. Define a function f with domain α' as follows: $f \text{ ‘ } \delta = \delta'$ if $\delta \in \omega$; $f \text{ ‘ } \delta = \delta$ if $\delta \notin \omega$ and $\delta \neq \alpha$; $f \text{ ‘ } \alpha = 0$. Then $\alpha' \underset{f}{\simeq} \alpha$.

(2) Assume false, and let α be the least ordinal such that $\alpha \in \omega$, and there is a $\beta \neq \alpha$ such that $\alpha \simeq \beta$. Hence, $\alpha <_0 \beta$. (Otherwise, β would be a smaller ordinal than α, and β would be equinumerous with some ordinal $\neq \beta$.) Let $\alpha \underset{f}{\simeq} \beta$. If $\alpha = 0$, then $f = 0$ and $\beta = 0$, contradicting $\alpha \neq \beta$. So, $\alpha \neq 0$. Since $\alpha \in \omega$, $\alpha = \delta'$ for some $\delta \in \omega$. We may assume that $\beta = \gamma'$ for some γ. (For, if $\beta \in \omega$, then $\beta \neq 0$; and if $\beta \notin \omega$, then, by Part (a), $\beta \simeq \beta'$, and we can take β' instead of β.) Thus, $\delta' = \alpha \underset{f}{\simeq} \gamma'$. Also, $\delta \neq \gamma$, since $\alpha \neq \beta$. Case 1: $f \text{ ‘ } \delta = \gamma$. Then $\delta \underset{\delta 1 f}{\simeq} \gamma$. Case 2: $f \text{ ‘ } \delta \neq \gamma$. Then there is some $\mu \in \delta$ such that $f \text{ ‘ } \mu = \gamma$. Let $h = ((\delta \mathbf{1} f) - \{\langle \mu, \gamma \rangle\}) \cup \{\langle \mu, f \text{ ‘ } \delta \rangle\}$, i.e., let $h \text{ ‘ } \tau = f \text{ ‘ } \tau$ if $\tau \notin \{\delta, \mu\}$; $h \text{ ‘ } \mu = f \text{ ‘ } \delta$. Then $\delta \underset{h}{\simeq} \gamma$. In both cases, δ is a finite ordinal smaller than α which is equinumerous with a different ordinal γ, contradicting the minimality of α.

(3) Assume $\beta \in \omega \land x \subset \beta \land \beta \simeq x$ holds for some β, and let α be the least such β. Clearly, $\alpha \neq 0$; hence, $\alpha = \gamma'$ for some γ; but, as in the proof of Part (2), one can then show that γ is also equinumerous with a proper subset of itself, contradicting the minimality of α.

PROPOSITION 4.25

(1) $\vdash Fin(X) \land Y \subseteq X \supset Fin(Y)$

(2) $\vdash Fin(X) \land Fin(Y) \supset Fin(X \cup Y)$

(3) A set is said to be *Dedekind-finite* if and only if it is equinumerous with no proper subset of itself. Then every finite set is Dedekind-finite. (The converse is not provable without use of an additional axiom, the Axiom of Choice.)

PROOF

(1) Assume $Fin(X) \land Y \subseteq X$. Then $X \underset{f}{\simeq} \alpha$, where $\alpha \in \omega$. Let $g = Y \mathbf{1} f$ and $W = g \text{ “ } Y \subseteq \alpha$. W is a set of ordinals, and so, E_W is a well-ordering of W. By Proposition 4.17, $\langle E_W, W \rangle$ is similar to $\langle E_\beta, \beta \rangle$ for some ordinal β. Hence, $W \simeq \beta$. In addition, $\beta \leqslant_0 \alpha$.

(For, if $\beta >_0 \alpha$, then $\langle E_\beta, \beta\rangle$ is similar to $\langle E_W, W\rangle$, contradicting Corollary 4.15.) Since $\alpha \in \omega$, $\beta \in \omega$. Since $W \underset{g}{\simeq} Y$, $Fin(Y)$.

(2) Let $Z = \hat{u}(u \in \omega \ \wedge \ (x)(y)(f)(x \underset{f}{\simeq} u \wedge Fin(y) \supset Fin(x \cup y)))$. We must show that $Z = \omega$. Clearly, $0 \in Z$, for, if $x \simeq 0$, then $x = 0$ and $x \cup y = y$. Assume that $\alpha \in Z$. Let $x \underset{f}{\simeq} \alpha'$ and $Fin(y)$. Let $f \text{`} w = \alpha$, and $x_1 = x - \{w\}$. Then $x_1 \simeq \alpha$. Since $\alpha \in Z$, $Fin(x_1 \cup y)$. But $x \cup y = (x_1 \cup y) \cup \{w\}$. Hence, $Fin(x \cup y)$. (For, $\vdash (v)(v_1)(Fin(v) \supset Fin(v \cup \{v_1\}))$.) Thus, $\alpha' \in Z$. Hence, by Proposition 4.10(3), $Z = \omega$.

(3) This follows from Proposition 4.24(3).

DEFINITIONS. $Inf(X)$ for $\sim Fin(X)$. (X is infinite.)
$Den(X)$ for $X \simeq \omega$. (X is denumerable.)

Clearly, $\vdash Inf(X) \wedge X \simeq Y \supset Inf(Y)$ and $\vdash Den(X) \wedge X \simeq Y \supset Den(Y)$. By the Replacement Axiom R and the fact that $M(\omega)$, it follows that $\vdash Den(X) \supset M(X)$.

PROPOSITION 4.26

(1) $\vdash Inf(X) \wedge X \subseteq Y \supset Inf(Y)$

(2) $\vdash Inf(X) \equiv Inf(X \cup \{y\})$

(3) A class is called *Dedekind-infinite* if and only if it is equinumerous with a proper subset of itself. Then every Dedekind-infinite class is infinite.

(4) $\vdash Inf(\omega)$

PROOF

(1) From Proposition 4.25(1).

(2) $\vdash Inf(X) \supset Inf(X \cup \{y\})$ by Part (1). $\vdash Inf(X \cup \{y\}) \supset Inf(X)$, by Proposition 4.25(2).

(3) Use Proposition 4.25(3).

(4) $\vdash \omega \notin \omega$

PROPOSITION 4.27. $\vdash Den(v) \wedge z \subseteq v \supset (Den(z) \vee Fin(z))$

PROOF. It suffices to prove: $z \subseteq \omega \supset (Den(z) \vee Fin(z))$. Assume $z \subseteq \omega \wedge \sim Fin(z)$. Since $\sim Fin(z)$, for any $\alpha \in z$, there is some $\beta \in z$ with $\alpha <_0 \beta$. (Otherwise, $z \subseteq \alpha'$ and, since $Fin(\alpha')$, $Fin(z)$.) Let X be a function such that, for any $\alpha \in \omega$, $X \text{`} \alpha$ is the least ordinal $\beta$ in $z$ with $\alpha <_0 \beta$. Then, by Proposition 4.13(3) (with $\delta = \omega$), there is a function $Y$ with domain $\omega$ such that $Y \text{`} 0$ is the least ordinal in z, and for any γ in ω, $Y \text{`} (\gamma')$ is the least ordinal $\beta$ in $z$ with $\beta >_0 (Y \text{`} \gamma)$. Clearly, Y is one-one, $\mathscr{D}(Y) = \omega$, and $Y \text{``} \omega \subseteq z$. Also, $Y \text{``} \omega = z$; for, if $z - Y \text{``} \omega \neq 0$, $\delta$ is the least ordinal in $z - Y \text{``} \omega$, and τ is the least ordinal in $Y \text{``} \omega$ with $\tau >_0 \delta$, then $\tau = Y \text{`} \sigma$ for some σ in ω.

Since $\delta <_0 \tau$, $\sigma \neq 0$. So, $\sigma = \mu'$ for some μ in ω. Then $\tau = Y ` \sigma =$ the least ordinal in $z$ which is greater than $Y ` \mu$. But $\delta >_0 Y ` \mu$, since τ is the least ordinal in $Y `` \omega$ which is greater than δ. Hence, $\tau = \delta$, which yields a contradiction.

EXERCISES

1. $\vdash Fin(x) \supset Fin(\mathscr{P}(x))$. (Induction on α in $(x)(x \simeq \alpha \wedge \alpha \in \omega \supset Fin(\mathscr{P}(x)))$.)
2. $\vdash (Fin(x) \wedge (y)(y \in x \supset Fin(y)) \supset Fin(\bigcup(x))$. (Hint: induction on the α such that $x \simeq \alpha$.)
3. $\vdash x \preceq y \wedge Fin(y) \supset Fin(x)$
4. $\vdash Fin(\mathscr{P}(x)) \supset Fin(x)$
5. $\vdash Fin(\bigcup(x)) \supset (Fin(x) \wedge (y)(y \in x \supset Fin(y)))$
6. $\vdash Fin(x) \supset (x \preceq y \vee y \preceq x)$
7. $\vdash Fin(x) \wedge Inf(Y) \supset x \prec Y$
8. $\vdash Fin(x) \wedge y \subset x \supset y \prec x$
9. $\vdash Fin(x) \wedge Fin(y) \supset Fin(x \times y)$
10. $\vdash Fin(x) \wedge Fin(y) \supset Fin(x^y)$
11. $\vdash Fin(x) \wedge y \notin x \supset x \prec (x \cup \{y\})$
12. Define x to be a minimal (respectively, maximal) element of Y if and only if $x \in Y$ and $(y)(y \in Y \supset \sim y \subset x)$ (respectively, $(y)(y \in Y \supset \sim x \subset y)$). Prove that a class Z is finite if and only if every non-empty set of subsets of Z has a minimal (respectively, maximal) element (Tarski [1925]).
13. (a) $\vdash Fin(x) \wedge Den(y) \supset Den(x \cup y)$. (Hint: induction on α, where $\alpha \simeq x$.)

    (b) $\vdash Fin(x) \wedge Den(y) \wedge x \neq 0 \supset Den(x \times y)$.

    (c) A set y contains a denumerable subset if and only if y is Dedekind-infinite. (Hint: (i) Assume $x \subseteq y$ and $Den(x)$. Let $x \underset{f}{\simeq} \omega$. Define a function g on y: $g ` u = u$ if $u \in y - x$; $g ` u = (\check{f}) ` ((f ` u)')$ if $u \in x$. (ii) Assume y Dedekind-infinite. Assume $x \subset y$ and $y \underset{f}{\simeq} x$. Let $v \in y - x$. Define a function h on ω such that $h ` 0 = v$ and $h ` (\alpha') = f ` (h ` \alpha)$ if $\alpha \in \omega$. Then h is one-one; so, $Den(h `` \omega)$ and $h `` \omega \subseteq y$.)

§4. Hartogs' Theorem. Initial Ordinals. Ordinal Arithmetic.

An unjustly neglected proposition with manifold uses in set theory is Hartogs' Theorem.

PROPOSITION 4.28 (Hartogs [1915]). *For any set x, there is an ordinal which is not equinumerous with any subset of x (and hence there is a least such ordinal).*

PROOF. Assume that every ordinal α is equinumerous with some subset y of x. Hence, $y \underset{f}{\simeq} \alpha$ for some f. Define a relation R on y by stipulating that $\langle u, v\rangle \in R$ if and only if $(f \text{ ‘ } u) \in (f \text{ ‘ } v)$. Then R is a well-ordering of y such that $\langle R, y\rangle$ is similar to $\langle E_\alpha, \alpha\rangle$. Now, define a function F with domain On such that, for any α, $F \text{ ‘ } \alpha$ is the set w of all pairs $\langle z, y\rangle$ such that $y \subseteq x$, z is a well-ordering of y, and $\langle E_\alpha, \alpha\rangle$ is similar to $\langle z, y\rangle$. (w is a set, since $w \subseteq \mathscr{P}(x \times x) \times \mathscr{P}(x)$.) Hence, $F \text{ “ } On \subseteq \mathscr{P}(\mathscr{P}(x \times x) \times \mathscr{P}(x))$, and therefore $F \text{ “ } (On)$ is a set. F is one-one; hence, $On = \check{F} \text{ “ } (F \text{ “ } (On))$ is a set, by the Replacement Axiom R, contradicting Proposition 4.7(8).

Let $\mathscr{H}$ be the function which assigns to each set x the least ordinal α which is not equinumerous with any subset of x.

By an *initial ordinal* α we mean an ordinal α which is not equinumerous with any smaller ordinal. In particular, by Proposition 4.24(2), every finite ordinal is an initial ordinal, and ω is the smallest infinite initial ordinal. Also, for any x, $\mathscr{H} \text{ ‘ } x$ is an initial ordinal.

By transfinite induction (Proposition 4.13(2)), there is a function G with domain On such that

$$G \text{ ‘ } 0 = \omega$$
$$G \text{ ‘ } (\alpha') = \mathscr{H} \text{ ‘ } (G \text{ ‘ } \alpha)$$
$$G \text{ ‘ } \lambda = \bigcup(G \text{ “ } \lambda) \quad \text{if } \lambda \text{ is a limit ordinal.}$$

G is an increasing function, i.e., $\alpha \in \beta \supset G \text{ ‘ } \alpha \in G \text{ ‘ } \beta$; therefore, if λ is a limit ordinal, and each $G \text{ ‘ } \alpha$, for $\alpha <_0 \lambda$, is an initial ordinal, then $\bigcup(G \text{ “ } \lambda)$ is also an initial ordinal. (For, $\delta = \bigcup(G \text{ “ } \lambda)$ is the least upper bound of $G \text{ “ } \lambda$. Assume $\delta \simeq \gamma$ with $\gamma <_0 \delta$. Hence, there is some $\alpha <_0 \lambda$ such that $\gamma <_0 G \text{ ‘ } \alpha$. But $G \text{ ‘ } (\alpha') <_0 \delta$. So, by the Schröder-Bernstein Theorem (Proposition 4.21(4)), using $G \text{ ‘ } \alpha \preceq G \text{ ‘ } (\alpha')$ and $G \text{ ‘ } (\alpha') \preceq \delta \simeq \gamma \preceq G \text{ ‘ } \alpha$, we have $G \text{ ‘ } \alpha \simeq G \text{ ‘ } (\alpha') = \mathscr{H} \text{ ‘ } (G \text{ ‘ } \alpha)$, contradicting the definition of $\mathscr{H}$.) Hence $G \text{ ‘ } \alpha$ is an initial ordinal, for all α. In addition, every infinite initial ordinal is equal to $G \text{ ‘ } \alpha$ for some α. (Assume not. Let σ be the least infinite initial ordinal not in $G \text{ “ } On$. By the Replacement Axiom R, $G \text{ “ } On$ is not a set; hence there is some ordinal greater than σ in $G \text{ “ } On$. Let μ be the least such ordinal, and let $\mu = G \text{ ‘ } \beta$. Clearly, $\beta \neq 0$; if $\beta = \gamma'$ for some γ, then $G \text{ ‘ } \gamma <_0 \sigma <_0 G \text{ ‘ } (\gamma') = \mathscr{H} \text{ ‘ } (G \text{ ‘ } \gamma)$, contradicting the definition of $\mathscr{H}$. If β is a limit ordinal, then there is some $\alpha <_0 \beta$ such that $\sigma <_0 G \text{ ‘ } \alpha <_0 G \text{ ‘ } \beta$, contradicting the definition of β.) Thus, G is an $\in$-preserving "isomorphism" of On with the class of infinite initial ordinals.

We denote $G \text{ ‘ } \alpha$ by ω_α. Thus, $\omega_0 = \omega$; $\omega_{\alpha'}$ is the least initial ordinal greater than ω_α; and, for limit ordinals λ, ω_λ is the initial ordinal which is the least upper bound of the set of all ω_α with $\alpha <_0 \lambda$. It follows from Proposition 4.14 that $\omega_\alpha \geqslant_0 \alpha$ for all α. Also, any ordinal α is equinumerous with a unique initial ordinal $\omega_\beta \leqslant_0 \alpha$, namely, with the least ordinal equinumerous with α.

Let us turn now to ordinal arithmetic. We have already defined (see page 178) addition, multiplication, and exponentiation:

(I)
$$\begin{aligned} \beta +_0 0 &= \beta \\ \beta +_0 \gamma' &= (\beta +_0 \gamma)' \\ Lim(\alpha) \supset \beta +_0 \alpha &= \bigcup_{\tau <_0 \alpha} (\beta +_0 \tau) \end{aligned}$$

(II)
$$\begin{aligned} \beta \times_0 0 &= 0 \\ \beta \times_0 (\gamma') &= (\beta \times_0 \gamma) +_0 \beta \\ Lim(\alpha) \supset \beta \times_0 \alpha &= \bigcup_{\tau <_0 \alpha} (\beta \times_0 \tau) \end{aligned}$$

(III)
$$\begin{aligned} \beta^0 &= 1 \\ \beta^{\gamma'} &= (\beta^\gamma) \times_0 \beta \\ Lim(\alpha) \supset \beta^\alpha &= \bigcup_{0 <_0 \tau <_0 \alpha} (\beta^\tau) \end{aligned}$$

PROPOSITION 4.29. *The following* wfs *are theorems.*

(1) $\beta +_0 1 = \beta'$
(2) $0 +_0 \beta = \beta$
(3) $\beta >_0 0 \supset \alpha +_0 \beta >_0 \alpha \wedge \alpha +_0 \beta \geqslant_0 \beta$
(4) $\beta <_0 \gamma \supset \alpha +_0 \beta <_0 \alpha +_0 \gamma$
(5) $\alpha +_0 \beta = \alpha +_0 \delta \supset \beta = \delta$
(6) $\alpha <_0 \beta \supset (E_1\delta)(\alpha +_0 \delta = \beta)$
(7) $x \subseteq On \supset \alpha +_0 \bigcup_{\beta \in x} \beta = \bigcup_{\beta \in x} (\alpha +_0 \beta)$
(8) $0 <_0 \alpha \wedge 1 <_0 \beta \supset \alpha \times_0 \beta >_0 \alpha$
(9) $0 <_0 \alpha \wedge 0 <_0 \beta \supset \alpha \times_0 \beta \geqslant_0 \beta$
(10) $\gamma <_0 \beta \wedge 0 <_0 \alpha \supset \alpha \times_0 \gamma <_0 \alpha \times_0 \beta$
(11) $x \subseteq On \supset \alpha \times_0 \bigcup_{\beta \in x} \beta = \bigcup_{\beta \in x} (\alpha \times_0 \beta)$

PROOF

(1) $\beta +_0 1 = \beta +_0 (0') = (\beta +_0 0)' = (\beta)'$.

(2) Prove $0 +_0 \beta = \beta$ by transfinite induction (Proposition 4.12). Let $X = \hat{\beta}(0 +_0 \beta = \beta)$. First, $0 \in X$, since $0 +_0 0 = 0$. If $0 +_0 \gamma = \gamma$, then $0 +_0 (\gamma') = (0 +_0 \gamma)' = \gamma'$. If $Lim(\alpha)$ and $0 +_0 \tau = \tau$ for all $\tau <_0 \alpha$, then $0 +_0 \alpha = \bigcup_{\tau <_0 \alpha} (0 +_0 \tau) = \bigcup_{\tau <_0 \alpha} \tau = \alpha$, since $\bigcup_{\tau <_0 \alpha} \tau$ is the least upper bound of the set of all $\tau <_0 \alpha$.

(3) Let $X = \hat{\beta}(\beta >_0 0 \supset \alpha +_0 \beta >_0 \alpha)$. Prove $X = On$ by transfinite induction. Clearly, $0 \in X$. If $\gamma \in X$, then $\alpha +_0 \gamma \geqslant_0 \alpha$; hence, $\alpha +_0 (\gamma') = (\alpha +_0 \gamma)' >_0 \alpha +_0 \gamma \geqslant_0 \alpha$. If $Lim(\lambda)$ and $\tau \in X$ for all $\tau <_0 \lambda$, then $\alpha +_0 \lambda = \bigcup_{\tau <_0 \lambda} (\alpha +_0 \tau) \geqslant_0 \alpha +_0 1 = \alpha' >_0 \alpha$. The second part is left as an exercise.

(4) Use transfinite induction: $X = \hat{\gamma}((\alpha)(\beta)(\beta <_0 \gamma \supset \alpha +_0 \beta <_0 \alpha +_0 \gamma))$. Clearly, $0 \in X$. Assume $\gamma \in X$. Assume $\beta <_0 \gamma'$. Then $\beta <_0 \gamma$ or $\beta = \gamma$. If $\beta <_0 \gamma$, then, since $\gamma \in X$, $\alpha +_0 \beta <_0 \alpha +_0 \gamma <_0 (\alpha +_0 \gamma)' = \alpha +_0 \gamma'$. If $\beta = \gamma$, then $\alpha +_0 \beta = \alpha +_0 \gamma <_0 (\alpha +_0 \gamma)' = \alpha +_0 \gamma'$. Hence, $\gamma' \in X$. Assume $Lim(\lambda)$ and $\tau \in X$ for all $\tau <_0 \lambda$. Assume $\beta <_0 \lambda$. Then $\beta <_0 \tau$ for some $\tau <_0 \lambda$, since $Lim(\lambda)$. Hence, since $\tau \in X$, $\alpha +_0 \beta <_0 \alpha +_0 \tau \leqslant_0 \bigcup_{\tau <_0 \lambda} (\alpha +_0 \tau) = \alpha +_0 \lambda$. Hence, $\lambda \in X$.

(5) Assume $\alpha +_0 \beta = \alpha +_0 \delta$. Now, either $\beta <_0 \delta$ or $\delta <_0 \beta$ or $\delta = \beta$. If $\beta <_0 \delta$, then $\alpha +_0 \beta <_0 \alpha +_0 \delta$, and if $\delta <_0 \beta$, then $\alpha +_0 \delta <_0 \alpha +_0 \beta$, by Part (4), contradicting $\alpha +_0 \beta = \alpha +_0 \delta$. Hence, $\delta = \beta$.

(6) The uniqueness follows from Part (5). Prove the existence by induction on β. Let $X = \hat{\beta}(\alpha <_0 \beta \supset (E_1\delta)(\alpha +_0 \delta = \beta))$. Clearly $0 \in X$. Assume $\gamma \in X$ and $\alpha <_0 \gamma'$. Hence, $\alpha <_0 \gamma$ or $\alpha = \gamma$. If $\alpha <_0 \gamma$, then $(E_1\delta)(\alpha +_0 \delta = \gamma)$. Take an ordinal σ such that $\alpha +_0 \sigma = \gamma$. Then $(\alpha +_0 \sigma') = (\alpha +_0 \sigma)' = \gamma'$; thus, $(E\delta)(\alpha +_0 \delta = \gamma')$, i.e., $\gamma' \in X$. Assume now that $Lim(\lambda)$ and $\tau \in X$ for all $\tau <_0 \lambda$. Assume $\alpha <_0 \lambda$. Now define a function f such that, for $\alpha <_0 \mu <_0 \lambda$, $f`\mu$ is the unique ordinal $\delta$ such that $\alpha +_0 \delta = \mu$. But $\lambda = \bigcup_{\alpha <_0 \mu <_0 \lambda} \mu = \bigcup_{\alpha <_0 \mu <_0 \lambda} (\alpha +_0 f`\mu)$. Let $\rho = \bigcup_{\alpha <_0 \mu <_0 \lambda} (f`\mu)$. (Notice that, if $\alpha <_0 \mu <_0 \lambda$, then $f`\mu <_0 f`(\mu')$; hence if $\alpha <_0 \mu <_0 \lambda$, $f`\mu <_0 \lambda$.) Then $\lambda = \bigcup_{\alpha <_0 \mu <_0 \lambda} (\alpha +_0 f`\mu) = \bigcup_{\sigma < \rho} (\alpha +_0 \sigma) = \alpha +_0 \rho$.

(7) Assume $x \subseteq On$. By Part (6), there is some δ such that $\alpha +_0 \delta = \bigcup_{\beta \in x} (\alpha +_0 \beta)$. We must show that $\delta = \bigcup_{\beta \in x} \beta$. If $\beta \in x$, $\alpha +_0 \beta \leqslant_0 \alpha +_0 \delta$. Hence, $\beta \leqslant_0 \delta$, by Part (4). Therefore, δ is an upper bound of the set of all $\beta \in x$. So, $\bigcup_{\beta \in x} \beta \leqslant_0 \delta$. On the other hand, if $\beta \in x$, then $\alpha +_0 \beta \leqslant_0 \alpha +_0 \bigcup_{\beta \in x} \beta$. Hence, $\alpha +_0 \delta = \bigcup_{\beta \in x} (\alpha +_0 \beta) \leqslant_0 \alpha +_0 \bigcup_{\beta \in x} \beta$, and so, by Part (4), $\delta \leqslant_0 \bigcup_{\beta \in x} \beta$. Therefore, $\delta = \bigcup_{\beta \in x} \beta$.

(8)–(11) are left as exercises.

PROPOSITION 4.30. *The following* wfs *are theorems.*

(1) $\beta \times_0 1 = \beta \wedge 1 \times_0 \beta = \beta$
(2) $0 \times_0 \beta = 0$
(3) $(\alpha +_0 \beta) +_0 \gamma = \alpha +_0 (\beta +_0 \gamma)$
(4) $(\alpha \times_0 \beta) \times_0 \gamma = \alpha \times_0 (\beta \times_0 \gamma)$
(5) $\alpha \times_0 (\beta +_0 \gamma) = (\alpha \times_0 \beta) +_0 (\alpha \times_0 \gamma)$
(6) $\beta^1 = \beta \wedge 1^\beta = 1$
(7) $(\beta^\gamma)^\delta = \beta^{\gamma \times_0 \delta}$

(8) $\beta^{\gamma +_0 \delta} = \beta^{\gamma} \times_0 \beta^{\delta}$
(9) $\alpha >_0 1 \wedge \beta <_0 \gamma \supset \alpha^{\beta} <_0 \alpha^{\gamma}$

PROOF

(1) $\beta \times_0 1 = \beta \times_0 0' = (\beta \times_0 0) +_0 \beta = 0 +_0 \beta = \beta$, by Proposition 4.29(2). Prove $1 \times_0 \beta = \beta$ by transfinite induction on β.

(2) Prove $0 \times_0 \beta = 0$ by transfinite induction on β.

(3) Let $X = \hat{\gamma}((\alpha)(\beta)((\alpha +_0 \beta) +_0 \gamma = \alpha +_0 (\beta +_0 \gamma)))$. $(\alpha +_0 \beta) +_0 0 = \alpha +_0 \beta = \alpha +_0 (\beta +_0 0)$. Hence, $0 \in X$. Assume $\gamma \in X$. Then $(\alpha +_0 \beta) +_0 \gamma' = ((\alpha +_0 \beta) +_0 \gamma)' = (\alpha +_0 (\beta +_0 \gamma))' = \alpha +_0 (\beta +_0 \gamma)' = \alpha +_0 (\beta +_0 \gamma')$. Hence, $\gamma' \in X$. Assume now that $Lim(\lambda)$ and $\tau \in X$ for all $\tau <_0 \lambda$. Then $(\alpha +_0 \beta) +_0 \lambda = \bigcup_{\tau <_0 \lambda} ((\alpha +_0 \beta) +_0 \tau) = \bigcup_{\tau <_0 \lambda} (\alpha +_0 (\beta +_0 \tau)) = \alpha +_0 \bigcup_{\tau <_0 \lambda} (\beta +_0 \tau)$ (by Proposition 4.29(7)), and this is equal to $\alpha +_0 (\beta +_0 \lambda)$.

(5)–(9) are left as exercises.

We should like to consider for a moment the properties of ordinal addition and multiplication when restricted to ω.

PROPOSITION 4.31. Assume α, β, γ are in ω. Then

(1) $\alpha +_0 \beta \in \omega$
(2) $\alpha \times_0 \beta \in \omega$
(3) $\alpha^{\beta} \in \omega$
(4) $\alpha +_0 \beta = \beta +_0 \alpha$
(5) $\alpha \times_0 \beta = \beta \times_0 \alpha$
(6) $(\alpha +_0 \beta) \times_0 \gamma = (\alpha \times_0 \gamma) +_0 (\beta \times_0 \gamma)$
(7) $(\alpha \times_0 \beta)^{\gamma} = \alpha^{\gamma} \times_0 \beta^{\gamma}$

PROOF

(1) Induction on β. $X = \hat{\beta}((\alpha)(\alpha \in \omega \supset \alpha +_0 \beta \in \omega))$. Clearly $0 \in X$. Assume $\beta \in X$ and $\alpha \in \omega$. Then $\alpha +_0 \beta \in \omega$. Hence, $\alpha +_0 (\beta') = (\alpha +_0 \beta)' \in \omega$ by Proposition 4.10(2). So, by Proposition 4.10(3), $X \subseteq \omega$.

(2) and (3) are exercises.

(4) Lemma: $\vdash \alpha \in \omega \wedge \beta \in \omega \supset \alpha' +_0 \beta = \alpha +_0 \beta'$.

Let $Y = \hat{\beta}(\beta \in \omega \wedge (\alpha)(\alpha \in \omega \supset \alpha' +_0 \beta = \alpha +_0 \beta'))$. Observe that $0 \in Y$. Assume $\beta \in Y$, and let $\alpha \in \omega$. So, $\alpha' +_0 \beta = \alpha +_0 \beta'$. Then $(\alpha)' +_0 \beta' = ((\alpha)' +_0 \beta)' = (\alpha +_0 (\beta)')' = \alpha +_0 (\beta')'$. Hence, $\beta' \in Y$.

Now, to prove Part (4), let $X = \hat{\beta}(\beta \in \omega \wedge (\alpha)(\alpha \in \omega \supset \alpha +_0 \beta = \beta +_0 \alpha.)$ Then $0 \in X$, and it is easy to prove that $\beta \in X \supset \beta' \in X$.

(5)–(7) are left as exercises.

The reader will have noticed that we have not stated for ordinals certain well-known laws which hold for other well-known number systems, e.g., the commutative laws for addition and multiplication. In fact, these laws fail for ordinals, as the following examples show.

Examples

1. $(E\alpha)(E\beta)(\alpha +_0 \beta \neq \beta +_0 \alpha)$

$$1 +_0 \omega = \bigcup_{\alpha <_0 \omega} (1 +_0 \alpha) = \omega$$

But
$$\omega +_0 1 = \omega' >_0 \omega$$

2. $(E\alpha)(E\beta)(\alpha \times_0 \beta \neq \beta \times_0 \alpha)$

$$2 \times_0 \omega = \bigcup_{\alpha <_0 \omega} (2 \times_0 \alpha) = \omega$$

$$\omega \times_0 2 = \omega \times_0 (1 +_0 1) = (\omega \times_0 1) +_0 (\omega \times_0 1) = \omega +_0 \omega >_0 \omega$$

3. $(E\gamma)(E\alpha)(E\beta)((\alpha +_0 \beta) \times_0 \gamma \neq (\alpha \times_0 \gamma) +_0 (\beta \times_0 \gamma))$

$$(1 +_0 1) \times_0 \omega = 2 \times_0 \omega = \omega$$

$$(1 \times_0 \omega) +_0 (1 \times_0 \omega) = \omega +_0 \omega >_0 \omega$$

4. $(E\alpha)(E\beta)(E\gamma)((\alpha \times_0 \beta)^\gamma \neq \alpha^\gamma \times_0 \beta^\gamma)$

$$(2 \times_0 2)^\omega = 4^\omega = \bigcup_{\alpha <_0 \omega} (4^\alpha) = \omega$$

$$2^\omega = \bigcup_{\alpha <_0 \omega} 2^\alpha = \omega$$

So,
$$2^\omega \times_0 2^\omega = \omega \times_0 \omega >_0 \omega$$

Given any wf $\mathscr{A}$ of formal number theory S (cf. Chapter III), we can associate with $\mathscr{A}$ a wf $\mathscr{A}^\star$ of NBG as follows: first, replace every "+" by "$+_0$", and every "$\cdot$" by "$\times_0$"; then, if $\mathscr{A}$ is $\mathscr{B} \supset \mathscr{C}$, or $\sim\mathscr{B}$, respectively, and we already have found $\mathscr{B}^\star$ and $\mathscr{C}^\star$, let $\mathscr{A}^\star$ be $\mathscr{B}^\star \supset \mathscr{C}^\star$, or $\sim(\mathscr{B}^\star)$, respectively; if $\mathscr{A}$ is $(x)\mathscr{B}(x)$, replace it by $(x)(x \in \omega \supset \mathscr{B}^\star(x))$. This completes the definition of $\mathscr{A}^\star$. Now, if $x_1, \ldots, x_n$ are the free variables of $\mathscr{A}$, prefix $(x_1 \in \omega \wedge x_2 \in \omega \wedge \ldots \wedge x_n \in \omega) \supset$ to $\mathscr{A}^\star$, obtaining a wf $\mathscr{A}\#$. This amounts to restricting all variables to ω and interpreting addition, multiplication, and the successor function on integers as the corresponding operations on ordinals. Then every axiom $\mathscr{A}$ of S is transformed into a theorem $\mathscr{A}\#$ of NBG. (Axioms (S1)–(S3) are obviously transformed into theorems. (S4)# is a theorem, by Proposition 4.9(3), and (S5)#–(S8)# are properties of ordinal addition and multiplication (cf. page 178). Now, for any wf $\mathscr{A}$ of S, $\mathscr{A}\#$ is predicative. Hence, all instances of (S9)# are provable by transfinite induction (Proposition 4.12(2)). Assume $\mathscr{A}\#(0) \wedge (x)(x \in \omega \supset \mathscr{A}\#(x) \supset \mathscr{A}\#(x')))$; let $X = \hat{y}(y \in \omega \wedge \mathscr{A}\#(y))$; then, by Proposition 4.13(2), $(x)(x \in \omega \supset \mathscr{A}\#(x))$.) Applications of modus ponens are preserved under the transformation of $\mathscr{A}$ into $\mathscr{A}\#$. Also, if $\mathscr{A}(x)$ is provable in S, then $\mathscr{A}\#(x)$ is provable in NBG. But $\mathscr{A}\#(x)$

is of the form $x \in \omega \wedge y_1 \in \omega \wedge \ldots \wedge y_m \in \omega \supset \mathscr{A}^\star(x)$. Hence, $y_1 \in \omega \wedge \ldots \wedge y_m \in \omega \supset (x)(x \in \omega \supset \mathscr{A}^\star(x))$ is provable in NBG. But this wf is just $((x)\mathscr{A}(x))\#$. Hence, applications of the Generalization Rule lead from theorems to theorems. Therefore, for every theorem $\mathscr{A}$ of S, $\mathscr{A}\#$ is a theorem of NBG, and we can translate into NBG all the theorems of S proved in Chapter III.

One can check that the number-theoretic function h such that, if x is the Gödel number of a wf $\mathscr{A}$ of S, then h(x) is the Gödel number of $\mathscr{A}\#$ in NBG, and if x is not the Gödel number of a wf of S, then h(x) = 0, is recursive (in fact, primitive recursive). Let K be any consistent extension of NBG. As we saw above, if x is the Gödel number of a theorem of S, h(x) is the Gödel number of a theorem of NBG, and, hence, also a theorem of K. Let S′ be the extension of S obtained by taking as axioms all wfs $\mathscr{A}$ of S such that $\mathscr{A}\#$ is a theorem of K. Since K is consistent, S′ must be consistent. Therefore, since S is essentially recursively undecidable (by Corollary 3.37), S′ is recursively undecidable, i.e., the set $T_{S'}$ of Gödel numbers of theorems of S′ is not recursive. Now, assume K is recursively decidable, i.e., the set T_K of Gödel numbers of theorems of K is recursive. But, $C_{T_{S'}}(x) = C_{T_K}(h(x))$ for any x, where $C_{T_{S'}}$ and C_{T_K} are the characteristic functions of $T_{S'}$ and T_K. Hence $T_{S'}$ would be recursive, contradicting the recursive undecidability of S′. Therefore K is recursively undecidable, and, thus, if NBG is consistent, NBG is essentially recursively undecidable. Recursive undecidability of a recursively axiomatizable theory implies incompleteness (cf. Exercise 1(b), page 151). Hence NBG is also essentially incomplete. Thus, we have the following result: *If* NBG *is consistent, then* NBG *is essentially recursively undecidable and essentially incomplete.* (It is possible to prove this result directly in the same way that the corresponding result was proved for S in Chapter III. Also cf. Exercises on page 158.) Since NBG apparently can serve as a foundation for all of present-day mathematics (i.e., it is clear to every mathematician that every mathematical theorem can be translated and proved within NBG, or within extensions of NBG obtained by adding various extra axioms such as the Axiom of Choice), the essential incompleteness of NBG seems to indicate that the "axiomatic approach to mathematics" is inadequate. This conclusion does not depend upon the peculiarities of the theory NBG. Any other consistent theory (including "higher-order theories" as well as first-order theories) in which the theory of natural numbers can be developed far enough so as to include all the theorems of S (or even of RR) must also be essentially recursively undecidable and essentially incomplete, as the proof given above for NBG shows. (In fact, it suffices to prove that all recursive functions are representable in the theory (cf. Corollary 3.36); for further study of undecidability and incompleteness, cf. Smullyan [1961] and Tarski [1953].)

EXERCISE

Verify that the function h defined above is recursive. (Notice that, because $+_0$, $\times_0$, 0 are introduced into NBG as additional function letters and individual constants, one has to prove that the transformation given in Proposition 2.29 is recursive.)

There are a few facts about the "cardinal arithmetic" of ordinals that we should like to deal with now. By "cardinal arithmetic", we mean properties connected with the operations of union ($\cup$) and Cartesian product ($\times$) and X^Y, as opposed to the properties of $+_0$ and $\times_0$ and ordinal exponentiation. Observe that $\times$ is distinct from $\times_0$; also notice that ordinal exponentiation α^β, in spite of the ambiguous notation, has nothing to do with the operation of forming X^Y, the class of all functions from Y into X. (From Example 4 on page 192, we see that 2^ω, in the sense of ordinal exponentiation, is ω; while, from Cantor's Theorem, $\omega \prec 2^\omega$, where, in the latter formula, we mean by 2^ω the set of functions from ω into 2.) If necessary, denote ordinal exponentiation by exp (α, β).

PROPOSITION 4.32

(a) $\vdash \omega \times \omega \simeq \omega$

(b) *If each of X and Y contains at least two elements, then* $X \cup Y \preceq X \times Y$

(c) $Den(x) \wedge Den(y) \supset Den(x \cup y)$

PROOF

(a) Let f be a function with domain ω such that, if $\alpha \in \omega$, then $f\,`\,\alpha = \langle \alpha, 0 \rangle$. Then f is a one-one function from ω into a subset of $\omega \times \omega$. Hence, $\omega \preceq \omega \times \omega$. Conversely, let g be a function with domain $\omega \times \omega$ such that, for any $\langle \alpha, \beta \rangle \in \omega \times \omega$, $g\,`\,\langle \alpha, \beta \rangle = 2^\alpha \times_0 3^\beta$. We leave it as an exercise to show that g is one-one. Hence, $\omega \times \omega \preceq \omega$. So, by the Schröder-Bernstein Theorem, $\omega \times \omega \simeq \omega$.

(b) Assume $a_1 \in X$, $a_2 \in X$, $a_1 \neq a_2$ and $b_1 \in Y$, $b_2 \in Y$, and $b_1 \neq b_2$. Define:

$$f\,`\,x = \begin{cases} \langle x, b_1 \rangle & \text{if} \quad x \in X \\ \langle a_1, x \rangle & \text{if} \quad x \in Y - X \quad \text{and} \quad x \neq b_1 \\ \langle a_2, b_2 \rangle & \text{if} \quad x = b_1 \quad \text{and} \quad x \in Y - X \end{cases}$$

Then f is a one-one function with domain $X \cup Y$ and range a subset of $X \times Y$. Hence, $X \cup Y \preceq X \times Y$.

(c) Assume $Den(A)$ and $Den(B)$. Hence, each of A and B contains at least two elements. Then, by Part (b), $A \cup B \preceq A \times B$. But $A \simeq \omega$ and $B \simeq \omega$. Hence, $A \times B \simeq \omega \times \omega$. Therefore $A \cup B \preceq \omega \times \omega \simeq \omega$. By Proposition 4.27, either $Den(A \cup B)$ or $Fin(A \cup B)$. But $A \subseteq A \cup B$ and $Den(A)$; hence, $\sim Fin(A \cup B)$.

For the further study of ordinal addition and multiplication, it is quite useful to obtain concrete interpretations of these operations.

PROPOSITION 4.33 (Addition). *Assume that* $\langle R, A\rangle$ *is similar to* $\langle E_\alpha, \alpha\rangle$, *that* $\langle S, B\rangle$ *is similar to* $\langle E_\beta, \beta\rangle$, *and that* $A \cap B = 0$. *Define the relation* T *on* $A \cup B$ *as follows*: $\langle x, y\rangle \in T \equiv (x \in A \wedge y \in B) \vee (x \in A \wedge y \in A \wedge \langle x, y\rangle \in R) \vee (x \in B \wedge y \in B \wedge \langle x, y\rangle \in S)$; (i.e., T is the same as R in the set A, the same as S in the set B, and every element of A T-precedes every element of B). Then T is a well-ordering of $A \cup B$, and $\langle T, A \cup B\rangle$ is similar to $\langle E_{\alpha +_0 \beta}, \alpha +_0 \beta\rangle$.

PROOF. First, it is simple to verify that T is a well-ordering of $A \cup B$, since R is a well-ordering of A and S is a well-ordering of B. To show that $\langle T, A \cup B\rangle$ is similar to $\langle E_{\alpha +_0 \beta}, \alpha +_0 \beta\rangle$, perform transfinite induction on β. For $\beta = 0$, $B = 0$. Hence, $T = R$, $A \cup B = A$, and $\alpha +_0 \beta = \alpha$. So, $\langle T, A \cup B\rangle$ is similar to $\langle E_{\alpha +_0 \beta}, \alpha +_0 \beta\rangle$. Assume the proposition for γ, and let $\beta = \gamma'$. Since $\langle S, B\rangle$ is similar to $\langle E_\beta, \beta\rangle$, we have a function f with domain B and range β such that, for any x, y in B, $\langle x, y\rangle \in S$ if and only if $f\,{}^{\backprime}\,x \in f\,{}^{\backprime}\,y$. Let $b = (\breve{f})\,{}^{\backprime}\,\gamma$, let $B_1 = B - \{b\}$, and let $S_1 = S \cap (B_1 \times B_1)$. Since b is the S-maximum of B, it follows easily that S_1 well-orders B_1. Also, $B_1 \upharpoonright f$ is a similarity mapping of B_1 onto γ. Let $T_1 = T \cap ((A \cup B_1) \times (A \cup B_1))$. By inductive hypothesis, $\langle T_1, A \cup B_1\rangle$ is similar to $\langle E_{\alpha +_0 \gamma}, \alpha +_0 \gamma\rangle$, by means of some similarity mapping g with domain $A \cup B_1$ and range $\alpha +_0 \gamma$. Extend g to $g_1 = g \cup \{\langle b, \alpha +_0 \gamma\rangle\}$, which is a similarity mapping of $A \cup B$ onto $(\alpha +_0 \gamma)' = \alpha +_0 \gamma' = \alpha +_0 \beta$. Finally, if $Lim(\beta)$, and our proposition holds for all $\tau <_0 \beta$, assume that f is a similarity mapping of B onto β. Now, for each $\tau <_0 \beta$, let $B_\tau = (\breve{f})\,{}^{\backprime\backprime}\,\tau$, $S_\tau = S \cap (B_\tau \times B_\tau)$, and $T_\tau = T \cap ((A \cup B_\tau) \times (A \cup B_\tau))$. By inductive hypothesis, and Corollary 4.16(2), there is a unique similarity mapping g_τ of $\langle T_\tau, A \cup B_\tau\rangle$ with $\langle E_{\alpha +_0 \tau}, \alpha +_0 \tau\rangle$; also, if $\tau_1 <_0 \tau_2 <_0 \beta$, then, since $T_{\tau_1} \upharpoonright g_{\tau_2}$ is a similarity mapping of $\langle T_{\tau_1}, A \cup B_{\tau_1}\rangle$ with $\langle E_{\alpha +_0 \tau_1}, \alpha +_0 \tau_1\rangle$ and, by the uniqueness of g_{τ_1}, $T_{\tau_1} \upharpoonright g_{\tau_2} = g_{\tau_1}$, i.e., g_{τ_2} is an extension of g_{τ_1}. Hence, if $g = \bigcup_{\tau <_0 \beta} (g_\tau)$, then g is a similarity mapping of $\langle T, \bigcup_{\tau <_0 \beta} (A \cup B_\tau)\rangle$ with $\langle E_{\bigcup_{\tau <_0 \beta} (\alpha +_0 \tau)}, \bigcup_{\tau <_0 \beta} (\alpha +_0 \tau)\rangle$. But, $\bigcup_{\tau <_0 \beta} (A \cup B_\tau) = A \cup B$, and $\bigcup_{\tau <_0 \beta} (\alpha +_0 \tau) = \alpha +_0 \beta$. This completes the transfinite induction.

PROPOSITION 4.34 (Multiplication). *Assume that* $\langle R, A\rangle$ *is similar to* $\langle E_\alpha, \alpha\rangle$ *and that* $\langle S, B\rangle$ *is similar to* $\langle E_\beta, \beta\rangle$. *Define the relation* W *on* $A \times B$ *as follows*: $\langle\langle x, y\rangle, \langle u, v\rangle\rangle \in W \equiv (x \in A \wedge u \in A \wedge y \in B \wedge v \in B) \wedge ((\langle y, v\rangle \in S) \vee (y = v \wedge \langle x, u\rangle \in R))$. *Then* W *is a well-ordering of* $A \times B$ *and* $\langle W, A \times B\rangle$ *is similar to* $\langle E_{\alpha \times_0 \beta}, \alpha \times_0 \beta\rangle$.

PROOF. Exercise (proceed as in the proof of Proposition 4.33).

Examples

1. $2 \times_0 \omega = \omega$. Let $\langle R, A\rangle = \langle E_2, 2\rangle$, and $\langle S, B\rangle = \langle E_\omega, \omega\rangle$. Then the pairs in $2 \times \omega$ can be well-ordered as follows: $\langle 0, 0\rangle$, $\langle 1, 0\rangle$, $\langle 0, 1\rangle$, $\langle 1, 1\rangle$, $\langle 0, 2\rangle$, $\langle 1, 2\rangle, \ldots, \langle 0, n\rangle$, $\langle 1, n\rangle$, $\langle 0, n + 1\rangle$, $\langle 1, n + 1\rangle, \ldots$.

2. By Proposition 4.30(5), $\omega \times_0 2 = \omega +_0 \omega$. Let $\langle R, A\rangle = \langle E_\omega, \omega\rangle$ and $\langle S, B\rangle = \langle E_2, 2\rangle$. Then $\omega \times 2$ can be well-ordered (cf. Proposition 4.34) as follows: $\langle 0, 0\rangle$, $\langle 1, 0\rangle$, $\langle 2, 0\rangle, \ldots, \langle 0, 1\rangle$, $\langle 1, 1\rangle$, $\langle 2, 1\rangle, \ldots$.

PROPOSITION 4.35. *For all* α, $\omega_\alpha \times \omega_\alpha \simeq \omega_\alpha$.

PROOF (Sierpinski [1958]). Assume false, and let α be the least ordinal such that $\sim(\omega_\alpha \times \omega_\alpha \simeq \omega_\alpha)$. Then $\omega_\beta \times \omega_\beta \simeq \omega_\beta$ for all $\beta <_0 \alpha$. By Proposition 4.32(1), $\alpha >_0 0$. Now, let $P = \omega_\alpha \times \omega_\alpha$, and, for $\beta <_0 \omega_\alpha$, let $P_\beta = \hat{\gamma}\hat{\delta}(\gamma +_0 \delta = \beta)$. We wish to show that $P = \bigcup_{\beta <_0 \omega_\alpha} P_\beta$. First, if $\gamma +_0 \delta = \beta <_0 \omega_\alpha$, then $\gamma \leqslant_0 \beta <_0 \omega_\alpha$ and $\delta \leqslant_0 \beta <_0 \omega_\alpha$; hence, $\langle \gamma, \delta\rangle \in \omega_\alpha \times \omega_\alpha = P$. Thus, $\bigcup_{\beta <_0 \omega_\alpha} P_\beta \subseteq P$. To show that $P \subseteq \bigcup_{\beta <_0 \omega_\alpha} P_\beta$, it suffices to show that, if $\gamma <_0 \omega_\alpha$ and $\delta <_0 \omega_\alpha$, then $\gamma +_0 \delta <_0 \omega_\alpha$. Now, γ and δ are equinumerous with initial ordinals $\omega_\sigma \leqslant_0 \gamma$ and $\omega_\rho \leqslant_0 \delta$, respectively. Let ζ be the larger of σ and ρ. Since $\gamma <_0 \omega_\alpha$ and $\delta <_0 \omega_\alpha$, then $\omega_\zeta <_0 \omega_\alpha$. Hence, by the minimality of α, $\omega_\zeta \times \omega_\zeta \simeq \omega_\zeta$. Let $A = \gamma \times \{0\}$, $B = \delta \times \{1\}$. Then, by Proposition 4.33, $A \cup B \simeq \gamma +_0 \delta$. Since $\gamma \simeq \omega_\sigma$ and $\delta \simeq \omega_\rho$, $A \simeq \omega_\sigma \times \{0\}$ and $B \simeq \omega_\rho \times \{1\}$. Hence, since $A \cap B = 0$, $A \cup B \simeq (\omega_\sigma \times \{0\}) \cup (\omega_\rho \times \{1\})$. But, by Proposition 4.32(2), $(\omega_\sigma \times \{0\}) \cup (\omega_\rho \times \{1\}) \preceq (\omega_\sigma \times \{0\}) \times (\omega_\rho \times \{1\}) \simeq \omega_\sigma \times \omega_\rho \preceq \omega_\zeta \times \omega_\zeta \simeq \omega_\zeta$. Hence, $\gamma +_0 \delta \preceq \omega_\zeta <_0 \omega_\alpha$. Since ω_α is an initial ordinal, $\gamma +_0 \delta <_0 \omega_\alpha$. (For, if $\omega_\alpha \leqslant_0 \gamma +_0 \delta$, then $\omega_\alpha \preceq \omega_\zeta$ and $\omega_\zeta \preceq \omega_\alpha$; so, by the Schröder-Bernstein Theorem, $\omega_\alpha = \omega_\zeta$, contradicting $\omega_\zeta <_0 \omega_\alpha$.) Thus, $P = \bigcup_{\beta <_0 \omega_\alpha} P_\beta$. Consider P_β for any $\beta <_0 \omega_\alpha$. By Proposition 4.29(6), for each $\gamma \leqslant_0 \beta$, there is exactly one ordinal δ such that $\gamma +_0 \delta = \beta$. Hence there is a similarity mapping from β' onto P_β, where P_β is ordered according to the size of the first component γ of the pairs $\langle\gamma, \delta\rangle$. Define the following relation R on P. For any $\gamma <_0 \omega_\alpha$, $\delta <_0 \omega_\alpha$, $\mu <_0 \omega_\alpha$, $\nu <_0 \omega_\alpha$, $\langle\langle\gamma, \delta\rangle, \langle\mu, \nu\rangle\rangle \in R$ if and only if either $\gamma +_0 \delta <_0 \mu +_0 \nu$ or $(\gamma +_0 \delta = \mu +_0 \nu \wedge \gamma <_0 \mu)$. Thus, if $\beta_1 <_0 \beta_2 <_0 \omega_\alpha$, the pairs in P_{β_1} R-precede the pairs in P_{β_2}, and, within each P_β, the pairs are R-ordered according to the size of their first components. One easily verifies that R well-orders P. Since $P = \omega_\alpha \times \omega_\alpha$, it suffices now to show that $\langle R, P\rangle$ is similar to $\langle E_{\omega_\alpha}, \omega_\alpha\rangle$. By Proposition 4.17, $\langle R, P\rangle$ is similar to some $\langle E_\xi, \xi\rangle$, where ξ is an ordinal. Hence, $P \simeq \xi$. Assume that $\xi >_0 \omega_\alpha$. There is a similarity mapping f between $\langle E_\xi, \xi\rangle$ and $\langle R, P\rangle$. Let $b = f \text{‘} \omega_\alpha$; then b is an ordered pair $\langle\gamma, \delta\rangle$ with $\gamma <_0 \omega_\alpha$, $\delta <_0 \omega_\alpha$, and ω_α **1** f is a similarity mapping between $\langle E_{\omega_\alpha}, \omega_\alpha\rangle$ and the R-segment $Y = Seg_R(P, \langle\gamma, \delta\rangle)$ of P determined by $\langle\gamma, \delta\rangle$. Then $Y \simeq \omega_\alpha$. Also, letting $\beta = \gamma +_0 \delta$, if $\langle\sigma, \rho\rangle \in Y$, we have $\sigma +_0 \rho \leqslant_0 \gamma +_0 \delta = \beta$; hence, $\sigma \leqslant_0 \beta$ and $\rho \leqslant_0 \beta$. Therefore, $Y \subseteq \beta' \times \beta'$. But $\beta' <_0 \omega_\alpha$. Hence, $\beta' \simeq \omega_\mu$ with $\mu <_0 \alpha$. By the minimality of α, $\omega_\mu \times \omega_\mu \simeq \omega_\mu$. So, $\omega_\alpha \simeq Y \preceq \omega_\mu$, contradicting $\omega_\mu \prec \omega_\alpha$. Thus, $\xi \leqslant_0 \omega_\alpha$, and, therefore, $P \preceq \omega_\alpha$. Let h be the function with domain ω_α such that $h \text{‘} \beta = \langle\beta, 0\rangle$ for every $\beta <_0 \omega_\alpha$. Then h is a one-one correspondence between β and the subset $\omega_\alpha \times \{0\}$, and, therefore, $\omega_\alpha \preceq P$. By the Schröder-Bernstein Theorem, $\omega_\alpha \simeq P$, contradicting the definition of α. Hence, $\omega_\beta \times \omega_\beta \simeq \omega_\beta$ for all β.

COROLLARY 4.36. *If $A \simeq \omega_\alpha$ and $B \simeq \omega_\beta$, and if γ is the maximum of α and β, then $A \times B \simeq \omega_\gamma$ and $A \cup B \simeq \omega_\gamma$. In particular, $\omega_\alpha \times \omega_\beta \simeq \omega_\gamma$.*

PROOF. By Proposition 4.35 and 4.32(2), $\omega_\gamma \preceq A \cup B \preceq A \times B \simeq \omega_\alpha \times \omega_\beta \preceq \omega_\gamma \times \omega_\gamma \simeq \omega_\gamma$. Hence, by the Schröder-Bernstein Theorem, $A \times B \simeq \omega_\gamma$ and $A \cup B \simeq \omega_\gamma$.

This is really only the beginning of ordinal arithmetic. For further study, cf. Sierpinski [1958] and Bachmann [1955].

§ 5. The Axiom of Choice. The Axiom of Restriction.

The Axiom of Choice is one of the most celebrated and contested statements of the theory of sets. We shall state it in the next proposition and show its equivalence to several other important assertions.

PROPOSITION 4.37. *The following* wfs *are equivalent.*

(1) Axiom of Choice (AC): *For any set x, there is a function f such that, for any non-empty subset y of x, $f \text{‘} y \in y$ (f is called a* choice function *for x).*

(2) Multiplicative Axiom (Mult): *If x is a set of disjoint non-empty sets, then there is a set y (called a* choice set *for x) such that y contains exactly one element of each set in x.* $(u)(u \in x \supset u \neq 0 \wedge (v)(v \in x \wedge v \neq u \supset v \cap u = 0)) \supset (Ey)(u)(u \in x \supset (E_1 w)(w \in u \cap y))$.

(3) Well-ordering Principle (*W.O.*): *Every set can be well-ordered.* $(x)(Ey)(y\ We\ x)$.

(4) Trichotomy (*Trich*): $(x)(y)(x \preceq y \vee y \preceq x)$.

(5) Zorn's Lemma (*Zorn*): *Any non-empty partially-ordered set x, in which every chain* (i.e., *every totally-ordered subset*) *has an upper bound, has a maximal element.* $(x)(y)((y\ Part\ x) \wedge ((u)(u \subseteq x \wedge y\ Tot\ u \supset (Ev)(v \in x \wedge (w)(w \in u \supset w = v \vee \langle w, v\rangle \in y))) \supset (Ev)(v \in x \wedge (w)(w \in x \supset \langle v, w\rangle \notin y)))$.

PROOF

(1) $\vdash (W.O.) \supset Trich$. Given sets x, y, then, by (*W.O.*), x and y can be well-ordered; hence, by Proposition 4.17, $x \simeq \alpha$ and $y \simeq \beta$ for some ordinals α, β. But $\alpha \preceq \beta$ or $\beta \preceq \alpha$. Hence, $x \preceq y$ or $y \preceq x$.

(2) $\vdash Trich \supset (W.O.)$. Given a set x, then, by Hartogs' Theorem, there is an ordinal α such that α is not equinumerous with any subset of x. By *Trich*, x is equinumerous with some subset y of α. Hence, by translating the well-ordering E_y of y to x, x can be well-ordered.

(3) $\vdash (W.O.) \supset Mult$. Let x be a set of non-empty disjoint sets. By (*W.O.*), there is a well-ordering R of $\bigcup(x)$. Hence, there is a function f with domain x such that, for any u in x, $f\,{}^\backprime\, u$ is the R-least element of u. (Notice that $u \subseteq \bigcup(x)$.)

(4) $\vdash Mult \supset AC$. For any set x, we may define a one-one function g such that, for each non-empty subset u of x, $g\,{}^\backprime\, u = u \times \{u\}$. Let x_1 be the range of g. Then x_1 is a set of non-empty disjoint sets. Hence, by *Mult*, there is a choice set y for x_1. Therefore, if $0 \neq u$ and $u \subseteq x$, then $u \times \{u\}$ is in x_1, and so, y contains exactly one element $\langle v, u\rangle$ in $u \times \{u\}$. Then the function f such that $f\,{}^\backprime\, u = v$ is a choice function for x.

(5) $\vdash AC \supset Zorn$. Let y partial-order a non-empty set x such that every y-chain in x has an upper bound in x. By *AC*, there is a choice function f for x. Let b be any element of x. By transfinite induction (Proposition 4.13), we define a function F such that $F\,{}^\backprime\, 0 = b$, and, for any α, $F\,{}^\backprime\, \alpha$ is $f\,{}^\backprime\, u$, where u is the set of y-upper bounds v in x of $F\,{}^{\backprime\backprime}\, \alpha$ such that $v \notin F\,{}^{\backprime\backprime}\, \alpha$. Let β be the least ordinal such that the set of y-upper bounds in x of $F\,{}^{\backprime\backprime}\, \beta$ which are not in $F\,{}^{\backprime\backprime}\, \beta$ is empty. (There must be such an ordinal; otherwise, F is a one-one function with domain On and range a subset of x, which, by the Replacement Axiom R, implies that On is a set.) Let $g = \beta \upharpoonright F$. Then it is an easy exercise to check that g is one-one, and, if $\alpha <_0 \gamma <_0 \beta$, $\langle g\,{}^\backprime\, \alpha, g\,{}^\backprime\, \gamma\rangle \in y$.

Hence, $g``\beta$ is a $y$-chain in $x$; by hypothesis, there is an upper bound $w$ of $g``\beta$. Since the set of upper bounds of $F``\beta(= g``\beta)$ which are not in $g``\beta$ is empty, $w \in g``\beta$ and w is the only upper bound of $g``\beta$ (because a set can contain at most one upper bound). Hence, $w$ is a $y$-maximal element. (For, if $\langle w, z\rangle \in y$ and $z \in x$, then $z$ is a $y$-upper bound of $g``\beta$, which is impossible.)

(6) $\vdash$ *Zorn* $\supset$ (*W.O.*). Given a set z, let X be the class of all one-one functions with domain an ordinal and range a subset of z. By Hartogs' Theorem, X is a set. Clearly, $0 \in X$. X is partially-ordered by the proper inclusion relation $\subset$. Given any chain of functions in X, of any two, one is an extension of the other. Hence, the union of all the functions in the chain is also a one-one function from an ordinal into z, which is an $\subset$-upper bound of the chain. Hence, by *Zorn*, X has a maximal element g, which is a one-one function from an ordinal α into z. Assume $z - g``\alpha \neq 0$, and let $b \in z - g``\alpha$. Let $f = g \cup \{\langle\alpha, b\rangle\}$. Then $f \in X$ and $g \subset f$, contradicting the maximality of g. So, $g``\alpha = z$. Thus, $\alpha \underset{g}{\simeq} z$. We can transfer by means of g the well-ordering E_α of α to a well-ordering of z.

EXERCISES

1. Show that the following are equivalent to the Axiom of Choice.

(a) Any set x is equinumerous with some ordinal.

(b) (Special case of Zorn's Lemma) If x is a non-empty set, and if the union of each non-empty $\subset$-chain in x is also in x, then x has a $\subset$-maximal element.

(c) (Hausdorff Maximal Principle) If x is a set, then every $\subset$-chain in x is a subset of some maximal $\subset$-chain in x.

(d) (Teichmüller-Tukey Lemma) Any set of finite character has an $\subset$-maximal element. (A non-empty set x is said to be of finite character if and only if (i) every finite subset of an element of x is also an element of x; (ii) if every finite subset of a set y is a member of x, then $y \in x$.)

(e) $(x)((Rel(x) \supset (Ey)(Fnc(y) \wedge \mathscr{D}(x) = \mathscr{D}(y) \wedge y \subseteq x)$.

2. Show that the following Finite Axiom of Choice is provable in NBG: if x is a finite set of non-empty disjoint sets, then there is a choice set y for x. (Hint: assume $x \simeq \alpha$ where $\alpha \in \omega$. Use induction on α.)

PROPOSITION 4.38. The following are consequences of the Axiom of Choice.

(I) Any infinite set has a denumerable subset.

(II) Any infinite set is Dedekind-infinite.

(III) If x is a denumerable set whose elements are denumerable sets, then $\bigcup(x)$ is denumerable.

PROOF

(I) Assume AC. Let x be an infinite set. By Exercise 1(a), page 199, x is equinumerous with some ordinal α. Since x is infinite, so is α. Hence, $\omega \leqslant_0 \alpha$; therefore, ω is equinumerous with some subset of x.

(II) By (I) and Exercise 13(c), page 187.

(III) Assume x is a denumerable set of denumerable sets. Let f be a function assigning to each $u \in x$ the set of all one-one correspondences between u and ω. Let z be the union of the range of f. Then, by AC applied to z, there is a function g such that $g \text{ ‘ } v \in v$ for each non-empty $v \subseteq z$. In particular, if $u \in x$, then $g \text{ ‘ } (f \text{ ‘ } u)$ is a one-one correspondence between u and ω. Let h be a one-one correspondence between ω and x. Define a function F on $\bigcup(x)$ as follows: Let $y \in \bigcup(x)$ and let n be the smallest element of ω such that $y \in h \text{ ‘ } n$. Now, $h \text{ ‘ } n \in x$; so, $g \text{ ‘ } (f \text{ ‘ } (h \text{ ‘ } n))$ is a one-one correspondence between $h \text{ ‘ } n$ and ω. Define $F \text{ ‘ } y = \langle n, (g \text{ ‘ } (f \text{ ‘ } (h \text{ ‘ } n))) \text{ ‘ } y\rangle$. Then F is a one-one function with domain $\bigcup(x)$ and range a subset of $\omega \times \omega$. Hence, $\bigcup(x) \preceq \omega \times \omega$. But $\omega \times \omega \simeq \omega$ and, therefore, $\bigcup(x) \preceq \omega$. If $v \in x$, then $v \subseteq \bigcup(x)$ and $v \simeq \omega$. Hence, $\omega \preceq \bigcup(x)$. By the Schröder-Bernstein Theorem, $\bigcup(x) \simeq \omega$.

EXERCISES

1. If x is a set, the Cartesian product $\prod_{u \in x} u$ is the set of functions f with domain x such that $f \text{ ‘ } u \in u$ for all $u \in x$. Show that AC is equivalent to the proposition that the Cartesian product of any set x of non-empty sets is also non-empty.

2. Show that AC implies that any partial ordering of a set x is included in a total ordering of x.

3. Prove that the following assertion is a consequence of AC: for any ordinal α, if x is a set such that $x \preceq \omega_\alpha$ and such that $(u)(u \in x \supset u \preceq \omega_\alpha)$, then $\bigcup(x) \preceq \omega_\alpha$. (Hint: proof is analogous to that of Proposition 4.38(III).)

An apparently stronger form of the Axiom of Choice is the following wf. (UCF): $(EX)(Fnc(X) \wedge (u)(u \neq 0 \supset X \text{ ‘ } u \in u))$. (There is a *universal choice function*, i.e., a function which assigns to every non-empty set u an element of u.)

UCF obviously implies AC, but it is not known whether, conversely, AC implies UCF.

The theory of cardinal numbers is simplified if we assume AC; for, AC implies that every set is equinumerous with some ordinal, and, therefore, that every set x is equinumerous with a unique initial ordinal ω_α. We then designate ω_α the *cardinal number* of x. Thus, the cardinal numbers are identified with the initial ordinals. To conform with the standard notation for ordinals, we let $\aleph_\alpha$ stand for ω_α. Propositions 4.35–4.36 establish some of the basic properties of addition and multiplication of cardinal numbers.

The status of the Axiom of Choice has become less controversial in recent years. To most mathematicians it seems quite plausible and it has so many important applications in practically all branches of mathematics that not to accept it would seem to be a wilful hobbling of the practicing mathematician. We shall discuss its consistency and independence later in this section.

Another hypothesis which has been proposed as a basic principle of set theory is the so-called *Axiom of Restriction* (Axiom D): $(X)(X \neq 0 \supset (Ey)(y \in X \wedge y \cap X = 0))$. (Every non-empty class X contains a member which is disjoint from X.)

PROPOSITION 4.39

(1) *The Axiom of Restriction implies the* Fundierungsaxiom:

$$\sim(Ex)(Fnc(x) \wedge \mathscr{D}(x) = \omega \wedge (u)(u \in \omega \supset x\text{ ‘ }(u') \in x\text{ ‘ }u))$$

i.e., there is no infinitely-descending $\in$*-sequence* $x_1 \ni x_2 \ni x_3 \ni \ldots$.

(2) *If we assume the Axiom of Choice, then the Fundierungsaxiom implies the Axiom of Restriction.*

(3) *The Axiom of Restriction implies the non-existence of finite* $\in$*-cycles, i.e., of functions* f *on a non-zero finite ordinal* α' *such that* $f\text{ ‘ }0 \in f\text{ ‘ }1 \in \ldots \in f\text{ ‘ }\alpha \in f\text{ ‘ }0$; *in particular, it implies that there is no set* y *such that* $y \in y$.

PROOF

(1) Assume $Fnc(x) \wedge \mathscr{D}(x) = \omega \wedge (u)(u \in \omega \supset x\text{ ‘ }(u') \in x\text{ ‘ }u)$. Let $z = x\text{ “ }\omega$. By the Axiom of Restriction, there is some element y in z such that $y \cap z = 0$. Since $y \in z$, there is some finite ordinal α such that $y = f\text{ ‘ }\alpha$. Then $f\text{ ‘ }(\alpha') \in y \cap z$, contradicting $y \cap z = 0$.

(2) First, we define the *transitive closure* of a set u. Define by induction a function g on ω such that $g\text{ ‘ }0 = \{u\}$, and $g\text{ ‘ }(\alpha') = \bigcup(g\text{ ‘ }\alpha)$ for each $\alpha \in \omega$. Thus, $g\text{ ‘ }1 = u$, $g\text{ ‘ }2 = \bigcup(u)$, etc. Let $TC(u) = \bigcup(g\text{ “ }\omega)$ be called the transitive closure of u. For any u, $TC(u)$ is transitive, i.e., $(v)(v \in TC(u) \supset v \subseteq TC(u))$. Now, assume AC and the *Fundierungsaxiom*; also, assume $X \neq 0$ but there is no $y \in X$ such that $y \cap X = 0$. Let b be some element of X; hence, $b \cap X \neq 0$. Let $c = TC(b) \cap X$. By AC, let h be a choice function for c. Define a function f on ω such that $f\text{ ‘ }0 = b$, and, for any $\alpha \in \omega$, $f\text{ ‘ }(\alpha') = h\text{ ‘ }((f\text{ ‘ }\alpha) \cap X)$. It follows easily that, for each $\alpha \in \omega$, $f\text{ ‘ }(\alpha') \in f\text{ ‘ }\alpha$, contradicting the Fundierungsaxiom. (The proof can be summarized as follows: we start with an element b of X; then, using h, we pick

an element $f\text{ ‘ }1$ in $b \cap X$; since, by assumption, $f\text{ ‘ }1$ and X cannot be disjoint, we pick an element $f\text{ ‘ }2$ in $f\text{ ‘ }1 \cap X$, etc.)

(3) Assume given a finite $\in$-cycle: $f\text{ ‘ }0 \in f\text{ ‘ }1 \in \ldots \in f\text{ ‘ }n \in f\text{ ‘ }0$. Let X be the range of f: $\{f\text{ ‘ }0, f\text{ ‘ }1, \ldots, f\text{ ‘ }n\}$. By the Axiom of Restriction, there is some $f\text{ ‘ }i \in X$ such that $f\text{ ‘ }i \cap X = 0$. But each element of X has an element in common with X.

Remark: The use of the Axiom of Choice in deriving the Axiom of Restriction from the Fundierungsaxiom is necessary. It can be shown (cf. Mendelson [1958]) that, if NBG is consistent, and if we add the Fundierungsaxiom as an axiom, then the Axiom of Restriction is not provable in this enlarged theory.

Let us define by transfinite induction a function Ψ, which was originally devised by von Neumann.

$$\Psi\text{ ‘ }0 = 0$$

$$\Psi\text{ ‘ }(\alpha') = \mathscr{P}(\Psi\text{ ‘ }\alpha)$$

$$Lim(\lambda) \supset \Psi\text{ ‘ }\lambda = \bigcup_{\beta <_0 \lambda} (\Psi\text{ ‘ }\beta)$$

Let $H = \bigcup(\Psi\text{ “ }On)$, and let H_β stand for $\bigcup(\Psi\text{ “ }\beta)$. Define a function ρ on H such that, for any $x \in H$, $\rho\text{ ‘ }x$ is the least ordinal α such that $x \in \Psi\text{ ‘ }\alpha$. $\rho\text{ ‘ }x$ is called the *rank* of x. Observe that $\rho\text{ ‘ }x$ must be a successor ordinal.

EXERCISES

1. $\vdash On \subseteq H$ (Hint: by transfinite induction)
2. $\vdash (\alpha)(\rho\text{ ‘ }\alpha = \alpha')$ (Hint: by transfinite induction)
3. $\vdash Trans(H)$, i.e., $u \in H \supset u \subseteq H$
4. $\vdash u \in H \wedge v \in H \wedge (u \in v) \supset \rho\text{ ‘ }u <_0 \rho\text{ ‘ }v$
5. $\vdash u \subseteq H \supset u \in H$ (Hint: let λ be a limit ordinal greater than the ranks of all the elements of u. Then $u \subseteq \Psi\text{ ‘ }\lambda$; hence, $u \in \mathscr{P}(\Psi\text{ ‘ }\lambda) = \Psi\text{ ‘ }(\lambda')$.)

PROPOSITION 4.40. *The Axiom of Restriction is equivalent to the assertion that* $V = H$, *i.e., that every set is a member of* H.

PROOF

(1) Assume $V = H$, and let $X \neq 0$. Let α be the least of the ranks of all the elements of X, and let b be an element of X such that $\rho\text{ ‘ }b = \alpha$. Then $b \cap X = 0$; for, if $u \in b \cap X$, then, by Exercise 4 above, $\rho\text{ ‘ }u \in \rho\text{ ‘ }b = \alpha$ contradicting the minimality of α.

(2) Assume the Axiom of Restriction, and assume that $V - H \neq 0$. By the Axiom of Restriction, there is some $y \in V - H$ such that $y \cap (V - H) = 0$. Hence, $y \subseteq H$, and so, by Exercise 5 above, $y \in H$, contradicting $y \in V - H$.

EXERCISES

1. Show that the Axiom of Restriction is equivalent to the special case: $x \neq 0 \supset (Ey)(y \in x \wedge y \cap x = 0)$.

2. Show that, if we assume the Axiom of Restriction, then $x \in On$ is equivalent to: $Trans(x) \wedge E\ Con\ x$, i.e., to $(u)(u \in x \supset u \subseteq x) \wedge (u)(v)(u \in x \wedge v \in x \wedge u \neq v \supset u \in v \vee v \in u)$. Thus, with the Axiom of Restriction, a much simpler definition of the notion of ordinal number is possible.

Proposition 4.40 certainly increases the attractiveness of adding the Axiom of Restriction as a new axiom to NBG. The proposition $V = H$ asserts that every set can be obtained by starting with 0 and applying the power set and union operations any transfinite number of times, and the assumption that this is so would clarify our rather hazy ideas about sets. By Exercise 2 above, the Axiom of Restriction would also simplify the definition of ordinal numbers. In addition, we can develop the theory of cardinal numbers on the basis of the Axiom of Restriction: namely, just define the cardinal number of a set x to be the set of all those y of lowest rank such that $y \simeq x$. (The basic requirement of the theory of cardinal numbers is that there be a function *Card* whose domain is V such that $Card \text{`}\, x = Card \text{`}\, y \equiv x \simeq y$.) There is no unanimity among mathematicians about whether we have sufficient grounds for adding the Axiom of Restriction as a new axiom, for, although it has great simplifying power, it does not have the immediate plausibility that even the Axiom of Choice has, nor has it had any mathematical applications.

The class H defined above determines an *inner model* of NBG in the following sense. For any wf $\mathscr{A}$ (written in unabbreviated notation) containing the free variables $Y_1, \ldots, Y_n$, let $\mathrm{Rel}_H(\mathscr{A})$ be the wf obtained from $\mathscr{A}$ by replacing every subformula $(X)\mathscr{B}(X)$ by $(X)(X \subseteq H \supset \mathscr{B}(X))$ (in making the replacements, we start with the innermost subformulas), and then prefixing $(Y_1 \subseteq H \wedge Y_2 \subseteq H \wedge \ldots \wedge Y_n \subseteq H) \supset$. In other words, in forming $\mathrm{Rel}_H(\mathscr{A})$, we interpret "class" as "subclass of H". Then, for any theorem $\mathscr{A}$ of NBG, $\mathrm{Rel}_H(\mathscr{A})$ is also a theorem of NBG.

EXERCISE. Verify that, for each axiom $\mathscr{A}$ of NBG, $\mathrm{Rel}_H(\mathscr{A})$ is a theorem of NBG. Notice that $\mathrm{Rel}_H((x)\mathscr{B})$ is equivalent to $(x)(x \in H \supset \mathscr{B}^{\#})$, where $\mathscr{B}^{\#}$ is $\mathrm{Rel}_H(\mathscr{B})$. In particular, $\mathrm{Rel}_H(M(X))$ is $(EY)(Y \subseteq H \wedge X \in Y)$, which is equivalent to $X \in H$; thus, the "sets" of the model are the elements of H. If we adopt a semantic approach, then one need only observe that, if N is a model for NBG (in the usual sense of "model"), then the objects X of N that satisfy the wf $X \subseteq H$ also form a model for NBG. In addition, one can verify that the Axiom of Restriction holds in this model; this is just Part (1) of Proposition 4.40. A direct consequence of this fact is the consistency of the Axiom of Restriction, i.e., if NBG is consistent, so is the theory obtained by adding the Axiom of Restriction as a new axiom. That the Axiom of Restriction is independent of NBG can also be proved (cf. Bernays [1954], Part VII) by means of a suitable model, though the model is more complex than that given above for the consistency proof. Thus, the Axiom of Restriction is both consistent and independent with respect to NBG: we can consistently add either it or its negation as an axiom to NBG, if NBG is consistent. (Practically the same proofs also show the independence and consistency of the Axiom of Restriction with respect to NBG + (AC).)

The Axiom of Choice also turns out to be consistent and independent with respect to NBG. In fact, Gödel [1940] has shown that if NBG is consistent then the theory NBG + (AC) + (Axiom of Restriction) + (GCH) is also consistent, where (GCH) stands for the Generalized Continuum Hypothesis: $(x)(y) \sim (Inf(x) \wedge x \prec y \wedge y \prec \mathscr{P}(x))$. (The assertion just made is a bit redundant, since $\vdash$ (GCH) $\supset$ (AC) has been proved by Sierpinski [1947] and Specker [1954].) On the other hand, it has been shown by Mendelson [1958] that, if NBG is consistent, then (AC) is not provable from NBG even if we add the Fundierungsaxiom as a new axiom to NBG. Thus, if NBG is consistent, we can either accept or reject the Axiom of Choice without fear of inconsistency. (However, the independence of the Axiom of Choice from NBG + (Axiom of Restriction) is still an open question.)

EXERCISES

1. Show that the model H_α, the "classes" of which are the subclasses of H_α, satisfies all axioms of NBG, except possibly the Axiom of Infinity and the Replacement Axiom, if and only if $Lim(\alpha)$. Prove also that H_α satisfies the Axiom of Infinity if and only if $\alpha >_0 \omega$.

2. Show that the Axiom of Infinity is not provable from the other axioms of NBG, if the latter are consistent. (Hint: assume that the other axioms of NBG are consistent, and assume that the Axiom of Infinity is provable from them. Show that H_ω is a model for the other axioms but not for the Axiom of Infinity; the "classes" are the subsets of H_ω.)

3. Show that the Axiom of Replacement R is not provable from the other axioms (T, P, N, B1–B7, U, W, S) if these latter are consistent. (Hint: show that $H_{\omega +_0 \omega}$ is a model for the other axioms but not for Axiom R.)

D4. An ordinal α such that H_α is a model for NBG is called *inaccessible*.

Since NBG has only a finite number of proper axioms, the assertion that α is inaccessible can be expressed by the conjunction of the relativization to H_α of the proper axioms of NBG. The existence of inaccessible ordinals is not provable in NBG if the latter is consistent, and the same is true even if the Axiom of Choice and the Generalized Continuum Hypothesis are added as axioms. (Compare Shepherdson [1951–1953], Montague-Vaught [1959], and, for related results, Bernays [1961] and Levy [1960].) Inaccessible ordinals have been shown to have connections with problems in measure theory and algebra (cf. Ulam [1930], Zeeman [1955], and Erdos-Tarski [1961]). The consistency of the theory obtained from NBG by adding an axiom asserting the existence of an inaccessible ordinal is still an open question.

5. An *α-sequence* is a function w whose domain is α. If the range of w consists of ordinals, w is called an *ordinal α-sequence*, and if, in addition, $\beta <_0 \gamma <_0 \alpha$ implies $w(\beta) <_0 w(\gamma)$, w is called an *increasing ordinal α-sequence*. By Proposition 4.11, if w is an increasing ordinal α-sequence, then $\bigcup(w\text{``}\alpha)$ is the least upper bound of the range of $w$. An ordinal $\delta$ is said to be *regular* if, for any increasing ordinal $\alpha$-sequence $w$ such that $\alpha <_0 \delta$ and the ordinals in the range of $w$ are all $<_0 \delta$, then $\bigcup(w\text{``}\alpha) +_0 1 <_0 \delta$. Non-regular ordinals are called *singular* ordinals.

(i) Which finite ordinals are regular?
(ii) Show that ω_0 is regular and that ω_ω is singular.
(iii) Prove that every regular ordinal is an initial ordinal.
(iv) Assuming the Axiom of Choice (AC), prove that every ordinal of the form $\omega_{\gamma +_0 1}$ is regular.
(v) If ω_α is regular and $Lim(\alpha)$, prove that $\omega_\alpha = \alpha$. (A regular ordinal ω_α such that $Lim(\alpha)$ is called a *weakly inaccessible* ordinal.)
(vi) Show that, if ω_α has the property that $\gamma <_0 \omega_\alpha$ implies $\mathscr{P}(\gamma) \prec \omega_\alpha$, then $Lim(\alpha)$. The converse is implied by the Generalized Continuum Hypothesis. A regular ordinal ω_α such that $\alpha >_0 0$, and $\gamma <_0 \omega_\alpha$ implies $\mathscr{P}(\gamma) \prec \omega_\alpha$, is called *strongly inaccessible*. Thus, every strongly inaccessible ordinal is weakly inaccessible, and, if the (GCH) holds, the strongly inaccessible ordinals coincide with the weakly inaccessible ordinals.
(vii) (Shepherdson [1951–53], Montague-Vaught [1959]) (a) If γ is inaccessible (i.e., if H_γ is a model of NBG), then γ is weakly inaccessible. ^{D}(b) In the theory NBG + (AC), γ is inaccessible if and only if γ is strongly inaccessible. (c) If (NBG) is consistent, then in the theory NBG + (AC) + (GCH) it is impossible to prove the existence of weakly inaccessible ordinals.

We have chosen to develop axiomatic set theory on the basis of NBG because it is probably the simplest and most convenient for the practicing mathematician. Of course, there are many other varieties of axiomatic set theory.

(1) Strengthening NBG, we can replace Axioms B1–B7 by the Axiom Schema: $(EX)(y_1)(y_2)\ldots(y_n)(\langle y_1, y_2, \ldots, y_n\rangle \in X \equiv \varphi(y_1, y_2, \ldots, y_n))$, where φ is any wf (not necessarily predicative) of NBG. This new theory NBG^+ is an extension of NBG; Mostowski [1951] has shown that, if NBG is consistent, NBG^+ is a proper extension of NBG. Although NBG^+ is simpler and more powerful than NBG, its strength makes its consistency a riskier gamble. In addition, Gödel's relative consistency proof for the Axiom of Choice [1940] no longer seems to apply when we extend NBG to NBG^+.

(2) Zermelo-Skolem-Fraenkel (ZSF) set theory is essentially the part of NBG which refers only to sets. We use $x_1, x_2, \ldots$ as variables in ZSF. There is a single binary predicate $\in$. The axioms are Axioms T (Extensionality), P (Pairing), N (Null Set), U (Sum Set), W (Power Set), I (Infinity), plus an axiom schema corresponding to Axiom R (Replacement): for any wf $\varphi(v, u)$, the following is an axiom.

$$((v)(w)(u)(\varphi(v, u) \wedge \varphi(v, w) \supset u = w)) \\ \supset (Ey)(u)(u \in y \equiv (Ev)(v \in x \wedge \varphi(v, u)))$$

Every wf of ZSF can be considered a wf of NBG, with the variables of ZSF playing the role of restricted set variables in NBG. It has been proved (cf. Novak-Gál [1951], Rosser-Wang [1950], Shoenfield [1954]) that, for any closed wf $\mathscr{A}$ of ZSF, if $\vdash_{NBG} \mathscr{A}$, then $\vdash_{ZSF} \mathscr{A}$; therefore, ZSF is consistent if and only if NBG is consistent. For a detailed development of ZSF, consult Suppes [1960].

For a survey of various axiomatic set theories, cf. Fraenkel-Bar Hillel [1958] and Wang-McNaughton [1953]. To obtain more detailed treatments of the theory of types, consult Church [1940] and Quine [1938]; for Quine's *New Foundations* (NF), cf. Rosser [1953] and Specker [1953] (where it is shown that the strong Axiom of Choice is disprovable in NF), and, for Quine's system ML, cf. Quine [1951].

CHAPTER 5

EFFECTIVE COMPUTABILITY

§ 1. Markov Algorithms

A function $f(x_1, \ldots, x_n)$ is thought of as being effectively computable if there is a mechanical procedure for determining the value $f(k_1, \ldots, k_n)$ when the arguments $k_1, \ldots, k_n$ are given. The phrase "mechanical procedure" is not at all precise; what we mean is a process which requires no ingenuity for its performance. An obvious example is the addition of two integers expressed in decimal notation. Another well-known case is the Euclidean algorithm for obtaining the greatest common divisor of two integers. In these two examples, it seems intuitively clear that the given functions are effectively computable. This is generally the case when an effective procedure has already been discovered. However, more and more in mathematics, we are faced with the task of showing that there is no effectively computable function of a certain kind or that there is no effective procedure for solving a large class of problems. To illustrate, we can cite on the one hand the well-known effective way of determining whether or not any given polynomial in one variable with integral coefficients has an integral root. On the other hand, it is still an open question, called Hilbert's Tenth Problem, to find out whether there is an effective procedure for testing any given polynomial in any finite number of variables with integral coefficients to see whether it has integral roots. If we attempt to prove that a certain function is not effectively computable, it is apparent that we have to give a precise, mathematical definition of the notion of effective computability. The situation is quite analogous to that which prevailed in mathematics before notions like continuity, curve, surface, area were explicated.

Any particular problem of a general class of problems can be formulated as an expression of some language. Any expression of a language can be considered as a sequence of symbols of that language, provided that the blank which is usually used to separate words is assumed to be a symbol in its own right. By an *alphabet* we mean a non-empty finite set of symbols. Most natural languages use only a finite number of symbols, and, for our purposes, it also suffices to treat only such alphabets. (Indeed, anything that can be done with an infinite alphabet $a_1, a_2, \ldots$ can be accomplished with a two-symbol alphabet $\{b, c\}$, if we let $b\underbrace{cc\ldots c}_{\text{n times}}b$ play the role of a_n.) For uniformity, we assume that the symbols of all alphabets are taken from the denumerable sequence $S_0, S_1, S_2, \ldots$, though, sometimes, for convenience, we shall use other letters.

A *word* in an alphabet A is any finite sequence of symbols of A. The empty sequence of symbols is called the *empty word*, and is denoted by Λ. If P denotes a word $S_{j_1} \ldots S_{j_k}$ and Q denotes a word $S_{r_1} \ldots S_{r_m}$, then we use PQ to denote the juxtaposition $S_{j_1} \ldots S_{j_k} S_{r_1} \ldots S_{r_m}$ of the two words. In particular, $P\Lambda = \Lambda P = P$; also, $(P_1P_2)P_3 = P_1(P_2P_3)$.

An alphabet A is an *extension* of an alphabet B if and only if B $\subseteq$ A. If A is an extension of B, any word of B is a word of A.

By an *algorithm in* an alphabet A, we mean an effectively computable function $\mathfrak{A}$ whose domain is a subset of the set of words of A and the values of which are also words in A. If P is a word in A, $\mathfrak{A}$ is said to be *applicable* to P if P is in the domain of $\mathfrak{A}$; if $\mathfrak{A}$ is applicable to P, we denote its value by $\mathfrak{A}(P)$. By an *algorithm over* an alphabet A we mean an algorithm $\mathfrak{A}$ in an extension B of A. Of course, the notion of algorithm is as hazy as that of effectively computable function.

Most familiar algorithms can be broken down into a few simple steps. Starting from this observation, and following Markov [1954], we select a particularly simple operation, substitution of one word for another, as the basic unit from which algorithms are to be constructed. To this end, if P and Q are words of an alphabet A, then we call the expressions $P \to Q$ and $P \to \cdot Q$ *productions* in the alphabet A. We assume here that "$\to$" and the dot "$\cdot$" are not symbols of A. Notice that P or Q can be the empty word. $P \to Q$ is called a *simple* production, while $P \to \cdot Q$ is a *terminal* production. Let us use $P \to (\cdot)Q$ to denote either $P \to Q$ or $P \to \cdot Q$. A finite list of productions in A

$$\begin{gathered} P_1 \to (\cdot)Q_1 \\ P_2 \to (\cdot)Q_2 \\ \vdots \\ P_r \to (\cdot)Q_r \end{gathered}$$

is called an *algorithm schema* and determines the following algorithm $\mathfrak{A}$ in A. As a preliminary definition, we say that a word T *occurs* in a word Q if there are words U, V (possibly empty) such that $Q = UTV$. Now, given a word P in A: (1) We write $\mathfrak{A}$: $P\sqsupset$ if none of the words $P_1, \ldots, P_r$ occurs in P. (2) Otherwise, if m is the least integer, with $1 \leqslant m \leqslant r$, such that P_m occurs in P, and if R is the word which results from replacing the left-most occurrence of P_m in P by Q_m, then we write

(a) $$\mathfrak{A}: P \vdash R$$

if $P_m \to (\cdot)Q_m$ is simple (and we say that $\mathfrak{A}$ simply transforms P into R);

(b) $$\mathfrak{A}: P \vdash \cdot R$$

if $P_m \to (\cdot)Q_m$ is terminal (and we say that $\mathfrak{A}$ terminally transforms P into R).

We then define $\mathfrak{A}: P \models R$ to mean that there is a sequence $R_0, R_1, \ldots, R_k$ such that $P = R_0$; $R = R_k$; if $0 \leqslant j \leqslant k - 2$, $\mathfrak{A}: R_j \vdash R_{j+1}$; and either $\mathfrak{A}: R_{k-1} \vdash R_k$ or $\mathfrak{A}: R_{k-1} \vdash \cdot R_k$. (In the second case, we write $\mathfrak{A}: P \models \cdot R$.) We set $\mathfrak{A}(P) = R$ if and only if either $\mathfrak{A}: P \models \cdot R$, or $\mathfrak{A}: P \models R$ and $\mathfrak{A}: R\sqsupset$. The algorithm thus defined is called a *normal* algorithm (or Markov algorithm) in the alphabet A.

The action of $\mathfrak{A}$ can be described as follows: given a word P, we find the first production $P_m \to (\cdot)Q_m$ in the schema such that P_m occurs in P. We then substitute Q_m for the left-most occurrence of P_m in P. Let R_1 be the new word obtained in this way. If $P_m \to (\cdot)Q_m$ is a terminal production, the process stops and the value of the algorithm is R_1. If $P_m \to (\cdot)Q_m$ is simple, then we apply the same process to R_1 as was just applied to P, and so on. If we ever obtain a word R_i such that $\mathfrak{A}$: $R_i\sqsupset$, i.e., no P_m occurs in R_i for $1 \leqslant m \leqslant r$, then the process stops and the value of $\mathfrak{A}$ is R_i. It is possible that the process just described never stops. In that case, $\mathfrak{A}$ is not applicable to the given word P.

Our exposition of the theory of normal algorithms will closely follow that of Markov [1954].

Examples

1. Let A be the alphabet $\{b, c\}$. Consider the schema

$$b \to \cdot \Lambda$$
$$c \to c$$

The normal algorithm $\mathfrak{A}$ defined by this schema transforms any word containing at least one occurrence of b into the word obtained by erasing the left-most occurrence of b. $\mathfrak{A}$ transforms the empty word Λ into itself. $\mathfrak{A}$ is not applicable to any non-empty word not containing b.

2. Let A be the alphabet $\{a_0, a_1, \ldots, a_n\}$. Consider the schema

$$\begin{aligned} a_0 &\rightarrow \Lambda \\ a_1 &\rightarrow \Lambda \\ &\vdots \\ a_n &\rightarrow \Lambda \end{aligned}$$

We can abbreviate this schema as follows:

$$\xi \rightarrow \Lambda \qquad (\xi \text{ in A})$$

(Whenever we use such abbreviations, the productions intended may be listed in any order.) The corresponding normal algorithm transforms every word into the empty word. For example, $\mathfrak{A}\colon a_1a_2a_1a_3a_0 \vdash a_1a_2a_1a_3 \vdash a_2a_1a_3 \vdash a_2a_3 \vdash a_3 \vdash \Lambda$ and $\mathfrak{A}\colon \Lambda\sqsupset$. Hence $\mathfrak{A}(a_1a_2a_1a_3a_0) = \Lambda$.

3. Let A be an alphabet containing the symbol S_1, which we shall abbreviate 1. For natural numbers n, we define $\overline{\mathrm{n}}$ inductively as follows: $\overline{0} = 1$ and $\overline{\mathrm{n} + 1} = \overline{\mathrm{n}}1$. Thus, $\overline{1} = 11$, $\overline{2} = 111$, etc. The words $\overline{\mathrm{n}}$ are called numerals. Now consider the schema $\Lambda \rightarrow \cdot 1$, defining a normal algorithm $\mathfrak{A}$. For any word P in A, $\mathfrak{A}(P) = 1P$.† In particular, for every natural number n, $\mathfrak{A}(\overline{\mathrm{n}}) = \overline{\mathrm{n} + 1}$.

4. Let A be an arbitrary alphabet $\{a_0, a_1, \ldots, a_n\}$. Given a word $P = a_{j_0}a_{j_1}\ldots a_{j_k}$, let $\breve{P} = a_{j_k}\ldots a_{j_1}a_{j_0}$ be the *inverse* of P. We seek a normal algorithm $\mathfrak{A}$ such that $\mathfrak{A}(P) = \breve{P}$. Consider the following (abbreviated) algorithm schema in the alphabet $\mathrm{B} = \mathrm{A} \cup \{\alpha, \beta\}$.

(a) $\alpha\alpha \rightarrow \beta$

(b) $\beta\xi \rightarrow \xi\beta \qquad (\xi \text{ in A})$

(c) $\beta\alpha \rightarrow \beta$

(d) $\beta \rightarrow \cdot \Lambda$

(e) $\alpha\eta\xi \rightarrow \xi\alpha\eta \qquad (\xi, \eta \text{ in A})$

(f) $\Lambda \rightarrow \alpha$

† To see this, observe that Λ occurs at the beginning of any word P, since $P = \Lambda P$.

This determines a normal algorithm $\mathfrak{A}$ in B. Let $P = a_{j_0}a_{j_1}\ldots a_{j_k}$ be any word in A. Then, $\mathfrak{A}$: $P \vdash \alpha P$ by production (f); $\alpha P \vdash a_{j_1}\alpha a_{j_0}a_{j_2}\ldots a_{j_k} \vdash a_{j_1}a_{j_2}\alpha a_{j_0}a_{j_3}\ldots a_{j_k}\ldots \vdash a_{j_1}a_{j_2}\ldots a_{j_k}\alpha a_{j_0}$ by production (e). Thus, $\mathfrak{A}$: $P \models a_{j_1}a_{j_2}\ldots a_{j_k}\alpha a_{j_0}$. Then, by production (f), $\mathfrak{A}$: $P \models \alpha a_{j_1}a_{j_2}\ldots a_{j_k}\alpha a_{j_0}$. Applying, as before, production (e), $\mathfrak{A}$: $P \models a_{j_2}a_{j_3}\ldots a_{j_k}\alpha a_{j_1}\alpha a_{j_0}$. Iterating this process, we obtain $\mathfrak{A}$: $P \models \alpha a_{j_k}\alpha a_{j_{k-1}}\alpha\ldots\alpha a_{j_1}\alpha a_{j_0}$. Then, by production (f), $\mathfrak{A}$: $P \models \alpha\alpha a_{j_k}\alpha a_{j_{k-1}}\alpha\ldots\alpha a_{j_1}\alpha a_{j_0}$, and, by production (a), $\mathfrak{A}$: $P \models \beta a_{j_k}\alpha a_{j_{k-1}}\alpha\ldots\alpha a_{j_1}\alpha a_{j_0}$; applying productions (b) and (c), and, finally, (d), we arrive at $\mathfrak{A}$: $P \models\cdot \breve{P}$. Thus, $\mathfrak{A}$ is a normal algorithm over A which inverts every word of A.†

EXERCISES

1. Let A be an alphabet. Describe the action of the normal algorithms given by the following schemas.

(a) Let Q be a fixed word in A, and let the algorithm schema be: $\Lambda \rightarrow \cdot Q$.

(b) Let Q be a fixed word in A, and let α be a symbol not in A. Let B $= A \cup \{\alpha\}$. Consider the schema

$$\begin{array}{ll} \alpha\xi \rightarrow \xi\alpha & (\xi \text{ in A}) \\ \alpha \rightarrow \cdot Q & \\ \Lambda \rightarrow \alpha & \end{array}$$

(c) Let Q be a fixed word in A. Take the schema

$$\begin{array}{ll} \xi \rightarrow \Lambda & (\xi \text{ in A}) \\ \Lambda \rightarrow \cdot Q & \end{array}$$

(d) Let B $=$ A $\cup$ $\{1\}$. Consider the schema

$$\xi \rightarrow 1 \qquad (\xi \text{ in A} - \{1\})$$

2. Let A be an alphabet not containing the symbols α, β, γ. Let B $=$ A $\cup$ $\{\alpha\}$ and C $=$ A $\cup$ $\{\alpha, \beta, \gamma\}$.

(a) Construct a normal algorithm $\mathfrak{A}$ in B such that $\mathfrak{A}(\Lambda) = \Lambda$ and $\mathfrak{A}(\xi P) = P$ for any symbol ξ in A and any word P in A. Thus, $\mathfrak{A}$ erases the first letter of any non-empty word in A.

(b) Construct a normal algorithm $\mathfrak{B}$ in C such that, for any word P of A, $\mathfrak{B}(P) = PP$.

† The distinction between a normal algorithm in A and a normal algorithm over A is important. A normal algorithm in A uses only symbols of A, while a normal algorithm over A may employ additional symbols not in A. Every normal algorithm in A is a normal algorithm over A, but there are algorithms in A which are determined by normal algorithms over A but which are not normal algorithms in A (cf. Exercise 2(d), page 228).

3. Let A and B be alphabets, and let α be a symbol in neither A nor B. For certain symbols $a_1, \ldots, a_k$ in A, let $Q_1, \ldots, Q_k$ be corresponding words in B. Consider the algorithm which associates with each word of A the word $\mathrm{Sub}^{a_1,\ldots,a_k}_{Q_1,\ldots,Q_k}(P)$ obtained by simultaneous substitution of each Q_i for a_i (i = 1, ..., k). Show that this is given by a normal algorithm in $A \cup B \cup \{\alpha\}$. Hint: consider

$$\alpha a_i \to Q_i\alpha \qquad (i = 1, \ldots, k)$$
$$\alpha\xi \to \xi\alpha \qquad (\xi \in A - \{a_1, \ldots, a_k\})$$
$$\alpha \to \cdot\Lambda$$
$$\Lambda \to \alpha$$

4. Let $H = \{1\}$ and $M = \{1, *\}$. Every natural number n is represented by its numeral $\overline{n}$, which is a word in H. We represent every k-tuple $(n_1, n_2, \ldots, n_k)$ of natural numbers by the word $\overline{n}_1 * \overline{n}_2 * \ldots * \overline{n}_k$ in M. We shall denote this word by $\overline{(n_1, \ldots, n_k)}$. For example, $\overline{(3, 1, 2)}$ is $1111 * 11 * 111$.

(a) Show that the schema

$$* \to *$$
$$\alpha 11 \to \alpha 1$$
$$\alpha 1 \to \cdot 1$$
$$\Lambda \to \alpha$$

defines a normal algorithm $\mathfrak{A}_Z$ over M such that $\mathfrak{A}_Z(\overline{n}) = \overline{0}$ for any n, and $\mathfrak{A}_Z$ is applicable only to numerals in M.

(b) Show that the schema

$$* \to *$$
$$\alpha 1 \to \cdot 11$$
$$\Lambda \to \alpha$$

defines a normal algorithm $\mathfrak{A}_Z$ over M such that $\mathfrak{A}_Z(\overline{n}) = \overline{n + 1}$ for all n, and $\mathfrak{A}_Z$ is applicable only to numerals in M.

(c) Let $\alpha_1, \ldots, \alpha_{2k}$ be symbols not in M. Let $1 \leqslant j \leqslant k$. Let $\mathscr{S}_i$ be the list

$$\alpha_{2i-1}* \to \alpha_{2i-1}*$$
$$\alpha_{2i-1}1 \to \alpha_{2i}1$$
$$\alpha_{2i}1 \to \alpha_{2i}$$
$$\alpha_{2i}* \to \alpha_{2i+1}$$

If $1 < j < k$, consider the algorithm schema

$$\begin{array}{c} \mathscr{S}_1 \\ \vdots \\ \mathscr{S}_{j-1} \\ \alpha_{2j-1}* \to \alpha_{2j-1}* \\ \alpha_{2j-1}1 \to \alpha_{2j}1 \\ \alpha_{2j}1 \to 1\alpha_{2j} \\ \alpha_{2j}* \to \alpha_{2j+1} \\ \mathscr{S}_{j+1} \\ \vdots \\ \mathscr{S}_{k-1} \\ \alpha_{2k-1}* \to \alpha_{2k-1}* \\ \alpha_{2k-1}1 \to \alpha_{2k}1 \\ \alpha_{2k}1 \to \alpha_{2k} \\ \alpha_{2k}* \to \alpha_{2k}* \\ \alpha_{2k} \to \cdot\Lambda \\ \Lambda \to \alpha_1 \end{array}$$

If $j = 1$, consider the schema

$$\begin{array}{c} \alpha_1* \to \alpha_1* \\ \alpha_1 1 \to \alpha_2 1 \\ \alpha_2 1 \to 1\alpha_2 \\ \alpha_2* \to \alpha_3 \\ \mathscr{S}_2 \\ \vdots \\ \mathscr{S}_{k-1} \\ \alpha_{2k-1}* \to \alpha_{2k-1}* \\ \alpha_{2k-1}1 \to \alpha_{2k}1 \\ \alpha_{2k}1 \to \alpha_{2k} \\ \alpha_{2k}* \to \alpha_{2k}* \\ \alpha_{2k} \to \cdot\Lambda \\ \Lambda \to \alpha_1 \end{array}$$

If $j = k$, consider the schema

$$\begin{array}{c} \mathscr{S}_1 \\ \vdots \\ \mathscr{S}_{k-1} \\ \alpha_{2k-1}* \to \alpha_{2k-1}* \\ \alpha_{2k-1}1 \to \alpha_{2k}1 \\ \alpha_{2k}1 \to 1\alpha_{2k} \\ \alpha_{2k}* \to \alpha_{2k}* \\ \alpha_{2k}* \to \alpha_{2k}* \\ \alpha_{2k} \to \cdot\Lambda \\ \Lambda \to \alpha_1 \end{array}$$

Show that the corresponding normal algorithm $\mathfrak{A}_j^k$ is such that $\mathfrak{A}_j^k(\overline{(n_1, \ldots, n_k)}) = \overline{n}_j$; and $\mathfrak{A}_j^k$ is applicable only to words of the form $\overline{(n_1, \ldots, n_k)}$.

(d) Construct a schema for a normal algorithm in M transforming $\overline{(n_1, n_2)}$ into $\overline{|n_1 - n_2|}$.

(e) Construct normal algorithms over M for addition and multiplication.

Given algorithms $\mathfrak{A}$ and $\mathfrak{B}$ and a word P, we write $\mathfrak{A}(P) \approx \mathfrak{B}(P)$ if and only if either $\mathfrak{A}$ and $\mathfrak{B}$ are both applicable to P and $\mathfrak{A}(P) = \mathfrak{B}(P)$ or neither $\mathfrak{A}$ nor $\mathfrak{B}$ is applicable to P. More generally, if C and D are expressions, then $C \approx D$ is to hold if and only if neither C nor D is defined or both C and D are defined and denote the same object. If $\mathfrak{A}$ and $\mathfrak{B}$ are algorithms over an alphabet A, then we say that $\mathfrak{A}$ and $\mathfrak{B}$ are *fully equivalent* relative to A if and only if $\mathfrak{A}(P) \approx \mathfrak{B}(P)$ for every word P in A; we say that $\mathfrak{A}$ and $\mathfrak{B}$ are *equivalent* relative to A if and only if, for any word P in A, whenever $\mathfrak{A}(P)$ or $\mathfrak{B}(P)$ exists and is in A, then $\mathfrak{A}(P) \approx \mathfrak{B}(P)$.

Let M be the alphabet $\{1, *\}$, as in Exercise 4 above; let ω be the set of natural numbers. Given a partial effectively computable number-theoretic function φ of k arguments, i.e., a function from a subset of ω^k

into ω, we denote by $\mathfrak{B}_\varphi$ the corresponding algorithm in M; that is, $\mathfrak{B}_\varphi(\overline{(n_1, \ldots, n_k)}) = \overline{\varphi(n_1, \ldots, n_k)}$ whenever either of the two sides of the equation is defined; $\mathfrak{B}_\varphi$ is assumed to be inapplicable to words not of the form $\overline{(n_1, \ldots, n_k)}$. The function φ is said to be *partially Markov-computable* if and only if there is a normal algorithm $\mathfrak{A}$ over M which is fully equivalent to $\mathfrak{B}_\varphi$ relative to M.† If the function φ is total, i.e., if φ is defined for all k-tuples of natural numbers, and if φ is partially Markov-computable, then φ is said to be *Markov-computable.*

Let us generalize the notion of recursive function (cf. pages 120–121). A partial function φ of k arguments is called *partial recursive* if and only if φ can be obtained from the initial functions Z (zero function), U_j^n (projection functions), and N (successor function) by means of substitution, recursion, and the unrestricted μ-operator. (We say that ψ comes from τ by means of the unrestricted μ-operator if and only if $\psi(x_1, \ldots, x_n) = \mu y(\tau(x_1, \ldots, x_n, y) = 0)$. More precisely, $\mu y(\tau(x_1, \ldots, x_n, y) = 0)$ is the least number k (if such exists) such that, if $0 \leqslant i < k$, $\tau(x_1, \ldots, x_n, i)$ exists and is not 0, and $\tau(x_1, \ldots, x_n, k) = 0$. Notice that ψ may not be defined for certain n-tuples; in particular, for those n-tuples $(x_1, \ldots, x_n)$ for which there is no y such that $\tau(x_1, \ldots, x_n, y) = 0$.) Clearly, every recursive function is partial recursive. The assertion that every total partial recursive function is recursive is true, but not at all obvious, and will be proved later. We shall show that the partial recursive functions coincide with the partially Markov-computable functions and that the recursive functions are identical with the Markov-computable functions.

A normal algorithm is said to be *closed* if and only if one of the productions in its schema has the form $\Lambda \rightarrow \cdot Q$. Such an algorithm can only end terminally, i.e., by an application of a terminal production. Given an arbitrary normal algorithm $\mathfrak{A}$, add on at the end of the schema for $\mathfrak{A}$ the new production $\Lambda \rightarrow \cdot \Lambda$, and denote by $\mathfrak{A}^\bullet$ the normal algorithm determined by this enlarged schema. $\mathfrak{A}^\bullet$ is closed, and $\mathfrak{A}^\bullet$ is fully equivalent to $\mathfrak{A}$ relative to the alphabet of $\mathfrak{A}$.

Let us show now that the composition of two normal algorithms is again a normal algorithm. Let $\mathfrak{A}$ and $\mathfrak{B}$ be normal algorithms in an alphabet A. For each symbol b in A, form a new symbol $\bar{b}$, called the correlate of b. Let $\bar{A}$ be the alphabet consisting of the correlates of the symbols of A. Let α and β be two symbols not in $A \cup \bar{A}$. Let $\mathscr{S}_\mathfrak{A}$ be the schema of $\mathfrak{A}^\bullet$ except that the terminal dot in terminal productions

† In this and in all other definitions in this chapter, the existential quantifier "there is" is meant in the ordinary, "classical" sense. When we assert that there exists an object of a certain kind, we do not necessarily imply that any human being has found or ever will find such an object. Thus, a function φ may be partially Markov-computable without our ever knowing it to be so.

is replaced by α. Let $\mathscr{S}_{\mathfrak{B}}$ be the schema of $\mathfrak{B}^{\cdot}$ except that every symbol is replaced by its correlate, every terminal dot by β, productions of the form $\Lambda \to Q$ are replaced by $\alpha \to \alpha Q$, and productions $\Lambda \to \cdot Q$ are replaced by $\alpha \to \alpha\beta Q$. Consider the abbreviated schema

$$\begin{array}{ll} a\alpha \to \alpha a & (a \text{ in A}) \\ \alpha a \to \alpha\bar{a} & (a \text{ in A}) \\ \bar{a}b \to \bar{a}\bar{b} & (a, b \text{ in A}) \\ \bar{a}\beta \to \beta\bar{a} & (a \text{ in A}) \\ \beta\bar{a} \to \beta a & (a \text{ in A}) \\ a\bar{b} \to ab & (a, b \text{ in A}) \\ \alpha\beta \to \cdot\Lambda & \\ \quad\mathscr{S}_{\mathfrak{B}} & \\ \quad\mathscr{S}_{\mathfrak{A}} & \end{array}$$

This schema determines a normal algorithm $\mathfrak{C}$ over A such that $\mathfrak{C}(P) \approx \mathfrak{B}(\mathfrak{A}(P))$ for any word P in A. (Exercise.) $\mathfrak{C}$ is called the *composition* of $\mathfrak{A}$ and $\mathfrak{B}$, and is denoted $\mathfrak{B} \circ \mathfrak{A}$. In general, by $\mathfrak{A}_n \circ \ldots \circ \mathfrak{A}_1$, we mean $\mathfrak{A}_n \circ (\ldots \circ (\mathfrak{A}_3 \circ (\mathfrak{A}_2 \circ \mathfrak{A}_1))\ldots)$.

Let $\mathfrak{D}$ be a normal algorithm in an alphabet A, and let B be an extension of A. If we take a schema for $\mathfrak{D}$ and prefix to it the productions $b \to b$ for each symbol b in B − A, then the new schema determines a normal algorithm $\mathfrak{D}_{\text{B}}$ in B such that $\mathfrak{D}_{\text{B}}(P) \approx \mathfrak{D}(P)$ for every word P in A, and $\mathfrak{D}_{\text{B}}$ is not applicable to any word in B containing any symbol of B − A. $\mathfrak{D}_{\text{B}}$ is fully equivalent to $\mathfrak{D}$ relative to A and is called the *propagation* of $\mathfrak{D}$ onto B.

Assume that $\mathfrak{A}$ is a normal algorithm in an alphabet A_1 and $\mathfrak{B}$ is a normal algorithm in an alphabet A_2. Let $\text{A} = \text{A}_1 \cup \text{A}_2$. Let $\mathfrak{A}_{\text{A}}$ and $\mathfrak{B}_{\text{A}}$ be the propagations of $\mathfrak{A}$ and $\mathfrak{B}$, respectively, onto A. Then the composition $\mathfrak{C}$ of $\mathfrak{A}_{\text{A}}$ and $\mathfrak{B}_{\text{A}}$ is called the *normal composition* of $\mathfrak{A}$ and $\mathfrak{B}$, and is denoted by $\mathfrak{B} \circ \mathfrak{A}$. (When $\text{A}_1 = \text{A}_2$, the normal composition of $\mathfrak{A}$ and $\mathfrak{B}$ is identical with the composition of $\mathfrak{A}$ and $\mathfrak{B}$; hence the notation $\mathfrak{B} \circ \mathfrak{A}$ is unambiguous.) $\mathfrak{C}$ is a normal algorithm over A such that $\mathfrak{C}(P) \approx \mathfrak{B}(\mathfrak{A}(P))$ for any word P in A_1, and $\mathfrak{C}$ is applicable only to those words P of A such that P is a word of A_1, $\mathfrak{A}$ is applicable to P, and $\mathfrak{B}$ is applicable to $\mathfrak{A}(P)$.

Let an alphabet B be an extension of an alphabet A. Given a word P in B, the *projection* P^{A} of P on A is the word obtained by erasing in P all symbols in B − A. The abbreviated schema $\xi \to \Lambda$ (ξ in B − A) determines the *projection algorithm* $\mathfrak{P}$ of B on A, i.e., $\mathfrak{P}(P) = P^{\text{A}}$ for all words P in B.

Let A and C be alphabets without any symbols in common, and let $\mathrm{B} = \mathrm{A} \cup \mathrm{C}$. Then the abbreviated schema $ca \to ac$ (a in A; c in C) determines a normal algorithm $\mathfrak{L}_{\mathrm{A,C}}$ in B such that, for any word P in B, $\mathfrak{L}_{\mathrm{A,C}}(P) = P^{\mathrm{A}}P^{\mathrm{C}}$.

Given a normal algorithm $\mathfrak{A}$ in an alphabet A, and an extension B of A, then the *natural extension* $\mathfrak{B}$ of the algorithm $\mathfrak{A}$ to B is the normal algorithm in B determined by the given schema for $\mathfrak{A}$. Clearly, $\mathfrak{B}(P) \approx \mathfrak{A}(P)$ for any word P in A, and, in addition, if P is a word in A and Q is a word in $\mathrm{B} - \mathrm{A}$, then $\mathfrak{B}(PQ) \approx \mathfrak{A}(P)Q$. Notice that the natural extension of $\mathfrak{A}$ to B generally is different from the propagation of $\mathfrak{A}$ onto B, since the latter is not applicable to any word containing symbols of $\mathrm{B} - \mathrm{A}$.

PROPOSITION 5.1. *Let $\mathfrak{A}_1, \ldots, \mathfrak{A}_{\mathrm{k}}$ be normal algorithms, and let* A *be the union of their alphabets. Then there is a normal algorithm $\mathfrak{B}$ over* A, *called the* juxtaposition *of the algorithms $\mathfrak{A}_1, \ldots, \mathfrak{A}_{\mathrm{k}}$ such that*

$$\mathfrak{B}(P) \approx \mathfrak{A}_1{}^{\#}(P)\mathfrak{A}_2{}^{\#}(P)\ldots\mathfrak{A}_{\mathrm{k}}{}^{\#}(P) \quad \textit{for any word } P \textit{ in } \mathrm{A},$$

where $\mathfrak{A}_i{}^{\#}$ is the natural extension of $\mathfrak{A}_i$ to A.

PROOF. By induction on k. Clearly, it suffices to prove the result for $\mathrm{k} = 2$. For each symbol a in A, introduce a new symbol $\bar{a}$. Let $\bar{\mathrm{A}}$ be the alphabet made up of these new symbols, and let $\mathrm{B} = \mathrm{A} \cup \bar{\mathrm{A}}$. Let $\bar{\mathfrak{A}}_1$ be the normal algorithm in $\bar{\mathrm{A}}$ corresponding to the algorithm $\mathfrak{A}_1{}^{\#}$ in A. (The schema for $\bar{\mathfrak{A}}_1$ is obtained from that for $\mathfrak{A}_1$ by replacing each symbol a by $\bar{a}$.) Let $\bar{\mathfrak{A}}_1{}^{\#}$ and $\mathfrak{A}_2{}^{\#}$ be the natural extensions, respectively, of $\bar{\mathfrak{A}}_1$ and $\mathfrak{A}_2$ to B. Let $\mathrm{A} = \{a_1, \ldots, a_n\}$. By Exercise 3 (page 212), there exist normal algorithms $\mathfrak{W}_1 = \mathrm{Sub}_{a_1\bar{a}_1, a_2\bar{a}_2, \ldots, a_n\bar{a}_n}^{a_1, a_2, \ldots, a_n}$ and $\mathfrak{W}_2 = \mathrm{Sub}_{a_1, a_2, \ldots, a_n}^{\bar{a}_1, \bar{a}_2, \ldots, \bar{a}_n}$ over B such that $\mathfrak{W}_1$ simultaneously substitutes $a_1\bar{a}_1$ for a_1, $a_2\bar{a}_2$ for $a_2, \ldots$, and $\mathfrak{W}_2$ substitutes a_1 for $\bar{a}_1$, a_2 for $\bar{a}_2, \ldots$. We also have normal algorithms $\mathfrak{L}_{\mathrm{A},\bar{\mathrm{A}}}$ and $\mathfrak{L}_{\bar{\mathrm{A}},\mathrm{A}}$ such that $\mathfrak{L}_{\mathrm{A},\bar{\mathrm{A}}}(P) = P^{\mathrm{A}}P^{\bar{\mathrm{A}}}$ and $\mathfrak{L}_{\bar{\mathrm{A}},\mathrm{A}}(P) = P^{\bar{\mathrm{A}}}P^{\mathrm{A}}$. Then, take the normal composition $\mathfrak{B} = \mathfrak{W}_2 \circ \bar{\mathfrak{A}}_1{}^{\#} \circ \mathfrak{L}_{\bar{\mathrm{A}},\mathrm{A}} \circ \mathfrak{A}_2{}^{\#} \circ \mathfrak{B}_{\mathrm{A},\bar{\mathrm{A}}} \circ \mathfrak{W}_1$. It is easy to verify that $\mathfrak{B}(P) \approx \mathfrak{A}_1{}^{\#}(P)\mathfrak{A}_2{}^{\#}(P)$ for any word P in A.

COROLLARY 5.2. *Let $\mathfrak{A}_1, \ldots, \mathfrak{A}_{\mathrm{k}}$ be normal algorithms; let* A *be the union of their alphabets. Then there is a normal algorithm $\mathfrak{B}$ over* $\mathrm{A} \cup \{*\}$ *such that $\mathfrak{B}(P) \approx \mathfrak{A}_1{}^{\#}(P) * \mathfrak{A}_2{}^{\#}(P) * \ldots * \mathfrak{A}_{\mathrm{k}}{}^{\#}(P)$ for any word P in* A, *where $\mathfrak{A}_i{}^{\#}$ is the natural extension of $\mathfrak{A}_i$ to* A. *(Hence, $\mathfrak{B}(P) \approx \mathfrak{A}_1(P) * \mathfrak{A}_2(P) * \ldots * \mathfrak{A}_{\mathrm{k}}(P)$ for any word P common to the alphabets of all the $\mathfrak{A}_i$'s.)*

PROOF. There is a normal algorithm $\mathfrak{D}$ in $\mathrm{A} \cup \{*\}$ such that $\mathfrak{D}(P) = *$ for any word P in $\mathrm{A} \cup \{*\}$. Take as its defining schema

$$\begin{aligned} a &\rightarrow \Lambda \quad (a \text{ in A}). \\ \Lambda &\rightarrow \cdot * \end{aligned}$$

Let $\mathfrak{B}$ be the juxtaposition of $\mathfrak{A}_1, \mathfrak{D}, \mathfrak{A}_2, \mathfrak{D}, \ldots, \mathfrak{D}, \mathfrak{A}_k$, as in Theorem 5.1. Then $\mathfrak{B}(P) \approx \mathfrak{A}_1{}^{\#}(P) * \mathfrak{A}_2{}^{\#}(P) * \ldots * \mathfrak{A}_k{}^{\#}(P)$ for any word P in $\mathrm{A} \cup \{*\}$ (and $\mathfrak{B}(P) \approx \mathfrak{A}_1(P) * \mathfrak{A}_2(P) * \ldots * \mathfrak{A}_k(P)$ for any word P in the intersection of the alphabets of the $\mathfrak{A}_i$'s).

LEMMA 5.3

(1) *Let $\mathfrak{C}$ be a normal algorithm in an alphabet* A *and let α be any symbol. Then there is a normal algorithm $\mathfrak{D}$ over $\mathrm{A} \cup \{\alpha\}$ such that*

$$\mathfrak{D}(P) = \begin{cases} \alpha P & \text{if } P \text{ is a word in A such that } \mathfrak{C}(P) = \Lambda \\ P & \text{if } P \text{ is a word in A such that } \mathfrak{C}(P) \neq \Lambda \end{cases}$$

and $\mathfrak{D}$ applies only to those words to which $\mathfrak{C}$ applies.

(2) *If $\mathfrak{A}$ and $\mathfrak{B}$ are normal algorithms in an alphabet* A *and α is a symbol not in* A, *then there is a normal algorithm $\mathfrak{G}$ over $\mathrm{A} \cup \{\alpha\}$ such that*

$$\begin{aligned} \mathfrak{G}(P) &\approx \mathfrak{A}(P) \quad \text{if } P \text{ is a word in A, and} \\ \mathfrak{G}(\alpha P) &\approx \mathfrak{B}(P) \quad \text{if } P \text{ is a word in A.} \end{aligned}$$

PROOF

(1) There is a normal algorithm $\mathfrak{H}_1$ over $\mathrm{A} \cup \{\alpha\}$ taking Λ into α and any other word of $\mathrm{A} \cup \{\alpha\}$ into Λ. Let β be any symbol not in $\mathrm{A} \cup \{\alpha\}$. Consider the abbreviated schema for $\mathfrak{H}_1$

$$\begin{aligned} a &\rightarrow \beta \quad (a \text{ in } \mathrm{A} \cup \{\alpha\}) \\ \beta\beta &\rightarrow \beta \\ \beta &\rightarrow \cdot \Lambda \\ \Lambda &\rightarrow \cdot \alpha \end{aligned}$$

Let $\mathfrak{H}_2 = \mathfrak{H}_1 \circ \mathfrak{C}$. For any word P in A, if $\mathfrak{C}(P) = \Lambda$, then $\mathfrak{H}_2(P) = \alpha$ and if $\mathfrak{C}(P) \neq \Lambda$, then $\mathfrak{H}_2(P) = \Lambda$. Let $\mathfrak{I}$ be the identity algorithm in A (with the schema $\Lambda \rightarrow \cdot \Lambda$). Let $\mathfrak{D}$ be the juxtaposition of $\mathfrak{H}_2$ and $\mathfrak{I}$. If $\mathfrak{C}(P) = \Lambda$, then $\mathfrak{D}(P) = \alpha P$, and, if $\mathfrak{C}(P) \neq \Lambda$, then $\mathfrak{D}(P) = P$.

(2) For each symbol a of A, let $\bar{a}$ be a new symbol, and let $\bar{\mathrm{A}}$ be the alphabet consisting of these $\bar{a}$'s. Let $\mathrm{B} = \mathrm{A} \cup \bar{\mathrm{A}} \cup \{\alpha, \beta\}$, where β is not in $\mathrm{A} \cup \bar{\mathrm{A}} \cup \{\alpha\}$. If we replace in the schema of algorithm $\mathfrak{B}^{\cdot}$ all symbols a by the corresponding symbols $\bar{a}$, all terminal dots by β, every production $\Lambda \rightarrow Q$ by $\alpha \rightarrow \alpha Q$, and every production $\Lambda \rightarrow \cdot Q$ by

$\alpha \rightarrow \alpha\beta Q$, we obtain a new algorithm schema $\mathscr{S}_{\overline{\mathfrak{B}}}$. Let $\mathscr{S}_{\mathfrak{A}^{\cdot}}$ be the schema for $\mathfrak{A}^{\cdot}$. Form the schema

$$\begin{array}{ll} \alpha a \rightarrow \alpha \bar{a} & (a \text{ in A}) \\ \bar{a} b \rightarrow \bar{a} \bar{b} & (a, b \text{ in A}) \\ \bar{a} \beta \rightarrow \beta \bar{a} & (a \text{ in A}) \\ \beta \bar{a} \rightarrow \beta a & (a \text{ in A}) \\ a \bar{b} \rightarrow ab & (a, b \text{ in A}) \\ \alpha\beta \rightarrow \cdot \Lambda & \\ \quad \mathscr{S}_{\overline{\mathfrak{B}}} & \\ \quad \mathscr{S}_{\mathfrak{A}^{\cdot}} & \end{array}$$

This determines a normal algorithm $\mathfrak{G}$ over $\text{A} \cup \{\alpha\}$ such that $\mathfrak{G}(P) \approx \mathfrak{A}(P)$ and $\mathfrak{G}(\alpha P) \approx \mathfrak{B}(P)$ if P is a word in A.

PROPOSITION 5.4. *Let $\mathfrak{A}$, $\mathfrak{B}$, $\mathfrak{C}$ be normal algorithms and* A *the union of their alphabets. Then there is a normal algorithm $\mathfrak{E}$ over* A *such that*

$$\mathfrak{E}(P) \approx \begin{cases} \mathfrak{B}(P) & \textit{if } P \textit{ is a word in } \text{A} \textit{ and } \mathfrak{C}(P) = \Lambda \\ \mathfrak{A}(P) & \textit{if } P \textit{ is a word in } \text{A} \textit{ and } \mathfrak{C}(P) \neq \Lambda \end{cases}$$

and $\mathfrak{E}$ applies only to those words in A *to which $\mathfrak{C}$ is applicable. The algorithm $\mathfrak{E}$ is called the* ramification *of $\mathfrak{A}$ and $\mathfrak{B}$ governed by $\mathfrak{C}$.*

PROOF. Let $\mathfrak{A}_1$, $\mathfrak{B}_1$, $\mathfrak{C}_1$ be the propagations of $\mathfrak{A}$, $\mathfrak{B}$, $\mathfrak{C}$ to A. Let α be a symbol not in A. By Lemma 5.3(1), there is a normal algorithm $\mathfrak{D}$ over $\text{A} \cup \{\alpha\}$ such that

$$\mathfrak{D}(P) = \begin{cases} \alpha P & \text{if } P \text{ is a word in A and } \mathfrak{C}(P) = \Lambda \\ P & \text{if } P \text{ is a word in A and } \mathfrak{C}(P) \neq \Lambda \end{cases}$$

By Lemma 5.3(2), there is a normal algorithm $\mathfrak{G}$ over $\text{A} \cup \{\alpha\}$ such that $\mathfrak{G}(P) \approx \mathfrak{A}_1(P)$, and $\mathfrak{G}(\alpha P) \approx \mathfrak{B}_1(P)$ if P is a word in A. Let $\mathfrak{E} = \mathfrak{G} \circ \mathfrak{D}$.

Suppose that $\mathfrak{A}$ and $\mathfrak{C}$ are algorithms in an alphabet A and that P_0 is a word in A. First, apply $\mathfrak{A}$ to P_0, and, if a word P_1 results, apply $\mathfrak{C}$ to P_1. If $\mathfrak{C}(P_1) = \Lambda$, stop; if $\mathfrak{C}(P_1) \neq \Lambda$, apply $\mathfrak{A}$ to P_1. If a word P_2 results, test P_2 by $\mathfrak{C}$: if $\mathfrak{C}(P_2) = \Lambda$, stop; if $\mathfrak{C}(P_2) \neq \Lambda$, apply $\mathfrak{A}$ to P_2, and so on. The algorithm $\mathfrak{B}$ defined in this way is called the *iteration* of $\mathfrak{A}$ governed by $\mathfrak{C}$. Clearly, $\mathfrak{B}(P_0) = Q$ when and only when there is a sequence of words $P_0, P_1, \ldots, P_n$ ($\text{n} > 0$) such that $P_n = Q$, $\mathfrak{C}(P_n) = \Lambda$, $P_i = \mathfrak{A}(P_{i-1})$ if $0 < \text{i} \leqslant \text{n}$, and $\mathfrak{C}(P_i) \neq \Lambda$ if $0 < \text{i} < \text{n}$.

PROPOSITION 5.5. *Let $\mathfrak{A}$ and $\mathfrak{C}$ be normal algorithms,* A *the union of their alphabets, and $\mathfrak{A}_1$ and $\mathfrak{C}_1$ the propagations of $\mathfrak{A}$ and $\mathfrak{C}$ to* A. *Then the iteration of $\mathfrak{A}_1$ governed by $\mathfrak{C}_1$ is a normal algorithm over* A.

PROOF. It clearly suffices to prove the result when $\mathfrak{A}$ and $\mathfrak{C}$ have the same alphabet A, in which case $\mathfrak{A}_1 = \mathfrak{A}$ and $\mathfrak{C}_1 = \mathfrak{C}$. Let α be a symbol not in A. By Lemma 5.3(1), there is a normal algorithm $\mathfrak{D}$ over $\mathrm{B} = \mathrm{A} \cup \{\alpha\}$ such that

$$\mathfrak{D}(P) = \begin{cases} \alpha P & \text{if } P \text{ is a word in A such that } \mathfrak{C}(P) = \Lambda \\ P & \text{if } P \text{ is a word in A such that } \mathfrak{C}(P) \neq \Lambda \end{cases}$$

Let $\mathfrak{F} = \mathfrak{D} \circ \mathfrak{A}$. $\mathfrak{F}$ is a normal algorithm in an extension F of B. Let β be a symbol not in the alphabet F. Consider the following schema.

$$\xi\beta \rightarrow \beta\xi \qquad (\xi \text{ in F})$$

$$\beta\alpha \rightarrow \cdot\alpha$$

$$\beta \rightarrow \Lambda$$

$$\mathscr{S}_{\mathfrak{F}^\beta}$$

where $\mathscr{S}_{\mathfrak{F}^\beta}$ is a schema for $\mathfrak{F}^\cdot$ in which all terminal dots are replaced by β. The normal algorithm $\mathfrak{G}$ defined by this schema is such that $\mathfrak{G}(P_0) = Q$ when and only when there is a sequence $P_0, P_1, \ldots, P_n$, where $P_n = Q$, $P_i = \mathfrak{F}(P_{i-1})$ $(0 < \mathrm{i} \leqslant \mathrm{n})$, and P_n is the only word among $P_1, \ldots, P_n$ beginning with α. Let $\mathfrak{P}$ be the projection algorithm of F on $\mathrm{F} - \{\alpha\}$ (cf. page 215; $\mathfrak{P}$ erases all occurrences of α). Then $\mathfrak{B} = \mathfrak{P} \circ \mathfrak{G}$ is the desired normal algorithm.

COROLLARY 5.6. *Let $\mathfrak{A}$ and $\mathfrak{C}$ be normal algorithms and* A *the union of their alphabets. Then there is a normal algorithm $\mathfrak{H}$ over* A *such that, for any word P_0 in* A, *$\mathfrak{H}(P_0) = Q$ if and only if there is a sequence $P_0, \ldots, P_n$ $(\mathrm{n} \geqslant 0)$ such that $P_n = Q$, $\mathfrak{C}(P_n) = \Lambda$, $P_{i+1} = \mathfrak{A}(P_i)$ and $\mathfrak{C}(P_i) \neq \Lambda$ for $0 \leqslant i < n$.*

PROOF. Let $\mathfrak{I}$ be the identity algorithm and $\mathfrak{B}$ the iteration of $\mathfrak{A}$ governed by $\mathfrak{C}$. Take $\mathfrak{H}$ to be the ramification of $\mathfrak{B}$ and $\mathfrak{I}$ governed by $\mathfrak{C}$ (cf. Proposition 5.4). This algorithm $\mathfrak{H}$ is called the *full iteration* of $\mathfrak{A}$ governed by $\mathfrak{C}$.

PROPOSITION 5.7. *Let $\mathfrak{A}$ be a normal algorithm in an alphabet* A. *Then there is normal algorithm $\mathfrak{A}^{\mathrm{I}}$ over the alphabet* $\mathrm{B} = \mathrm{A} \cup \mathrm{M}$ *(where* $\mathrm{M} = \{*, 1\}$*) such that, for any word P_0 in* A *and any natural number* n, *$\mathfrak{A}^{\mathrm{I}}(\bar{\mathrm{n}} * P_0) = Q$ if and only if there is a sequence $P_0, \ldots, P_n$ $(\mathrm{n} \geqslant 0)$ with $P_n = Q$ and $P_i = \mathfrak{A}(P_{i-1})$ for $0 < \mathrm{i} \leqslant \mathrm{n}$.*

PROOF. Let α be a symbol not in B, and let $\mathrm{C} = \mathrm{B} \cup \{\alpha\}$. Consider the normal algorithms in C given by the following schemas.

$$\mathfrak{H}_1: \begin{cases} \alpha 11 \to \cdot 1 \\ \alpha 1 * \to \alpha * \\ \alpha * \xi \to \alpha * \qquad (\xi \text{ in B}) \\ \alpha * \to \cdot \Lambda \\ \Lambda \to \alpha \end{cases}$$

Clearly, $\mathfrak{H}_1(\overline{0} * P) = \Lambda$ and $\mathfrak{H}_1(\overline{n} * P) \neq \Lambda$, for $n > 0$, where P is any word in B.

$$\mathfrak{H}_2: \begin{cases} * \xi \to * \qquad (\xi \text{ in B}) \\ * \to \Lambda \end{cases}$$

If P does not contain $*$, then $\mathfrak{H}_2(P * Q) = P$.

$$\mathfrak{H}_3: \qquad \begin{cases} \alpha 1 \to \alpha \\ \alpha * \to \cdot \Lambda \\ \Lambda \to \alpha \end{cases}$$

Then $\mathfrak{H}_3(\overline{n} * P) = P$.

$$\mathfrak{H}_4: \qquad 1 \to \cdot \Lambda$$

$$\mathfrak{H}_5: \qquad 1* \to \cdot \Lambda$$

Clearly, $\mathfrak{H}_4(\overline{n} * P) = \overline{(n-1)} * P$ if $n > 0$, and $\mathfrak{H}_4(\overline{0} * P) = *P$. Also, $\mathfrak{H}_5(\overline{0} * P) = P$.

Let $\mathfrak{E}$ be the normal algorithm given by Corollary 5.2 such that $\mathfrak{E}(P) = (\mathfrak{H}_2 \circ \mathfrak{H}_4)(P) * (\mathfrak{A} \circ \mathfrak{H}_3)(P)$ for any word P in C. For any word P in A,

$$\mathfrak{E}(\overline{n} * P) = \begin{cases} \overline{n-1} * \mathfrak{A}(P) & \text{if n is a positive integer} \\ * \mathfrak{A}(P) & \text{if } n = 0 \end{cases}$$

Let E be the alphabet of $\mathfrak{E}$. By Corollary 5.6, let $\mathfrak{F}$ be a normal algorithm over E such that $\mathfrak{F}(P_0) = Q$ if and only if there is a sequence $P_0, \ldots, P_k$ $(k \geqslant 0)$ with $P_k = Q$, $\mathfrak{H}_1(P_k) = \Lambda$, $P_i = \mathfrak{E}(P_{i-1})$ for $0 < i \leqslant k$, and $\mathfrak{H}_1(P_i) \neq \Lambda$ for $0 \leqslant i < k$. Now let $\mathfrak{A}^I = \mathfrak{H}_5 \circ \mathfrak{F}$. We leave as an exercise the verification that this is the required normal algorithm.

PROPOSITION 5.8. *Every partial recursive function is partially Markov-computable, and every recursive function is Markov-computable.*

PROOF

(1) The initial functions Z, N, I_j^k $(1 \leqslant j \leqslant k)$ are Markov-computable (cf. Exercise 4, pages 212–213).

(2) Substitution. Assume that ψ arises from $\tau, \varphi_1, \ldots, \varphi_k$ by substitution: $\psi(x_1, \ldots, x_n) = \tau(\varphi_1(x_1, \ldots, x_n), \ldots, \varphi_k(x_1, \ldots, x_n))$, where

$\tau, \varphi_1, \ldots, \varphi_k$ are partial recursive. Suppose that there are normal algorithms $\mathfrak{A}_\tau, \mathfrak{A}_{\varphi_1}, \ldots, \mathfrak{A}_{\varphi_k}$ over $M = \{1, *\}$ which partially compute the functions $\tau, \varphi_1, \ldots, \varphi_k$. By Corollary 5.2, there is an algorithm $\mathfrak{B}$ over M such that $\mathfrak{B}(P) \approx \mathfrak{A}_{\varphi_1}(P) * \mathfrak{A}_{\varphi_2}(P) * \ldots * \mathfrak{A}_{\varphi_k}(P)$ for any word P in M. In particular,

$$\mathfrak{B}(\overline{(x_1, \ldots, x_n)}) \approx \overline{\varphi_1(x_1, \ldots, x_n)} * \overline{\varphi_2(x_1, \ldots, x_n)} * \ldots * \overline{\varphi_k(x_1, \ldots, x_n)}$$

for any natural numbers $x_1, \ldots, x_n$. Now, let $\mathfrak{C} = \mathfrak{A}_\tau \circ \mathfrak{B}$. Then

$$\begin{aligned} \mathfrak{C}(\overline{(x_1, \ldots, x_n)}) &\approx \mathfrak{A}_\tau(\overline{\varphi_1(x_1, \ldots, x_n)} * \ldots * \overline{\varphi_k(x_1, \ldots, x_n)}) \\ &\approx \overline{\tau(\varphi_1(x_1, \ldots, x_n), \ldots, \varphi_k(x_1, \ldots, x_n))} \end{aligned}$$

for any natural numbers $x_1, \ldots, x_n$.

(3) Recursion. Assume that ψ arises from τ and φ by recursion:

$$\begin{aligned} \psi(x_1, \ldots, x_k, 0) &= \tau(x_1, \ldots, x_k) \\ \psi(x_1, \ldots, x_k, y + 1) &= \varphi(x_1, \ldots, x_k, y, \psi(x_1, \ldots, x_k, y)) \end{aligned}$$

Suppose that τ and φ are partial recursive and that $\mathfrak{A}_\tau$ and $\mathfrak{A}_\varphi$ are normal algorithms over M which partially compute τ and φ. Let $\mathfrak{A}_Z$ be the normal algorithm computing the zero function, $\mathfrak{A}_N$ the normal algorithm computing the successor function, and let $\mathfrak{A}_j^k$ be the normal algorithm computing the projection function U_j^k. By Corollary 5.2, using the algorithms $\mathfrak{A}_i^{k+1}$, there is a normal algorithm $\mathfrak{B}_1$ over M such that $\mathfrak{B}_1(\bar{x}_1 * \ldots * \bar{x}_k * \bar{y}) = \bar{x}_1 * \ldots * \bar{x}_k$. Let $\mathfrak{K} = \mathfrak{A}_\tau \circ \mathfrak{B}_1$. Again by Corollary 5.2, applied to $\mathfrak{A}_{k+1}^{k+1}, \mathfrak{A}_1^{k+1}, \ldots, \mathfrak{A}_k^{k+1}, \mathfrak{A}_Z, \mathfrak{K}$, there is a normal algorithm $\mathfrak{B}_2$ over M such that $\mathfrak{B}_2(\bar{x}_1 * \ldots * \bar{x}_k * \bar{y}) \approx \bar{y} * \bar{x}_1 * \ldots * \bar{x}_k * \bar{0} * \overline{\tau(x_1, \ldots, x_k)}$. Let $\mathfrak{B}_3 = \mathfrak{A}_N \circ \mathfrak{A}_{k+1}^{k+2}$. Thus, $\mathfrak{B}_3(\bar{x}_1 * \ldots * \bar{x}_k * \bar{y} * \bar{x}) = \overline{y + 1}$. By Corollary 5.2, applied to $\mathfrak{A}_1^{k+2}, \ldots, \mathfrak{A}_k^{k+2}, \mathfrak{B}_3, \mathfrak{A}_\varphi$, we obtain the juxtaposition algorithm $\mathfrak{B}_4$ over M such that

$$\mathfrak{B}_4(\bar{x}_1 * \ldots * \bar{x}_k * \bar{y} * \bar{x}) \approx \bar{x}_1 * \ldots * \bar{x}_k * \overline{y + 1} * \overline{\varphi(x_1, \ldots, x_k, y, z)}$$

By Proposition 5.7, there is a normal algorithm $\mathfrak{B}_4^I$ such that, if $n \geqslant 0$, $\mathfrak{B}_4^I(\bar{n} * P_0) = Q$ when and only when there is a sequence $P_0, \ldots, P_n$ such that $Q = P_n$ and $P_i = \mathfrak{B}_4(P_{i-1})$ for $0 < i \leqslant n$. Then $\mathfrak{B} = \mathfrak{A}_{k+2}^{k+2} \circ \mathfrak{B}_4^I \circ \mathfrak{B}_2$ is a normal algorithm over M computing ψ. Notice that

$$\mathfrak{B}_2(\bar{x}_1 * \ldots * \bar{x}_k * \bar{y}) \approx \bar{y} * \bar{x}_1 * \ldots * \bar{x}_k * \bar{0} * \overline{\tau(x_1, \ldots, x_k)}$$

If we then apply $\mathfrak{B}_4^I$, this produces a y-fold iteration of $\mathfrak{B}_4$ starting with $\bar{x}_1 * \ldots * \bar{x}_k * \bar{0} * \overline{\tau(x_1, \ldots, x_k)}$. It is easy to see that the result is then $\bar{x}_1 * \ldots * \bar{x}_k * \bar{y} * \overline{\psi(x_1, \ldots, x_k, y)}$. Then, applying $\mathfrak{A}_{k+2}^{k+2}$, we obtain $\overline{\psi(x_1, \ldots, x_k, y)}$.

(4) μ-operator. Suppose that $\psi(x_1, \ldots, x_n) = \mu y(\varphi(x_1, \ldots, x_n, y) = 0)$ and assume that φ is partially computable by a normal algorithm $\mathfrak{A}_\varphi$ over M. By Corollary 5.2, applied to the algorithms $\mathfrak{A}_1^{n+1}, \ldots, \mathfrak{A}_n^{n+1}$, $\mathfrak{A}_N \circ \mathfrak{A}_{n+1}^{n+1}$, there is a normal algorithm $\mathfrak{W}$ such that $\mathfrak{W}(\overline{x}_1 * \ldots * \overline{x}_n * \overline{y}) = \overline{x}_1 * \ldots * \overline{x}_n * \overline{y+1}$. Let $\mathfrak{D}$ be the normal algorithm over M given by the schema

$$11 \rightarrow \cdot 11$$

$$1 \rightarrow \Lambda$$

Then $\mathfrak{D}(\overline{n}) = \Lambda$ if $n = 0$ and $\mathfrak{D}(\overline{n}) \neq \Lambda$ if $n > 0$. Let $\mathfrak{C} = \mathfrak{D} \circ \mathfrak{A}_\varphi$. Then

$$\mathfrak{C}(\overline{x}_1 * \ldots * \overline{x}_n * \overline{y}) \begin{cases} = \Lambda & \text{if } \varphi(x_1, \ldots, x_n, y) = 0 \\ \neq \Lambda & \text{if } \varphi(x_1, \ldots, x_n, y) \neq 0 \end{cases}$$

Let $\mathfrak{K}$ be a normal algorithm over M such that

$$\mathfrak{K}(\overline{x}_1 * \ldots * \overline{x}_n) = \overline{x}_1 * \ldots * \overline{x}_n * \overline{0}$$

By Corollary 5.6, applied to $\mathfrak{W}$ and $\mathfrak{C}$, there is a normal algorithm $\mathfrak{H}$ over M such that $\mathfrak{H}(P_0) = Q$ if and only if there is a sequence $P_0, \ldots, P_n$ ($n \geqslant 0$) such that $P_n = Q$, $\mathfrak{C}(P_n) = \Lambda$, $P_{i+1} = \mathfrak{W}(P_i)$ and $\mathfrak{C}(P_i) \neq \Lambda$ for $0 \leqslant i < n$. Let $\mathfrak{B} = \mathfrak{A}_{n+1}^{n+1} \circ \mathfrak{H} \circ \mathfrak{K}$. Then

$$\mathfrak{B}(\overline{x}_1 * \ldots * \overline{x}_n) \approx \overline{\mu y(\varphi(x_1, \ldots, x_n, y) = 0)} \approx \overline{\psi(x_1, \ldots, x_n)}$$

From Parts (1)–(4), if ψ is a partial recursive function of k arguments, there is a normal algorithm $\mathfrak{A}_\psi$ over M such that

$$\mathfrak{A}_\psi(\overline{x}_1, * \ldots * \overline{x}_k) \approx \overline{\psi(x_1, \ldots, x_k)}$$

Let $\mathfrak{R}$ be a normal algorithm over M such that $\mathfrak{R}$ is defined only for words of M of the form $\overline{x}_1 * \ldots * \overline{x}_k$, where $x_1, \ldots, x_k$ are natural numbers, and $\mathfrak{R}(\overline{x}_1 * \ldots * \overline{x}_k) = \overline{x}_1 * \ldots * \overline{x}_k$. (We leave the construction of a schema for $\mathfrak{R}$ as an exercise.) Take $\mathfrak{E}_\psi = \mathfrak{A}_\psi \circ \mathfrak{R}$. Then $\mathfrak{E}_\psi(\overline{x}_1 * \ldots * \overline{x}_k) \approx \overline{\psi(x_1, \ldots, x_k)}$ and $\mathfrak{E}_\psi$ is defined only for those words of M of the form $\overline{x}_1 * \ldots * \overline{x}_k$ such that $\psi(x_1, \ldots, x_k)$ is defined. Hence, every partial recursive function is partially Markov-computable. Every recursive function is, a fortiori, partially Markov-computable, and, since it is total, it is Markov-computable.

We shall now assign Gödel numbers to the symbols $S_0, S_1, S_2, \ldots$ out of which alphabets are constructed: $g(S_i) = 2i + 3$. Then, to any word $P = S_{j_0} \ldots S_{j_k}$ we assign the number

$$g(P) = 2^{g(S_{j_0})} 3^{g(S_{j_1})} \ldots p_k^{g(S_{j_k})} = 2^{2j_0+3} 3^{2j_1+3} \ldots p_k^{2j_k+3}$$

where p_k is the kth prime number; we define $g(\Lambda) = 1$. To a sequence of words $P_0, \ldots, P_k$, we assign the number $2^{g(P_0)}3^{g(P_1)}\ldots p_k{}^{g(P_k)}$.

We make the convention that S_1 is abbreviated by 1, and S_2 by $*$. Considering the numerals as words, we have $g(\overline{0}) = 2^5$; $g(\overline{1}) = 2^5 \cdot 3^5$, and, in general, $g(\overline{n}) = \prod_{i=0}^{n} p_i{}^5$.

There are normal algorithms $\mathfrak{T}_1, \mathfrak{T}_2$ over $A \cup M$ such that $\mathfrak{T}_1(P) = \overline{g(P)}$ for any word P in the alphabet A, and $\mathfrak{T}_2(\overline{g(P)}) = P$ for any word P in A. First, there is a normal algorithm $\mathfrak{B}_1$ over $A \cup M$ such that, for any non-empty word $P = a_{m_0}a_{m_1}\ldots a_{m_r}$ of A,

$$\mathfrak{B}_1(P) = \overline{g(a_{m_0})} * \overline{g(a_{m_1})} * \ldots * \overline{g(a_{m_r})} * \quad \text{and} \quad \mathfrak{B}_1(a_{m_0}) = \overline{g(a_{m_0})} *$$

If $A = \{S_{j_0}, \ldots, S_{j_k}\}$, then the schema for $\mathfrak{B}_1$ is

$$\begin{aligned} \alpha S_{j_0} &\rightarrow \overline{2j_0 + 3} * \alpha \\ \alpha S_{j_1} &\rightarrow \overline{2j_1 + 3} * \alpha \\ &\vdots \\ \alpha S_{j_k} &\rightarrow \overline{2j_k + 3} * \alpha \\ \alpha &\rightarrow \cdot \Lambda \\ \Lambda &\rightarrow \alpha \end{aligned}$$

Second, there is a normal algorithm $\mathfrak{B}_2$ such that $\mathfrak{B}_2(\overline{n} * Q) = \overline{0} * \overline{2^n} * Q$. (Exercise. Note that the function 2^x is recursive; so, by Proposition 5.8, there is a normal algorithm computing it.) Let $\mathfrak{B}_3 = \mathfrak{B}_2 \circ \mathfrak{B}_1$. Then, for any non-empty word $P = S_{m_0}\ldots S_{m_r}$,

$$\mathfrak{B}_3(P) = \overline{0} * \overline{2^{g(S_{m_0})}} * \overline{g(S_{m_1})} * \ldots * \overline{g(S_{m_r})} *$$

Let $\mathfrak{A}$ be a normal algorithm such that

$$\mathfrak{A}(\overline{n} * \overline{u} * \overline{v} * Q) = \overline{n+1} * \overline{u \cdot (p_{n+1})^v} * Q$$

(Exercise. Notice that the function $f(x, y, n) = x \cdot (p_{n+1})^y$ is recursive and hence computable by a normal algorithm.) Let $\mathfrak{C}$ be a normal algorithm such that $\mathfrak{C}(P) = \Lambda$ when and only when P contains exactly two occurrences of $*$. Using Corollary 5.6, let $\mathfrak{H}$ be the full iteration of $\mathfrak{A}$ governed by $\mathfrak{C}$; let $\mathfrak{E}$ be a normal algorithm such that $\mathfrak{E}(\overline{x} * \overline{y} *) = \overline{y}$, and let $\mathfrak{F} = \mathfrak{E} \circ \mathfrak{H} \circ \mathfrak{B}_3$. Then, for any non-empty word P of A, $\mathfrak{F}(P) = \overline{g(P)}$. Hence, if we use Proposition 5.4 to take care of the case $P = \Lambda$, there is a normal algorithm $\mathfrak{T}_1$ over A $\cup$ M such that $\mathfrak{T}_1(P) = \overline{\mathrm{g}(P)}$ for any word P in A. (Remember that $\mathrm{g}(\Lambda) = 1$.)

EXERCISE

Prove that there is a normal algorithm $\mathfrak{T}_2$ over A $\cup$ M such that $\mathfrak{T}_2(\overline{\mathrm{g}(P)}) = P$ for any word P in A.

Hint: construct a normal algorithm $\mathfrak{D}$ such that $\mathfrak{D}(\overline{2\mathrm{i} + 3}) = S_i$ for each symbol S_i of A, but $\mathfrak{D}$ is not defined for any other words. Construct a normal algorithm $\mathfrak{K}$ such that $\mathfrak{K}(\overline{\mathrm{u}}) = \overline{0} * \overline{\mathrm{u}} *$, for any positive integer u but $\mathfrak{K}$ is not defined for any other words. Construct a normal algorithm $\mathfrak{F}$ such that

$$\mathfrak{F}(\overline{\mathrm{n}} * \overline{\mathrm{u}} * \mathrm{P}) = \overline{\mathrm{n} + 1} * \overline{\mathrm{Qt}(\mathrm{p}_{\mathrm{n}}{}^{(\mathrm{u})_{\mathrm{n}}}, \mathrm{u})} * P\mathfrak{D}(\overline{(\mathrm{u})_{\mathrm{n}}})$$

for any non-negative integers n, u and any word P. Let $\mathfrak{C}$ be a normal algorithm such that $\mathfrak{C}(\overline{\mathrm{n}} * \overline{1} * P) = \Lambda$ for any non-negative integer n and word P, and $\mathfrak{C}$ is defined but not equal to Λ for words not of the form $\overline{\mathrm{n}} * \overline{1} * P$. By Proposition 5.5, let $\mathfrak{R}$ be the normal algorithm which is the iteration of $\mathfrak{F}$ governed by $\mathfrak{C}$. Let $\mathfrak{G}$ be a normal algorithm such that $\mathfrak{G}(\overline{\mathrm{n}} * \overline{1} * P) = P$ for any non-negative integer n and any word P of A. Let $\mathfrak{L} = \mathfrak{G} \circ \mathfrak{R} \circ \mathfrak{K}$. Then $\mathfrak{L}(\overline{\mathrm{g}(Q)}) = Q$ for any non-empty word Q of A. Use Proposition 5.4 to take care of the empty word.

Let $\mathfrak{A}$ be any algorithm (not necessarily normal) over an alphabet A. We can associate with $\mathfrak{A}$ a partial function $\psi_{\mathfrak{A}}$ such that $\psi_{\mathfrak{A}}(\mathrm{n}) = \mathrm{m}$ if and only if either n is not the Gödel number of a word of A and $\mathrm{m} = 0$ or n and m are Gödel numbers of words P and Q of A such that $\mathfrak{A}(P) = Q$. Suppose that $\psi_{\mathfrak{A}}$ is partial recursive. (We then call $\mathfrak{A}$ a *recursive algorithm.*) By Proposition 5.8, there is a normal algorithm $\mathfrak{B}$ over M such that $\mathfrak{B}(\overline{\mathrm{n}}) \approx \overline{\psi_{\mathfrak{A}}(\mathrm{n})}$ for any natural number n and $\mathfrak{B}$ is defined only for those $\overline{\mathrm{n}}$ for which $\psi_{\mathfrak{A}}(\mathrm{n})$ is defined. Let $\mathfrak{A}'$ be the normal algorithm $\mathfrak{T}_2 \circ \mathfrak{B} \circ \mathfrak{T}_1$. Then $\mathfrak{A}'$ is a normal algorithm over A which is fully equivalent to $\mathfrak{A}$ relative to A. Thus:

PROPOSITION 5.9. *If $\mathfrak{A}$ is any algorithm over* A, *and $\psi_{\mathfrak{A}}$ is partial recursive, then $\mathfrak{A}$ is fully equivalent relative to* A *to some normal algorithm over* A.

PROPOSITION 5.10. *If $\mathfrak{A}$ is a normal algorithm over* A, *then $\psi_{\mathfrak{A}}$ is partial recursive, and, if $\mathfrak{A}$ is applicable to all words in* A, *$\psi_{\mathfrak{A}}$ is recursive.*

PROOF. Given a simple production $P \to Q$, we call $2^1 3^{\mathrm{g}(P)} 5^{\mathrm{g}(Q)}$ its index; given a terminal production $P \to \cdot Q$, we let $2^2 3^{\mathrm{g}(P)} 5^{\mathrm{g}(Q)}$ be its index. If $P_0 \to (\cdot)Q_0, \ldots, P_r \to (\cdot)Q_r$ is an algorithm schema, we let its *index* be the number $2^{k_0}3^{k_1}\ldots p_r^{k_r}$, where k_i is the index of $P_i \to (\cdot)Q_i$. Let Word (u) be the recursive predicate which holds if and only if u is the Gödel number of a word: $u = 1 \vee (z)(z < lh(u) \supset (Ey)(y < u \wedge (u)_z = 2y + 3))$. Let SI(u) be the recursive predicate which holds if and only if u is the index of a simple production: $lh(u) = 3 \wedge (u)_0 = 1 \wedge Word((u)_1) \wedge Word((u)_2)$. Similarly, let TI(u) be the recursive predicate which holds if and only if u is the index of a terminal production: $lh(u) = 3 \wedge (u)_0 = 2 \wedge Word((u)_1) \wedge Word((u)_2)$. Let Ind(u) be the recursive predicate which holds if and only if u is the index of an algorithm schema: $u > 1 \wedge (z)(z < lh(u) \supset SI((u)_z) \vee TI((u)_z))$. Let $x \square y$ stand for the recursive function which we denoted $x * y$ on page 126(4). Then, if $x = \prod_{i=0}^{n} p_i^{\alpha_i}$ and each $\alpha_i > 0$, and $y = \prod_{i=0}^{m} p_i^{\beta_i}$, $x \square y = \prod_{i=0}^{n} p_i^{\alpha_i} \cdot \prod_{i=0}^{m} p_{i+n+1}^{\beta_i}$. In addition, $x \square 1 = 1 \square x = x$.

$\square$ corresponds to the juxtaposition operation on words. Let Lsub(x, y, e) be the recursive predicate which holds if and only if e is the index of a production $P \to (\cdot)Q$ and x and y are Gödel numbers of words U and V such that P occurs in U, and V is the result of substituting Q for the left-most occurrence of P in U: $Word(x) \wedge Word(y) \wedge (SI(e) \vee TI(e)) \wedge (Eu)_{u \leqslant x}(Ev)_{v \leqslant x}(x = u \square (e)_1 \square v \wedge y = u \square (e)_2 \square v \wedge \sim(Ew)_{w \leqslant x}(Ez)_{z \leqslant x}(x = w \square (e)_1 \square z \wedge w < u))$. Let Occ(x, y) be the recursive predicate which holds if and only if x and y are Gödel numbers of words U and V, and V occurs in U: $Word(x) \wedge Word(y) \wedge (Ev)_{v \leqslant x}(Ez)_{z \leqslant x}(x = v \square y \square z)$. Let End(e, z) be the recursive predicate holding if and only if z is the Gödel number of a word P, e is the index of an algorithm schema, and any algorithm $\mathfrak{A}$ defined by this schema cannot be applied to P (i.e., $\mathfrak{A}$: $P\sqsupset$): $Ind(e) \wedge Word(z) \wedge (w)_{w < lh(e)}(\sim Occ(z, ((e)_w)_1))$. Let SCons (e, y, x) be the recursive predicate which holds if and only if e is the index of an algorithm schema and y and x are Gödel numbers of words V and U such that V arises from U by a simple production of the schema:

$$Ind(e) \wedge Word(x) \wedge Word(y) \wedge (Ev)_{v < lh(e)}(SI((e)_v) \wedge Lsub(x, y, (e)_v) \wedge (z)_{z<v}(\sim Occ(x, ((e)_z)_1)))$$

Similarly, one defines the recursive predicate TCons(e, y, x) which differs from SCons(e, y, x) only in that the production in question is terminal. Let Der(e, x, y) be the recursive predicate which is true when and only when e is the index of an algorithm schema, x is the Gödel number of a word U_0, y is the Gödel number of a sequence of words $U_0, \ldots, U_k$ ($k \geqslant 0$) such that, for $0 \leqslant i < k \dot{-} 1$, U_{i+1} arises from U_i according to an algorithm $\mathfrak{A}$ determined by the schema, and,

either $\mathfrak{A}$: $U_{k \dot{-} 1} \vdash \cdot U_k$, or $\mathfrak{A}$: $U_{k \dot{-} 1} \vdash U_k$ and $\mathfrak{A}$: $U_k \sqsupset$ (or, if k = 0, just $\mathfrak{A}$: $U_k \sqsupset$)) : $\mathrm{Ind(e)} \wedge \mathrm{Word(x)} \wedge (z)_{z < lh(y)}(\mathrm{Word}((y)_z) \wedge$
$(y)_0 = x \wedge (z)_{z < lh(y) \dot{-} 2}(\mathrm{SCons}(e, (y)_{z+1}, (y)_z)) \wedge$
$((lh(y) = 1 \wedge \mathrm{End}(e, (y)_0)) \vee (lh(y) > 1 \wedge (\mathrm{TCons}(e, (y)_{lh(y) \dot{-} 1},$
$(y)_{lh(y) \dot{-} 2}) \vee (\mathrm{SCons}(e, (y)_{lh(y) \dot{-} 1}, (y)_{lh(y) \dot{-} 2}) \wedge \mathrm{End}(e, (y)_{lh(y) \dot{-} 1})))))$

Let A be any alphabet $\{S_{j_0}, \ldots, S_{j_m}\}$, and let $W_A(u)$ be the recursive predicate which holds if and only if u is the Gödel number of a word of A: $u = 1 \vee (z)_{z < lh(u)}((u)_z = 2j_0 + 3 \vee \ldots \vee (u)_z = 2j_m + 3)$. Now, let $\mathfrak{A}$ be any normal algorithm over the alphabet A, and let e be the index of the algorithm schema for $\mathfrak{A}$. Define the partial recursive function $\varphi(x) = \mu y((W_A(x) \wedge \mathrm{Der}(e, x, y)) \vee \sim W_A(x))$. But, $\psi_{\mathfrak{A}}(x) = (\varphi(x))_{lh(\varphi(x)) \dot{-} 1}$, and so, $\psi_{\mathfrak{A}}$ is partial recursive. If $\mathfrak{A}$ is applicable to every word in A, then φ is recursive; hence, so is $\psi_{\mathfrak{A}}$.

EXERCISE

Let A be an alphabet. Show that there is a normal algorithm $\mathfrak{B}$ over A ∪ M such that, for any normal algorithm $\mathfrak{A}$ in A determined by an algorithm schema with index e, $\mathfrak{B}(\bar{e} * P) \approx \mathfrak{A}(P)$ for any word P in A. ($\mathfrak{B}$ can be considered a *universal* algorithm for A.)

COROLLARY 5.11. *Let φ be a partial function. If φ is partially Markov-computable, then φ is partial recursive, and, if φ is Markov-computable, then φ is recursive.*

PROOF. Let $\mathfrak{A}$ be a normal algorithm over M such that $\varphi(n_1, \ldots, n_k) = m$ if and only if $\mathfrak{A}(\overline{(n_1, \ldots, n_k)}) = \overline{m}$. The function $\psi_{\mathfrak{A}}$ is partial recursive. Let $\tau(n) = g(\overline{n})$. τ is recursive, since $g(\overline{n}) = g(1^{n+1}) = \prod_{i=0}^{n} (p_i)^5$. Define the recursive function $\gamma(x) = lh(x) \dot{-} 1$. If $x = \prod_{i=0}^{n} (p_i)^5$, then $n = \gamma(x)$. Let

$$\xi(n_1, \ldots, n_k) = g(\overline{(n_1, \ldots, n_k)}) = g(1^{n_1+1} * 1^{n_2+1} * \ldots * 1^{n_k+1})$$

$$= \left[\prod_{i=0}^{n_1+1} (p_i)^5\right] \cdot (p_{n_1+2})^7 \cdot \left[\prod_{i=0}^{n_2+1} (p_{i+n_1+3})^5\right] \cdot (p_{n_1+n_2+5})^7 \cdot \ldots$$

$$\ldots \cdot (p_{(n_1+\ldots+n_{k-1}+2k \dot{-} 3)})^7 \cdot \left[\prod_{i=0}^{n_k+1} (p_{i+n_1+\ldots+n_{k-1}+2k \dot{-} 2})^5\right]$$

ξ is clearly recursive. Then $\varphi = \gamma \circ \psi_{\mathfrak{A}} \circ \xi$ is partial recursive. If φ is Markov-computable, then $\mathfrak{A}$ can be assumed applicable to every word in M. (Set up the algorithm schema for $\mathfrak{A}$ so that it takes every word in M not of the form $\bar{n}_1 * \ldots * \bar{n}_k$ into the empty word.) Then, by Proposition 5.10, $\psi_{\mathfrak{A}}$ is recursive. Hence $\varphi = \gamma \circ \psi_{\mathfrak{A}} \circ \tau$ is recursive.

EXERCISE. Show that every total partial recursive function is recursive.

Thus, the equivalence between partial recursiveness and partial Markov-computability (and between recursiveness and Markov-computability) has been established by Corollary 5.11 and Proposition 5.8. Church's Thesis asserts that recursiveness is equivalent to effective computability (and, in an extended form, that partial recursiveness is equivalent to partial effective computability). In terms of algorithms, Markov has formulated the corresponding *Normalization Principle*: Every algorithm in A is fully equivalent relative to A to some normal algorithm over A. Now, Church's Thesis (in the extended form) and Markov's Principle are equivalent. First, assume Church's Thesis. Let $\mathfrak{A}$ be an algorithm in an alphabet A. Then $\psi_{\mathfrak{A}}$ is a partial effectively computable function. Hence, by Church's Thesis, $\psi_{\mathfrak{A}}$ is partial recursive, and so, by Proposition 5.9, $\mathfrak{A}$ is fully equivalent relative to A to some normal algorithm $\mathfrak{B}$, i.e., Markov's Principle holds. Conversely, assume Markov's Principle. Let φ be a partial effectively computable function. Let $\mathfrak{B}_\varphi$ be the corresponding algorithm in M. By Markov's Principle, $\mathfrak{B}_\varphi$ is fully equivalent to a normal algorithm relative to M. Hence, φ is partially Markov-computable, and, by Corollary 5.11, φ is partial recursive. Thus, Church's Thesis holds.

Of course, because of the vagueness of the intuitive notions of effectively computable function and algorithm, it is impossible to *prove* the validity of Church's Thesis or Markov's Principle. Nor is there any a priori reason to support these hypotheses. There is no apparent reason why the use of productions alone should account for all effective operations. One can only expect incomplete confirmation, not a rigorous proof. It is clear that every partial recursive function is a partial effectively computable function.† The converse assertion, that every partial effectively computable function is partial recursive (or, equivalently, that every algorithm in an alphabet A is fully equivalent relative to A to some normal algorithm) has been confirmed for every known partial effectively computable function. There is some additional evidence in favor of Church's Thesis, namely, the odd fact that quite dissimilar attempts to precisely define the notion of partial

† The reader should notice that partial effective computability does not necessarily imply human computability. Partial effective computability means that the values of the function can be computed, according to a fixed procedure, in a finite number of steps. Some of the computations needed to obtain the values of a partial recursive function involve so many steps that the human race may not exist long enough to carry them out.

effectively computable function have all proved to be equivalent. We have seen this already for partial recursiveness and partial Markov-computability. Other approaches, by Turing and by Herbrand and Gödel, will be shown later to lead to the same result. In addition, Church's theory of λ-computability [1941] and Post's theory of normal systems [1943] also yield notions equivalent to that of partial-recursive function or normal algorithm. (Arguments for Church's Thesis may be found in Kleene [1952], §§ 62, 70. Also consult Hermes [1961].)

EXERCISES

1. Show that the Normalization Principle is equivalent to the assertion that every algorithm in an alphabet A is equivalent relative to A to some normal algorithm over A.

2. Given an alphabet B and an alphabet $A = \{a_1, \ldots, a_k\}$ disjoint from B. Let b, c be distinct symbols not in $B \cup A$. For any symbol a, we denote by a^i the word $\underbrace{aa\ldots a}_{i \text{ times}}$. The *translation* $T(a_i)$ of a_i is defined to be the word cb^ic, and the translation $T(u)$ of any symbol u in B is u itself; the translation $T(P)$ of a word $P = d_1 \ldots d_n$ in $B \cup A$ is defined to be $T(d_1)\ldots T(d_n)$, while $T(\Lambda) = \Lambda$. Note that $T(P) = P$ for any word P in B.

(a) Show that the schema

$$\begin{aligned} &\alpha\xi \rightarrow T(\xi)\alpha \qquad (\xi \text{ in } B \cup A) \\ &\alpha \rightarrow \cdot\Lambda \\ &\Lambda \rightarrow \alpha \end{aligned}$$

defines a normal algorithm $\mathfrak{T}$ over $B \cup A \cup \{b, c\}$ such that $\mathfrak{T}(P) = T(P)$ for any word P in $B \cup A$. (Assume that α is not in $B \cup A \cup \{b, c\}$.)

(b) Give the schema for a normal algorithm $\mathfrak{B}$ over $B \cup A \cup \{b, c\}$ such that $\mathfrak{B}(T(P)) = P$ for any word P in $B \cup A$.

(c) Let $\mathfrak{C}$ be any normal algorithm in $B \cup A$. For any production $P \rightarrow (\cdot)Q$ of the schema for $\mathfrak{C}$, the translation of this production is taken to be the production $T(P) \rightarrow (\cdot)T(Q)$. The translation of all the productions in the schema for $\mathfrak{C}$ gives an algorithm schema defining a normal algorithm $T(\mathfrak{C})$ in $B \cup \{b, c\}$. If $\mathfrak{T}$ is the algorithm of Part (a), show that $(T(\mathfrak{C}))(\mathfrak{T}(P)) \approx \mathfrak{T}(\mathfrak{C}(P))$.

(d) Prove that any normal algorithm over B is fully equivalent relative to B to some normal algorithm in $B \cup \{b, c\}$. (That the number of additional symbols can be reduced from two to one has been shown by Nagornyi [1953]. However, in the same paper, Nagornyi states that there is a normal algorithm over B, the doubling algorithm (Exercise 2(b), page 211), which is not equivalent relative to B to any normal algorithm in B itself. This is an easy exercise for the reader.)

§2. Turing Algorithms

Attempting to give a precise definition of effective computability, Turing [1936] proposed that a certain class of abstract machines could perform any "mechanical" computing procedure. Such machines are now called Turing machines in honor of their inventor, and can be described in the following way.

There is a two-way potentially infinite tape divided up into squares.

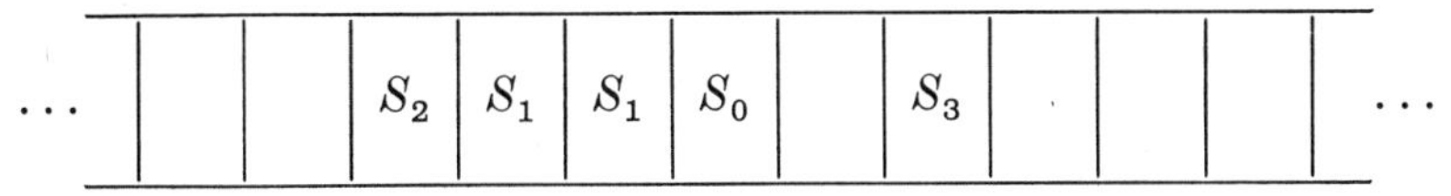

The tape is said to be potentially infinite in the sense that, although at any moment it is finite in length, additional squares always can be added to the right- and left-hand ends of the tape. There is a finite set of *tape symbols* $S_0, S_1, \ldots, S_n$ called the *alphabet* of the machine; at every moment, each square of the tape is occupied by at most one symbol. The machine has a finite set of *internal states* $\{q_0, q_1, \ldots, q_m\}$. At any given moment, the machine is in exactly one of these states. Finally, there is a reading head which, at any given time, stands over some square of the tape. The machine does not act continuously, but only at discrete moments of time. If, at any moment t, the reading head is scanning (i.e., is standing over) a square containing a symbol S_i and the machine is in the internal state q_j, then the action of the machine is determined, and it will do one of four things: (1) it may erase the symbol S_i and print a new symbol S_k; (2) it may move left one square; (3) it may move right one square; (4) it may stop. In cases (1)–(3), the machine goes into a new internal state q_r, and is ready to act again at time t + 1. We shall assume that the symbol S_0 represents a blank, so that the reading head may always be assumed to be scanning a symbol. The first three actions of the machine just described can be represented by quadruples: either (1) $q_jS_iS_kq_r$, or (2) $q_jS_iLq_r$, or (3) $q_jS_iRq_r$. The first two symbols stand for the present internal state and scanned symbol, the third symbol represents the action of the machine (print S_k, or move left, or move right one square), and the fourth symbol gives the internal state of the machine after the action has been performed.

If a tape is put into a Turing machine and the reading head is placed on a certain square, and if the machine is started off in one of its internal states, then the machine begins to operate on the tape: printing and erasing symbols and moving from one square to an adjacent one. If the machine ever stops, the resulting tape is said to be the output of the machine applied to the given tape. Now we can associate with any

Turing machine T the following algorithm $\mathfrak{B}$ in the alphabet A of T. Take any word P in the alphabet A and print it from left to right in the squares of an empty tape. Place this tape in the machine with the reading head scanning the left-most square. Start the machine in the internal state q_0. If the machine ever stops, the word of A appearing on the tape is the value of the algorithm $\mathfrak{B}$. $\mathfrak{B}$ is called a *Turing algorithm*. (The word appearing on the tape is defined to be the sequence of symbols beginning with the left-most symbol and moving right to the right-most symbol. Remember that a blank square encountered in this motion is assumed to have the symbol S_0 printed in it.) We have not specified yet the mechanism by which a machine knows when to stop; this will be done below.

Any Turing machine can be determined precisely by a finite set of quadruples of the three kinds: (1) $q_jS_iS_kq_r$; (2) $q_jS_iLq_r$; (3) $q_jS_iRq_r$, such that no two quadruples have the same first two symbols. In fact, we now shall define a *Turing machine* to be such a finite set of quadruples. The *alphabet* of any Turing machine T is the set of tape symbols S_m appearing in any of the quadruples. The *internal states* of the machine are the symbols q_s appearing in the quadruples. We assume that q_0 is an internal state of every Turing machine.

An *instantaneous tape description* of a Turing machine T is a word such that (i) all symbols in the word but one are tape symbols S_m; (ii) the only symbol which is not a tape symbol is an internal state q_s; (iii) q_s is not the last symbol of the word.† We say that T *moves* one instantaneous tape description α into another one β (abbreviated $\alpha \underset{T}{\rightarrow} \beta$) if and only if either (a) α is of the form Pq_jS_iQ, β is of the form Pq_rS_kQ, and $q_jS_iS_kq_r$ is one of the quadruples of T; or (b) α is of the form $PS_sq_jS_iQ$, β is $Pq_rS_sS_iQ$, and $q_jS_iLq_r$ is one of the quadruples of T; or (c) α is of the form q_jS_iQ, β is $q_rS_0S_iQ$, and $q_jS_iLq_r$ is one of the quadruples of T; or (d) α is of the form $Pq_jS_iS_kQ$, β is $PS_iq_rS_kQ$, and $q_jS_iRq_r$ is one of the quadruples of T; or (e) α is of the form Pq_jS_i, β is $PS_iq_rS_0$, and $q_jS_iRq_r$ is one of the quadruples of T.‡

† An instantaneous tape description describes the condition of the machine and the tape at a given moment. When read from left to right, the tape symbols in the description represent the symbols on the tape at the moment. The internal state q_s in the description is the internal state of the machine at the moment, and the tape symbol occurring immediately to the right of q_s in the tape description represents the symbol being scanned by the machine at the moment.

‡ Observe that, according to our intuitive picture, "T moves α into β" implies that if the condition at time t of the Turing machine and tape is described by α, then the condition at time t + 1 is described by β. Notice that, according to clause (c), whenever the machine reaches the left-hand end of the tape and is ordered to move left, a blank square is attached to the tape on the left; similarly, by clause (e), a blank square is added on the right when the machine reaches the right-hand end of the tape and has to move right.

We say that T *stops* at an instantaneous tape description α if and only if there is no instantaneous tape description β such that $\alpha \underset{T}{\rightarrow} \beta$. (This happens when $q_j S_i$ occurs in α but $q_j S_i$ are not the first two symbols of a quadruple of T.)

A *computation* of a Turing machine T is a finite sequence of instantaneous tape descriptions $\alpha_0, \ldots, \alpha_m$ ($m \geqslant 0$) such that the internal state occurring in α_0 is q_0; for $0 \leqslant i < m$, $\alpha_i \underset{T}{\rightarrow} \alpha_{i+1}$; and T stops at α_m. This computation is said to begin with α_0 and end with α_m. The algorithm $\mathfrak{B}_{T,C}$ in any alphabet C containing the alphabet A of T is defined as follows: for any words P, Q in C, $\mathfrak{B}_{T,C}(P) = Q$ if and only if there is a computation of T which begins with the instantaneous tape description $q_0 P$ and ends with an instantaneous tape description of the form $R_1 q_j R_2$, where $Q = R_1 R_2$. An algorithm $\mathfrak{A}$ in an alphabet D is called Turing-computable if and only if there is a Turing machine T with alphabet A and an alphabet C containing $A \cup D$ such that $\mathfrak{B}_{T,C}$ and $\mathfrak{A}$ are fully equivalent relative to D.

We let 1 stand for S_1. Remember that $\overline{m}$ stands for 1^{m+1}, for any natural number m. Also, let $*$ be an abbreviation of S_2. Given a partial number-theoretic function $f(x_1, \ldots, x_n)$, we say that a Turing machine T (whose alphabet A includes $\{1, *\}$) *computes* f if and only if, for any natural numbers $k_1, \ldots, k_n$, and any word Q, $\mathfrak{B}_{T,A}(\overline{k_1} * \overline{k_2} * \ldots * \overline{k_n}) = Q$ if and only if Q is $R_1 \overline{f(k_1, \ldots, k_n)} R_2$, where both R_1 and R_2 are certain (possibly empty) words consisting only of S_0's. (The form $R_1 \overline{f(k_1, \ldots, k_n)} R_2$ is allowed for the result since S_0 is interpreted as a blank.) The function f is called *Turing-computable* if and only if there is a Turing machine T which computes f.

Examples

1. Consider the Turing machine T defined by the following quadruples.

$$q_0 1 L q_1$$
$$q_1 S_0 1 q_2$$

The alphabet of T is $\{1, S_0\}$. T computes the successor function, since $q_0 \overline{k} \underset{T}{\rightarrow} q_1 S_0 \overline{k} \underset{T}{\rightarrow} q_2 \overline{k+1}$. In general, T takes any $q_0 1 P$ into $q_2 1 1 P$, and T takes any word not beginning with 1 into itself.

2. The machine defined by the quadruples

$$q_0 1 L q_1$$
$$q_1 S_0 1 q_0$$

when started on a word beginning with 1 keeps on adding 1's to the left and never stops.

3. The Turing machine given by the quadruples

$$\begin{gathered} q_0 S_0 R q_0 \\ q_0 S_2 R q_0 \\ \vdots \\ q_0 S_k R q_0 \\ q_0 1\; 1 q_1 \end{gathered}$$

moves right until it locates the first occurrence (if any) of the symbol 1 and then stops.

4. Let us find a Turing machine T which computes the addition function. Take as the quadruples for T:

$$\begin{gathered} q_0 1\; S_0 q_0 \\ q_0 S_0 R\, q_1 \\ q_1 1\; R\, q_1 \\ q_1 *\; 1\; q_2 \\ q_2 1\; R\, q_2 \\ q_2 S_0 L\, q_3 \\ q_3 1\; S_0 q_3 \end{gathered}$$

Then $q_0\overline{\mathrm{m}} * \overline{\mathrm{n}} = q_0 1^{\mathrm{m}+1} * 1^{\mathrm{n}+1} \underset{\mathrm{T}}{\rightarrow} q_0 S_0 1^{\mathrm{m}} * 1^{\mathrm{n}+1} \underset{\mathrm{T}}{\rightarrow} S_0 q_1 1^{\mathrm{m}} * 1^{\mathrm{n}+1} \underset{\mathrm{T}}{\rightarrow}$ $S_0 1 q_1 1^{\mathrm{m}\dot{-}1} * 1^{\mathrm{n}+1} \underset{\mathrm{T}}{\rightarrow} \ldots \underset{\mathrm{T}}{\rightarrow} S_0 1^{\mathrm{m}} q_1 * 1^{\mathrm{n}+1} \underset{\mathrm{T}}{\rightarrow} S_0 1^{\mathrm{m}} q_2 1 1^{\mathrm{n}+1} \underset{\mathrm{T}}{\rightarrow} S_0 1^{\mathrm{m}+1} q_2 1^{\mathrm{n}+1}$ $\underset{\mathrm{T}}{\rightarrow} S_0 1^{\mathrm{m}+1} 1 q_2 1^{\mathrm{n}} \underset{\mathrm{T}}{\rightarrow} \ldots \underset{\mathrm{T}}{\rightarrow} S_0 1^{\mathrm{m}+1} 1^{\mathrm{n}+1} q_2 S_0 \underset{\mathrm{T}}{\rightarrow} S_0 1^{\mathrm{m}+1} 1^{\mathrm{n}} q_3 1 S_0 \underset{\mathrm{T}}{\rightarrow}$ $S_0 1^{\mathrm{m}+1} 1^{\mathrm{n}} q_3 S_0 S_0 = S_0 1^{\mathrm{m}+\mathrm{n}+1} q_3 S_0 S_0 = S_0 \overline{\mathrm{m}+\mathrm{n}} q_3 S_0 S_0.$

EXERCISES

1. Show that the function $\mathrm{m} \dot{-} \mathrm{n}$ is Turing-computable.

2. Show that the initial primitive recursive functions $\mathrm{U}_{\mathrm{i}}^{\mathrm{n}}(\mathrm{x}_1, \ldots, \mathrm{x}_{\mathrm{n}})$ are Turing-computable. (For more examples, cf. Davis [1958, Chapter I].)

PROPOSITION 5.12. *Let* T *be a Turing machine with alphabet* A. *Let* C *be an extension of* A, *i.e.*, C ⊇ A. *Then there is a normal algorithm* $\mathfrak{A}$ *over* C *which is fully equivalent to the Turing algorithm* $\mathfrak{B}_{\mathrm{T,C}}$ *relative to* C.

PROOF. Let $\mathrm{D} = \mathrm{C} \cup \{q_{k_0}, \ldots, q_{k_m}\}$, where $q_{k_0}, \ldots, q_{k_m}$ are the internal states of T, and $q_{k_0} = q_0$. Write down the algorithm schema for $\mathfrak{A}$ as follows: first, for all quadruples $q_j S_i S_k q_r$ of T, take the productions $q_j S_i \rightarrow q_r S_k$. Second, for each quadruple $q_j S_i L q_r$, take the productions $S_l q_j S_i \to q_r S_l S_i$ for all symbols S_l of C; then take the production $q_j S_i \to q_r S_0 S_i$. Third, for each quadruple $q_j S_i R q_r$, take the productions $q_j S_i S_l \to S_i q_r S_l$ for all symbols S_l of C; then take the production $q_j S_i \to S_i q_r S_0$. Fourth, write down the productions $q_{k_i} \to \cdot \Lambda$ for each internal state q_{k_i} of T, and, finally, take $\Lambda \to q_0$. This schema defines an algorithm $\mathfrak{A}$ over C, and it is easy to see that, for any word P of C, $\mathfrak{B}_{T,C}(P) \approx \mathfrak{A}(P)$.

COROLLARY 5.13. *Every Turing-computable function f is partially Markov-computable; hence (by Corollary 5.11), f is partial recursive, and, if f is total, then f is recursive.*

PROOF. Let $f(x_1, \ldots, x_n)$ be Turing-computable by a Turing machine T with alphabet $A \supseteq \{1, *\}$. Then by Proposition 5.12, there is a normal algorithm $\mathfrak{A}$ over A such that $\mathfrak{A}$ is fully equivalent to $\mathfrak{B}_{T,A}$ relative to A, where $\mathfrak{B}_{T,A}(\overline{k_1} * \ldots * \overline{k_n}) \approx R_1 \overline{f(k_1, \ldots, k_n)} R_2$, R_1 and R_2 being (possibly empty) sequences of S_0's. Let $\mathfrak{C}_1$ be a normal algorithm over $\{1, *, S_0\}$ such that $\mathfrak{C}_1$ erases all S_0's occurring before the first 1 or $*$; as a schema for $\mathfrak{C}_1$ we may take

$$\begin{aligned} \alpha S_0 &\to \alpha \\ \alpha 1 &\to \cdot 1 \\ \alpha * &\to \cdot * \\ \alpha &\to \cdot \Lambda \\ \Lambda &\to \alpha \end{aligned}$$

Also, let $\mathfrak{C}_2$ be a normal algorithm over $\{1, *, S_0\}$ such that $\mathfrak{C}_2$ erases all S_0's occurring after the last 1 or $*$ of a word in $\{1, *\}$; a schema for $\mathfrak{C}_2$ is

$$\begin{aligned} \alpha * &\to * \alpha \\ \alpha 1 &\to 1 \alpha \\ \alpha S_0 &\to \alpha \\ \alpha &\to \cdot \Lambda \\ \Lambda &\to \alpha \end{aligned}$$

Now, let $\mathfrak{C}$ be the normal algorithm $\mathfrak{C}_2 \circ \mathfrak{C}_1 \circ \mathfrak{A}$. Then for any $k_1, \ldots, k_n$, $\mathfrak{A}(\overline{k_1} * \ldots * \overline{k_n}) \approx \mathfrak{B}_{T,A}(\overline{k_1} * \ldots * \overline{k_n}) \approx R_1 \overline{f(k_1, \ldots, k_n)} R_2$, where R_1 and R_2 are sequences of S_0's. Then

$$\mathfrak{C}_1(R_1 \overline{f(k_1, \ldots, k_n)} R_2) = \overline{f(k_1, \ldots, k_n)} R_2$$

and $\mathfrak{C}_2(\overline{f(k_1, \ldots, k_n)} R_2) = \overline{f(k_1, \ldots, k_n)}$. Hence, f is partially Markov-computable by $\mathfrak{C}$.

Proposition 5.14. *Let $\mathfrak{A}$ be a normal algorithm in an alphabet* A *not containing S_0 or δ. Then there is a Turing machine* T *such that the Turing algorithm $\mathfrak{B} = \mathfrak{B}_{\mathrm{T},(\mathrm{A} \cup \{S_0, \delta\})}$ in the alphabet $\mathrm{A} \cup \{S_0, \delta\}$ has the following property: for any word W in* A, *$\mathfrak{B}$ is applicable to W if and only if $\mathfrak{A}$ is, and $\mathfrak{B}(W)$ is of the form $S_0{}^m\mathfrak{A}(W)S_0{}^n$, where m and n are non-negative integers.* (The reason for the difference between $\mathfrak{A}$ and $\mathfrak{B}$ is that, while we agree to consider S_0 as a blank on a Turing machine tape, S_0 is treated like any other symbol in the theory of algorithms.)

PROOF. We may assume, by suitable reindexing, that $\mathrm{A} = \{S_1, S_2, \ldots, S_k\}$. Let $P \rightarrow (\cdot)Q$ be an arbitrary production. We shall construct Turing machine quadruples which will have the effect of replacing the left-most occurrence (if any) of P in a word W by Q. If $P \neq \Lambda$, let P be $b_0 \ldots b_r$. Then, take the following quadruples.

q_0	S_i	R	q_0	$(S_i \in \mathrm{A}, S_i \neq b_0)$
q_0	b_0	δ	q_0	
q_0	δ	R	q_2	
q_2	b_1	R	q_3	
q_2	S_i	S_i	q_{r+2}	$(S_i \in \mathrm{A} \cup \{S_0\}, S_i \neq b_1)$
q_3	b_2	R	q_4	
q_3	S_i	S_i	q_{r+2}	$(S_i \in \mathrm{A} \cup \{S_0\}, S_i \neq b_2)$
		$\vdots$		
q_r	b_{r-1}	R	q_{r+1}	
q_r	S_i	S_i	q_{r+2}	$(S_i \in \mathrm{A} \cup \{S_0\}, S_i \neq b_{r-1})$
q_{r+1}	b_r	R	q_{r+4}	
q_{r+1}	S_i	S_i	q_{r+2}	$(S_i \in \mathrm{A} \cup \{S_0\}, S_i \neq b_r)$
q_{r+2}	S_i	L	q_{r+2}	$(S_i \in \mathrm{A} \cup \{S_0\})$
q_{r+2}	δ	b_0	q_{r+3}	
q_{r+3}	b_0	R	q_0	
q_0	S_0	L	q_{r+5}	
q_{r+5}	S_i	L	q_{r+5}	$(S_i \in \mathrm{A})$
q_{r+5}	δ	b_0	q_{r+5}	
q_{r+5}	S_0	R	q_Y	(where Y is an integer greater than all the other indices, to be specified later)

These quadruples have the following effect on a word W. (Notice that we have not used q_1; q_1 will have a special purpose later on.) If W has no occurrence of P, then we wind up with the instantaneous tape description $q_Y W$; if W has an occurrence of P, and $W = W_1PW_2$, where the indicated P is the left-most occurrence of P in W, then we wind up with $W_1Pq_{r+4}W_2$. In the latter case, we must now add some quadruples which will replace the indicated occurrence of P by Q. Let Q be $c_0 \ldots c_s$. There are three cases:

(1) s = r, i.e., P and Q have the same length. Then we add:

q_{r+4}	S_i	L	q_{r+7}	$(S_i \in A \cup \{S_0\})$
q_{r+7}	b_r	c_r	q_{r+8}	
q_{r+8}	c_r	L	q_{r+9}	
q_{r+9}	b_{r-1}	c_{r-1}	q_{r+10}	
q_{r+10}	c_{r-1}	L	q_{r+11}	
		$\vdots$		
q_{3r+7}	b_0	c_0	q_{3r+8}	
q_{3r+8}	S_i	L	q_{3r+8}	$(S_i \in A)$
q_{3r+8}	S_0	R	q_u	$u = \begin{cases} 0 & \text{if } P \to (\cdot)Q \text{ is simple} \\ 1 & \text{if } P \to (\cdot)Q \text{ is terminal} \end{cases}$

Then, applying these quadruples to $W_1Pq_{r+4}W_2$, we obtain $q_uW_1QW_2$.

(2) s < r. Q is shorter than P. Add the quadruples

q_{r+4}	S_i	L	q_{r+7}	$(S_i \in A \cup \{S_0\})$
q_{r+7}	b_r	c_s	q_{r+8}	
q_{r+8}	c_s	L	q_{r+8}	
		$\vdots$		
q_{r+7+2s}	b_{r-s}	c_0	$q_{r+7+2s+1}$	
$q_{r+7+2s+1}$	c_0	L	$q_{r+7+2s+2}$	
$q_{r+7+2s+2}$	b_{r-s-1}	S_0	$q_{r+7+2s+2}$	
$q_{r+7+2s+2}$	S_0	L	$q_{r+7+2s+3}$	
$q_{r+7+2s+3}$	b_{r-s-2}	S_0	$q_{r+7+2s+3}$	
$q_{r+7+2s+3}$	S_0	L	$q_{r+7+2s+4}$	
	$\vdots$			
q_{2r+s+8}	b_0	S_0	q_{2r+s+8}	

After these quadruples work on $W_1Pq_{r+4}W_2$, we have

$$W_1 q_{2r+s+8} S_0^{r-s} Q W_2$$

Now we must provide some quadruples which will move W_1 r − s squares to the right to obtain W_1QW_2 (preceded by some S_0's). Let M be an integer larger than all the indices of the q_i's and S_i's above, say, M = 3r + 9.

$$
\begin{array}{llll}
q_{2r+s+8} & S_0 & L & q_M
\end{array}
$$

$$
(j = 1, 2, \ldots, k)\left\{
\begin{array}{lllll}
q_M & S_j & \delta & q_{M+j} & (S_j \in \mathrm{A}) \\
q_{M+j} & \delta & R & q_{M+j} & \\
q_{M+j} & S_0 & R & q_{M+j} & \\
q_{M+j} & S_l & L & q_{2M+j} & (S_l \in \mathrm{A}) \\
q_{2M+j} & S_0 & S_j & q_{2M+j} & \\
q_{2M+j} & S_j & L & q_{3M+j} & \\
q_{3M+j} & S_0 & L & q_{3M+j} & \\
q_{3M+j} & \delta & S_0 & q_{4M+j} & \\
q_{4M+j} & S_0 & L & q_{5M+j} & \\
q_{5M+j} & S_0 & R & q_{6M+j} & \\
q_{6M+j} & S_0 & R & q_{6M+j} & \\
q_{6M+j} & S_l & S_l & q_u & (S_l \in \mathrm{A}) \\
 & & & & u = \begin{cases} 0 & \text{if } P \rightarrow (\cdot)Q \text{ is simple} \\ 1 & \text{if } P \rightarrow (\cdot)Q \text{ is terminal} \end{cases} \\
q_{5M+j} & S_l & S_l & q_M & (S_l \in \mathrm{A})
\end{array}\right.
$$

Beginning with $W_1q_{2r+s+8}S_0{}^{r-s}QW_2$, these quadruples produce $(S_0)^pq_uW_1QW_2$ (where p is a positive integer).

(3) $s > r$, i.e., Q is longer than P. This is left to the reader as an exercise. The treatment is analogous to that of case (2). (If P or Q is empty, the slight modifications necessary in the above constructions are left to be filled in by the reader.)

Now, let us assume that $\mathfrak{A}$ is a normal algorithm in the alphabet A = $\{S_1, \ldots, S_k\}$ not containing S_0 or δ, and that the algorithm $\mathfrak{A}$ is defined by the algorithm schema $P_1 \rightarrow (\cdot)Q_1, \ldots, P_h \rightarrow (\cdot)Q_h$. We define a Turing machine T as follows: in the work above, take $P \rightarrow (\cdot)Q$ to be $P_1 \rightarrow (\cdot)Q_1$ and list the appropriate quadruples (it will suffice to take Y to be a number 100 times greater than the sum of k and the number of occurrences of symbols in the schema). These quadruples have the following effect: given q_1W, if W does not contain P_1, we wind up with q_YW; if $W = W_1PW_2$, and this indicates the left-most occurrence of P in W, then we finally obtain $(S_0)^vq_uW_1QW_2$ (where v is a non-negative integer; and u = 0 if $P_1 \to (\cdot)Q_1$ is simple, and u = 1 if $P_1 \to (\cdot)Q_1$ is terminal). Next, we consider $P_2 \to (\cdot)Q_2$ and form the quadruples for this production as indicated above, except that we raise the subscripts on all q_i's by the amount Y (but q_u is left untouched). The subscripts are raised by Y so that these quadruples will not interfere with the action of the quadruples corresponding to $P_1 \to (\cdot)Q_1$. The new quadruples will go into action only after a word W has been found not to contain P_1; they have the effect of searching W for an occurrence of P_2, and, if one is found, replacing the left-most occurrence of P_2 by Q_2, and winding up back in the initial state q_0 ready for action again by the first group of quadruples if $P_2 \to (\cdot)Q_2$ is simple or winding up in the terminal state q_1 if $P_2 \to (\cdot)Q_2$ is terminal. We now repeat the same process with $P_3 \to (\cdot)Q_3$, this time adding 2Y to the subscripts of the q_i's, etc. It should be clear that the Turing machine T so defined mimics the action of the normal algorithm $\mathfrak{A}$ in such a way that, for any word W in A, $\mathfrak{B} = \mathfrak{B}_{T, A \cup \{S_0, \delta\}}$ is applicable to W if and only if $\mathfrak{A}$ is, and $\mathfrak{B}(W)$ is of the form $(S_0)^m \mathfrak{A}(W)(S_0)^n$, where m and n are non-negative integers. (For a similar proof, cf. Asser [1959]. An indirect proof could have been given by showing that every partial recursive function is Turing-computable and then using Corollary 5.11. Study of Hermes' method of linking Turing machines and his flow-charts (cf. Hermes [1961], II, § 7) would clarify the procedures used in the proof above).

COROLLARY 5.15. *Every partially Markov-computable function is Turing-computable.* (Hence, every partial recursive function is Turing-computable. For another proof, cf. Kleene [1952], § 68.)

PROOF. From Proposition 5.14 and the definition of Turing-computable function.

Thus, the Turing-machine approach to effective computability is equivalent to that by means of normal algorithms or by recursive functions. A Turing machine seems to be an abstract form of a digital computer (except that no attention is given to speed or convenience of operation). Intuitively, then, the fact that Turing-computable functions are identical with partial recursive functions further substantiates Church's Thesis. In addition, one can show that making additional complications in the structure of Turing machines (such as adding more tapes and reading heads, or using a two-dimensional tape) does not change the class of Turing-computable functions. (Further arguments along these lines may be found in Kleene [1952], pp. 317–323 and 376–381.)

§3. Herbrand-Gödel Computability. Recursively Enumerable Sets.

The idea of defining all computable functions in terms of fairly simple systems of equations was proposed by Herbrand and developed by Gödel [1934]. The exposition given here is a version of the presentation in Kleene [1952], Chapter XI.

We define first the *terms*.

(a) All variables are terms.
(b) 0 is a term.
(c) If t is a term, then $(t)'$ is a term.
(d) If $t_1, \ldots, t_n$ are terms and f_j^n is a function letter, $f_j^n(t_1, \ldots, t_n)$ is a term.

For every natural number n, we define the corresponding *numeral* $\overline{\mathrm{n}}$ as follows: (1) $\overline{0}$ is 0; (2) $\overline{\mathrm{n}+1}$ is $(\overline{\mathrm{n}})'$. Thus, every numeral is a term.

An *equation* is a formula $r = s$ where r and s are terms. A *system* E of equations is a finite sequence $r_1 = s_1, r_2 = s_2, \ldots, r_k = s_k$ of equations such that r_k is of the form $f_j^n(t_1, \ldots, t_n)$. The function letter f_j^n is called the *principal letter* of the system E. Those function letters (if any) which appear only on the right side of equations of E are called the *initial letters* of E; any function letter other than the principal letter which appears on the left side of some equations and also on the right side of some equations is called an *auxiliary letter* of E.

We have two rules of inference:

R_1: An equation e_2 is a consequence of an equation e_1 by R_1 if and only if e_2 arises from e_1 by substituting any numeral $\overline{\mathrm{n}}$ for all occurrences of a variable.

R_2: An equation e is a consequence by R_2 of equations $f_{\mathrm{h}}^{\mathrm{m}}(\overline{\mathrm{n}}_1, \ldots, \overline{\mathrm{n}}_{\mathrm{m}}) = \overline{\mathrm{p}}$ and $r = s$ if and only if e arises from $r = s$ by replacing one or more occurrences of $f_{\mathrm{h}}^{\mathrm{m}}(\overline{\mathrm{n}}_1, \ldots, \overline{\mathrm{n}}_{\mathrm{m}})$ in s by $\overline{\mathrm{p}}$, and $r = s$ contains no variables.

A *proof* of an equation e from a set B of equations is a sequence $e_0, \ldots, e_q$ of equations such that $e_q = e$ and, if $0 \leqslant \mathrm{i} \leqslant \mathrm{q}$, then either (1) e_i is an equation of B, or (2) e_i is a consequence by R_1 of a preceding equation e_j ($\mathrm{j} < \mathrm{i}$), or (3) e_i is a consequence by R_2 of two preceding equations e_j and e_m ($\mathrm{j} < \mathrm{i}$, $\mathrm{m} < \mathrm{i}$). We use the notation $B \vdash e$ to state that there is a proof from B of e (or, in other words, that e is *derivable* from B).

Example. Let E be the system

$$f_1^1(x_1) = (x_1)'$$
$$f_1^2(x_1, x_2) = f_1^3(\overline{2}, x_2, f_1^1(x_1))$$

The principal letter of E is f_1^2; f_1^1 is an auxiliary letter, and f_1^3 an initial letter. The sequence of equations

$$\begin{aligned} f_1^2(x_1, x_2) &= f_1^3(\overline{2}, x_2, f_1^1(x_1)) \\ f_1^2(\overline{2}, x_2) &= f_1^3(\overline{2}, x_2, f_1^1(\overline{2})) \\ f_1^2(\overline{2}, \overline{1}) &= f_1^3(\overline{2}, \overline{1}, f_1^1(\overline{2})) \\ f_1^1(x_1) &= (x_1)' \\ f_1^1(\overline{2}) &= (\overline{2})' \qquad (\text{i.e., } f_1^1(\overline{2}) = \overline{3}) \\ f_1^2(\overline{2}, \overline{1}) &= f_1^3(\overline{2}, \overline{1}, \overline{3}) \end{aligned}$$

is a proof of $f_1^2(\overline{2}, \overline{1}) = f_1^3(\overline{2}, \overline{1}, \overline{3})$ from E.

A number-theoretic partial function $\varphi(x_1, \ldots, x_n)$ is said to be *computable by a system* E of equations if and only if the principal letter of E is a letter f_j^n with n arguments, and, for any natural numbers $k_1, \ldots, k_n, p$,

$$E \vdash f_j^n(\overline{k_1}, \ldots, \overline{k_n}) = \overline{p} \text{ if and only if } \varphi(k_1, \ldots, k_n) = p.$$

The function φ is called *Herbrand-Gödel computable* (for short, HG-computable) if and only if there is some system E of equations by which φ is computable.

Examples

1. Let E be the system $f_1^1(x_1) = 0$. Then E computes the zero function Z. Hence, Z is HG-computable.
2. Let E be the system $f_1^1(x_1) = (x_1)'$. Then E computes the successor function N. Hence, N is HG-computable.
3. Let E be the system $f_i^n(x_1, \ldots, x_n) = x_i$. Then E computes the projection function U_i^n. Hence, U_i^n is HG-computable.
4. Let E be the system

$$\begin{aligned} f_1^2(x_1, 0) &= x_1 \\ f_1^2(x_1, (x_2)') &= (f_1^2(x_1, x_2))' \end{aligned}$$

Then E computes the addition function.

PROPOSITION 5.16. *Every partial recursive function is* HG-*computable.*

PROOF

(1) Examples 1–3 above have shown that the initial functions Z, N, U_i^n are HG-computable.

(2) Substitution (Rule IV). Let $\varphi(x_1, \ldots, x_n) = \eta(\psi_1(x_1, \ldots, x_n), \ldots, \psi_m(x_1, \ldots, x_n))$ where $\eta, \psi_1, \ldots, \psi_m$ have been shown to be HG-computable. Let E_i be a system of equations computing ψ_i, with principal

letter f_i^n, and let E_{m+1} be a system of equations computing η, with principal letter f_{m+1}^m. By changing indices, we may assume that no two of $E_1, \ldots, E_m, E_{m+1}$ have any function letters in common. Construct a system E for φ by listing $E_1, \ldots, E_{m+1}$, and then adding the equation $f_{m+2}^n(x_1, \ldots, x_n) = f_{m+1}^m(f_1^n(x_1, \ldots, x_n), \ldots, f_m^n(x_1, \ldots, x_n))$. (We may assume that f_{m+2}^n does not occur in $E_1, \ldots, E_{m+1}$.) It is clear that, if $\varphi(k_1, \ldots, k_n) = p$, then $E \vdash f_{m+2}^n(\overline{k_1}, \ldots, \overline{k_n}) = \overline{p}$. Conversely, if $E \vdash f_{m+2}^n(\overline{k_1}, \ldots, \overline{k_n}) = \overline{p}$, then $E \vdash f_1^n(\overline{k_1}, \ldots, \overline{k_n}) = \overline{p}_1, \ldots, E \vdash f_m^n(\overline{k_1}, \ldots, \overline{k_n}) = \overline{p}_m$ and $E \vdash f_{m+1}^m(\overline{p}_1, \ldots, \overline{p}_m) = \overline{p}$. Hence, it readily follows that $E_1 \vdash f_1^n(\overline{k_1}, \ldots, \overline{k_n}) = \overline{p}_1, \ldots, E_m \vdash f_m^n(\overline{k_1}, \ldots, \overline{k_n}) = \overline{p}_m$ and $E_{m+1} \vdash f_{m+1}^n(\overline{p}_1, \ldots, \overline{p}_m) = \overline{p}$. Consequently, $\psi_1(k_1, \ldots, k_n) = p_1, \ldots, \psi_m(k_1, \ldots, k_n) = p_m$ and $\eta(p_1, \ldots, p_m) = p$. So, $\varphi(k_1, \ldots, k_n) = p$. (The details of this proof are left as an exercise. Hints may be found in Kleene [1952], Chapter XI, especially pages 262–270.) Hence φ is HG-computable.

(3) Recursion (Rule V). Let

$$\varphi(x_1, \ldots, x_n, 0) = \psi(x_1, \ldots, x_n)$$
$$\varphi(x_1, \ldots, x_n, (x_{n+1}) + 1) = \theta(x_1, \ldots, x_{n+1}, \varphi(x_1, \ldots, x_{n+1}))$$

where ψ and θ are HG-computable. Assume that E_1 is a system of equations computing ψ with principal letter f_1^n, and that E_2 is a system of equations computing θ, with principal letter f_1^{n+2}. Then form a system for computing φ by adding to E_1 and E_2

$$f_1^{n+1}(x_1, \ldots, x_n, 0) = f_1^n(x_1, \ldots, x_n)$$
$$f_1^{n+1}(x_1, \ldots, x_n, (x_{n+1})') = f_1^{n+2}(x_1, \ldots, x_{n+1}, f_1^{n+1}(x_1, \ldots, x_{n+1}))$$

(We assume that E_1 and E_2 have no function letters in common.) Clearly, if $\varphi(k_1, \ldots, k_n, k) = p$, then $E \vdash f_1^{n+1}(\overline{k_1}, \ldots, \overline{k_n}, \overline{k}) = \overline{p}$. Conversely, one can prove easily by induction on k that, if $E \vdash f_1^{n+1}(\overline{k_1}, \ldots, \overline{k_n}, \overline{k}) = \overline{p}$, then $\varphi(k_1, \ldots, k_n, k) = p$. Therefore, φ is HG-computable. (The case when the recursion has no parameters is even easier to handle, and is left as an exercise.)

(4) μ-operator (Rule VI). Let $\varphi(x_1, \ldots, x_n) = \mu y(\psi(x_1, \ldots, x_n, y) = 0)$ and assume that ψ is HG-computable by a system E_1 of equations with principal letter f_1^{n+1}. By Parts (1)–(3), we know that every primitive recursive function is HG-computable. In particular, multiplication is HG-computable; hence there is a system E_2 of equations, having no function letters in common with E_1, and with principal letter f_2^2 such that $E_2 \vdash f_2^2(\overline{k_1}, \overline{k_2}) = \overline{p}$ if and only if $k_1 \cdot k_2 = p$. We form a system E_3 by adding to E_1 and E_2 the equations

$$f_2^{n+1}(x_1, \ldots, x_n, 0) = 1$$

$$f_2^{n+1}(x_1, \ldots, x_n, (x_{n+1})') = f_2^2(f_2^{n+1}(x_1, \ldots, x_n, x_{n+1}), f_1^{n+1}(x_1, \ldots, x_n, x_{n+1}))$$

One can prove by induction that E_3 computes the function $\prod_{y<z} \psi(x_1, \ldots, x_n, y)$, i.e., $E_3 \vdash f_2^{n+1}(\overline{k_1}, \ldots, \overline{k_n}, \overline{k}) = \overline{p}$ if and only if $\prod_{y<k} \psi(k_1, \ldots, k_n, y) = p$. Now construct the system E by adding to E_3 the equations

$$f_2^3((x_1)', 0, x_3) = x_3$$

$$f_3^n(x_1, \ldots, x_n) = f_2^3(f_2^{n+1}(x_1, \ldots, x_n, x_{n+1}), f_2^{n+1}(x_1, \ldots, x_n, (x_{n+1})'), x_{n+1})$$

Then E computes the function $\varphi(x_1, \ldots, x_n) = \mu y(\psi(x_1, \ldots, x_n, y) = 0)$. For, if $\mu y(\psi(k_1, \ldots, k_n, y) = 0) = q$, then $E_3 \vdash f_2^{n+1}(\overline{k_1}, \ldots, \overline{k_n}, \overline{q}) = \overline{p}'$, where $p + 1 = \prod_{y<q} \psi(k_1, \ldots, k_n, y)$, and $E_3 \vdash f_2^{n+1}(\overline{k_1}, \ldots, \overline{k_n}, \overline{q}') = 0$. Hence $E \vdash f_3^n(\overline{k_1}, \ldots, \overline{k_n}) = f_2^3(\overline{p}', 0, \overline{q})$. But, $E \vdash f_2^3(\overline{p}', 0, \overline{q}) = \overline{q}$, and so, $E \vdash f_3^n(\overline{k_1}, \ldots, \overline{k_n}) = \overline{q}$. Conversely, if $E \vdash f_3^n(\overline{k_1}, \ldots, \overline{k_n}) = \overline{q}$, then $E \vdash f_2^3(\overline{m}', 0, \overline{q}) = \overline{q}$, where $E_3 \vdash f_2^{n+1}(\overline{k_1}, \ldots, \overline{k_n}, \overline{q}) = (\overline{m})'$ and $E_3 \vdash f_2^{n+1}(\overline{k_1}, \ldots, \overline{k_n}, \overline{q}') = 0$. Hence, $\prod_{y<q} \psi(k_1, \ldots, k_n, y) = m + 1 \neq 0$ and $\prod_{y<q+1} \psi(k_1, \ldots, k_n, y) = 0$. So, $\psi(k_1, \ldots, k_n, y) \neq 0$ for $y < q$, and $\psi(k_1, \ldots, k_n, q) = 0$. Thus, $\mu y(\psi(k_1, \ldots, k_n, y) = 0) = q$. Therefore, φ is HG-computable.

We now shall proceed to show that every Herbrand-Gödel computable function is partial recursive, by means of an arithmetization of the apparatus of Herbrand-Gödel computability. We shall use the same arithmetization that was used for first-order theories (cf. Chapter III, § 4). (We take the symbol ′ to be an abbreviation for f_1^1. Remember that $r = s$ is an abbreviation for $A_1^2(r, s)$. The only individual constant is 0.) In particular (cf. pages 137–141), the following relations and functions are primitive recursive:

FL(x): x is the Gödel number of a function letter.

$$(Ey)_{y<x}(Ez)_{z<x}(x = 9 + 8(2^y \cdot 3^z) \wedge y > 0 \wedge z > 0)$$

EVbl(x): x is the Gödel number of an expression consisting of a variable.

EFL(x): x is the Gödel number of an expression consisting of a function letter.

Nu(x): x is the Gödel number of a numeral.

Trm(x): x is the Gödel number of a term.

Num(x) = the Gödel number of the numeral $\overline{x}$.

$Arg_T(x)$ = the number of arguments of a function letter f, if x is the Gödel number of f.

$x * y$ = the Gödel number of an expression AB if x is the Gödel number of the expression A and y is the Gödel number of the expression B.

Subst(a, b, u, v): v is the Gödel number of a variable x_i, u is the Gödel number of a term t, b is the Gödel number of an expression $\mathscr{A}$, and a is the Gödel number of the result of substituting t for all occurrences of x_i in $\mathscr{A}$.

The following are also primitive recursive.

Eqt(x): x is the Gödel number of an equation:

$$\mathrm{lh}(x) = 3 \wedge \mathrm{Trm}((x)_1) \wedge \mathrm{Trm}((x)_2) \wedge (x)_0 = 107$$

(Remember that $=$ is A_1^2, whose Gödel number is 107.)

Syst(x): x is the Gödel number of a system of equations:

$$(y)_{y<\mathrm{lh}(x)}\mathrm{Eqt}((x)_y) \wedge \mathrm{FL}((((x)_{\mathrm{lh}(x)\dot{-}1})_1)_0)$$

Occ(u, v): u is the Gödel number of a term t or equation $\mathfrak{B}$ and v is the Gödel number of a term which occurs in t or $\mathfrak{B}$.

$$(\mathrm{Trm}(u) \vee \mathrm{Eqt}(u)) \wedge \mathrm{Trm}(v) \wedge (Ex)_{x<u}(Ey)_{y<u}(u = x * v * y \vee$$
$$u = x * v \vee u = v * y \vee u = v)$$

Cons_1(u, v): u is the Gödel number of an equation e_1, and v is the Gödel number of an equation e_2, and e_2 is a consequence of e_1 by Rule R_1:

$$\mathrm{Eqt}(u) \wedge \mathrm{Eqt}(v) \wedge (Ex)_{x<u}(Ey)_{y<v}(\mathrm{Nu}(y) \wedge \mathrm{Subst}(v, u, y, x)$$
$$\wedge \mathrm{Occ}(u, x))$$

Cons_2(u, z, v): u, z, v are Gödel numbers of equations e_1, e_2, e_3, respectively, and e_3 is a consequence of e_1 and e_2 by Rule R_2.

$$\mathrm{Eqt}(u) \wedge \mathrm{Eqt}(z) \wedge \mathrm{Eqt}(v) \wedge \sim(Ex)_{x\leqslant z}(\mathrm{EVbl}(x) \wedge \mathrm{Occ}(z, x)) \wedge$$
$$\mathrm{FL}(((z)_1)_0) \wedge (x)_{0<x<\mathrm{lh}((z)_1)}\sim\mathrm{FL}(((z)_1)_x) \wedge$$
$$(x)_{x<\mathrm{lh}((z)_2)}\sim\mathrm{FL}(((z)_2)_x) \wedge \mathrm{Occ}((u)_2, (z)_1) \wedge ((Ey)_{y<u}$$
$$(Ew)_{w<u}((u)_2 = y * (z)_1 * w \wedge v = 2^{107}3^{(u)_1}5^{y*(z)_2*w}) \vee$$
$$((u)_2 = (z)_1 \wedge v = 2^{107}3^{(u)_1}5^{(z)_2})))$$

Ded(u, z): u is the Gödel number of a system of equations E, and z is the Gödel number of a proof from E.

$$\mathrm{Syst}(u) \wedge (x)_{x<\mathrm{lh}(z)}((Ew)_{w<\mathrm{lh}(u)}(u)_w = (z)_x \vee$$
$$(Ey)_{y<x}\mathrm{Cons}_1((z)_y, (z)_x) \vee (Ey)_{y<x}(Ev)_{v<x}\mathrm{Cons}_2((z)_y, (z)_v, (z)_x))$$

$S_n(u, x_1, \ldots, x_n, z)$: u is the Gödel number of a system of equations E whose principal letter is of the form f_j^n, and z is the Gödel number of a proof from E of an equation of the form $f_j^n(\overline{x}_1, \ldots, \overline{x}_n) = \overline{p}$.

$Ded(u, z) \wedge Arg_T(((u)_{lh(u)\dot{-}1})_1)_0) = n \wedge (((z)_{lh(z)\dot{-}1})_1)_0 =$
$(((u)_{lh(u)\dot{-}1})_1)_0 \wedge (y)_{0<y<lh(((z)_{lh(z)\dot{-}1})_1)} \sim FL((((z)_{lh(z)\dot{-}1})_1)_y)$
$\wedge Nu(((z)_{lh(z)\dot{-}1})_2) \wedge$
$((z)_{lh(z)\dot{-}1})_1 = 2^{(((u)_{lh(u)\dot{-}1})_1)_0} * 2^3 * 2^{Num(x_1)} * 2^7 *$
$2^{Num(x_2)} * 2^7 * \ldots * 2^7 * 2^{Num(x_n)} * 2^5$

Remember that g(( ) = 3, g( )) = 5, g(,) = 7.

$U(x) = \mu y_{y<x}(Num(y) = ((x)_{lh(x)\dot{-}1})_2)$ (If x is the Gödel number of a proof of an equation $r = \bar{p}$, then $U(x) = p$.)

PROPOSITION 5.17 (Kleene [1936a]). *If* $\varphi(x_1, \ldots, x_n)$ *is* HG-*computable by a system of equations* E *with Gödel number* e, *then*

$$\varphi(x_1, \ldots, x_n) = U(\mu y(S_n(e, x_1, \ldots, x_n, y)))$$

Hence, every HG-*computable function* φ *is partial recursive, and, if* φ *is total, then* φ *is recursive.*

PROOF. $\varphi(k_1, \ldots, k_n) = p$ if and only if $E \vdash f_j^n(\overline{k_1}, \ldots, \overline{k_n}) = \bar{p}$, where f_j^n is the principal letter of E. $\varphi(k_1, \ldots, k_n)$ is defined if and only if $(Ey)S_n(e, k_1, \ldots, k_n, y)$. If $\varphi(k_1, \ldots, k_n)$ is defined, $\mu y(S_n(e, k_1, \ldots, k_n, y))$ is the Gödel number of a proof from E of an equation $f_j^n(\overline{k_1}, \ldots, \overline{k_n}) = \bar{p}$. Hence, $U(\mu y(S_n(e, k_1, \ldots, k_n, y))) = p = \varphi(k_1, \ldots, k_n)$. Also, since S_n is primitive recursive, $\mu y(S_n(e, x_1, \ldots, x_n, y))$ is partial recursive. If φ is total, then $(x_1)\ldots(x_n)(Ey)S_n(e, x_1, \ldots, x_n, y)$; hence, $\mu y(S_n(e, x_1, \ldots, x_n, y))$ is recursive, and then, so is $U(\mu y(S_n(e, x_1, \ldots, x_n, y)))$.

Thus, the class of Herbrand-Gödel computable functions is identical with the class of partial recursive functions. This is further evidence for Church's Thesis.

It is sometimes more convenient to use instead of S_n the predicate

$T_n(z, x_1, \ldots, x_n, y)$: $S_n(z, x_1, \ldots, x_n, y) \wedge (u)_{u<y} \sim S_n(z, x_1, \ldots, x_n, u)$

Clearly, if $T_n(z, x_1, \ldots, x_n, y)$, then $S_n(z, x_1, \ldots, x_n, y)$. In addition, in contrast to S_n, if $T_n(z, x_1, \ldots, x_n, y)$ and $T_n(z, x_1, \ldots, x_n, v)$, then $y = v$. It is obvious that

$$(Ey)S_n(z, x_1, \ldots, x_n, y) \equiv (Ey)T_n(z, x_1, \ldots, x_n, y)$$

and

$$U(\mu y S_n(z, x_1, \ldots, x_n, y)) = U(\mu y T_n(z, x_1, \ldots, x_n, y))$$

whenever either side is defined. From Propositions 5.16 and 5.17, it follows that every partial recursive function is expressible in the form $U(\mu y T_n(e, x_1, \ldots, x_n, y))$ where e is the Gödel number of a system of equations computing the function. Conversely, for any natural number e, $U(\mu y T_n(e, x_1, \ldots, x_n, y))$ is a partial recursive function. Thus, as z varies over all natural numbers, $U(\mu y T_n(z, x_1, \ldots, x_n, y))$ gives an enumeration (with repetitions) of *all* partial recursive functions of n arguments. A number e such that $\varphi(x_1, \ldots, x_n) = U(\mu y T_n(e, x_1, \ldots, x_n, y))$ is called an *index* of the function φ. The Gödel number of any system of equations computing φ is an index of φ; there are infinitely many indices of φ. (Exercise.)

By an index of a recursive relation R we mean an index of the characteristic function of R. Then

$$R(x_1, \ldots, x_n) \equiv (Ey)(T_n(e, x_1, \ldots, x_n, y) \wedge U(y) = 0)$$

where e is an index of R.

LEMMA 5.18

(1) *For* $n > 0$, *if* $R(x_1, \ldots, x_n, y)$ *is a recursive predicate, then there exist natural numbers* e_1, e_2 *such that*

$$(Ey)R(x_1, \ldots, x_n, y) \equiv (Ey)T_n(e_1, x_1, \ldots, x_n, y)$$

and

$$(y)R(x_1, \ldots, x_n, y) \equiv (y) \sim T_n(e_2, x_1, \ldots, x_n, y)$$

(2) *For* $n > 0$, *if* $R(x_1, \ldots, x_n, z, y)$ *is a recursive predicate, there exist natural numbers* e_3, e_4 *such that*

$$(z)(Ey)R(x_1, \ldots, x_n, z, y) \equiv (z)(Ey)T_{n+1}(e_3, x_1, \ldots, x_n, z, y)$$

and

$$(Ez)(y)R(x_1, \ldots, x_n, z, y) \equiv (Ez)(y) \sim T_{n+1}(e_4, x_1, \ldots, x_n, z, y)$$

and so on, for three or more quantifiers.

PROOF

(1) Let $\varphi(x_1, \ldots, x_n, y)$ be the characteristic function of R; then φ is recursive, and $\mu y(\varphi(x_1, \ldots, x_n, y) = 0)$ is partial recursive. Let e_1 be the Gödel number of a system of equations computing $\mu y(\varphi(x_1, \ldots, x_n, y) = 0)$. Then, $(Ey)R(x_1, \ldots, x_n, y)$ if and only if $\mu y(\varphi(x_1, \ldots, x_n, y) = 0)$ is defined; hence, $(Ey)R(x_1, \ldots, x_n, y) \equiv (Ey)(T_n(e_1, x_1, \ldots, x_n, y))$. Applying this result to $\sim R$, we obtain a number e_2 such that $(Ey) \sim R(x_1, \ldots, x_n, y) \equiv (Ey)T_n(e_2, x_1, \ldots, x_n, y)$. Hence, $(y)R(x_1, \ldots, x_n, y) \equiv (y) \sim T_n(e_2, x_1, \ldots, x_n, y)$.

(2) follows from (1), taking $n + 1$ instead of n. (Thus, as u varies, $(Ey)T_n(u, x_1, \ldots, x_n, y)$ enumerates all relations $(Ey)R(x_1, \ldots, x_n, y)$, where R is recursive, and $(y) \sim T_n(u, x_1, \ldots, x_n, y)$ enumerates all relations $(y)R(x_1, \ldots, x_n, y)$, where R is recursive; etc.)

PROPOSITION 5.19 (Kleene [1943; 1952, § 57], Mostowski [1947]).

(1) *If* $R(x, y)$ *is recursive, there are natural numbers* e_1, e_2 *such that*

$$\sim((Ey)R(e_1, y) \equiv (y)\sim T_1(e_1, e_1, y))$$

and

$$\sim((y)R(e_2, y) \equiv (Ey)T_1(e_2, e_2, y))$$

(2) *If* $R(x)$ *is recursive, there are natural numbers* e_1, e_2 *such that*

$$\sim(R(e_1) \equiv (y)\sim T_1(e_1, e_1, y))$$

and

$$\sim(R(e_2) \equiv (Ey)T_1(e_2, e_2, y))$$

(3) *Both* $(y)\sim T_1(x, x, y)$ *and* $(Ey)T_1(x, x, y)$ *are not recursive.*

(4) *Consider the following list* (where R is any recursive relation):

$$R(x_1, \ldots, x_n) \quad \begin{matrix} (Ey_1)R(x_1, \ldots, x_n, y_1) & (Ey_1)(y_2)R(x_1, \ldots, x_n, y_1, y_2) \\ (y_1)R(x_1, \ldots, x_n, y_1) & (y_1)(Ey_2)R(x_1, \ldots, x_n, y_1, y_2) \end{matrix}$$

$$\begin{matrix} (Ey_1)(y_2)(Ey_3)R(x_1, \ldots, x_n, y_1, y_2, y_3)\ldots \\ (y_1)(Ey_2)(y_3)R(x_1, \ldots, x_n, y_1, y_2, y_3)\ldots \end{matrix}$$

If we let $\Pi_0^n = \Sigma_0^n =$ the set of all recursive relations with n arguments; and, for $k > 0$, $\Sigma_k^n =$ the set of all relations with n arguments expressible in the "prenex form" $(Ey_1)(y_2)\ldots(Qy_k)R(x_1, \ldots, x_n, y_1, y_2, \ldots, y_k)$, consisting of k alternating quantifiers beginning with an existential quantifier and followed by a recursive relation R; and $\Pi_k^n =$ the set of all relations with n arguments expressible in "prenex form" $(y_1)(Ey_2)\ldots(Qy_k)R(x_1, \ldots, x_n, y_1, y_2, \ldots, y_k)$, consisting of k alternating quantifiers beginning with a universal quantifier and followed by a recursive relation R, then the list above can be written

$$\Sigma_0^n \quad \begin{matrix} \Sigma_1^n & \Sigma_2^n & \Sigma_3^n & \ldots \\ \Pi_1^n & \Pi_2^n & \Pi_3^n & \ldots \end{matrix}$$

(In the "prenex form", (Qy_k) represents either a universal or existential quantifier.)

(a) Every relation of any form listed above is expressible in any form indicated in any of the succeeding columns on the right, i.e., $\Sigma_k^n \subseteq \Sigma_j^n \cap \Pi_j^n$ and $\Pi_k^n \subseteq \Sigma_j^n \cap \Pi_j^n$ for all $j > k$.

(b) There is a relation of each form, except the left-most, which is not expressible in the other form indicated in the same column, and, hence, by (a), not in any of the previous columns on the left, i.e., $\Sigma_k^n - \Pi_k^n \neq 0$ and $\Pi_k^n - \Sigma_k^n \neq 0$ for $k > 0$.

(c) Every arithmetic relation (cf. page 135, Exercise 2) is expressible in at least one of these forms.

(d) (Post) For any relation $Q(x_1, \ldots, x_n)$, Q is recursive if and only if both Q and $\sim Q$ are both expressible in the form $(Ey_1)R(x_1, \ldots, x_n, y_1)$, where R is recursive, i.e., $\Sigma_1^n \cap \Pi_1^n = \Sigma_0^n$.

(e) If $Q_1 \in \Sigma_k^n$ and $Q_2 \in \Sigma_k^n$, then $Q_1 \vee Q_2$ and $Q_1 \wedge Q_2$ are in Σ_k^n; if Q_1 and Q_2 are in Π_k^n, then $Q_1 \vee Q_2$ and $Q_1 \wedge Q_2$ are in Π_k^n.

(f) In contradistinction to (d), if $k > 0$,

$$(\Sigma_{k+1}^n \cap \Pi_{k+1}^n) - (\Sigma_k^n \cup \Pi_k^n) \neq 0$$

PROOF

(1) Assume $R(x, y)$ recursive. Then, by Lemma 5.18, there are numbers e_1, e_2 such that $(Ey)R(x, y) \equiv (Ey)T_1(e_1, x, y)$ and

$(y)R(x, y) \equiv (y) \sim T_1(e_2, x, y)$

(2) Assume $R(x)$ recursive. Then $R(x) \wedge y = y$ is recursive; clearly, $(Ey)(R(x) \wedge y = y) \equiv R(x)$ and $(y)(R(x) \wedge y = y) \equiv R(x)$. Apply (1).

(3) Assume $(y) \sim T_1(x, x, y)$ is recursive. By (2), there is an integer e_1 such that $\sim((y) \sim T_1(e_1, e_1, y) \equiv (y) \sim T_1(e_1, e_1, y))$, which is a contradiction. Similarly, if $(Ey)T_1(x, x, y)$ is recursive, then, by (2), there is an integer e_2 such that $\sim((Ey)T_1(e_2, e_2, y) \equiv (Ey)T_1(e_2, e_2, y))$, which is a contradiction.

(4) (a) $(Ez_1)(y_1)(Ez_2)(y_2) \ldots (Ez_k)(y_k)R(x_1, \ldots, x_n, z_1, y_1, \ldots, z_k, y_k) \equiv (u)(Ez_1)(y_1) \ldots (Ez_k)(y_k)(R(x_1, \ldots, x_n, z_1, y_1, \ldots, z_k, y_k) \wedge u = u) \equiv (Ez_1)(y_1) \ldots (Ez_k)(y_k)(Eu)(R(x_1, \ldots, x_n, z_1, y_1, \ldots, z_k, y_k) \wedge u = u)$. Hence any relation expressible in one of the forms in the list is expressible in both forms in any succeeding column.

(b) Let us just take a typical case. Consider $(Ev)(z)(Ey)T_{n+2}(x_1, x_1, x_2, \ldots, x_n, v, z, y)$. Assume that this is expressible in the form $(v)(Ez)(y)R(x_1, \ldots, x_n, v, z, y)$, where R is recursive. By Lemma 5.18, this relation is equivalent to $(v)(Ez)(y) \sim T_{n+2}(e, x_1, \ldots, x_n, v, z, y)$ for some e. But when $x_1 = e$, this is a contradiction.

(c) Every wf of the first-order theory S can be put into prenex normal form. It suffices to note that, if R is recursive, then $(Eu)(Ev)R(u, v)$ is equivalent to $(Ez)R(\sigma_1^2(z), \sigma_2^2(z))$, where σ_1^2, σ_2^2 are the recursive inverse mappings of the one-one correspondence σ^2 between pairs of natural numbers and natural numbers (cf. page 128). Also, $(u)(v)R(u, v)$ is equivalent to $(z)R(\sigma_1^2(z), \sigma_2^2(z))$. Hence, successive quantifiers of the same kind (existential or universal) can be condensed into one such quantifier.

(d) If Q is recursive, so is $\sim Q$; if $P(x_1, \ldots, x_n)$ is recursive, then $P(x_1, \ldots, x_n) \equiv (Ey)(P(x_1, \ldots, x_n) \wedge y = y)$. Conversely, assume Q is expressible as $(Ey)R_1(x_1, \ldots, x_n, y)$, and $\sim Q$ as $(Ey)R_2(x_1, \ldots, x_n, y)$, where R_1 and R_2 are recursive. Hence, $(x_1) \ldots (x_n)(Ey)(R_1(x_1, \ldots, x_n, y)$

$\vee R_2(x_1, \ldots, x_n, y))$. So, $\varphi(x_1, \ldots, x_n) = \mu y(R_1(x_1, \ldots, x_n, y) \vee R_2(x_1, \ldots, x_n, y))$ is recursive. Then $Q(x_1, \ldots, x_n) \equiv R_1(x_1, \ldots, x_n, \varphi(x_1, \ldots, x_n))$, and, therefore, Q is recursive.

(e) Use the following facts: If x is not free in $\mathfrak{A}$, $\vdash (Ex)(\mathfrak{A} \vee \mathfrak{B}) \equiv (\mathfrak{A} \vee (Ex)\mathfrak{B})$, $\vdash (Ex)(\mathfrak{A} \wedge \mathfrak{B}) \equiv (\mathfrak{A} \wedge (Ex)\mathfrak{B})$, $\vdash (x)(\mathfrak{A} \vee \mathfrak{B}) \equiv (\mathfrak{A} \vee (x)\mathfrak{B})$, $\vdash (x)(\mathfrak{A} \wedge \mathfrak{B}) \equiv (\mathfrak{A} \wedge (x)\mathfrak{B})$.

(f) We shall suggest here a proof in the case $n = 1$; the other cases are then easy consequences. Let $Q(x) \in \Sigma^1_k - \Pi^1_k$. Define P(x) as $(Ez)((x = 2z \wedge Q(z)) \vee (x = 2z + 1 \wedge \sim Q(z)))$. It is easy to prove that $P \notin \Sigma^1_k \cup \Pi^1_k$ and that $P \in \Sigma^1_{k+1}$. To show that $P \in \Pi^1_{k+1}$, note that P(x) holds if and only if

$$(Ez)(x = 2z \wedge Q(z)) \vee ((Ez_{z<x}(x = 2z + 1) \wedge (z)(x = 2z + 1 \supset \sim Q(z)))$$

(Cf. Rogers [1959]).

EXERCISE

This exercise will show the existence of a recursive, non-primitive recursive function.

1. Let $[\sqrt{n}]$ be the largest integer $\leqslant \sqrt{n}$. Show that $[\sqrt{n}]$ is defined by the recursion

$$\kappa(0) = 0$$
$$\kappa(n + 1) = \kappa(n) + \overline{sg}|(n + 1) - (\kappa(n) + 1)^2|$$

Hence, $[\sqrt{n}]$ is primitive recursive.

2. The function $\text{Quadrem}(n) = n \dot{-} [\sqrt{n}]^2$ is primitive recursive and represents the difference between n and the largest square $\leqslant n$.

3. Let $\rho(x, y) = ((x + y)^2 + y)^2 + x$; $\rho_1(n) = \text{Quadrem}(n)$ and $\rho_2(n) = \text{Quadrem}([\sqrt{n}])$. These functions are primitive recursive. Prove:

(a) $\rho_1(\rho(x, y)) = x$ and $\rho_2(\rho(x, y)) = y$.
(b) $\rho(\rho_1(n), \rho_2(n)) = n$.
(c) ρ is a one-one function from ω^2 into ω.
(d) $\rho_1(0) = \rho_2(0) = 0$ and

$$\left.\begin{aligned}\rho_1(n + 1) &= \rho_1(n) + 1\\ \rho_2(n + 1) &= \rho_2(n)\end{aligned}\right\} \quad \text{if } \rho_1(n + 1) \neq 0$$

(e) Define, for each $n \geqslant 3$, $\rho^n(x_1, \ldots, x_n) = \rho(\rho^{n-1}(x_1, \ldots, x_{n-1}), x_n)$. Let $\rho^2 = \rho$. Then each ρ^n is primitive recursive. Define $\rho^n_i(k) = \rho^{n-1}_i(\rho_1(k))$ for $1 \leqslant i \leqslant n - 1$, and $\rho^n_n(k) = \rho_2(k)$. Then each $\rho^n_i(1 \leqslant i \leqslant n)$ is primitive recursive, $\rho^n_i(\rho^n(x_1, \ldots, x_n)) = x_i$ and $\rho^n(\rho^n_1(k), \rho^n_2(k), \ldots, \rho^n_n(k)) = k$. Hence, ρ^n is a one-one mapping of ω^n

into ω, and the ρ_i^n's are the corresponding "inverse" functions. The ρ^n's and ρ_i^n's are obtained from ρ, ρ_1, ρ_2 by substitution.

4. The recursion rule (V) (cf. page 120) can be limited to the form

$$\psi(x_1, \ldots, x_{n+1}, 0) = x_{n+1} \quad (n \geqslant 0)$$
$$\psi(x_1, \ldots, x_{n+1}, y + 1) = \varphi(x_1, \ldots, x_{n+1}, y, \psi(x_1, \ldots, x_{n+1}, y))$$

Suggestion: given

$$\theta(x_1, \ldots, x_n, 0) = \gamma(x_1, \ldots, x_n)$$
$$\theta(x_1, \ldots, x_n, y + 1) = \delta(x_1, \ldots, x_n, y, \theta(x_1, \ldots, x_n, y))$$

Define ψ as above, letting $\varphi(x_1, \ldots, x_{n+1}, y, z) = \delta(x_1, \ldots, x_n, y, z)$. Then $\theta(x_1, \ldots, x_n, y) = \psi(x_1, \ldots, x_n, \gamma(x_1, \ldots, x_n), y)$.

5. Assuming ρ, ρ_1, ρ_2 as additional initial functions, we can limit uses of the recursion rule (V) to the one-parameter form:

$$\psi(x, 0) = \alpha(x)$$
$$\psi(x, y + 1) = \beta(x, y, \psi(x, y))$$

Hint: let $n \geqslant 2$. Given

$$\theta(x_1, \ldots, x_n, 0) = \gamma(x_1, \ldots, x_n)$$
$$\theta(x_1, \ldots, x_n, y + 1) = \delta(x_1, \ldots, x_n, y, \theta(x_1, \ldots, x_n, y)$$

Let $\eta(u, y) = \theta(\rho_1^n(u), \ldots, \rho_n^n(u), y)$. Define η by a permissible recursion.

6. Assuming ρ, ρ_1, ρ_2 as additional initial functions, we can use $\delta(y, \psi(x, y))$ instead of $\beta(x, y, \psi(x, y))$ in Part (5). (Hint: given

$$\psi(x, 0) = \alpha(x)$$
$$\psi(x, y + 1) = \beta(x, y, \psi(x, y))$$

let $\psi_1(x, y) = \rho(x, \psi(x, y))$. Then $x = \rho_1(\psi_1(x, y))$ and $\psi(x, y) = \rho_2(\psi_1(x, y))$. Define ψ_1 by an appropriate recursion.)

7. Assuming ρ, ρ_1, ρ_2 as additional initial functions, we can limit uses of the recursion rule (V) to the form

$$\psi(x, 0) = x$$
$$\psi(x, y + 1) = \beta(y, \psi(x, y))$$

Hint: use Part (6). Given

$$\varphi(x, 0) = \alpha(x)$$
$$\varphi(x, y + 1) = \beta(y, \varphi(x, y))$$

Define ψ as above. Then $\varphi(x, y) = \psi(\alpha(x), y)$.

8. Assuming $\rho, \rho_1, \rho_2, +, \cdot, \overline{sg}$, as additional initial functions, we

can limit all uses of the recursion rule (V) to those with one parameter of the form

$$f(0) = 0$$
$$f(y + 1) = h(y, f(y))$$

Hint: given, by Part (7),

$$\psi(x, 0) = x$$
$$\psi(x, y + 1) = \beta(y, \psi(x, y))$$

Let $f(n) = \psi(\rho_2(n), \rho_1(n))$. Then

$$\begin{aligned}
f(0) &= \psi(\rho_2(0), \rho_1(0)) = \psi(0, 0) = 0 \\
f(n + 1) &= \psi(\rho_2(n + 1), \rho_1(n + 1)) \\
&= \begin{cases} \rho_2(n + 1) & \text{if } \rho_1(n + 1) = 0 \\ \beta(\rho_1(n + 1) \dot{-} 1, \psi(\rho_2(n + 1), \rho_1(n + 1) \dot{-} 1)) & \text{if } \rho_1(n + 1) \neq 0 \end{cases} \\
&= \begin{cases} \rho_2(n + 1) & \text{if } \rho_1(n + 1) = 0 \\ \beta(\rho_1(n), \psi(\rho_1(n), \rho_2(n))) & \text{if } \rho_1(n + 1) \neq 0 \end{cases} \\
&= \begin{cases} \rho_1(n + 1) & \text{if } \rho_2(n + 1) = 0 \\ \beta(\rho_1(n), f(n)) & \text{if } \rho_1(n + 1) \neq 0 \end{cases} \\
&= \rho_2(n + 1)\cdot\overline{sg}(\rho_1(n + 1)) + \beta(\rho_1(n), f(n))\cdot sg(\rho_1(n + 1)) \\
&= h(n, f(n))
\end{aligned}$$

(Note that sg is obtainable by a recursion of the appropriate kind.)

Then $\psi(x, y) = f(\rho(x, y))$.

9. All primitive recursive functions are obtainable from the initial functions $Z, N, U_i^n, \rho, \rho_1, \rho_2, +, \cdot, \overline{sg}$ by substitution and the recursion rule (V) in the form

$$f(0) = 0$$
$$f(y + 1) = h(y, f(y))$$

(Restatement of Part (8).)

10. In Part (9), $h(y, f(y))$ can be replaced by $h(f(y))$. Hint: given

$$f(0) = 0$$
$$f(y + 1) = h(y, f(y))$$

Let $g(u) = \rho(u, f(u))$, and $\varphi(w) = \rho(\rho_1(w) + 1, h(\rho_1(w), \rho_2(w)))$. Then

$$g(0) = 0$$
$$g(y + 1) = \varphi(g(y))$$

and

$$f(u) = \rho_2(g(u))$$

11. Show that the equations

$$\psi(n, 0) = n + 1$$
$$\psi(0, m + 1) = \psi(1, m)$$
$$\psi(n + 1, m + 1) = \psi(\psi(n, m + 1), m)$$

define a recursive function. (Hint: show that ψ is Herbrand-Gödel computable by the given equations, and then use Proposition 5.17.) In addition, prove:

(I) $\psi(n, m) > n$.
(II) ψ is monotonic in each variable, i.e., if $x < z$, then $\psi(x, y) < \psi(z, y)$ and $\psi(y, x) < \psi(y, z)$.
(III) $\psi(n, m + 1) \geqslant \psi(n + 1, m)$.
(IV) For every primitive recursive function $f(x_1, \ldots, x_n)$, there is some fixed m such that $f(x_1, \ldots, x_n) < \psi(\max(x_1, \ldots, x_n), m)$ for all $x_1, \ldots, x_n$. (Hint: prove this first for the initial functions Z, N, U_i^n, ρ, ρ_1, ρ_2, $+$, $\cdot$, $\overline{sg}$, and then show that it is preserved by substitution and the recursion of Part (10) above.) Hence, for every primitive recursive function f(x) of one argument, there is some m such that $f(x) < \psi(x, m)$ for all x.
(V) Prove that $\psi(x, x) + 1$ is recursive, but not primitive recursive. (Hint: Part (IV).)

For other proofs of the existence of recursive, non-primitive recursive functions, cf. Ackermann [1928], Péter [1935, 1951], R. Robinson [1948].

A very important metamathematical notion is that of recursively enumerable set. A set of natural numbers is called *recursively enumerable* (r.e.) if and only if it is either empty or is the range of a recursive function. Intuitively, if we accept Church's Thesis, then a recursively enumerable set is a collection of natural numbers which is generated by some mechanical process.

PROPOSITION 5.20

(1) *A set* B *is* r.e. *if and only if* $x \in B$ *is expressible in the form* (Ey)R(x, y), *where* R *is recursive.* (*We can also allow* R *here to be primitive recursive.*)

(2) *A set* B *is* r.e. *if and only if it is empty or is the range of a partial recursive function* (*or of a primitive recursive function*).

(3) *A set* B *is* r.e. *if and only if it is the domain of definition of a partial recursive function.*

(4) *A set* B *is recursive if and only if both* B *and its complement* $\bar{B}$† *are* r.e.

(5) *The set* $\{x|(Ey)T_1(x, x, y)\}$ *is* r.e., *but not recursive.*‡

PROOF

(1) Assume B is r.e. If B is empty, then $x \in B \equiv (Ey)(x \neq x \wedge y \neq y)$. If B is non-empty, it is the range of a recursive function φ. Then $x \in B \equiv (Ey)(\varphi(y) = x)$. Conversely, assume $x \in B \equiv (Ey)R(x, y)$. If B is empty, B is r.e. If B is non-empty, let k be a fixed element of B. Define:

$$\theta(z) = \begin{cases} k & \text{if } \sim R((z)_0, (z)_1) \\ (z)_0 & \text{if } R((z)_0, (z)_1) \end{cases}$$

Clearly, B is the range of θ, and θ is recursive. (By Lemma 5.8, if R is recursive, $(Ey)R(x, y) \equiv (Ey)T_1(e, x, y)$ for some e; but $T_1(e, x, y)$ is primitive recursive.)

(2) Assume B is the range of a partial recursive function φ. If B is empty, then B is r.e. If B is non-empty, let k be a fixed element of B. Now, there is a number e such that $\varphi(x) = U(\mu y T_1(e, x, y))$. Let

$$\theta(z) = \begin{cases} U((z)_1) & \text{if } T_1(e, (z)_0, (z)_1) \\ k & \text{if } \sim T_1(e, (z)_0, (z)_1) \end{cases}$$

Then θ is primitive recursive and B is the range of θ. Hence, B is r.e. This proof also shows that every non-empty r.e. set is the range of a primitive recursive function.

(3) Assume B r.e. If B is empty, B is the domain of the partial recursive function $\mu y(x + y + 1 = 0)$. If B is non-empty, B is the range of a recursive function f. Let g be the partial recursive function such that $g(y) = \mu x(f(x) = y)$. Then B is the domain of g. Conversely, assume B is the domain of a partial recursive function φ. Then there is a number e such that $\varphi(x) = U(\mu y T_1(e, x, y))$. Hence, $\varphi(x) = z \equiv (Ey)(T_1(e, x, y) \wedge U(y) = z)$. But $x \in B \equiv (Ez)(\varphi(x) = z)$. So, $x \in B$ if and only if $(Ez)(Ey)(T_1(e, x, y) \wedge U(y) = z)$, and the latter is equivalent to $(Eu)(T_1(e, x, (u)_1) \wedge U((u)_1) = (u)_0)$; moreover, $T_1(e, x, (u)_1) \wedge U((u)_1) = (u)_0$ is recursive. Thus, by (1), B is r.e.

(4) From (1) and Proposition 5.19(5). (The intuitive meaning of Part (4) is the following: if there are mechanical procedures for generating B and $\bar{B}$, then to determine whether any number n is in B we need only wait until n is generated by one of the machines and then observe which machine produced it.)

(5) From (1) and (4), and Proposition 5.19(3).

† I.e., $\omega - B$, where ω is the set of non-negative integers.
‡ Remember that $\{x \mid P(x)\}$ stands for the set of all x such that P(x) holds.

EXERCISES

1. The inverse image of an r.e. set under a recursive function is r.e. (i.e., if f is recursive and B r.e., then $\{x \mid f(x) \in B\}$, is r.e.). The inverse image of a recursive set under a recursive function is recursive. The image of an r.e. set under a recursive function is r.e., but the image of a recursive set under a recursive function is not necessarily a recursive set.

2. An infinite set is recursive if and only if it is the range of a strictly increasing recursive function.

3. Any infinite set is r.e. if and only if it is the range of a one-one recursive function.

4. Every infinite r.e. set contains an infinite recursive subset.

5. If A and B are r.e. sets, so are $A \cup B$ and $A \cap B$, but there exists an r.e. set A such that $\omega - A$ is not r.e.

By Proposition 5.20(3), a set is r.e. if and only if it is the domain ζ_n of the partial recursive function $U(\mu y T_1(n, x, y))$ for some n; hence, $x \in \zeta_n$ if and only if $(Ey)T_1(n, x, y)$. We call n an *index* of the r.e. set ζ_n. We thus have an enumeration (with repetitions) $\zeta_1, \zeta_2, \ldots$ of all r.e. sets.

An example of an r.e. set which is not recursive is the set of all x such that $(Ey)T_1(x, x, y)$. That it is r.e. follows from Proposition 5.20(2), and that it is not recursive follows from Proposition 5.19(3). By Proposition 5.20(4), it also follows that $(y) \sim T_1(x, x, y)$ is not r.e.

EXERCISES

1. A set B is called *creative* if and only if B is r.e. and there is a partial recursive function φ such that, for any n, if $\zeta_n \subseteq \bar{B}$, then $\varphi(n) \in \bar{B} - \zeta_n$. Prove that $\{x \mid (Ey)T_1(x, x, y)\}$ is creative. (Hint: let $\varphi(n) = n$ for all n.) Show that every creative set is non-recursive.

2. A partial recursive function φ is called *potentially recursive* if and only if there is a recursive function ψ such that $\varphi(x_1, \ldots, x_n) = \psi(x_1, \ldots, x_n)$ whenever $\varphi(x_1, \ldots, x_n)$ is defined. Prove that $\mu y T_1(x, x, y)$ is not potentially recursive. (Hint: if $\psi(x)$ were a recursive function which is an extension of $\mu y T_1(x, x, y)$, then $(Ey)T_1(x, x, y)$ would be equivalent to $T_1(x, x, \psi(x))$, which is recursive.)

D3. A set B is called *simple* if and only if B is r.e., $\bar{B}$ is infinite, and $\bar{B}$ contains no infinite r.e. set. Every simple set is non-recursive. Show that a simple set exists. (Hint: let $\varphi(z) = \sigma_1^2(\mu y[T_1(z, \sigma_1^2(y), \sigma_2^2(y)) \wedge \sigma_1^2(y) > 2z])$, and let B be the range of φ.)

4. A *recursive permutation* is a one-one recursive function from ω onto ω. Sets X and Y are called *isomorphic* (written $X \simeq Y$) if there is a recursive permutation which maps X onto Y.

[A](a) Show that the recursive permutations form a group under the operation of composition.

(b) $\cong$ is an equivalence relation.

(c) If X is recursive (r.e., creative, simple) and $X \cong Y$, then Y is recursive (r.e., creative, simple).

Myhill [1955] has shown that any two creative sets are isomorphic. (Also cf. Bernays [1957].)

5. X is *many-one reducible* to Y (written $X\ R_m\ Y$) if there is a recursive function f such that $u \in X$ if and only if $f(u) \in Y$. X and Y are called *many-one equivalent* (written $X \equiv_m Y$) if $X\ R_m\ Y$ and $Y\ R_m\ X$. X is *one-one reducible* to Y (written $X\ R_1\ Y$) if there is a one-one recursive function f such that $u \in X$ if and only if $f(u) \in Y$. X and Y are called *one-one equivalent* (written $X \equiv_1 Y$) if $X\ R_1\ Y$ and $Y\ R_1\ X$.

(a) $\equiv_m$ and $\equiv_1$ are equivalence relations.

(b) If X is creative, Y is r.e., and $X\ R_m\ Y$, then Y is creative. It can be shown (Myhill [1955]) that if X is creative and Y is r.e. then $Y\ R_m\ X$.

(c) (Myhill [1955]) If $X\ R_1\ Y$ then $X\ R_m\ Y$, and if $X \equiv_1 Y$ then $X \equiv_m Y$. However, many-one reducibility does not imply one-one reducibility, and many-one equivalence does not imply one-one equivalence. (Hint: let X be a simple set, Z an infinite recursive subset of X, and $Y = X - Z$. Then $X\ R_1\ Y$, $Y\ R_m\ X$, but not $(Y\ R_1\ X)$.) It can be proved that $X \equiv_1 Y$ if and only if $X \cong Y$.

6. (Dekker [1955]) X is said to be *productive* if there is a partial recursive function f such that if $\zeta_n \subseteq X$ then $f(n) \in X - \zeta_n$. (a) If X is productive, then X is not r.e.; hence, both X and $\overline{X}$ are infinite. [D](b) If X is productive, then X has an infinite r.e. subset. Hence, if X is productive, $\overline{X}$ is not simple. (c) If X is r.e., then X is creative if and only if $\overline{X}$ is productive. [D](d) There exist $2^{\aleph_0}$ productive sets.

7. (Dekker-Myhill [1960]) X is *recursively equivalent* to Y (written $X \sim Y$) if there is a one-one partial-recursive function which maps X onto Y. (a) $\sim$ is an equivalence relation. [D](b) X is *immune* if X is infinite and X has no infinite r.e. subset. X is *isolated* if X is not recursively equivalent to a proper subset of X. (The isolated sets may be considered the recursive counterparts of the Dedekind-finite sets.) Show that an infinite set is isolated if and only if it is immune. [D](c) There exist $2^{\aleph_0}$ immune sets.

Recursively enumerable sets are also important because, if we assume Church's Thesis, the set T_K of Gödel numbers of theorems of any axiomatizable first-order theory K is r.e. (The same holds true of arbitrary formal axiomatic systems.) For, the relation Pf(y, x) (y is the Gödel number of a proof in K of a wf with Gödel number x, cf. page 141) is recursive, if the set of Gödel numbers of the axioms is recursive, i.e., if the theory is axiomatic and Church's Thesis holds. Hence, $x \in T_K$ if and only if (Ey)Pf(y, x), and therefore, T_K is r.e. If we accept Church's Thesis, then K is effectively decidable if and only if the r.e. set T_K is recursive. We showed in Corollary 3.41 that every consistent extension K of the theory RR is recursively undecidable, i.e., T_K is not recursive.

Much more general results along these lines can be proved (cf. Smullyan [1961], Feferman [1957], Putnam [1957], Ehrenfeucht and Feferman [1960], Myhill [1955]). For example, (1) if every recursive set is expressible in K, then K is essentially recursively undecidable, i.e., for every consistent extension of K, T_K is not recursive (cf. Exercise 3 below); (2) for any consistent first-order theory with equality K in which every recursive function is representable and which satisfies (i′) and (ii) of pp. 146–147, the set T_K is creative. (We assume that K has among its terms the numerals $\overline{0}, \overline{1}, \overline{2}, \ldots$.) For further study of r.e. sets, cf. Post [1944] and Rogers [1956].

EXERCISES

1. Given a set A of natural numbers, define $A^\star$: $u \in A^\star$ if and only if u is a Gödel number of a wf $\mathfrak{A}(x_1)$ and the Gödel number of $\mathfrak{A}(\overline{u})$ is in A. If A is recursive, then $A^\star$ is recursive.

2. Let T_K be the set of Gödel numbers of the theorems of a consistent first-order theory K. Then, $(\overline{T}_K)^\star$ is not expressible in K. Hint: assume $\mathfrak{B}(x_1)$ expresses $(\overline{T}_K)^\star$ in K. Then, for any n, $\vdash_K \mathfrak{B}(\overline{n})$ if and only if $n \in (\overline{T}_K)^\star$. (This is a weaker assertion than the expressibility of $(\overline{T}_K)^\star$ by $\mathfrak{B}$ in K.) Let p = the Gödel number of $\mathfrak{B}(x_1)$. Then, $\vdash_K \mathfrak{B}(\overline{p})$ if and only if $p \in (\overline{T}_K)^\star$. Hence, $\vdash_K \mathfrak{B}(\overline{p})$ if and only if the Gödel number of $\mathfrak{B}(\overline{p})$ is in $\overline{T}_K$, i.e., $\vdash_K \mathfrak{B}(\overline{p})$ if and only if not-$\vdash_K \mathfrak{B}(\overline{p})$.

3. If every recursive set is expressible in K, then K is essentially recursively undecidable. (It suffices to prove that T_K is not recursive, since every recursive set is expressible in every extension of K. Assume T_K recursive. Then $\overline{T}_K$ is recursive. By 1., $(\overline{T}_K)^\star$ is recursive. Hence, $(\overline{T}_K)^\star$ is expressible in K, contradicting 2.)

§ 4. Undecidable Problems

A general class of problems is said to be undecidable if and only if there is no general effective (or mechanical) procedure for solving each problem in the given class. For example, given any polynomial in any number of variables with integral coefficients, is there a set of integral values of the variables for which the polynomial has the value 0? We may be able to answer this question for certain special polynomials, but it is still not known whether there is any generally applicable effective procedure (cf. Davis [1958], Chapter 7).

If we can arithmetize the formulation of a general class of problems and thus assign to each problem a natural number, then this class is undecidable if and only if there is no effectively computable function h such that, if n is the number of a given problem, then h(n) gives the solution of the problem. If we accept Church's Thesis (as we shall do in this section) the function h has to be partial recursive, and we then have a precise mathematical question. Examples of important mathematical decision problems which have been solved (negatively) are the word problem for semi-groups (Post [1947], Kleene [1952], § 71), and the very difficult word problem for groups (Boone [1959], Novikov [1955], Britton [1958], Higman [1961]). In addition, the decision problem for various first-order theories has been shown to have a negative solution, i.e., the general problem as to whether any given wf is provable in the theory is undecidable (cf. Corollary 3.36, Corollary 3.37, Proposition 3.41, Corollary 3.45, Proposition 3.46). We shall now present some more examples of undecidable problems.

The sequence of functions $\psi_n(x) = U(\mu y T_1(n, x, y))$ gives an enumeration of all partial recursive functions of one variable. Is there an effective procedure to determine for any n whether ψ_n is recursive (i.e., whether ψ_n is defined for all x)? A positive answer is equivalent to the recursiveness of the set A of all numbers n such that ψ_n is recursive. We shall show that A is not even r.e. Assume A r.e., and let h be a recursive function with range A. Define a new function $f(x) = [\psi_{h(x)}(x)] + 1 = [U(\mu y T_1(h(x), x, y))] + 1$. Hence, f is recursive and so there is some m such that $f = \psi_m$ and $m \in A$. Then $\psi_m(x) = \psi_{h(x)}(x) + 1$. Since $m \in A$, there is some k such that $m = h(k)$. Taking $x = k$, we have $\psi_m(k) = \psi_m(k) + 1$, which is a contradiction. Thus, there is no effective procedure by which we can tell whether any system of equations determines a recursive function.

We can obtain a "local" form of this result. Is there an effective procedure determining for any given m, n whether $\psi_n(m)$ is defined? The answer is negative. For, assume that $\theta(x, y)$ is a recursive function such that

$$\theta(x, y) = \begin{cases} 0 & \text{if } \psi_x(y) \text{ is defined} \\ 1 & \text{if } \psi_x(y) \text{ is not defined} \end{cases}$$

Now, let $\alpha(z) = \mu y(\theta(z, z) = 1 \wedge y = y)$. Clearly,

$$\alpha(z) = \begin{cases} 0 & \text{if } \psi_z(z) \text{ is undefined} \\ \text{undefined} & \text{if } \psi_z(z) \text{ is defined} \end{cases}$$

But α is partial recursive, and so, $\alpha = \psi_k$ for some k. Then

$$\psi_k(k) = \alpha(k) = \begin{cases} 0 & \text{if } \psi_k(k) \text{ is undefined} \\ \text{undefined} & \text{if } \psi_k(k) \text{ is defined} \end{cases}$$

which is a contradiction. (Other undecidable problems can be found in Rogers [1956].)

EXERCISES

1. Given a Turing machine T, can one effectively decide, given any instantaneous description α, whether or not there is a computation of T beginning with α? (*Halting problem* for T) Show that there is a Turing machine with undecidable halting problem. (Hint: let T be a Turing machine which computes $\mu y T_1(x, x, y)$; use Proposition 5.19(3).) For further discussion of this and similar problems, cf. Davis [1958], Chapter 5.

2. There is no normal algorithm $\mathfrak{B}$ over $M = \{1, *\}$ such that $\mathfrak{B}$ is applicable to exactly those words $\bar{n}$ such that n is an index of a normal algorithm $\mathfrak{A}$ over M such that $\mathfrak{A}$ is not applicable to $\bar{n}$.

For further examples of undecidable problems in the theory of algorithms, cf. Markov [1954], Chapter V. Because of the essential equivalence of normal algorithms, Turing machines, and Herbrand-Gödel systems of equations, any undecidability result established in terms of one of these approaches usually can be translated into corresponding results for the other two.

3. The function f such that

$$f(x) = \begin{cases} 0 & \text{if } \psi_x(x) \text{ is defined} \\ 1 & \text{otherwise} \end{cases}$$

is not recursive.

D4. Show that there is a recursive function $\eta(x)$ such that, for any x, $\eta(x)$ is the index of the partial recursive function v, where

$$v(y) = \begin{cases} 0 & \text{if } \psi_x(x) \text{ is defined} \\ \text{undefined} & \text{if } \psi_x(x) \text{ is undefined} \end{cases}$$

D5. (Rogers) Show that the following relations are not recursive (and, therefore, by Church's Thesis, are undecidable).

(a) y is in the range of ψ_x.
(b) $\psi_x(y) = z$.
(c) $\psi_x = \psi_y$. (Hint: use 4 and 3.)

The reader should not get the impression that all decision problems have a negative solution. In Chapter I it was shown that truth tables provide an effective procedure to determine whether any given statement form is a tautology. On page 156, it was shown that the pure monadic predicate calculus is effectively decidable (cf. Ackermann [1954] and Suranyi [1959] for many positive results of a similar kind). Presburger [1929] showed that the first-order theory obtained from first-order theory number theory S by omitting the multiplication symbol and the recursion axioms for multiplication is decidable (cf. pp. 116–117, Exercise 4); Szmielew [1955] proved the decidability of the first-order theory of abelian groups; and Tarski [1951] established the decidability of the first-order theory of real-closed fields, which is the elementary part of the theory of real numbers.

APPENDIX

A CONSISTENCY PROOF FOR FORMAL NUMBER THEORY

The first consistency proof for first-order number theory S was given by Gentzen [1936, 1938b]. Since then, other proofs along similar lines have been given by Ackermann [1940], Lorenzen [1951], Schütte [1951, 1960], and Hlodovskii [1959]. As can be expected from Gödel's Second Theorem (cf. page 148), all these proofs use methods which apparently are not available in S. Our exposition will follow Schütte's proof [1951].

The consistency proof will apply to a system S_∞ which is much stronger than S. S_∞ is to have the same individual constant 0 and the same function letters $+$, $\cdot$, $'$ as S (cf. pp. 102–103), and the same predicate letter $=$. Thus, S and S_∞ have the same terms and, hence, the same atomic formulas (i.e., formulas $s = t$, where s and t are terms). However, the primitive propositional connectives of S_∞ will be $\vee$ and $\sim$, whereas S had $\supset$ and $\sim$ as its basic connectives. We define a wf of S_∞ to be an expression built up from the atomic formulas by a finite number of applications of the connectives $\vee$ and $\sim$ and of the quantifiers (x_i) (i = 1, 2, . . .). We let $\mathscr{A} \supset \mathscr{B}$ stand for $(\sim\mathscr{A}) \vee \mathscr{B}$; then any wf of S is an abbreviation of a wf of S_∞.

A closed atomic wf $s = t$ (i.e., an atomic wf containing no variables) is called *correct*, if, when we evaluate s and t according to the usual recursion equations for $+$ and $\cdot$, the same value is obtained for s and t; if different values are obtained, $s = t$ is said to be *incorrect*. Clearly, one can effectively determine whether a given closed atomic wf is correct or incorrect.

As *axioms* of S_∞ we take: (a) all correct closed atomic wfs; (b) negations of all incorrect closed atomic wfs. Thus, for example, $(0'')\cdot(0'') + 0'' = (0''')\cdot(0'')$ and $0' + 0'' \neq 0'\cdot 0''$ are axioms of S_∞.

S_∞ has the following rules of inference:

I. Weak Rules

(a) Exchange: $\dfrac{\mathscr{C} \vee \mathscr{A} \vee \mathscr{B} \vee \mathscr{D}}{\mathscr{C} \vee \mathscr{B} \vee \mathscr{A} \vee \mathscr{D}}$

(b) Consolidation: $\dfrac{\mathscr{A} \vee \mathscr{A} \vee \mathscr{D}}{\mathscr{A} \vee \mathscr{D}}$

II. Strong Rules

(a) Dilution: $\dfrac{\mathscr{D}}{\mathscr{A} \vee \mathscr{D}}$ (where $\mathscr{A}$ is any closed wf)

(b) DeMorgan: $\dfrac{\sim\mathscr{A} \vee \mathscr{D} \qquad \sim\mathscr{B} \vee \mathscr{D}}{\sim(\mathscr{A} \vee \mathscr{B}) \vee \mathscr{D}}$

(c) Negation: $\dfrac{\mathscr{A} \vee \mathscr{D}}{\sim\sim\mathscr{A} \vee \mathscr{D}}$

(d) Quantification: $\dfrac{\sim\mathscr{A}(t) \vee \mathscr{D}}{(\sim(x)\mathscr{A}(x)) \vee \mathscr{D}}$ (where t is a closed term)

(e) Infinite Induction: $\dfrac{\mathscr{A}(\bar{\mathrm{n}}) \vee \mathscr{D} \quad \text{for all natural numbers n}}{((x)\mathscr{A}(x)) \vee \mathscr{D}}$

III. Cut: $\dfrac{\mathscr{C} \vee \mathscr{A} \qquad \sim\mathscr{A} \vee \mathscr{D}}{\mathscr{C} \vee \mathscr{D}}$

In all these rules, the wfs above the line are called *premisses*, and the wfs below the line, *conclusions*. The wfs denoted by $\mathscr{C}$ and $\mathscr{D}$ are called the *side* wfs of the rule; in every rule either or both side wfs may be absent—except that $\mathscr{D}$ must occur in a dilution (II(a)), and at least one of $\mathscr{C}$ and $\mathscr{D}$ in a cut (III). For example, $\dfrac{\mathscr{A} \qquad \sim\mathscr{A} \vee \mathscr{D}}{\mathscr{D}}$ is a cut, and $\dfrac{\sim\mathscr{A} \qquad \sim\mathscr{B}}{\sim(\mathscr{A} \vee \mathscr{B})}$ is an instance of DeMorgan's Rule, II(b). In any rule, the wfs which are not side wfs are called the *principal* wfs; these are the wfs denoted by $\mathscr{A}$ and $\mathscr{B}$ in the presentation above of the rules. The principal wf $\mathscr{A}$ of a cut is called the *cut wf*; the number of propositional connectives and quantifiers in $\sim\mathscr{A}$ is called the *degree* of the cut.

We still must define the notion of a proof in S_∞. Because of the Rule of Infinite Induction this is much more complicated than the notion of proof in S. A *G-tree* is defined to be a graph the points of which can be decomposed into disjoint "levels" as follows: At level 0, there is a single point, called the *terminal point*; each point at level i + 1 is connected by an edge to exactly one point at level i; each point P at level i is connected by edges to either zero, one, two, or denumerably many points at level i + 1 (these latter points at level i + 1 are called the *predecessors* of *P*); each point at level i is connected only to points at level i − 1 or i + 1; a point at level i not connected to any points at level i + 1 is called an *initial point.*

Examples of G-trees.

(1)

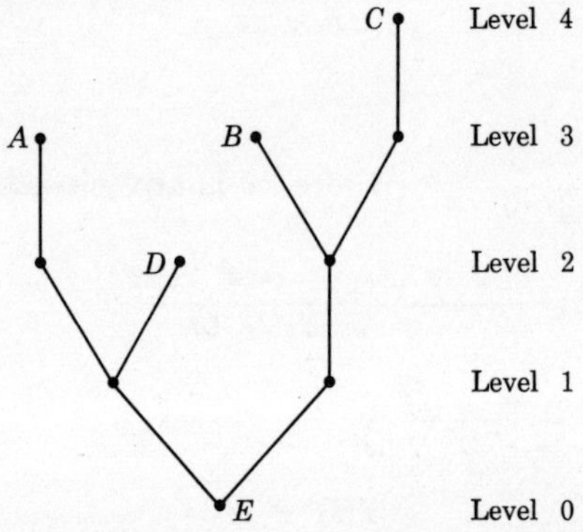

A, B, C, D, are initial points. E is the terminal point.

(2)

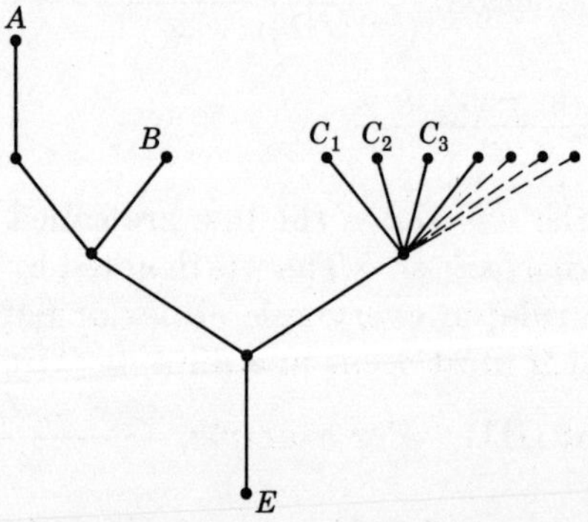

A, B, C_1, C_2, C_3,. . . are the initial points. E is the terminal point.

(3)

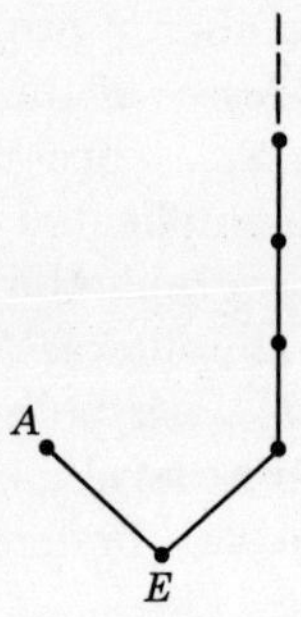

A is the only initial point.
E is the terminal point.

By a *proof-tree*, we mean an assignment of wfs of S_∞ to the points of a G-tree such that

(1) The wfs assigned to the initial points are axioms of S_∞;

(2) The wfs assigned to a non-initial point P and to the predecessors of P are, respectively, the conclusion and premisses of some rule of inference;

(3) There is a maximal degree of the cuts appearing in the proof-tree. This maximal degree is called the *degree* of the proof-tree. If there are no cuts, the degree is 0;

(4) There is an assignment of an ordinal number to each wf occurring in the proof-tree such that (a) the ordinal of the conclusion of a weak rule is the same as the ordinal of the premiss; (b) the ordinal of the conclusion of a strong rule or a cut is greater than the ordinals of the premisses.

The wf assigned to the terminal point of a proof-tree is called the *terminal wf*; the ordinal of the terminal wf is called the *ordinal* of the proof-tree. The proof-tree is said to be a *proof* of the terminal wf, and the *theorems* of S_∞ are defined to be the wfs which are terminal wfs of proof-trees. Notice that, since all axioms of S_∞ are closed wfs and the rules of inference take closed premisses into closed consequences, all theorems of S_∞ are closed wfs.

A *thread* in a proof-tree is a finite or denumerable sequence $\mathscr{A}_1, \mathscr{A}_2, \ldots$ of wfs starting with the terminal wf and such that each wf $\mathscr{A}_{i+1}$ is a predecessor of $\mathscr{A}_i$. Hence, the ordinals $\alpha_1, \alpha_2, \ldots$ assigned to the wfs in a thread do not increase, and they decrease at each application of a strong rule or a cut. Since there cannot exist a denumerably decreasing sequence of ordinals, it follows that only a finite number of applications of strong rules or cuts can be involved in a thread. Also, to a given wf, only a finite number of applications of weak rules are necessary. Hence, we can assume that there are only a finite number of consecutive applications of weak rules in any thread of a proof-tree. (Let us make this part of the definition of "proof-tree".) Then every thread of a proof-tree is finite.

If we restrict the class of ordinals which may be assigned to the wfs of a proof-tree, then this restricts the notion of a proof-tree, and, therefore, we obtain a (possibly) smaller set of theorems. If one uses various "constructive" segments of denumerable ordinals, then the systems so obtained and the methods used in the consistency proof below may be considered more or less "constructive".

EXERCISE

Prove that the associative rules $\dfrac{(\mathscr{C} \vee \mathscr{A}) \vee \mathscr{B}}{\mathscr{C} \vee (\mathscr{A} \vee \mathscr{B})}$ and $\dfrac{\mathscr{C} \vee (\mathscr{A} \vee \mathscr{B})}{(\mathscr{C} \vee \mathscr{A}) \vee \mathscr{B}}$ are derivable from the exchange rule, assuming association to the left. Hence, parentheses may be omitted from a disjunction.

LEMMA A-1. *Let $\mathscr{A}$ be a closed* wf *having* n *connectives and quantifiers. Then there is a proof of $\sim\mathscr{A} \vee \mathscr{A}$ of ordinal* $\leqslant 2n + 1$ *(in which no cut is used).*

PROOF. Induction on n.

(1) $n = 0$. Then $\mathscr{A}$ is a closed atomic wf. Hence, either $\mathscr{A}$ or $\sim\mathscr{A}$ is an axiom, because $\mathscr{A}$ is either correct or incorrect. Hence, by one application of the Dilution Rule, one of the following is a proof-tree.

$$\text{dilution}\ \frac{\mathscr{A}}{\sim\mathscr{A} \vee \mathscr{A}} \qquad \text{or} \qquad \dfrac{\dfrac{\sim\mathscr{A}}{\mathscr{A} \vee \sim\mathscr{A}}\ \text{dilution}}{\sim\mathscr{A} \vee \mathscr{A}}\ \text{exchange}$$

Hence, we can assign ordinals so that the proof of $\sim\mathscr{A} \vee \mathscr{A}$ has ordinal 1.

(2) Assume true for all $k < n$.

Case (i): $\mathscr{A}$ is $\mathscr{A}_1 \vee \mathscr{A}_2$. By inductive hypothesis, there are proofs of $\sim\mathscr{A}_1 \vee \mathscr{A}_1$ and $\sim\mathscr{A}_2 \vee \mathscr{A}_2$ of ordinals $\leqslant 2(n - 1) + 1 = 2n - 1$. By dilution, we obtain proofs of $\sim\mathscr{A}_1 \vee \mathscr{A}_1 \vee \mathscr{A}_2$ and $\sim\mathscr{A}_2 \vee \mathscr{A}_1 \vee \mathscr{A}_2$, respectively, of order 2n, and, by DeMorgan's Rule, a proof of $\sim(\mathscr{A}_1 \vee \mathscr{A}_2) \vee \mathscr{A}_1 \vee \mathscr{A}_2$ of ordinal $2n + 1$.

Case (ii): $\mathscr{A}$ is $\sim\mathscr{B}$. Then, by inductive hypothesis, there is a proof of $\sim\mathscr{B} \vee \mathscr{B}$ of ordinal $2n - 1$. By the Exchange Rule, we obtain a proof of $\mathscr{B} \vee \sim\mathscr{B}$ of ordinal $2n - 1$, and then, applying the Negation Rule, we have a proof of $\sim\sim\mathscr{B} \vee \sim\mathscr{B}$, i.e., of $\sim\mathscr{A} \vee \mathscr{A}$, of ordinal $2n \leqslant 2n + 1$.

Case (iii): $\mathscr{A}$ is $(x)\mathscr{B}(x)$. By inductive hypothesis, for every natural number k, there is a proof of $\sim\mathscr{B}(\bar{k}) \vee \mathscr{B}(\bar{k})$ of ordinal $\leqslant 2n - 1$. Then, by the Quantification Rule, for each k there is a proof of $(\sim(x)\mathscr{B}(x)) \vee \mathscr{B}(\bar{k})$ of ordinal $\leqslant 2n$ and, hence, by the Exchange Rule, a proof of $\mathscr{B}(\bar{\text{k}}) \vee \sim (x)\mathscr{B}(x)$ of ordinal $\leqslant 2\text{n}$. Finally, by an application of the Infinite Induction Rule, we obtain a proof of $((x)\mathscr{B}(x)) \vee \sim (x)\mathscr{B}(x)$ of ordinal $\leqslant 2\text{n} + 1$, and, by the Exchange Rule, a proof of $(\sim (x)\mathscr{B}(x)) \vee (x)\mathscr{B}(x)$ of ordinal $\leqslant 2\text{n} + 1$.

LEMMA A-2. *For any closed terms t and s, and any* wf $\mathscr{A}(x)$ *with x as its only free variable, the* wf $s \neq t \vee \sim\mathscr{A}(s) \vee \mathscr{A}(t)$ *is a theorem of* S_∞ *and is provable without applying the Cut Rule.*

PROOF. In general, if a closed wf $\mathscr{B}(t)$ is provable in S_∞, and s has the same value as t, then $\mathscr{B}(s)$ is also provable in S_∞. (Simply replace all occurrences of t which are "deductively connected" with the t in the terminal wf $\mathscr{B}(t)$ by s.) Now, if s has the same value $\bar{\text{n}}$ as t, then, since $\sim\mathscr{A}(\bar{\text{n}}) \vee \mathscr{A}(\bar{\text{n}})$ is provable, it follows by the previous remark that $\sim\mathscr{A}(s) \vee \mathscr{A}(t)$ is provable. Hence, by dilution, $s \neq t \vee \sim\mathscr{A}(s) \vee \mathscr{A}(t)$ is provable. If s and t have different values, $s = t$ is incorrect; hence, $s \neq t$ is an axiom. So, by dilution and exchange, $s \neq t \vee \sim\mathscr{A}(s) \vee \mathscr{A}(t)$ is a theorem.

LEMMA A-3, *Every closed* wf *which is a theorem of* S *is also a theorem of* S_∞.

PROOF. Let $\mathscr{A}$ be a closed wf which is a theorem of S. Clearly, every proof in S can be represented in the form of a finite proof-tree, where the initial wfs are axioms of S and the rules of inference are modus ponens and generalization. Let n be an ordinal assigned to such a proof-tree for $\mathscr{A}$.

If $\text{n} = 0$, then $\mathscr{A}$ is an axiom of S (cf. page 103).

(1) $\mathscr{A}$ is $\mathscr{B} \supset (\mathscr{C} \supset \mathscr{B})$, i.e., $\sim\mathscr{B} \vee (\sim\mathscr{C} \vee \mathscr{B})$. But, $\sim\mathscr{B} \vee \mathscr{B}$ is provable in S_∞ (Lemma A-1). Hence, so is $\sim\mathscr{B} \vee \sim\mathscr{C} \vee \mathscr{B}$ by a dilution and an exchange.

(2) $\mathscr{A}$ is $(\mathscr{B} \supset (\mathscr{C} \supset \mathscr{D}) \supset ((\mathscr{B} \supset \mathscr{C}) \supset (\mathscr{B} \supset \mathscr{D}))$, i.e., $\sim(\sim\mathscr{B} \vee \sim\mathscr{C} \vee \mathscr{D}) \vee \sim(\sim\mathscr{B} \vee \mathscr{C}) \vee (\sim\mathscr{B} \vee \mathscr{D})$. By Lemma A-1, we have $\sim(\sim\mathscr{B} \vee \mathscr{C}) \vee \sim\mathscr{B} \vee \mathscr{C}$ and $(\sim\mathscr{B} \vee \sim\mathscr{C} \vee \mathscr{D}) \vee \sim(\sim\mathscr{B} \vee \sim\mathscr{C} \vee \mathscr{D})$. Then, by exchange, a cut (with $\mathscr{C}$ as cut formula), and consolidation, $\sim(\sim\mathscr{B} \vee \sim\mathscr{C} \vee \mathscr{D}) \vee \sim(\sim\mathscr{B} \vee \mathscr{C}) \vee \sim\mathscr{B} \vee \mathscr{D}$ is provable.

(3) $\mathscr{A}$ is $(\sim\mathscr{B} \supset \sim\mathscr{A}) \supset ((\sim\mathscr{B} \supset \mathscr{A}) \supset \mathscr{B}))$, i.e., $\sim(\sim\sim\mathscr{B} \vee \sim\mathscr{A}) \vee \sim(\sim\sim\mathscr{B} \vee \mathscr{A}) \vee \mathscr{B}$. Now, by Lemma A-1 we have $\sim\mathscr{B} \vee \mathscr{B}$, and then, by the Negation Rule, $\sim\sim\sim\mathscr{B} \vee \mathscr{B}$, and, by dilution and exchange,

(a) $\sim\sim\sim\mathscr{B} \vee \sim(\sim\sim\mathscr{B} \vee \mathscr{A}) \vee \mathscr{B}$.

Similarly, we obtain $\sim\sim\sim\mathscr{B} \vee \mathscr{B} \vee \sim\sim\mathscr{A}$ and $\sim\mathscr{A} \vee \mathscr{B} \vee \sim\sim\mathscr{A}$, and by DeMorgan's Rule, $\sim(\sim\sim\mathscr{B} \vee \mathscr{A}) \vee \mathscr{B} \vee \sim\sim\mathscr{A}$; then, by exchange,

(b) $\sim\sim\mathscr{A} \vee \sim(\sim\sim\mathscr{B} \vee \mathscr{A}) \vee \mathscr{B}$.

From (a) and (b), by DeMorgan's Rule, we have $\sim(\sim\sim\mathscr{B} \vee \sim\mathscr{A}) \vee \sim(\sim\sim\mathscr{B} \vee \mathscr{A}) \vee \mathscr{B}$.

(4) $\mathscr{A}$ is $(x)\mathscr{B}(x) \supset \mathscr{B}(t)$, i.e., $(\sim(x)\mathscr{B}(x)) \vee \mathscr{B}(t)$. Then, by Lemma A-1, we have $\sim\mathscr{B}(t) \vee \mathscr{B}(t)$; by the Quantification Rule, $(\sim(x)\mathscr{B}(x)) \vee \mathscr{B}(t)$.

(5) $\mathscr{A}$ is $(x)(\mathscr{B} \supset \mathscr{C}) \supset (\mathscr{B} \supset (x)\mathscr{C})$, where x is not free in $\mathscr{B}$, i.e., $\sim(x)(\sim\mathscr{B} \vee \mathscr{C}(x)) \vee \sim\mathscr{B} \vee (x)\mathscr{C}(x)$. Now, by Lemma A-1, for every natural number n, there is a proof of $\sim(\sim\mathscr{B} \vee \mathscr{C}(\overline{\mathrm{n}})) \vee \sim\mathscr{B} \vee \mathscr{C}(\overline{\mathrm{n}})$. (Note that the ordinals of these proofs are bounded by 2k + 1, where k is the number of propositional connectives and quantifiers in $\sim\mathscr{B} \vee \mathscr{C}(x)$.)

Hence, by the Quantification Rule, for each n, there is a proof of

$$\sim(x)(\sim\mathscr{B} \vee \mathscr{C}(x)) \vee \sim\mathscr{B} \vee \mathscr{C}(\overline{\mathrm{n}}) \quad \text{(of ordinal } \leqslant 2\mathrm{k} + 2)$$

Hence, by exchange and infinite induction, there is a proof of

$$\sim(x)(\sim\mathscr{B} \vee \mathscr{C}(x)) \vee \sim\mathscr{B} \vee (x)\mathscr{C}(x) \quad \text{(of ordinal } \leqslant 2\mathrm{k} + 3)$$

(S1) $\mathscr{A}$ is $t_1 = t_2 \supset (t_1 = t_3 \supset t_2 = t_3)$, i.e., $t_1 \neq t_2 \vee t_1 \neq t_3 \vee t_2 = t_3$. Apply Lemma A-2, with $x = t_3$ as $\mathscr{A}(x)$, t_1 as s, t_2 as t.

(S2) $\mathscr{A}$ is $t_1 = t_2 \supset (t_1)' = (t_2)'$, i.e., $t_1 \neq t_2 \vee (t_1)' = (t_2)'$. If t_1 and t_2 have the same value, then so do $(t_1)'$ and $(t_2)'$. Hence $(t_1)' = (t_2)'$ is correct and therefore an axiom. By dilution, we obtain $t_1 \neq t_2 \vee (t_1)' = (t_2)'$. If t_1 and t_2 have different values, $t_1 \neq t_2$ is an axiom; hence, by dilution and exchange, $t_1 \neq t_2 \vee (t_1)' = (t_2)'$ is provable.

(S3) $\mathscr{A}$ is $0 \neq t'$. 0 and t' have different values; hence, $0 \neq t'$ is an axiom.

(S4) $\mathscr{A}$ is $(t_1)' = (t_2)' \supset t_1 = t_2$, i.e., $(t_1)' \neq (t_2)' \vee t_1 = t_2$. (Exercise.)

(S5) $\mathscr{A}$ is $t + 0 = t$. $t + 0$ and t have the same values. Hence, $t + 0 = t$ is an axiom.

(S6)–(S8) follow similarly from the recursion equations for evaluating closed terms.

(S9) $\mathscr{A}$ is $\mathscr{B}(0) \supset ((x)(\mathscr{B}(x) \supset \mathscr{B}(x')) \supset (x)\mathscr{B}(x))$, i.e.,

$$\sim\mathscr{B}(0) \vee \sim(x)(\sim\mathscr{B}(x) \vee \mathscr{B}(x')) \vee (x)\mathscr{B}(x)$$

(1) Clearly, by Lemma A-1, exchange and dilution,

$\sim\mathscr{B}(0) \vee \sim(x)(\sim\mathscr{B}(x) \vee \mathscr{B}(x')) \vee \mathscr{B}(0)$ is provable.

(2) For k $\geqslant$ 0, let us prove by induction that the following wf is provable:

$$\sim\mathscr{B}(0) \vee \sim(\sim\mathscr{B}(0) \vee \mathscr{B}(\overline{1})) \vee \ldots \vee \sim(\sim\mathscr{B}(\overline{\mathrm{k}}) \vee \mathscr{B}(\overline{\mathrm{k}'})) \vee \mathscr{B}(\overline{\mathrm{k}'}).$$

(a) For $\mathrm{k} = 0$; $\vdash_{S_\infty} \sim\sim\mathscr{B}(0) \vee \sim\mathscr{B}(0) \vee \mathscr{B}(\bar{1})$ by Lemma A-1, dilution, and exchange; similarly, $\vdash_{S_\infty} \sim\mathscr{B}(\bar{1}) \vee \sim\mathscr{B}(0) \vee \mathscr{B}(\bar{1})$. Hence, by DeMorgan's Rule, $\vdash_{S_\infty} \sim(\sim\mathscr{B}(0) \vee \mathscr{B}(\bar{1})) \vee \sim\mathscr{B}(0) \vee \mathscr{B}(\bar{1})$, and, by exchange,

$$\vdash_{S_\infty} \sim\mathscr{B}(0) \vee \sim(\sim\mathscr{B}(0) \vee \mathscr{B}(\bar{1})) \vee \mathscr{B}(\bar{1})$$

(b) Assume for k:

$$\vdash_{S_\infty} \sim\mathscr{B}(0) \vee \sim(\sim\mathscr{B}(0) \vee \mathscr{B}(\bar{1})) \vee \dots \vee \sim(\sim\mathscr{B}(\bar{\mathrm{k}}) \vee \mathscr{B}(\bar{\mathrm{k}}')) \vee \mathscr{B}(\bar{\mathrm{k}}')$$

Hence, by exchange, negation, and dilution,

$$\vdash_{S_\infty} \sim\sim\mathscr{B}(\bar{\mathrm{k}}') \vee \sim\mathscr{B}(0) \vee \sim(\sim\mathscr{B}(0) \vee \mathscr{B}(\bar{1})) \vee \dots \vee \sim(\sim\mathscr{B}(\mathrm{k}) \vee \mathscr{B}(\bar{\mathrm{k}}')) \vee \mathscr{B}(\bar{\mathrm{k}}'')$$

Also, by Lemma A-1 for $\mathscr{B}(\bar{\mathrm{k}}'')$, dilution and exchange,

$$\vdash_{S_\infty} \sim\mathscr{B}(\bar{\mathrm{k}}'') \vee \sim\mathscr{B}(0) \vee \sim(\sim\mathscr{B}(0) \vee \mathscr{B}(\bar{1})) \vee \dots \vee \sim(\sim\mathscr{B}(\bar{\mathrm{k}}) \vee \mathscr{B}(\bar{\mathrm{k}}')) \vee \mathscr{B}(\bar{\mathrm{k}}'')$$

Hence, by DeMorgan's Rule,

$$\vdash_{S_\infty} \sim(\sim\mathscr{B}(\bar{\mathrm{k}}') \vee \mathscr{B}(\bar{\mathrm{k}}'') \vee \sim\mathscr{B}(0) \vee \sim(\sim\mathscr{B}(0) \vee \mathscr{B}(\bar{1})) \vee \dots \vee \sim(\sim\mathscr{B}(\bar{\mathrm{k}}) \vee \mathscr{B}(\bar{\mathrm{k}}')) \vee \mathscr{B}(\bar{\mathrm{k}}'')$$

and, by exchange, the result follows for $\mathrm{k} + 1$.

Now, applying the exchange and quantification rules k times to the result of (2), we have, for each $\mathrm{k} \geqslant 0$,

$$\vdash_{S_\infty} \sim\mathscr{B}(0) \vee \sim(x)(\mathscr{B}(x) \vee \mathscr{B}(x')) \vee \dots \vee \sim(x)(\sim\mathscr{B}(x) \vee \mathscr{B}(x')) \vee \mathscr{B}(\bar{\mathrm{k}}')$$

and, by consolidation, $\vdash_{S_\infty} \sim\mathscr{B}(0) \vee \sim(x)(\sim\mathscr{B}(x) \vee \mathscr{B}(x')) \vee \mathscr{B}(\bar{\mathrm{k}}')$. Hence, together with (1), we have, for all $\mathrm{k} \geqslant 0$,

$$\vdash_{S_\infty} \sim\mathscr{B}(0) \vee \sim(x)(\sim\mathscr{B}(x) \vee \mathscr{B}(x')) \vee \mathscr{B}(\bar{\mathrm{k}})$$

Then, by infinite induction,

$$\vdash_{S_\infty} \sim\mathscr{B}(0) \vee \sim(x)(\sim\mathscr{B}(x) \vee \mathscr{B}(x')) \vee (x)\mathscr{B}(x)$$

Thus, all the closed axioms of S are provable in S_∞. We assume now that $\mathrm{n} > 0$. Then, (i) $\mathscr{A}$ may arise by modus ponens from $\mathscr{B}$ and $\mathscr{B} \supset \mathscr{A}$, where $\mathscr{B}$ and $\mathscr{B} \supset \mathscr{A}$ have smaller ordinals in the proof-tree. We may assume that $\mathscr{B}$ contains no free variables, since we can replace any such free variables by 0 in $\mathscr{B}$ and its predecessors in the proof-tree.

Hence, by inductive hypothesis, $\vdash_{S_\infty} \mathscr{B}$ and $\vdash_{S_\infty} \mathscr{B} \supset \mathscr{A}$, i.e., $\vdash_{S_\infty} \sim\mathscr{B} \vee \mathscr{A}$. Hence, by a cut, we obtain $\vdash_{S_\infty} \mathscr{A}$. The other possibility (ii) is that $\mathscr{A}$ is $(x)\mathscr{B}(x)$ and comes by generalization from $\mathscr{B}(x)$. Now, in the proof-tree, working backwards from $\mathscr{B}(x)$, replace the appropriate free occurrences of x by $\bar{\mathrm{n}}$. We then obtain a proof of $\mathscr{B}(\bar{\mathrm{n}})$, of the same ordinal. This holds for all n; by inductive hypothesis, $\vdash_{S_\infty} \mathscr{B}(\bar{\mathrm{n}})$ for all n. Hence, by infinite induction, $\vdash_{S_\infty} (x)\mathscr{B}(x)$, i.e., $\vdash_{S_\infty} \mathscr{A}$.

COROLLARY A-4. *If* S_∞ *is consistent*, S *is consistent.*

PROOF. If S is inconsistent, then $\vdash_S 0 \neq 0$. Hence, by Lemma A-3, $\vdash_{S_\infty} 0 \neq 0$. But, $\vdash_{S_\infty} 0 = 0$, since $0 = 0$ is correct. For any wf $\mathscr{A}$ of S_∞, we would have, by dilution, $\vdash_{S_\infty} 0 \neq 0 \vee \mathscr{A}$, and, together with $\vdash_{S_\infty} 0 = 0$, by a cut, $\vdash_{S_\infty} \mathscr{A}$. Thus, any wf of S_∞ is provable; so, S_∞ is inconsistent.

By Corollary A-4, to prove the consistency of S it suffices to show the consistency of S_∞.

LEMMA A-5. *The rules of DeMorgan, negation, and infinite induction are invertible, i.e., from a proof of a* wf *which is a consequence of some premisses by one of these rules one can obtain a proof of the premisses (and the ordinal and degree of such a proof are no higher than the ordinal and degree of the original proof).*

PROOF

(1) DeMorgan. $\mathscr{A}$ is $\sim(\mathscr{B} \vee \mathscr{E}) \vee \mathscr{D}$. Take a proof of $\mathscr{A}$. Take all those subformulas $\sim(\mathscr{B} \vee \mathscr{E})$ of wfs of the proof-tree obtained by starting with $\sim(\mathscr{B} \vee \mathscr{E})$ in $\mathscr{A}$ and working back up the proof-tree. This process continues through all applications of weak rules and through all strong rules in which $\sim(\mathscr{B} \vee \mathscr{E})$ is part of a side wf. It can end only at dilutions $\dfrac{\mathscr{F}}{\sim(\mathscr{B} \vee \mathscr{E}) \vee \mathscr{F}}$ or applications of DeMorgan's Rule: $\dfrac{\sim\mathscr{B} \vee \mathscr{F} \quad \sim\mathscr{E} \vee \mathscr{F}}{\sim(\mathscr{B} \vee \mathscr{E}) \vee \mathscr{F}}$. The set of all occurrences of $\sim(\mathscr{B} \vee \mathscr{E})$ obtained by this process is called the *history* of $\sim(\mathscr{B} \vee \mathscr{E})$. Let us replace all occurrences of $\sim(\mathscr{B} \vee \mathscr{E})$ in its history by $\sim\mathscr{B}$. Then we still have a proof-tree (after unnecessary formulas are erased), and the terminal wf is $\sim\mathscr{B} \vee \mathscr{D}$. Similarly, if we replace $\sim(\mathscr{B} \vee \mathscr{E})$ by $\sim\mathscr{E}$ we obtain a proof of $\sim\mathscr{E} \vee \mathscr{D}$.

(2) Negation. $\mathscr{A}$ is $\sim\sim\mathscr{B} \vee \mathscr{D}$. Define the history of $\sim\sim\mathscr{B}$ as was done for $\sim(\mathscr{B} \vee \mathscr{E})$ in (1); replace all occurrences of $\sim\sim\mathscr{B}$ in its history by $\mathscr{B}$; the result is a proof of $\mathscr{B} \vee \mathscr{D}$.

(3) Infinite Induction. $\mathscr{A}$ is $((x)\mathscr{B}(x)) \vee \mathscr{D}$. Define the history of $(x)\mathscr{B}(x)$ as in (1); replace $(x)\mathscr{B}(x)$ in its history by $\mathscr{B}(\overline{n})$ (and if one of the initial occurrences in its history appears as the consequence of an infinite induction, erase the tree above all the premisses except the one involving $\overline{n}$); we then obtain a proof of $\mathscr{B}(\overline{n}) \vee \mathscr{D}$.

LEMMA A-6 (Schütte [1951]: Reduktionssatz). *Given a proof of* $\mathscr{A}$ *in* S_∞ *of positive degree m and ordinal* α, *there is a proof of* $\mathscr{A}$ *in* S_∞ *of lower degree and ordinal* 2^α (cf. page 178).

PROOF. By transfinite induction on the ordinal α of the given proof of $\mathscr{A}$. $\alpha = 0$: this proof can contain no cuts and, hence, has degree 0. Assume the theorem proved for all ordinals $<\alpha$. Starting from the terminal wf $\mathscr{A}$, find the first application of a non-weak rule, i.e., of a strong rule or a cut. If it is a strong rule, each premiss has ordinal $\alpha_i < \alpha$. By inductive hypothesis, for these premisses, there are proof-trees of lower degree and ordinal 2^{α_i}. Substitute these proof-trees for the proof-trees above the premisses in the original proof. We thus obtain a new proof for $\mathscr{A}$ except that the ordinal of $\mathscr{A}$ should be taken to be 2^α, which is greater than every 2^{α_i} (cf. Proposition 4.30(9)).

The remaining case is that of a cut.

$$\frac{\mathscr{C} \vee \mathscr{B} \qquad \sim\mathscr{B} \vee \mathscr{D}}{\mathscr{C} \vee \mathscr{D}}$$

If the ordinals of $\mathscr{C} \vee \mathscr{B}$ and $\sim\mathscr{B} \vee \mathscr{D}$ are α_1, α_2, then, by inductive hypothesis, we can replace the proof-trees above them so that the degrees are reduced and the ordinals are 2^{α_1}, 2^{α_2}, respectively. We shall distinguish various cases according to the form of the cut formula $\mathscr{B}$.

(a) $\mathscr{B}$ is an atomic wf. Either $\mathscr{B}$ or $\sim\mathscr{B}$ must be an axiom. Let $\mathscr{K}$ be the non-axiom of $\mathscr{B}$ and $\sim\mathscr{B}$. By inductive hypothesis, the proof-tree above the premiss containing $\mathscr{K}$ can be replaced by a proof-tree with lower degree having ordinal 2^{α_i} ($i = 1$ or 2). In this new proof-tree, consider the history of $\mathscr{K}$ (as defined in the proof of Lemma A-5). The initial wfs in this history can arise only by dilutions. So, if we erase all occurrences of $\mathscr{K}$ in this history, we obtain a proof-tree for $\mathscr{C}$ or for $\mathscr{D}$ of ordinal 2^{α_i}; then, by a dilution, we obtain $\mathscr{C} \vee \mathscr{D}$, of ordinal 2^α. The degree of the new proof-tree is less than m.

(b) $\mathscr{B}$ is $\sim\mathscr{E}$: $$\frac{\mathscr{C} \vee \sim\mathscr{E} \qquad \sim\sim\mathscr{E} \vee \mathscr{D}}{\mathscr{C} \vee \mathscr{D}}$$

There is a proof-tree for $\sim\sim\mathscr{E} \vee \mathscr{D}$ of degree $<$m and ordinal 2^{α_2}. By Lemma A-5, there is a proof-tree for $\mathscr{E} \vee \mathscr{D}$ of degree $<$m and ordinal 2^{α_2}. There is also, by inductive hypothesis, a proof-tree for $\mathscr{C} \vee \sim\mathscr{E}$ of degree $< \mathrm{m}$ and ordinal 2^{α_1}. Now, construct

$$\text{Exchange}\ \frac{\begin{matrix}\vdots\\ \mathscr{E} \vee \mathscr{D}\end{matrix}}{\mathscr{D} \vee \mathscr{E}} \qquad\qquad \frac{\begin{matrix}\vdots\\ \mathscr{C} \vee \sim\mathscr{E}\end{matrix}}{\sim\mathscr{E} \vee \mathscr{C}}\ \text{Exchange}$$

$$\text{Cut}$$

$$\frac{\mathscr{D} \vee \mathscr{C}}{\mathscr{C} \vee \mathscr{D}}\quad \text{Exchange}$$

The degree of the indicated cut is the degree of $\sim\mathscr{E}$ which is one less than the degree of $\sim\sim\mathscr{E}$, which, in turn, is $\leqslant \mathrm{m}$. The ordinal of $\mathscr{D} \vee \mathscr{C}$ can be taken to be 2^{α}. Hence, we have a proof of lower degree and ordinal 2^{α}.

(c) $\mathscr{B}$ is $\mathscr{E} \vee \mathscr{F}$: $\dfrac{\mathscr{C} \vee \mathscr{E} \vee \mathscr{F} \qquad \sim(\mathscr{E} \vee \mathscr{F}) \vee \mathscr{D}}{\mathscr{C} \vee \mathscr{D}}$

There is a proof-tree for $\sim(\mathscr{E} \vee \mathscr{F}) \vee \mathscr{D}$ of lower degree and ordinal 2^{α_2}. Hence, by Lemma A-5, there are proof-trees for $\sim\mathscr{E} \vee \mathscr{D}$ and $\sim\mathscr{F} \vee \mathscr{D}$ of degree $< \mathrm{m}$ and ordinal 2^{α_2}. There is also a proof-tree for $\mathscr{C} \vee \mathscr{E} \vee \mathscr{F}$ of degree $< \mathrm{m}$ and ordinal 2^{α_1}. Construct:

$$\begin{array}{lll}
 & \begin{matrix}\vdots & & \vdots\\ \mathscr{C} \vee \mathscr{E} \vee \mathscr{F} & & \sim\mathscr{F} \vee \mathscr{D}\end{matrix} & \\
\text{Cut} & & \\
 & \mathscr{C} \vee \mathscr{E} \vee \mathscr{D} & \\
\text{Exchange} & & \vdots \\
 & \mathscr{C} \vee \mathscr{D} \vee \mathscr{E} & \sim\mathscr{E} \vee \mathscr{D} \\
\text{Cut} & & \\
 & \qquad\mathscr{C} \vee \mathscr{D} \vee \mathscr{D} & \\
\text{Consolidation} & & \\
 & \qquad\quad\mathscr{C} \vee \mathscr{D} &
\end{array}$$

The cuts indicated have degrees $<$m; hence, the new proof-tree has degree $<$m; the ordinal of $\mathscr{C} \vee \mathscr{E} \vee \mathscr{D}$ can be taken as $2^{\max(\alpha_1, \alpha_2)} +_0 1$, and then the ordinal of $\mathscr{C} \vee \mathscr{D} \vee \mathscr{D}$ and $\mathscr{C} \vee \mathscr{D}$ as 2^α.

(d) $\mathscr{B}$ is $(x)\mathscr{E}$: $$\frac{\mathscr{C} \vee (x)\mathscr{E} \quad (\sim(x)\mathscr{E}) \vee \mathscr{D}}{\mathscr{C} \vee \mathscr{D}}$$

By inductive hypothesis, the proof-tree above $\mathscr{C} \vee (x)\mathscr{E}$ can be replaced by one with smaller degree and ordinal 2^{α_1}. By Lemma A-5 and the remark at the beginning of the proof of Lemma A-2, we can obtain proofs of $\mathscr{C} \vee \mathscr{E}(t)$ of degree $<$m and ordinal 2^α, for any closed term t. Now, the proof-tree above the right-hand formula $(\sim(x)\mathscr{E}) \vee \mathscr{D}$ can be replaced, by inductive hypothesis, by one with smaller degree and ordinal 2^{α_2}. The history of $\sim(x)\mathscr{E}$ in this proof terminates above either at dilutions or as principal wfs in applications of the Quantification Rule:

$$\frac{\sim\mathscr{E}(t_i) \vee \mathscr{G}_i}{(\sim(x)\mathscr{E}) \vee \mathscr{G}_i}$$

Replace every such application by the cut

$$\frac{\mathscr{C} \vee \mathscr{E}(t_i) \qquad (\sim\mathscr{E}(t_i)) \vee \mathscr{G}_i}{\mathscr{C} \vee \mathscr{G}_i}$$

Replace all occurrences in the history of $\sim(x)\mathscr{E}(x)$ by $\mathscr{C}$. The result is still a proof-tree, and the terminal wf is $\mathscr{C} \vee \mathscr{D}$. The proof-tree has degree $<$m, since the degree of $\sim\mathscr{E}(t_i)$ is less than the degree of $\sim(x)\mathscr{E}$. Replace each old ordinal β of the proof-tree by $2^{\alpha_1} +_0 \beta$. If β was the ordinal of the premiss $\sim\mathscr{E}(t) \vee \mathscr{G}_i$ of an eliminated Quantification Rule application above, and if γ was the ordinal of the conclusion $(\sim(x)\mathscr{E}) \vee \mathscr{G}_i$, then, in the new cut introduced, $\mathscr{C} \vee \mathscr{E}(t)$ has ordinal 2^{α_1}, $\sim\mathscr{E}(t_i) \vee \mathscr{G}_i$ has ordinal $2^{\alpha_1} +_0 \beta$, and the conclusion $\mathscr{C} \vee \mathscr{G}_i$ has ordinal $2^{\alpha_1} +_0 \gamma > \max(2^{\alpha_1}, 2^{\alpha_1} +_0 \beta)$. At all other places, the ordinal of the conclusion is still greater than the ordinal of the premisses, since $\delta <_0 \mu$ implies $2^{\alpha_1} +_0 \delta <_0 2^{\alpha_1} +_0 \mu$. Finally, the right-hand premiss $(\sim(x)\mathscr{E}) \vee \mathscr{D}$ (originally of ordinal α_2) goes over into $\mathscr{C} \vee \mathscr{D}$ with ordinal $2^{\alpha_1} +_0 2^{\alpha_2} \leqslant 2^{\max(\alpha_1, \alpha_2)} +_0 2^{\max(\alpha_1, \alpha_2)} = 2^{\max(\alpha_1, \alpha_2)} \times_0 2 = 2^{\max(\alpha_1, \alpha_2) +_0 1} \leqslant 2^\alpha$. If this is $<_0 2^\alpha$, the ordinal of $\mathscr{C} \vee \mathscr{D}$ can be raised to 2^α.

Corollary A-7. *Every proof of $\mathscr{A}$ of ordinal α and degree m can be replaced by a proof of $\mathscr{A}$ of ordinal $2^{2^{\cdot^{\cdot^{\cdot^{2^{(2^\alpha)}}}}}}$ and degree* 0 (*i.e., a cut-free proof*).

Proposition A-8. S_∞ *is consistent.*

PROOF. Consider any wf $\mathscr{A}$ of the form $(0 \neq 0) \vee (0 \neq 0) \vee \ldots \vee (0 \neq 0)$. If there is a proof of $\mathscr{A}$, then by Corollary A-7, there is a cut-free proof of $\mathscr{A}$. By inspection of the rules of inference, $\mathscr{A}$ can be derived only from other wfs of the same form: $(0 \neq 0) \vee \ldots \vee (0 \neq 0)$. Hence, the axioms of the proof would have to be of this form. But there are no axioms of this form; hence, $\mathscr{A}$ is unprovable. Therefore, S_∞ is consistent.

EXERCISE

If no restriction is placed upon the class of ordinals which can be attached to proofs: (1) S_∞ is ω-consistent (Hint: Corollary A-7, Proposition A-8, and the Rule of Infinite Induction). (2) Every closed wf of S_∞ which is true for the standard model is provable. Hence, S_∞ would be complete.

To reduce the non-constructive aspect of the consistency proof, one can restrict the class of ordinals which can be assigned to wfs of a proof-tree. Consider the set of ordinals $\{\omega, \omega^\omega, \omega^{\omega^\omega}, \ldots\}$ (defined inductively by: $\gamma_0 = \omega, \gamma_{n+1} = \omega^{\gamma_n}$). Let us denote the least upper bound of this set by ε_0. If we use only ordinals $<_0 \varepsilon_0$, then all the proofs given above still go through (for, if $\delta <_0 \varepsilon_0$, then $2^\delta <_0 \varepsilon_0$). In addition, the ordinals $<_0 \varepsilon_0$ can be written down in a certain standard "polynomial" notation: (i) the ordinals $<_0 \omega^\omega$ can be written in the form

$$(\omega^{k_1} \times_0 n_1) +_0 (\omega^{k_2} \times_0 n_2) +_0 \ldots +_0 (\omega^{k_l} \times_0 n_l)$$

where $k_1, k_2, \ldots, k_l$ is a decreasing sequence of finite ordinals, and $n_1, n_2, \ldots, n_l$ are finite ordinals; (ii) the ordinals between ω^ω and ω^{ω^ω} can be written in the form $(\omega^{\alpha_1} \times_0 n_1) +_0 (\omega^{\alpha_2} \times_0 n_2) +_0 \ldots +_0 (\omega^{\alpha_l} \times_0 \eta_l)$ where $\alpha_1, \alpha_2, \ldots, \alpha_l$ is a decreasing sequence of ordinals $<_0 \omega^\omega$ and $n_1, n_2, \ldots, n_l$ are finite ordinals, etc. (cf. Bachmann [1955], III; Gentzen [1938b]).

The chief non-constructive aspect of the consistency proof was the use of transfinite induction in the proof of Lemma A-6. The principle of transfinite induction up to a given ordinal has been formalized and studied by Gentzen [1943] and Schütte [1951, 1960]; as was to be expected, transfinite induction up to ε_0, is not derivable in S. Whether or not certain concepts and assumptions (such as denumerable ordinals and transfinite induction up to ε_0) should really be considered "constructive" seems ultimately to be a subjective matter. For further details and discussion, in addition to the references already given, cf. Hilbert-Bernays [1939], Rosser [1937], Müller [1961], and Shoenfield [1959].

BIBLIOGRAPHY

Listed here are not only books and papers mentioned in the text but also other material which will be helpful in a further study of mathematical logic. Additional references may be found in the reviews in the *Journal of Symbolic Logic* and *Mathematical Reviews.* We shall use the following abbreviations.

Arch for *Archiv für mathematische Logik und Grundlagenforschung.*
FM for *Fundamenta Mathematicae.*
JSL for *Journal of Symbolic Logic.*
ZML for *Zeitschrift für mathematische Logik und Grundlagen der Mathematik.*

Ackermann, W.
1928. Zum Hilbertschen Aufbau der reelen Zahlen, *Math. Annalen*, 99, pp. 118–133.
1940. Zur Widerspruchsfreiheit der Zahlentheorie, *Math. Annalen*, 117, pp. 162–194.
1951. Konstruktiver Aufbau eines Abschnittes der zweiten Cantorschen Zahlenklasse, *Math. Zeitschr.*, 53, pp. 403–413.
1954. *Solvable Cases of the Decision Problem*, Amsterdam, 114 pp.
See Hilbert, D., and W. Ackermann.

Asser, G.
1955. Das Repräsentantenproblem im Prädikatenkalkül der ersten Stufe mit Identitat, *ZML*, 1, pp. 252–263.
1959. Turing-Maschinen und Markowsche Algorithmen, *ZML*, 5, pp. 346–365.

Bachmann, H.
1955. *Transfinite Zahlen.* Berlin, Göttingen, Heidelberg, 204 pp.

Bar-Hillel, Y. See Fraenkel, A., and Y. Bar-Hillel.

Bernays, P.
1937–1954. A system of axiomatic set theory. *JSL.* I. Vol. 2 (1937), pp. 65–77; II. Vol. 6 (1941), pp. 1–17; III. Vol. 7 (1942), pp. 65–89; IV. Vol. 7 (1942), pp. 133–145; V. Vol. 8 (1943), pp. 89–106; VI. Vol. 13 (1948), pp. 65–79; VII. Vol. 19 (1954), pp. 81–96.
1957. Review of Myhill [1955], *JSL*, Vol. 22, pp. 73–76.
1958. *Axiomatic Set Theory*, Amsterdam, 225 pp.
1961. Zur Frage der Unendlichkeitsschemata in der axiomatischen Mengenlehre, *Essays on the Foundations of Mathematics*, Jerusalem, pp. 3–49.
See Hilbert, D., and P. Bernays.

Beth, E.
1951. A Topological Proof of the Theorem of Löwenheim-Skolem-Gödel, *Indag. Math.*, Vol. 13, pp. 436–444.
1953. Some consequences of the theorem of Löwenhein-Skolem-Gödel-Malcev, *Indag. Math.*, 15, pp. 66–71.
1959. *The Foundations of Mathematics*, Amsterdam, 741 pp.
1962. *Formal Methods*, New York, 178 pp.

Birkhoff, G.
1948. *Lattice Theory.* New York. Revised edition, 283 pp.

Boone, W.
1959. The Word Problem, *Annals of Math.*, 70, pp. 207–265.

Bourbaki, N.
1947. *Algebre.* Livre II, Chap. II, Paris.
1949. Foundations of mathematics for the working mathematician, *JSL*, Vol. 14, pp. 1–8.

Britton, J. L.
1958. The Word Problem for Groups. *Proc. London Math. Soc.*, 8, pp. 493–506.

Bruijn, N. G. de, and P. Erdös.
1951. A colour problem for infinite graphs and a problem in the theory of relations, *Indag. Math.*, 13, pp. 369–373.

Carnap, R.
1934. *The Logical Syntax of Language*, New York (Translation 1937), 352 pp.
1939. "Foundations of Logic and Mathematics", *Int. Enc. Unif. Sci.*, I, No. 3, 71 pp.
1942–43. *Studies in Semantics. Introduction to Semantics* and *Formalization of Logic*, Cambridge, Mass., 263 pp. and 159 pp.
1950. *Logical Foundations of Probability*, Chicago, 607 pp.
1958. *Introduction to Symbolic Logic*, New York, 241 pp.

Church, A.
1936a. A note on the Entscheidungsproblem, *JSL*, Vol. 1, pp. 40–41; Correction, ibid., pp. 101–102.
1936b. An unsolvable problem of elementary number theory, *Am. J. Math.*, Vol. 58, pp. 345–363.
1940. A formulation of the simple theory of types, *JSL*, Vol. 5, pp. 56–68.
1941. *The Calculi of Lambda-Conversion*, Princeton, Second printing 1951, 82 pp.
1956. *Introduction to Mathematical Logic, I*, Princeton, 376 pp.

Church, A., and S. C. Kleene.
1936. Formal definitions in the theory of ordinal numbers, *FM*, Vol. 28, pp. 11–21.

Church, A., and W. V. Quine
1951. Some theorems on definability and decidability, *JSL*, Vol. 17, pp. 179–187.

Craig, W.
1953. On axiomatizability within a system, *JSL*, Vol. 18, pp. 30–32.
1957a. Linear reasoning. A new form of the Herbrand-Gentzen theorem. *JSL*, Vol. 22, pp. 250–268.
1957b. Three uses of the Herbrand-Gentzen theorem in relating model theory and proof theory. *JSL*, Vol. 22, pp. 269–285.

Curry, H. B.
1950. *A Theory of Formal Deducibility*, Notre Dame, 126 pp.
1951. *Outlines of a Formalist Philosophy of Mathematics*, Amsterdam, 75 pp.
1952. *Leçons de logique algebrique*, Paris-Louvain, 163 pp.
Curry, H. B., and R. Feys
1958. *Combinatory Logic*, Amsterdam, 390 pp.

Davis, M.
1958. *Computability and Unsolvability*, New York, 210 pp.
Davis, M., H. Putnam, and J. Robinson
1961. The decision problem for exponential diophantine equations, *Ann. of Math.*, Vol. 74, pp. 425–436.
Dedekind, R.
1901. *Essays on the theory of numbers*, Chicago, 115 pp.
Dekker, J.
1953. Two notes on recursively enumerable sets, *Proc. Amer. Math. Soc.*, Vol. 4, pp. 495–501.
1955. Productive Sets, *Trans. Amer. Math. Soc.*, Vol. 78, pp. 129–149.
Dekker, J., and J. Myhill
1960. Recursive Equivalence Types, *Univ. Calif. Publ. Math.*, 3, pp. 67–213.
Detlovs, V. K.
1958. Equivalence of normal algorithms and recursive functions, *Tr. Mat. Inst. Steklov.*, LII, pp. 75–139 (in Russian).
Dickson, L. E.
1929. *Introduction to the Theory of Numbers*, Chicago, 183 pp.
Dreben, B.
1952. On the completeness of quantification theory, *Proc. Natl. Acad. Sci.*, U.S.A., 38, pp. 1047–1052.

Ehrenfeucht, A.
1957a. On theories categorical in power, *FM*, Vol. 44, pp. 241–248.
1957b. Two theories with axioms built by means of pleonasms, *JSL*, Vol. 22, pp. 36–38.
1958. Theories having at least continuum many non-isomorphic models in each infinite power (abstract), *Notices Amer. Math. Soc.*, Vol. 5, p. 680.
Ehrenfeucht, A., and S. Feferman
1960. Representability of recursively enumerable sets in formal theories, *Arch.*, Vol. 5, pp. 37–41.
Ehrenfeucht, A., and A. Mostowski
1957. Models of axiomatic theories admitting automorphisms, *FM*, XLIII, pp. 50–68.
Erdös, P., and N. G. de Bruijn. See Bruijn, N. G. de, and P. Erdös.
Erdös, P., and A. Tarski
1961. On some problems involving inaccessible cardinals, *Essays on the Foundations of Mathematics*, Jerusalem, pp. 50–82.

Feferman, S.
1957. Degrees of unsolvability associated with classes of formalized theories, *JSL*, Vol. 22, pp. 161–175.

1960a. Arithmetization of metamathematics in a general setting, *FM*, XLIX, pp. 35–92.
1960b. Transfinite Recursive Progressions of Axiomatic Theories, *Tech. Report No. 2, Appl. Math. & Stat. Lab.*, Stanford, 97 pp.
Feferman, S., and A. Ehrenfeucht. See Ehrenfeucht, A., and S. Feferman.
Feferman, S., G. Kreisel, and S. Orey
1961. 1-Consistency and Faithful Interpretations, *Arch*, Vol. 6, pp. 52–63.
Feferman, S., and R. Montague
196_. *The method of arithmetization and some of its applications*, Amsterdam (forthcoming).
Feferman, S., and R. L. Vaught
1959. The first order properties of products of algebraic systems, *Fund. Math.*, 47, pp. 57–103.
Feys, R., and H. B. Curry. See Curry, H. B., and R. Feys.
Fraenkel, A. A.
1953. *Abstract Set Theory*, Amsterdam. (Second Edition, 1961, 303 pp.)
Fraenkel, A. A., and Y. Bar-Hillel
1958. *Foundations of Set Theory*, Amsterdam, 414 pp.
Frege, G.
1884. *Grundlagen der Arithmetik* (English translation, New York 1950), 119 pp.
1893, 1903. *Grundgesetze der Arithmetik*, Vols. I and II, 254 pp. and 265 pp.
Friedberg, R.
1957. Two recursively enumerable sets of incomparable degrees of unsolvability, *Proc. Natl. Acad. Sci.*, U.S.A., Vol. 43, pp. 236–238.
Friedberg, R., and H. Rogers Jr.
1959. Reducibility and completeness for set of integers, *ZML*, Vol. 5, pp. 117–125.

Galler, B. A.
1957. Cylindric and polyadic algebras, *Proc. Amer. Math. Soc.*, Vol. 8, pp. 176–183.
Gentzen, G.
1934. Untersuchungen über das Logische Schliessen, *Math. Zeitschr.*, Vol. 39, pp. 176–210, 405–431.
1936. Die Widerspruchsfreiheit der reinen Zahlentheorie, *Math. Ann.*, Vol. 112, pp. 493–565.
1938a. Die gegenwärtige Lage in der mathematischen Grundlagenforschung, *Forschungen zur Logik*, N.S., No. 4, pp. 5–18.
1938b. Neue Fassung des Widerspruchsfreiheitsbeweises für die reine Zahlentheorie, ibid., pp. 19–44.
1943. Beweisbarkeit und Unbeweisbarkeit von Anfangsfällen der transfiniten Induktion in der reinen Zahlentheorie, *Math. Ann.*, Vol. 119, pp. 140–161.
Gödel, K.
1930. Die Vollständigkeit der Axiome des logischen Funktionenkalküls, *Monatsh. Math. Phys.*, Vol. 37, pp. 349–360.
1931. Ueber formal unentscheidbare Sätze der Principia Mathematica und verwandter Systeme I, ibid., Vol. 38, pp. 173–198. (An English translation was published in 1962 by Oliver and Boyd, Edinburgh–London.)

1933. Zum intuitionistischen Aussagenkalkül; Zur intuitionistischen Arithmetik und Zahlentheorie, *Ergeb. math. Koll.*, Vol. 4, pp. 34–38, 40.
1934. *On undecidable propositions of formal mathematical systems*, Princeton, 30 pp.
1936. Über die Länge der Beweise, *Ergeb. math. Koll.*, Vol. 7, pp. 23–24.
1940. *The consistency of the axiom of choice and of the generalized continuum hypothesis with the axioms of set theory*, Princeton (Second printing 1951, 74 pp.)
1944. Russell's Mathematical Logic, in *The Philosophy of Bertrand Russell* (ed. Schilpp), Evanston, pp. 123–153.
1947. What is Cantor's continuum problem? *Amer. Math. Monthly*, Vol. 54, pp. 515–525.
1958. Über eine bisher noch nicht benutzte Erweiterung des finiten Standpunkts, *Dialectica*, Vol. 12, pp. 280–287.

Grzegorczyk, A.
1956. Some proofs of undecidability of arithmetic, *FM*, XLIII, pp. 166–177.

Grzegorczyk, A., A. Mostowski, and C. Ryll-Nardzewski
1958. The classical and the ω-complete arithmetic, *JSL*, Vol. 23, pp. 188–206.

Hall, M., Jr.
1949. The word problem for semigroups with two generators, *JSL*, Vol. 14, pp. 115–118.

Halmos, P.
1960. *Naive Set Theory*, Van Nostrand, Princeton, 104 pp.
1962. *Algebraic Logic.* New York, 271 pp.

Halmos, P., and H. Vaughn
1950. The marriage problem, *Amer. J. Math.*, Vol. 72, pp. 214–215.

Hartogs, F.
1915. Ueber das Problem der Wohlordnung, *Math. Ann.*, Vol. 76, pp. 438–443.

Hasenjaeger, G.
1952. Über ω-Unvollständigkeit in der Peano-Arithmetik, *JSL*, Vol. 17, pp. 81–97.
1953. Eine Bemerkung zu Henkin's Beweis für die Vollständigkeit des Prädikatenkalküls der ersten Stufe, *JSL*, Vol. 18, pp. 42–48.
1960. Unabhangigkeitsbeweise in Mengenlehre und Stufenlogik der Modelle, *Jahresber. Deutsch. Math Ver.*, Vol. 63, pp. 141–162.

Hasenjaeger, G., and H. Scholz
1961. *Grundzüge der mathematischen Logik*, Berlin-Göttingen-Heidelberg, 504 pp.

Hellman, M.
1961. A short proof of an equivalent form of the Schröder-Bernstein Theorem, *Amer. Math. Monthly*, Vol. 68, p. 770.

Henkin, L.
1949. The completeness of the first-order functional calculus, *JSL*, Vol. 14, pp. 159–166.
1950. Completeness in the theory of types, ibid., Vol. 15, pp. 81–91.
1953. Some interconnections between modern algebra and mathematical logic, *Trans. Am. Math. Soc.*, Vol. 74, pp. 410–427.

1954. Boolean representation through propositional calculus, *FM*, XLI, pp. 89–96.
1955a. The representation theorem for cylindrical algebras, *Mathematical Interpretations of Formal Systems*, Amsterdam, pp. 85–97.
1955b. On a theorem of Vaught, *JSL*, Vol. 20, pp. 92–93.
1956. *La structure algébrique des théories mathématiques*, Paris, 52 pp.

Henkin, L., and A. Tarski
1961. Cylindric Algebras, *Proc. Symp. Pure Math. A.M.S.*, II, Lattice Theory, pp. 83–113.

Herbrand, J.
1930. Recherches sur la théorie de la démonstration, *Travaux de la Soc. des Sci. et des Lettres de Varsovie*, III, Vol. 33, pp. 33–160.
1931. Sur le problème fondamental de la logique mathématique, *Comptes Rend.*, Warsaw, Vol. 24, pp. 12–56.
1932. Sur la non-contradiction de l'arithmetique, *J. f. Math.*, Vol. 166, pp. 1–8.

Hermes, H.
1961. *Aufzählbarkeit, Entscheidbarkeit, Berechenbarkeit*, Berlin-Gottingen-Heidelberg, 246 pp.

Heyting, A.
1956. *Intuitionism*, Amsterdam, 133 pp.

Higman, G.
1961. Subgroups of finitely presented groups, *Proc. Roy. Soc.*, Ser. A. 262, pp. 455–475.

Hilbert, D., and W. Ackermann
1950. *Principles of Mathematical Logic*, New York.

Hilbert, D., and P. Bernays
1934, 1939. *Grundlagen der Mathematik*, Vol. I (1934), Vol. II (1939), Berlin, I (471 pp.), II (498 pp.).

Hintikka, K. J.
1954. An application of logic to algebra, *Math. Scand.*, Vol. 2, pp. 243–246.
1955a. Form and Content in Quantification Theory, *Acta Phil. Fennica*, pp. 11–55.
1955b. Notes on the Quantification Theory, Comment. Phys.-Math., *Soc. Sci. Fennica*, Vol. 17, pp. 1–13.
1956. Identity, Variables, and Impredicative Definitions, *JSL*, Vol. 21, pp. 225–245.
1957. Vicious Circle Principle and the Paradoxes, *JSL*, Vol. 22, pp. 245–249.

Hlodovskii, I.
1959. A new proof of the consistency of arithmetic, *Usp. Mat. Nauk*, Vol. 14, No. 6, pp. 105–140 (in Russian).

Hohn, F.
1960. *Applied Boolean Algebra*, New York, 139 pp.

Jaśkowski, S.
1936. Recherches sur le système de la logique intuitioniste, *Act. Sci. Ind.*, 393, Paris, pp. 58–61.

Kalmár, L.
1936. Zuruckführung des Entscheidungsproblems auf den Fall von Formeln mit einer einzigen binären Funktionsvariablen, *Comp. Math.*, Vol. 4, pp. 137–144.

1950a. Eine einfache Konstruktion unentscheidbarer Sätze in formalen Systemen, *Methodos*, Vol. 2, pp. 220–226.

1950b. Another proof of the Gödel-Rosser incompletability theorem, *Acta Szeged*, Vol. 12, pp. 38–43.

1956. Ein direkter Beweis für die allgemein-rekursive Unlösbarkeit des Entscheidungsproblems des Prädikatenkalküls der ersten Stufe mit Identität, *ZML*, Vol. 2, pp. 1–14.

Kemeny, J.

1948. Models of logical systems, *JSL*, Vol. 13, pp. 16–30.

1958. Undecidable problems of elementary number theory, *Math. Ann.*, Vol. 135, pp. 160–169.

Kamke, E.

1950. *Theory of Sets*, New York, 144 pp.

Kleene, S. C.

1936a. General Recursive Functions of Natural Numbers, *Math. Ann.*, 112, pp. 727–742.

1936b. λ-definability and recursiveness, *Duke Math. J.*, Vol. 2, pp. 340–353.

1938. On notation for ordinal numbers, *JSL*, Vol. 3, pp. 150–155.

1943. Recursive predicates and quantifiers, *Trans. Amer. Math. Soc.*, Vol. 53, pp. 41–73.

1944. On the forms of the predicates in the theory of constructive ordinals, *Amer. J. Math.*, Vol. 66, pp. 41–58

1945. On the interpretation of intuitionistic number theory, *JSL*, Vol. 10, pp. 109–124.

1952. *Introduction to Metamathematics*, Van Nostrand, Princeton, 550 pp.

1955a. Hierarchies of number-theoretic predicates, *Bull. Amer. Math. Soc.*, Vol. 61, pp. 193–213.

1955b. Arithmetical predicates and function quantifiers, *Trans. Amer. Math. Soc.*, Vol. 79, pp. 312–340.

1955c. On the form of the predicates in the theory of constructive ordinals II, *Amer. J. Math.*, Vol. 77, pp. 405–428.

1960. Mathematical logic: constructive and non-constructive operations, *Proc. Int. Cong. Math.*, Edinburgh, 1958, pp. 137–153.

Kleene, S. C., and A. Church. See Church, A., and S. C. Kleene.

Kleene, S. C., and E. L. Post

1954. The upper semi-lattice of degrees of recursive unsolvability, *Ann. of Math.*, Vol. 59, pp. 379–407.

Kreider, D. L., and H. Rogers, Jr.

1961. Constructive versions of ordinal number classes, *Trans. Amer. Math. Soc.*, Vol. 100, pp. 325–369.

Kreisel, G.

1950. Note on arithmetic models for consistent formulae of the predicate calculus, *FM*, Vol. 37, pp. 265–285.

1951–52. On the interpretation of non-finitist proofs, *JSL*, Vol. 16, pp. 241–267; Vol. 17, pp. 43–58.

1952a. On the concepts of completeness and interpretation of formal systems, *FM*, Vol. 39, pp. 103–127.

1952b. Some concepts concerning formal systems of number theory, *Math. Zeitschr.*, Vol. 57, pp. 1–12.

1953a. A variant to Hilbert's theory of the foundations of arithmetic, *British J. Phil. of Science*, Vol. 4, pp. 107–129.

1953b. On a problem of Henkin's, *Indag. Math.*, Vol. 15, pp. 405–406.
1955. Models, translations, and interpretations, *Mathematical Interpretations of Formal Systems*, Amsterdam, pp. 26–50.
1958a. Mathematical significance of consistency proofs, *JSL*, Vol. 23, pp. 155–182.
1958b. Hilbert's programme, *Dialectica*, Vol. 12, pp. 346–372.
1960. Ordinal logics and the characterization of informal concepts of proof, *Proc. Int. Cong. Math.*, Edinburgh, Cambridge, pp. 289–299.

Kreisel, G., S. Feferman, and S. Orey. See Feferman, S., G. Kreisel, and S. Orey.

Kreisel, G., and H. Wang
1955. Some applications of formalized consistency proofs, *FM*, Vol. 42, pp. 101–110.

Ladrière, J.
1957. *Les limitations internes des formalismes*, Paris, 715 pp.

Landau, E.
1951. *Foundations of Analysis*, New York, 134 pp.

Langford, C. H.
1927. Some theorems on deducibility, *Ann. of Math.* I., Vol. 28, pp. 16–40; II. Vol. 28, pp. 459–471.

Laüchli, H.
1962. Auswahlaxiom in der Algebra, *Comment. Math. Helvetici*, Vol. 37, pp. 1–18.

Levy, A.
1960. Axiom schemata of strong infinity, *Pacific J. Math.*, Vol. 10, pp. 223–238.

Löb, M. H.
1955. Solution of a problem of Leon Henkin, *JSL*, Vol. 20, pp. 115–118.

Lorenzen, P.
1951. Algebraische und logistische Untersuchungen über freie Verbände, *JSL*, Vol. 16, pp. 81–106.
1955. *Einführung in die operative Logik und Mathematik*, Berlin-Göttingen-Heidelberg, 298 pp.

Loś, J.
1954a. Sur le théorème de Gödel pour les théories indénombrables, *Bull. de l'Acad. Polon. des Sci.*, III, Vol. 2, pp. 319–320.
1954b. On the existence of linear order in a group, *Ibid.*, pp. 21–23.
1954c. On the categoricity in power of elementary deductive systems and some related problems, *Coll. Math.*, Vol. 3, pp. 58–62.
1955. The algebraic treatment of the methodology of elementary deductive systems, *Studia Logica*, 2, pp. 151–212.

Loś, J., and C. Ryll-Nardzewski
1954. Effectiveness of the representation theory for Boolean algebras, *FM*, XLI, pp. 49–56.

Löwenheim, L.
1915. Ueber Möglichkeiten im Relativkalkül, *Math. Ann.*, Vol. 76, pp. 447–470.

Lyndon, R. C.
1959. Properties preserved under algebraic constructions, *Bull. Amer. Math. Soc.*, Vol. 65, pp. 143–299.

Luxemburg, W. A. J.
1962. *Non-Standard Analysis*, Pasadena, 150 pp.

Macdowell, R., and E. Specker
1961. Modelle der Arithmetik, *Infinitistic Methods*, Warsaw, pp. 257–263.
Maclaughlin, T.
1961. A muted variation on a theme of Mendelson, *ZML*, Vol. 17, pp. 57–60.
Malcev, A.
1936. Untersuchungen aus dem Gebiet der mathematischen Logik, *Mat. Sbornik*, (*2*), pp. 323–336.
Markov, A.
1954. The Theory of Algorithms, *Tr. Mat. Inst. Steklov.*, XLII, 375 pp. (Translation: Office of Technical Services, U.S. Department of Commerce, Washington, D.C., 1962.)
Markwald, S.
1954. Zur Theorie der konstruktiven Wohlordnungen, *Math. Ann.*, Vol. 127, pp. 135–149.
McKinsey, J. C. C., and A. Tarski
1948. Some theorems about the sentential calculi of Lewis and Heyting, *JSL*, Vol. 13, pp. 1–15.
McNaughton, R., and H. Wang. See Wang, H., and R. McNaughton.
Mendelson, E.
1956a. Some proofs of independence in axiomatic set theory, *JSL*, Vol. 21, pp. 291–303.
1956b. The independence of a weak axiom of choice, ibid., pp. 350–366.
1958. The Axiom of Fundierung and the Axiom of Choice, *Arch*, Vol. 4, pp. 65–70.
1961. On Non-standard Models for Number Theory, *Essays on the Foundations of Mathematics*, Jerusalem, pp. 259–268.
Meredith, C. A.
1953. Single Axioms for the Systems (C, N), (C, O) and (A, N) of the Two-valued Propositional Calculus, *J. Comp. Syst.*, Vol. 3, pp. 155–164.
Montague, R., and R. L. Vaught
1959. Natural models of set theories, *FM*, Vol. 47, pp. 219–242.
Montague, R., and S. Feferman. See Feferman, S., and R. Montague.
Mostowski, A.
1939. Ueber die Unabhängigkeit des Wohlordnungsatzes vom Ordnungsprinzip, *FM*, 32, Vol. 32, pp. 201–252.
1947. On definable sets of positive integers, *FM*, Vol. 34, pp. 81–112.
1947a. On absolute properties of relations, *JSL*, Vol. 12, pp. 33–42.
1949. An undecidable arithmetic statement, *FM*, Vol. 36, pp. 143–164.
1951. Some impredicative definitions in the axiomatic set theory, *FM*, Vol. 37, pp. 111–124 (also, Vol. 38 (1952), p. 238).
1951a. A classification of logical systems, *Studia Philosophica*, Vol. 4, pp. 237–274.
1952a. *Sentences undecidable in formalized arithmetic*, Amsterdam, 117 pp.
1952b. On models of axiomatic systems, *FM*, Vol. 39, pp. 133–158.
1952c. On direct powers of theories, *JSL*, Vol. 17, pp. 1–31.
1955. The present state of investigations on the foundations of mathematics, Warsaw, 48 pp.

1956. Concerning a problem of H. Scholz, *ZML*, Vol. 2, pp. 210–214.
1957. On a generalization of quantifiers, *Fund. Math.*, Vol. 44, pp. 12–36.
1958. Quelques observations sur l'usage des methodes nonfinitistes dans la metamathematique, *Colloq. Int., Cent. Nat. Rech. Sci.*, Paris, pp. 19–32.
1961. A generalization of the incompleteness theorem, *FM*, Vol. 49, pp. 205–232.

Mostowski, A., and A. Ehrenfeucht. See Ehrenfeucht, A., and A. Mostowski.

Mostowski, A., A. Grzegorczyk, and C. Ryll-Nardzewski. See Grzegorczyk, A., A. Mostowski, and C. Ryll-Nardzewski.

Mostowski, A., A. Tarski, and R. Robinson. See Tarski, A., A. Mostowski, and R. Robinson.

Müller, G.
1961. Ueber die unendliche Induktion, *Infinitistic Methods*, Warsaw, pp. 75–95.

Myhill, J.
1955. Creative Sets, *ZML*, Vol. 1, pp. 97–108.

Myhill, J., and J. Dekker. See Dekker, J., and J. Myhill.

Nagornyi, N.
1953. Stronger reduction theorems for the theory of normal algorithms, *Dokl. Akad. Nauk*, USSR, Vol. 90, pp. 341–342 (in Russian).

von Neumann, J.
1925. Eine Axiomatisierung der Mengenlehre, *J. für Math.*, Vol. 154, pp. 219–240 (also, Vol. 155, p. 128).
1928. Die Axiomatisierung der Mengenlehre, *Math. Zeitschr.*, Vol. 27, pp. 669–752.

Nicod, J. G.
1917. A reduction in the number of primitive propositions of logic, *Proc. Camb. Phil. Soc.*, Vol. 19, pp. 32–41.

Novak, I. L. (Gál, L. N.)
1951. A construction for models of consistent systems, *FM*, Vol. 37, pp. 87–110.

Novikov, P.
1955. On the algorithmic unsolvability of the word problem for group theory, *Tr. Mat. Inst. Steklov.*, Vol. 44 (Amer. Math Soc. Translations, Series 2, Vol. 9, pp. 1–124).

Orey, S.
1956. On ω-consistency and related properties. *JSL*, Vol. 21, pp. 246–252.
1961. Relative interpretations, *ZML*, Vol. 7, pp. 146–153.

Orey, S., S. Feferman, and G. Kreisel. See Feferman, S., G. Kreisel, and S. Orey.

Peano, G.
1891. Sul concetto di numero. *Rivista di Mat.*, Vol. 1, pp. 87–102, 256–267.

Péter, R.
1935. Konstruktion nichtrekursiver Funktionen, *Math. Ann.*, Vol. 111, pp. 42–60.
1951. *Rekursive Funktionen*, Budapest 206 pp; Second enlarged edition, 1957.

Post, E.
1921. Introduction to a general theory of elementary propositions, *Amer. J. Math.*, Vol. 43, pp. 163–185.
1936. Finite combinatory processes—formulation 1, *JSL*, Vol. 1, pp. 103–105.
1943. Formal reductions of the general combinatorial decision problem, *Amer. J. Math.*, Vol. 65, pp. 197–215.
1944. Recursively enumerable sets of positive integers and their decision problems, *Bull. Amer. Math. Soc.*, Vol. 50, pp. 284–316.
1947. Recursive unsolvability of a problem of Thue, *JSL*, Vol. 12, pp. 1–11.

Post, E., and S. C. Kleene. See Kleene, S. C., and E. Post.

Presburger, M.
1929. Ueber die Vollständigkeit eines gewissen Systems der Arithmetik ganzer Zahlen in welchem die Addition als einzige Operation hervortritt, *Comptes Rendus, I Congrès des Math. des Pays Slaves*, Warsaw, pp. 192–201, 395.

Putnam, H.
1957. Decidability and Essential Undecidability, *JSL*, Vol. 22, pp. 39–54.

Putnam, H., M. Davis, and J. Robinson. See Davis, M., H. Putnam, and J. Robinson.

Quine, W. V.
1937. New foundations for mathematical logic, *Amer. Math. Monthly*, Vol. 44, pp. 70–80.
1938. On the theory of types, *JSL*, Vol. 3, pp. 125–139.
1950. *Methods of Logic*, New York, 264 pp.
1951. *Mathematical Logic*, Cambridge, Mass., 346 pp. (First edition 1940)
1953. *From a logical point of view*, Cambridge, Mass., 184 pp.
1955. On Frege's way out, *Mind*, Vol. 64, pp. 145–159.

Quine, W. V., and A. Church. See Church, A., and W. V. Quine.

Rabin, M.
1958. On recursively enumerable and arithmetic models of set theory, *JSL*, Vol. 23, pp. 408–416.
1959. Arithmetical extensions with prescribed cardinality, *Indag. Math.*, Vol. 21, pp. 439–446.
1960. Computable algebra, general theory and theory of computable fields, *Trans. Amer. Math. Soc.*, Vol. 95, pp. 341–360.
1961. Non-standard Models and Independence of the Induction Axiom, *Essays in the Foundations of Mathematics*, Jerusalem, pp. 287–299.
1962. Diophantine Equations and Non-Standard Models of Arithmetic, *Logic, Methodology, and Philosophy of Science* (Proc. Int. Cong., 1960), Stanford, pp. 151–158.

Rasiowa, H.
1951. Algebraic treatment of the functional calculi of Heyting and Lewis, *FM*, Vol. 38, pp. 99–126.
1955. Algebraic models of axiomatic theories, *FM*, Vol. 41, pp. 291–310.
1956. On the ϵ-theorems. *FM*, Vol. 43, pp. 156–165.

Rasiowa, H., and R. Sikorski
1951. A proof of the completeness theorem of Gödel, *FM*, Vol. 37, pp. 193–200.

1952. A proof of the Skolem-Löwenheim theorem, *FM*, Vol. 38, pp. 230–232.
1953. Algebraic treatment of the notion of satisfiability, *FM*, Vol. 40, pp. 62–95.

Rice, H. G.
1953. Classes of recursively enumerable sets and their decision problems, *Trans. Amer. Math. Soc.*, Vol. 74, pp. 358–366.

Robinson, A.
1951. *On the metamathematics of algebra*, Amsterdam, 195 pp.
1952. On the application of symbolic logic to algebra, *Int. Cong. Math.*, Cambridge, Mass., Vol. I., pp. 686–694.
1955. On ordered fields and definite functions, *Math. Ann.*, Vol. 130, pp. 257–271.
1956. *Complete Theories*, Amsterdam, 129 pp.
1961. Model theory and non-standard arithmetic, *Infinitistic Methods*, Warsaw, pp. 266–302.

Robinson, J.
1949. Definability and decision problems in arithmetic, *JSL*, Vol. 14, pp. 98–114.
1950. General recursive functions, *Proc. Amer. Math. Soc.*, Vol. 1, pp. 703–718.
1952. Existential definability in arithmetic, *Trans. Amer. Math. Soc.*, Vol. 72, pp. 437–449.

Robinson, J., M. Davis, and H. Putnam. See Davis, M., H. Putnam, and J. Robinson.

Robinson, R. M.
1937. The theory of classes. A modification of von Neumann's system, *JSL*, Vol. 2, pp. 69–72.
1947. Primitive recursive functions, *Bull. Amer. Math. Soc.*, Vol. 53, pp. 925–942.
1948. Recursion and double recursion, ibid., Vol. 54, pp. 987–993.
1950. An essentially undecidable axiom system, *Proc. Int. Cong. Math.*, Cambridge, 1950, Vol. 1, pp. 729–730.
1956. Arithmetical representation of recursively enumerable sets, *JSL*, Vol. 21, pp. 162–186.

Robinson, R., A. Tarski, and A. Mostowski. See Tarski, A., A. Mostowski, and R. Robinson.

Rogers, H., Jr.
1956. *Theory of Recursive Functions and Effective Computability*, Vols. I–II, MIT, Cambridge, Mass. (mimeographed).
1958. Gödel numberings of partial recursive functions, *JSL*, Vol. 23, pp. 331–341.
1959. Computing degrees of unsolvability, *Math. Annalen*, Vol. 138, pp. 125–140.

Rogers, H., Jr., and R. Friedberg. See Friedberg, R., and H. Rogers Jr.

Rogers, H., Jr., and D. L. Kreider. See Kreider, D. L., and H. Rogers Jr.

Rosenbloom, P.
1950. *Elements of Mathematical Logic*, New York, 214 pp.

Rosser, J. B.
1936a. Constructibility as a criterion for existence, *JSL*, Vol. 1, pp. 36–39.
1936b. Extensions of some theorems of Gödel and Church, ibid., pp. 87–91.

1937. Gödel theorems for non-constructive logics, *JSL*, Vol. 2, pp. 129–137.
1939a. On the consistency of Quine's "New foundations for mathematical logic", *JSL*, Vol. 4, pp. 15–24.
1939b. An informal exposition of proofs of Gödel's theorem and Church's Theorem, ibid., pp. 53–60.
1953. *Logic for Mathematicians*, New York, 540 pp.
1954. The relative strength of Zermelo's Set Theory and Quine's New Foundations, *Proc. Int. Cong. Math.*, Amsterdam, Vol. III, pp. 289–294.
1955. *Deux esquisses de logique*, Paris, 65 pp.

Rosser, J. B., and A. Turquette
1952. *Many-valued Logics*, Amsterdam, 124 pp.

Rosser, J. B., and H. Wang
1950. Non-standard models for formal logics, *JSL*, Vol. 15, pp. 113–129.

Russell, B.
1908. Mathematical logic as based on the theory of types, *Amer. J. Math.*, Vol. 30, pp. 222–262.

Russell, B., and A. N. Whitehead
1910–1913. *Principia Mathematica*, Vols. I–III, Cambridge Univ. Press.

Ryll-Nardzewski, C.
1953. The role of the axiom of induction in elementary arithmetic, *FM*, Vol. 39, pp. 239–263.

Ryll-Nardzewski, C., A. Grzegorczyk, and A. Mostowski. See Grzegorczyk, A., A. Mostowski, and C. Ryll-Nardzewski.

Ryll-Nardzewski, C., and J. Loś. See Loś, J., and C. Ryll-Nardzewski.

Schmidt, A.
1960. *Mathematische Gesetze der Logik I, Vorlesungen über Aussagenlogik*, Berlin, Göttingen, Heidelberg.

Scholz, H., and G. Hasenjaeger. See Hasenjaeger, G., and H. Scholz.

Schütte, K.
1951. Beweistheoretische Erfassung der unendlichen Induktion in der Zahlentheorie, *Math. Ann.*, Vol. 122, pp. 369–389.
1960. *Beweistheorie*, Berlin-Göttingen-Heidelberg, 355 pp.

Scott, D.
1961. On constructing models for arithmetic, *Infinitistic Methods*, Warsaw, pp. 235–255.

Seidenberg, A.
1954. A new decision method for elementary algebra, *Ann. of Math.*, Vol. 60, pp. 365–374.

Shannon, C.
1938. A symbolic analysis of relay and switching circuits, *Trans. Amer. Inst. Elect. Eng.*, Vol. 57, pp. 713–723.

Shapiro, N.
1956. Degrees of computability, *Trans. Amer. Math. Soc.*, Vol. 82, pp. 281–299.

Shepherdson, J.
1951–1953. Inner models for set theory, *JSL*, I, Vol. 16, pp. 161–190; II, Vol. 17, pp. 225–237; III, Vol. 18, pp. 145–167.
1961. Representability of recursively enumerable sets in formal theories, *Arch.*, Vol. 5, pp. 119–127.

Shoenfield, J.
1954. A relative consistency proof, *JSL*, Vol. 19, pp. 21–28.
1958. Degrees of formal systems, *JSL*, Vol. 23, pp. 389–392.
1959. On a restricted ω-rule. *Bull. Acad. Pol. Sci., Ser. Sci. Math. Astr. Phys.*, Vol. 7, pp. 405–407.
1961. Undecidable and creative theories. *FM*, Vol. 49, pp. 171–179.
Sierpinski, W.
1947. L'hypothèse généralisée du continu et l'axiome du choix, *FM*, Vol. 34, pp. 1–5.
1958. *Cardinal and Ordinal Numbers*, Warsaw, 487 pp.
Sikorski, R.
1960. *Boolean algebras*, Berlin-Göttingen-Heidelberg, 176 pp.
Sikorski, R., and H. Rasiowa. See Rasiowa, H., and R. Sikorski.
Skolem, T.
1919. Logisch-kombinatorische Untersuchungen über die Erfüllbarkeit oder Beweisbarkeit mathematische Sätze, *Skrifter Vidensk*, Kristiana, I, pp. 1–36.
1934. Ueber die Nicht-Charakterisierbarkeit der Zahlenreihe mittels endlich oder abzählbar unendlich vieler Aussagen mit ausschliesslich Zahlenvariablen, *FM*, Vol. 23, pp. 150–161.
1955. Peano's axioms and models of arithmetic, *Mathematical Interpretations of Formal Systems*, Amsterdam, pp. 1–14.
Smullyan, R.
1961. *Theory of Formal Systems*, Princeton, 142 pp.
Specker, E.
1949. Nicht-konstruktiv beweisbare Sätze der Analysis, *JSL*, Vol. 14, pp. 145–148.
1953. The axiom of choice in Quine's "New foundations for mathematical logic", *Proc. Acad. Sci. U.S.A.*, Vol. 39, pp. 972–975.
1954. Verallgemeinerte Kontinuumshypothese und Auswahlaxiom, *Archiv der Math.*, Vol. 5, pp. 332–337.
1957. Zur Axiomatik der Mengenlehre (Fundierungs und Auswahlaxiom), *ZML*, Vol. 3, pp. 173–210.
1962. Typical Ambiguity. *Logic, Methodology, and Philosophy of Science* (*Proc. Int. Cong.*, 1960), Stanford, pp. 116–124.
Specker, E., and R. Macdowell. See Macdowell, R., and E. Specker.
Spector, C.
1955. Recursive well-orderings, *JSL*, Vol. 20, pp. 151–163.
1956. On degrees of recursive unsolvability, *Ann. of Math.*, Vol. 64, pp. 581–592.
Stone, M.
1936. The representation theorem for Boolean algebras, *Trans. Amer. Math. Soc.*, Vol. 40, pp. 37–111.
Suppes, P.
1957. *Introduction to Logic*, Van Nostrand, Princeton, 312 pp.
1960. *Axiomatic Set Theory*, Van Nostrand, Princeton, 265 pp.
Suranyi, J.
1959. *Reduktionstheorie des Entscheidungproblems im Prädikatenkalkül der ersten Stufe*, Budapest, 216 pp.
Szmielew, W.
1955. Elementary properties of abelian groups, *FM*, Vol. 41, pp. 203–271.

Tarski, A.

1925. Sur les ensembles finis, *FM*, Vol. 6, pp. 45–95.

1933. Einige Betrachtungen über die Begriffe der ω-Widerspruchsfreiheit und der ω-Vollständigkeit, *Monats. Math. Phys.*, Vol. 40, pp. 97–112.

1936. Der Wahrheitsbegriff in den formalisierten Sprachen, *Studia Philos.*, Vol. 1, pp. 261–405 (also in [1956]).

1938. Ueber unerreichbare Kardinalzahlen, *FM*, Vol. 30, pp. 68–89.

1944. The semantic conception of truth and the foundations of semantics, *Philos. and Phenom. Res.*, Vol. 4, pp. 341–376.

1951. *A Decision Method for Elementary Algebra and Geometry*, Berkeley, 63 pp.

1952. Some notions and methods on the borderline of algebra and metamathematics, *Int. Cong. Math.*, Cambridge, Mass., pp. 705–720.

1954–55. Contributions to the Theory of Models, *Indag. Math.*, Vol. 16, pp. 572–588; Vol. 17, pp. 56–64.

1956. *Logic, Semantics, Metamathematics*, Oxford, 471 pp.

Tarski, A., and P. Erdös. See Erdös, P., and A. Tarski.

Tarski, A., and L. Henkin. See Henkin, L., and A. Tarski.

Tarski, A., and J. C. C. McKinsey. See McKinsey, J. C. C., and A. Tarski.

Tarski, A., A. Mostowski, and R. Robinson.

1953. *Undecidable Theories*, Amsterdam, 98 pp.

Tarski, A., and R. Vaught.

1957. Arithmetical extensions of relational systems, *Comp. Math.*, Vol. 18, pp. 81–102.

Turing, A.

1936–37. On computable numbers, with an application to the Entscheidungsproblem, *Proc. London Math. Soc.*, Vol. 42, pp. 230–265; Vol. 43, pp. 544–546.

1937. Computability and λ-definability, *JSL*, Vol. 2, pp. 153–163.

1939. Systems of logic based on ordinals, *Proc. London Math. Soc.*, Vol. 45, pp. 161–228.

1950a. The word problem in semigroups with cancellation, *Ann. of Math.*, Vol. 52, pp. 491–505.

1950b. Computing Machinery and Intelligence, *Mind*, 59, pp. 433–460.

Turquette, A., and J. B. Rosser. See Rosser, J. B., and A. Turquette.

Ulam, S.

1930. Zur Masstheorie in der allgemeinen Mengenlehre, *Fund. Math.*, Vol. 16, pp. 140–150.

Vaughn, H., and P. Halmos. See Halmos, P., and H. Vaughn.

Vaught, R.

1954. Applications of the Löwenheim-Skolem-Tarski theorem to problems of completeness and decidability, *Indag. Math.*, Vol. 16, pp. 467–472.

1959. Sentences true in all constructive models, *JSL*, Vol. 24, pp. 1–15.

1961. Denumerable models of complete theories, *Infinitistic Methods*, Warsaw, pp. 303–321.

1962. Cobham's Theorem on Undecidable Theories, *Logic, Methodology, and Philosophy of Science* (Proc. Int. Cong., 1960), Stanford, pp. 14–25.

Vaught, R., and S. Feferman. See Feferman, S., and R. Vaught.

Vaught, R., and R. Montague. See Montague, R., and R. Vaught.

Vaught, R., and A. Tarski. See Tarski, A., and R. Vaught.
Vinogradov, I.
1954. Elements of Number Theory, New York, 227 pp.
van der Waerden, B.
1949. *Modern Algebra,* New York, 264 pp.

Wajsberg, M.
1933. Untersuchungen über den Funktionenkalkül für endliche Individuenbereiche, *Math. Ann.*, Vol. 108, pp. 218–228.
Wang, Hao
1951a. Arithmetic translations of axiom systems, *Trans. Amer. Math. Soc.*, Vol. 71, pp. 283–291.
1951b. Arithmetic models for formal systems, *Methodos*, Vol. 3, pp. 217–232.
1954. The formalization of mathematics, *JSL*, Vol. 19, pp. 241–266.
1955. Undecidable sentences generated by semantical paradoxes, *JSL*, Vol. 20, pp. 31–43.
1957a. The axiomatization of arithmetic, *JSL*, Vol. 22, pp. 145–158.
1957b. Remarks on constructive ordinals and set theory, *Summer Inst. Symb. Logic*, Cornell, pp. 383–390.
1957c. A Variant to Turing's Theory of Computing Machines, *J. Assoc. Comp. Mach.*, 4, pp. 63–92.
1959. Ordinal numbers and predicative set theory, *ZML*, Vol. 5, pp. 216–239.
Wang, H., and R. McNaughton
1953. *Les systemes axiomatiques de la theorie des ensembles*, Paris, 55 pp.
Wang, H., and G. Kreisel. See Kreisel, G., and H. Wang.
Wang, H., and J. B. Rosser. See Rosser, J. B., and H. Wang.
Whitehead, A. N., and B. Russell. See Russell, B., and A. N. Whitehead.
Wilder, R.
1952. *Introduction to the Foundations of Mathematics*, New York, 305 pp.

Zeeman, E. C.
1955. On direct sums of free cycles, *J. London Math Soc.*, Vol. 30, pp. 195–212.
Zermelo, E.
1908. Untersuchungen über die Grundlagen der Mengenlehre I, *Math. Ann.*, Vol. 65, pp. 261–281.

NOTATION

INDEX